# MULTIPLE-FACTOR
# ANALYSIS

# MULTIPLE-FACTOR
# ANALYSIS

## A Development and Expansion of
### *The Vectors of Mind*

*By*

## L. L. THURSTONE

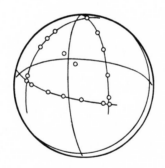

## THE UNIVERSITY OF CHICAGO PRESS
### CHICAGO AND LONDON

*151.2651*
*T42m*
*84038*
*aug 1973*

THE UNIVERSITY OF CHICAGO PRESS, CHICAGO 60637
The University of Chicago Press, Ltd., London W.C. 1

# PREFACE

The purpose of this volume is to make available the results of work that has been done during the past decade in the Psychometric Laboratory at the University of Chicago. The material is presented in the form of a text for students. Essentially all the material of the first edition, *The Vectors of Mind*, has been retained here, and much has been added both in multiple-factor theory and in computational method. Detailed computational office routine has not been featured because it will be covered in a workbook on multiple-factor analysis.

*The Vectors of Mind* has been out of print twice, and the current reprinting is now exhausted. When the writing of the present volume was started, it was my intention to revise *The Vectors of Mind*, re-writing certain sections and making additions of new material. This plan was altered by adopting a more complete expository style for the present text. The entire book has been re-written, and hence it has been given a new title. *The Vectors of Mind* will be referred to in this text as the "first edition."

It has not been my intention to produce a bibliographically complete treatise on multiple-factor analysis. That would be entirely beyond the scope of the present text. Only those references have been given that were directly in line with the subject of discussion, but I fear that even with this limitation I have not done justice to all the authors whose work should have been summarized in this text. Most of these references are readily available in the journal *Psychometrika* and in the bibliographies of its many papers on factorial theory. The subject is still advancing rapidly, so that a theoretically complete treatise would become obsolete in a few years. When the time comes for such a volume, it should be written by a mathematician or by an author who is competent to appraise the contributions of mathematicians and physicists in this field.

The brevity of *The Vectors of Mind* was probably responsible for much of the controversy about multiple-factor analysis. As far as I am aware, all the theorems in the first edition are as valid today as they were ten years ago. The theorems were stated, and, in general, they were proved; but I left them without the support of exposition as to their implications and interpretation in exploratory scientific work. Several concepts have been the subject of controversy. It has been a mystery to me why the fundamentally simple notion which I called "simple structure" has been twisted around by some critics into the most inconceivable nonsense. There has been misunderstanding about the communality concept by which multiple-factor analysis is limited to the common factors—just as it is in Spearman's single-factor case. Some students of this subject change their set in going to

v

the multiple-factor case by insisting that they must then include the total test space. There has also been confusion about the oblique reference frame which represents parameters or factors that are correlated in the general population as well as in the experimental population.

When multiple-factor analysis was introduced in 1931,* it constituted a shift of emphasis. Papers being published at that time were mainly concerned with the existence of Spearman's central intellective factor $g$, the tetrad difference criterion for the general factor $g$, probable error formulae for the tetrad difference, and group factors which were regarded as the disturbers of the general factor and which were nearly always regarded as residuals that were secondary to the general factor. There is nothing new in the recognition that more than one factor must be postulated to account for the observed test correlations. Instead of asking whether the central intellective factor $g$ can be demonstrated in any given set of correlations, with or without disturbing group factors, we ask how many factors are indicated by the correlations without restriction as to whether they are general or group factors. Instead of extracting, first, the postulated general factor and then investigating the residuals to determine whether any disturbing group factors must also be admitted, we start with an observation equation in $n$ terms which represent as many factors as may be required by the correlations. It becomes, then, a question of fact as to whether one or more of them are general factors and whether one or more of them are positive or bipolar.

Our matrix formulation of the problem led to the fundamental factor theorem $FF' = R$, where $F$ is a factor matrix and $R$ is the correlation matrix. The matrix formulation of factor analysis seems to have been generally accepted, and it has largely replaced the previous methods in factor analysis.

In 1931 I decided to investigate the relation between multiple-factor analysis and Spearman's tetrad differences. When I wrote the tetrad equation to begin this inquiry, I discovered that the tetrad was merely the expansion of a second-order minor, and the relation was then obvious. One might speculate as to whether multiple-factor analysis would have developed earlier if this interpretation had been stated earlier. If the second-order minors must vanish in order to established a single common factor, then must the third-order minors vanish in order to establish two common factors, and so on? To have put the matter in this way would have led to the matrix formulation of the problem much earlier, as well as to the immediate development of multiple-factor analysis. Instead of dealing with the proportional columns and rows of a hierarchy and the vanishing tetrads, we now deal with the same relations in terms of the properties of unit rank, namely, proportional columns and rows and vanishing second-order

* L. L. Thurstone, "Multiple Factor Analysis," *Psychological Review,* XXXVIII (September, 1931), 406–27.

minors. This formulation generalizes to the properties of higher rank. As far as I am aware, this formulation of the factor problem has been generally accepted.

The test correlations define a configuration of test vectors without a reference frame. Since the factors are represented by the axes of this frame, it is necessary to locate a reference frame somehow in the test configuration. Here we have to recognize a distinction between an arbitrary orthogonal reference frame that is used for computing purposes and the reference frame that should be used for scientific interpretation of the factors. The arbitrary orthogonal frame is defined by the method of factoring that the computer happens to use. In order to locate a reference frame for interpretation, I used, at first, a statistical criterion which led to the principal axes of the configuration; but I soon discarded this solution in favor of a principle that I called "simple structure." This principle of simple structure has been the cause of much controversy, and it is not yet accepted by all students of factorial theory. The fact that it very frequently gives a set of factors or parameters that can be interpreted as meaningful in scientific context would seem to be an argument in its favor, but even that result has been the object of controversy. I have found that the best way to convince a skeptic is to let him work with the rotational methods on a problem in which he is interested. As the reference frame begins to emerge in the rotational work with successively clearer interpretation, he convinces himself of the power of the method.

In locating a meaningful reference frame for a set of correlated variables, one may voluntarily impose the restriction that the reference frame shall be orthogonal, or one may allow it to become oblique according to the test configuration. If we impose the restriction that the reference frame shall be orthogonal, then we are imposing the condition that the factors or parameters shall be uncorrelated in the experimental population or in the general population. It is my own conviction that this restriction should not be imposed if we are looking for meaningful parameters. It seems just as unnecessary to require that mental traits shall be uncorrelated in the general population as to require that height and weight be uncorrelated in the general population. This admission of oblique axes has also been debated and is not yet generally accepted by students of factor theory.

The correlations among primary factors must be expected to vary from one experimental population to another, depending on selective conditions. This does not mean that the physical nature of each factor or parameter has altered. Just as the correlation between height and weight varies from one group to another by selective conditions, so the correlations between mental traits may also vary from one group to another without change in their meaning.

Second-order factors which are determined from the correlated primaries have only recently been introduced, so that it is not yet known how fruitful they will be. It seems likely that a second-order general factor, determined from correlated primaries, may turn out to be Spearman's general intellective factor $g$. Spearman's early admonition that the tests in each tetrad must not be very similar may be the equivalent of our present observation that a set of four tests can be selected so as to involve only one primary factor for each test. Such a set of four tests will have only the second-order general factor in common; hence the correlations will be of unit rank, and the second-order minors must then vanish. When two similar tests are included in a tetrad, they are likely to involve the same primary as well as the second-order general factor, and the unit rank is then disturbed.

In the scientific interpretation of factorial results it is necessary to differentiate between what we have called "configurational invariance" and the numerical invariance of correlations and saturation coefficients. In general, configurational invariance is more significant, since it transcends most selective conditions for the groups of experimental subjects. Those authors who insist on avoiding geometrical interpretations in factor analysis will almost certainly have some difficulty in dealing with configurational invariance and its important implications. The same results can usually be stated in analytical form, but it is likely that the geometrical ideas will precede the analytical forms.

Since the publication of *The Vectors of Mind*, there have been several texts on factorial theory. The text by Holzinger and Harman presents factor analysis as a statistical method.* This is a worth-while objective, but the mathematical statisticians have not yet accepted factor analysis as a part of statistical logic. Holzinger describes several factoring methods, including his own bi-factor method. The simple-structure concept is disposed of in a footnote, but the rotational problem is presented in variant forms of factorial resolution. It is unfortunate that the term "structure" has been defined in different ways. Holzinger accepts the matrix formulation of the multiple-factor problem and the interpretation of Spearman's single-factor hypothesis as a special case of unit rank. The oblique axes are described as alternative solutions.

Truman L. Kelley's monograph, *Essential Traits of Mental Life*,† describes an ingenious method of arriving at the principal-axes solution directly from the correlation matrix. Kelley does not accept the communalities, or the simple-structure concept, or rotation from the principal axes for the purpose of isolating simpler and more meaningful parameters. He attempts to interpret directly the principal axes of each test battery. Kelley insists that factor analysis must be made with unit diagonals to represent the total variance rather than the common-factor variance. His earlier

* Karl J. Holzinger and Harry H. Harman, *Factor Analysis* (Chicago: University of Chicago Press, 1941).

† Cambridge: Harvard University Press, 1935.

monograph, *Crossroads in the Mind of Man,*\* should also be acknowledged
as a significant contribution. In that publication he attempted to break
away from the dominant single general factor to the multiple-factor problem, but he did not then introduce the generalized factor problem.

Burt† accepts the communality concept, the matrix formulation of factor analysis, and the interpretation of Spearman's single-factor hypothesis
as a special case of unit rank, but he does not accept the necessity for rotating the reference frame for purposes of interpretation. Neither does he
accept the use of oblique reference axes. The configurational interpretations are evidently distasteful to Burt, for he does not have a single diagram in his text. Perhaps this is indicative of individual differences in
imagery types which lead to differences in methods and interpretation
among scientists.

The most provocative of the recent texts in factor theory is that of Godfrey H. Thomson.‡ Even when he differs from our interpretations of the
factor problem I find his discussion stimulating for our own work. Our
chapter on selective conditions and sections of the chapter on unit rank
resulted directly from the stimulus of his provocative papers. He does not
seem to be convinced about the necessity for rotating the reference frame,
although he is probably open-minded about the question. He is not opti-
mistic about the interpretation of primary factors as fundamental parameters in the description of mentality.

While there has been considerable controversy about multiple-factor
analysis, it is probably true that the large majority of factorial studies in
recent years have accepted the matrix formulation of the problem, the
interpretation of Spearman's single-factor theorems as a special case of
unit rank, the communalities, the simple-structure concept, the necessity
for rotating the reference frame for scientific interpretation, the desira-
bility of interpreting the primary factors as meaningful parameters, the
use of oblique reference axes, and the principles of configurational invariance.

No attempt has been made here to review the numerous applications of
factor analysis to psychological and other problems. Dael Wolfle's monograph, *Factor Analysis to 1940,*§ was a good summary of theory and of
applications, and such reviews should be made periodically either by new
monographs like Wolfle's or by periodic summaries in the *Psychological
Bulletin.* For several reasons in the present text I have used very few psychological test examples. When psychologists start to work with psycho-

---

\* Stanford, Calif.: Stanford University Press, 1928.

† Cyril Burt, *The Factors of the Mind* (New York: Macmillan Co., 1941).

‡ *The Factorial Analysis of Human Ability* (New York: Houghton Mifflin Co., 1939).

§ "Psychometric Monographs," No. 3 (Chicago: University of Chicago Press, 1940).

logical test correlations to find primary mental abilities, they sometimes
jump the track and fall into a discussion about faculty psychology. The
logic of the subject can be presented perhaps more clearly by using physical
objects. That is the reason we have used populations of rectangular boxes,
populations of cylinders, and a population of trapezoids. Here the student's
attention is directed to the interpretation of factors as parameters in the
usual scientific sense. In this way we attempt to make the relations of the
parameters in factorial representation as vivid as possible.

One of the limitations of factor analysis in its present stage of development is the absence of sampling-error formulae. It is perhaps natural that
factorial logic should be developed before the sampling-error formulae. It
is only recently that the influence of selection of tests and of experimental
subjects on factorial results have been investigated. These effects must be
distinguished as to the conditions that produce stable numerical values
and those in which configurational invariance is of primary interest. The
relations of second-order factors to factorial results have also only recently
been investigated. At present we are limited largely to the empirically observed stability of factorial findings. The availability of sampling-error
formulae for the principal-axes solution for a given correlation matrix is
good as far as it goes, but this is a trifle compared with the sampling-
error problems in factor analysis.

Factor analysis has not been generally accepted by mathematical statisticians. The present conceptual formulations of statistical theory do not
seem to lend themselves readily to the logical problems of factor analysis.
One might resolve this difficulty in one of two ways. One might insist that
multiple-factor analysis be re-written within the restrictions of current
statistical theory, or one might ask the statisticians to adapt and expand
their formulations to cover the logical problems of factor analysis. Perhaps
both ways will be tried.

When the mathematical statisticians eventually decide to assist the students of multiple-factor analysis, it will be helpful if certain fundamental
considerations are recognized at the outset. Some of these can be listed
here. First, let us recognize that when a scientist is trying to invent a theory
to cover the phenomena of a particular domain, a simple description of its
underlying order, he is certainly not concerned with sampling distributions.
Furthermore, he must restrict himself to some aspect of the phenomena in
the domain. He cannot hope to cover the total variation, for no scientific
formulation ever covers the total variance in any domain. When the statistician turns his attention to the multiple-factor problem, he must deal
with the communality concept and its effect on the rank of the correlation
matrix. If he denies this problem, he not only admits his inadequacy but
also his failure to understand the problem. If statistical theory is not now
adequate to cope with the communalities, then the statistician has the

challenge to adapt his formulations to the limitations that are inherent in a
very large class of scientific problems. He need not deal with the communalities as such because he may discover some equivalent resolution, but he
will not solve the problem by laughing it out of court.

Another consideration with which the statistician is already familiar is
the distortion introduced by the assumption of linearity in the exploratory
study of a new domain. Treatises in the more advanced sciences abound
with non-linear relations. Linear relations are the exception. There is no
good reason to believe that relations in the younger sciences are fundamentally simpler. When scientific inquiry enters upon a new domain with
hazy ideas about the underlying order or, perhaps, with no ideas at all, the
scientist is as naïve as we would be if we should make an experimental inquiry about the relation between the sizes and the weights of boxes without knowing their contents. He would measure and weigh the first one hundred boxes and determine the correlations and the regression equations,
and then he might worry about the standard errors of his coefficients.
Something would be gained by doing that, because it would affect the degree of assurance with which he could say something about the relations
that he had found. If the scientist takes his numerical coefficients very
seriously at the exploratory stage, he may be lacking in a desirable sense of
humor about the crudeness of all his tools in spite of their polished appearance. Too much concern with numerical minutiae at that stage may lead
him astray from the conceptual formulations that constitute his real goal.
If factor analysis is one of his tools for the exploration of a new domain, his
principal concern will be with the factor pattern, the presence or absence
of a significant coefficient in each cell of the oblique factor matrix, rather
than the numerical values of any of them. This consideration may simplify
the statistician's problem in factor analysis.

So far, one of the principal handicaps of the statistician in dealing with
multiple-factor analysis has been his failure to appreciate the significance
of the rotational problem. This is the problem of choosing the most fruitful
set of parameters to describe the variation in a domain. These parameters
represent scientific concepts. They are not merely numerical coefficients.
If these scientifically meaningful parameters happen to be correlated in
the experimental sample, such as height and weight, that is no reason for
rejecting them. The prior consideration is to find fruitful and meaningful
parameters. The question of whether the cross products vanish is a trivial
consideration of the computer's convenience. The statistician must understand this problem of oblique reference axes and associated scientific concepts. The statistician must not impose the arbitrary restriction that our
scientific concepts in the description of people must be uncorrelated either
in the experimental sample or in the general population.

In attempting to introduce sampling distributions in factor analysis, it will also be useful to recognize that when a simple structure is discovered in a new domain, it is rarely equally stable or clear in all the dimensions. Some of the hyperplanes may be overdetermined while others are even indeterminate. These hyperplanes are usually unknown at the start of the experiment, and no statistical jugglery can evade their different degrees of overdetermination unless the jugglery merely obscures them.

One of the most useful conceptual formulations in statistical theory is that of the sample and the universe from which the sample is drawn. A large part of statistical theory is built on this construct. This often leads to a concern as to whether any given sample is representative of a postulated universe. One might suppose in factor analysis that the experimental sample should be representative of the general population, but such is not the case. On the contrary, if a certain group of traits is to be investigated as to their underlying structure, we proceed as in many other types of scientific investigation by selecting a highly biased sample, including even freaks in the domain concerned. Another sample of freaks may be factorially studied without any question as to whether it is also an unbiased sample from the same universe. Such studies are much more likely to be revealing of the underlying nature of the domain than are carefully randomized samples from the general population. And, further, there is no necessity that the frequency distribution of anything shall be Gaussian. Let us also not forget a simple principle that every scientist takes for granted, namely, that he would rather measure something significant without any sampling distributions than measure something trivial or irrelevant because its sampling distribution is known.

In a recent paper Hotelling deplores the fact that students of factor analysis have not made use of the recent advances in mathematical statistics, and he dismisses the fundamental concepts of multiple-factor analysis because they have not been formulated in terms of current statistical theory. A fair appraisal of this situation would probably acknowledge that we should have succeeded better in getting the co-operation of the statisticians if recent advances in statistical theory had been recognized explicitly; but it would probably also acknowledge that, while statistical theory has made important advances in the last two decades, it has not advanced far enough to be immediately useful for factor analysis as a scientific method without still further advancement. Instead of dismissing the basic concepts of multiple-factor analysis, we must reach common ground in recognizing that these concepts represent difficult problems in the logic of science that need to be studied rather than ridiculed. Let us hope that competent students will begin soon to investigate these challenging problems, so that the factorial methods can be made generally available in the sciences without the handicap of distracting controversy.

A special acknowledgment is due Mr. Ledyard Tucker, who was my chief assistant for a number of years. His thorough mastery of the theory and computational methods of multiple-factor analysis has been of the greatest aid not only in preparing the present manuscript but also in the numerous factorial experiments that have been made here in recent years. Mrs. Virginia Brown, who succeeded Mr. Tucker, participated for several years in the development of factorial methods and computation, and she assisted in preparing this manuscript for publication. A large part of the computations for this text was done by Mr. Frank Medland. Miss Lorraine Bouthilet also assisted in editing the manuscript. The preparation of the manuscript was done by Miss Florence W. Brown, Miss Geri Blocker, and Miss Alexandra Thanos. The Index, which was prepared by Mrs. Dorothy C. Bechtoldt, was made quite extensive so as to be useful to the student reader. I have sincere appreciation for the loyalty and interest of these student assistants. My principal acknowledgment is to my wife, who has been a partner in the formulation of each problem, as well as in all the experimental studies of this laboratory.

The Social Science Research Committee of the University of Chicago has been generous in providing space and research funds for the Psychometric Laboratory. Our work has been greatly facilitated by several research grants from the Carnegie Corporation in New York for studies of primary mental abilities at different age levels. To the University of Chicago Press we want to express our appreciation for its interest and technical assistance in several publications of the Laboratory and, in particular, to Miss Mary Alexander of the publication department.

### A NOTE ON FUTURE WORK

In presenting this text as a summary of our work on multiple-factor analysis, it may be appropriate to mention some possibilities for the future development of this subject. One of the principal assumptions underlying factorial theory is that the scores are monotonic increasing or decreasing functions of the scores on the primary factors or parameters. The fundamental observation equation of factor analysis makes the further assumption that these functions can be expressed in linear form as a first approximation. It would be possible to start with a second-degree observation equation and to develop factorial methods on that basis. Instead of developing factorial theory more completely with observation equations of higher degree, it would probably be more profitable to develop non-metric methods of factor analysis. An idea for such a development would be to determine the number of independent parameters of a score matrix by analyzing successive differences in rank order on the assumption that they are monotonic functions of a limited number of independent parameters. A score would then be regarded as merely an index of rank order, and that is essentially what we are now doing. The raw scores are transmuted into a normal distribution of unit standard deviation, and these transmuted scores are used for the correlations. Instead of dealing with the transmuted scores in this manner, one might deal with the rank orders directly or with some equivalent indices of rank order. Analysis of successive differences in rank order, or their equivalents, should lead to the factor pattern, which would indicate the number of parameters involved in the variance of each test. That is the main object of factor analysis. The actual numerical values are of secondary importance in teasing out what we have called the underlying order of a new domain. The simple-structure concept is applicable as well to a non-metric form of factor pattern as to the more restricted linear metric form that we have been using. The scientific interpretation of the factors could be made from a factor pattern without putting it in metric form. If the mathematical theory has already been developed, it would be helpful if we knew what to call it in asking mathematicians for assistance. In putting the results to practical use, the problem would return to a metric form, with standardization and norms which call for statistical methods of the conventional kind. The main problem for factor analysis is the more fundamental one of charting the alternative factor patterns in new fields. To develop this subject with more powerful non-metric methods is future work that may leave our present efforts obsolete.

L. L. THURSTONE

CHICAGO, ILLINOIS
March 1945

# TABLE OF CONTENTS

# MATHEMATICAL INTRODUCTION

The matrix theory which is used in the development of factor analysis is not generally available to students whose training in mathematics is limited to undergraduate courses in analytical geometry and in the calculus. This mathematical introduction reviews the elementary theory of matrices as well as the closely related theory of determinants. Summation that involves double subscript notation is included in this section, since it is used in factor theory and since it is unfamiliar to most students of statistics. In the geometrical interpretation of the factorial matrix, only non-homogeneous co-ordinates are used. For this reason, the introduction includes non-homogeneous co-ordinates and omits homogeneous co-ordinates which are conventional. Orthogonal and oblique transformations have been illustrated geometrically. No provocation has been found so far in factor theory to introduce imaginaries and complex numbers, but the future development of factor analysis may call for them. *This mathematical introduction is limited to the real case,* and all theorems have been written with this restriction in mind.

If this introduction is not self-sufficient, perhaps it may serve as a useful guide to the student of factor theory who seeks mathematical assistance on specified topics. If a student has the intention of attaining some competence in factor theory and in related statistical work, there is no short cut for formal courses in the mathematics that is involved.*

## Matrices

Matrices and determinants involve rectangular arrangements of numbers. Any rectangular arrangement of numbers is called a *matrix*, irrespective of what the numbers mean. If the matrix has $m$ rows and $n$ columns, the matrix is said to be of *order* $m \times n$. In designating the order of a matrix,

* The following references will be found useful:

W. F. Osgood and W. C. Graustein, *Plane and Solid Analytic Geometry* (New York: Macmillan Co., 1929).

L. E. Dickson, *Modern Algebraic Theories* (New York: B. H. Sanborn, 1926), chap. iii.

Maxime Bôcher, *Introduction to Higher Algebra* (New York: Macmillan Co., 1931), chaps. i–vi, inc.

H. W. Turnbull and A. C. Aitken, *Canonical Matrices* (London: Blackie & Sons, 1932), chap. i.

V. Snyder and C. H. Sisam, *Analytical Geometry of Space* (New York: Henry Holt & Co., 1914).

A. Adrian Albert, *Introduction to Algebraic Theories* (Chicago: University of Chicago Press, 1941).

W. L. Ferrar, *Algebra* (Oxford University Press, 1941).

Arnold Dresden, *Solid Analytical Geometry and Determinants* (New York: John Wiley & Sons, 1930).

it is customary to refer to *rows first* and *columns second*. Thus a matrix of order $p \times q$ has $p$ rows and $q$ columns. *Tables 1a* and *1b* show a matrix of order $3 \times 4$ and a matrix of order $3 \times 3$. A *row* is horizontal. A *column* is vertical. The general name for either a row or a column is an *array*. Each of the small squares into which a matrix is divided is called a *cell*, and the number in each cell is called a *cell entry* or *element*.

| Table 1a | | | | | Table 1b | | |
|---|---|---|---|---|---|---|---|
| 2 | 3 | 1 | 5 | | 2 | 1 | 5 |
| 1 | 6 | 0 | 9 | | 4 | 8 | 3 |
| 0 | 2 | 6 | 7 | | 2 | 0 | 7 |

In order to designate a particular element, it is customary to use a double subscript, the first one for the row and the second one for the column. If a matrix is denoted $A$, then its elements may be denoted $a_{ij}$, where $i$ shows the row and $j$ shows the column at the intersection of which the element $a_{ij}$ is found. Thus, in *Table 1a* the element $a_{12} = 3$ and $a_{24} = 9$.

In developing the theory of matrices it is desirable to exhibit the elements as shown in *Table 2*. The elements in the first row are $a_{11}$, $a_{12}$, $a_{13}$, . . , $a_{1n}$, showing that the table represents a matrix of $n$ columns. The elements of the first column are $a_{11}$, $a_{21}$, $a_{31}$, . . . , $a_{m1}$, showing that the table represents $m$ rows. The general element in this matrix $A$ is $a_{ij}$, where $i$ takes the successive values 1, 2, 3, . . . , $m$, while $j$ takes the successive values 1, 2, 3, . . . , $n$. The first subscript refers to the row; the second subscript refers to the column.

*Table 2*

$$\begin{array}{ccccc}
a_{11} & a_{12} & a_{13} & \cdots & a_{1n} \\
a_{21} & a_{22} & a_{23} & \cdots & a_{2n} \\
a_{31} & a_{32} & a_{33} & \cdots & a_{3n} \\
\cdots & \cdots & \cdots & a_{ij} & \cdots \\
a_{m1} & a_{m2} & a_{m3} & \cdots & a_{mn}
\end{array}$$

The conventional representation of a matrix is shown in *Table 3*, where the rectangular arrangement of numbers is inclosed by double vertical lines on the left and on the right sides of the rectangle. It is also customary to denote specified matrices with letters. Thus, the matrix of *Table 3* might be conveniently designated $A$ or any other letter. A matrix $A$ might also be designated by its general element $a_{ij}$.

*Table 3*

$$\left\|\begin{array}{ccc}
2 & 1 & 5 \\
4 & 8 & 3 \\
2 & 0 & 7
\end{array}\right\|$$

If the successive rows of matrix $A$ are written as successive columns of a new matrix, the new matrix is called the *transpose* of $A$. It is denoted $A'$. *Table 4* shows a matrix $A$ and its transpose $A'$.

*Table 4*

$$
\begin{Vmatrix}
2 & 3 & 1 & 5 \\
1 & 6 & 0 & 9 \\
0 & 2 & 6 & 7
\end{Vmatrix}
\qquad\qquad
\begin{Vmatrix}
2 & 1 & 0 \\
3 & 6 & 2 \\
1 & 0 & 6 \\
5 & 9 & 7
\end{Vmatrix}
$$

$$A \qquad\qquad\qquad A'$$

## Determinants

One particular interpretation of a square matrix is called a *determinant*. This interpretation of a square matrix probably had its origin in the practical work of solving simultaneous equations, and it is indicated by single vertical lines on the left and on the right sides of a square table. It is illustrated in *Table 5*. *Table 3* is called a *matrix;* while *Table 5*, which implies a particular interpretation, is called a *determinant*. A determinant is always square. Hence its order is $n$, in which $n$ is the number of rows or the number of columns.

*Table 5*

$$
\begin{vmatrix}
2 & 1 & 5 \\
4 & 8 & 3 \\
2 & 0 & 7
\end{vmatrix}
$$

The diagonal from the upper left corner to the lower right corner of a determinant is called the *principal diagonal*. In *Table 5* the principal diagonal contains the elements 2, 8, 7. The other diagonal from the lower left corner to the upper right corner is called the *secondary diagonal*.

In many problems it is convenient to assign a plus sign and a minus sign to alternate cells in a determinant. A convenient rule is to designate the upper left cell as positive and all other cells as alternately negative and positive, as the cells can be moved over by the castle in a chess game. This sign arrangement is illustrated in *Table 6* for a determinant of order 5.

*Table 6*

$$
\begin{vmatrix}
+ & - & + & - & + \\
- & + & - & + & - \\
+ & - & + & - & + \\
- & + & - & + & - \\
+ & - & + & - & +
\end{vmatrix}
$$

Notice that the cells in the principal diagonal are all positive and that lines parallel to this diagonal are alternately negative and positive. The sign is positive for an even number of steps from the upper left cell, and it is negative when the number of steps is odd. The sign of a cell determined in this manner may be called the *position sign of the cell*. If the general element of the determinant is denoted $a_{ij}$, then the element with its position sign may be conveniently denoted $(-1)^{i+j}a_{ij}$. When the exponent $(i+j)$ is odd, the sign of the cell is negative; and when $(i+j)$ is even, the sign of the cell is positive.

The product of any $n$ elements of a square matrix, selected with only one element from each of the $n$ rows and only one element from each of the $n$ columns, is called a *term of the determinant* of the matrix. *Table 7* is a deter-

Table 7

$$\begin{vmatrix} a_{11} & a_{12} & a_{13} \\ a_{21} & a_{22} & a_{23} \\ a_{31} & a_{32} & a_{33} \end{vmatrix}$$

minant of order 3. From this determinant six terms may be written. These are shown in *Table 8*, in which the elements of each term are arranged in the order of their columns.

Table 8

1)  $a_{11}\ a_{22}\ a_{33}$

2)  $a_{11}\ a_{32}\ a_{23}$

3)  $a_{21}\ a_{12}\ a_{33}$

4)  $a_{21}\ a_{32}\ a_{13}$

5)  $a_{31}\ a_{12}\ a_{23}$

6)  $a_{31}\ a_{22}\ a_{13}$

Each of these six terms is the product of three elements so selected that each term contains only one element from each row and only one element from each column. If a square matrix is of order $n$, the total number of terms in its determinant is $n$. The term that contains all the elements of the principal diagonal is called the *leading term* of the determinant.

The sign of each of the $n$ terms of a determinant can be ascertained in the following manner. Let the $n$ elements of each term be arranged in ascending order according to columns, as shown in *Table 8*. This can evidently be done without affecting the numerical value of the terms. Consider the fourth term as an example, and list the rows as follows:

2   3   1.

Any interchange of two adjacent elements constitutes an *inversion*. It may be illustrated by interchanging 1 and 3. The resulting arrangement is

$$2 \quad 1 \quad 3 \, .$$

If, now, the adjacent elements 1 and 2 are interchanged, the arrangement becomes

$$1 \quad 2 \quad 3 \, ,$$

in which the rows are in consecutive order.

The sign of a term of a determinant is positive if it represents an even number of inversions from the consecutive order of rows and columns. The sign of the term is negative if the number of inversions in the term is odd.

Applying this rule to the six terms of *Table 8*, we have the same terms with proper signs as shown in *Table 9*.

Table 9

1) $\quad +a_{11} \; a_{22} \; a_{33}$

2) $\quad -a_{11} \; a_{32} \; a_{23}$

3) $\quad -a_{21} \; a_{12} \; a_{33}$

4) $\quad +a_{21} \; a_{32} \; a_{13}$

5) $\quad +a_{31} \; a_{12} \; a_{23}$

6) $\quad -a_{31} \; a_{22} \; a_{13}$

A complete definition of a determinant can now be given.

Definition: *If a square table is used as a symbol of the sum of* n *terms, each term being the product of* n *elements with only one element from each row and only one element from each column, the sign of each term taken positive or negative according as the term contains an even or an odd number of inversions, then the square table is called a* **determinant.** Hence the sum of the six terms of *Table 9* is implied by the determinant of *Table 7*. The determinantal interpretation of a square matrix is denoted by single vertical lines on the left and on the right sides of the square table, as shown in *Table 7*.

If a *square matrix* is denoted by a letter such as $A$, then the *determinant* of the matrix is denoted $|A|$. If $A$ represents a *number*, then $|A|$ means the *absolute value*, ignoring the sign of the number $A$. It should be noted that a matrix is merely a rectangular table of numbers, and hence *a matrix has no numerical value*. But a determinant is, by definition, a sum of terms, and hence it has a numerical value. If a matrix is denoted $a_{ij}$, then its determinant is denoted $|a_{ij}|$.

Consider the second-order determinant

$$
\begin{array}{cc}
1 & 5 \\
8 & 3
\end{array}
$$

and the $2=2$ terms that it implies. These are $1\times3$ and $8\times5$, in which the factors of each term are arranged in consecutive order by columns. The rows of the term $1\times3$ are 1 and 2. Since these are in consecutive order, the sign of this term is positive. Its value is therefore $+(1)(3)=+3$. The rows of the term $8\times5$ are 2 and 1. One inversion changes the order 2 and 1 into the consecutive order 1 and 2. Hence the sign of this term is negative. The determinant therefore has the numerical value $+3-40=-37$. Any second-order determinant can be evaluated as follows:

$$
\begin{array}{cc}
a & d \\
c & b
\end{array}
= ab - cd .
$$

An $x$-rowed minor of the matrix $A$ is a determinant of order $x$ which is formed by the intersections of any $x$ rows and any $x$ columns of the matrix $A$. If one or more columns of a determinant are eliminated and if the same number of rows are eliminated, the remaining cells constitute a *minor*. From the determinant of *Table 7* nine second-order minors may be drawn. A few of them are illustrated here:

$$
\begin{array}{cc}
a_{11} & a_{12} \\
a_{21} & a_{22}
\end{array}
\; , \quad
\begin{array}{cc}
a_{21} & a_{23} \\
a_{31} & a_{33}
\end{array}
\; , \quad
\begin{array}{cc}
a_{12} & a_{13} \\
a_{22} & a_{23}
\end{array}
\; .
$$

If any two columns and any two rows are eliminated from the determinant of *Table 7*, there remains a 1-rowed minor which is a single element. In this sense each element can be regarded as a minor of the determinant.

If corresponding rows and columns are eliminated, the remaining minor is symmetrically placed with regard to the principal diagonal, and it is called a *principal minor*. In the determinant of *Table 7*, three second-order principal minors may be drawn. These are

$$
\begin{array}{cc}
a_{11} & a_{12} \\
a_{21} & a_{22}
\end{array}
\; , \quad
\begin{array}{cc}
a_{11} & a_{13} \\
a_{31} & a_{33}
\end{array}
\; , \quad
\begin{array}{cc}
a_{22} & a_{23} \\
a_{32} & a_{33}
\end{array}
\; .
$$

There are three 1-rowed principal minors in this determinant, namely, the three elements in the principal diagonal.

If the row $i$ and the column $j$ which intersect in an element $a_{ij}$ are eliminated from a determinant, the remaining $(n-1)$-rowed determinant is called the *first minor* of $a_{ij}$. This definition is illustrated with the determinant of *Table 5*. The second row and the first column intersect in the element 4. If these two arrays are eliminated from the determinant, the remaining 2-rowed determinant is

$$\begin{vmatrix} 1 & 5 \\ 0 & 7 \end{vmatrix} = 7 - 0 = +7 .$$

This determinant, whose numerical value is $+7$, is the first minor of the element $a_{21} = 4$ in the determinant of *Table 5*. Let the first minor of the element $a_{ij}$ be denoted $m_{ij}$.

In some problems it is convenient to refer to the minor $m_{ij}$ with the position sign of the element $a_{ij}$. This quantity is called the *cofactor* of $a_{ij}$. It is defined by the relation

$$(\text{cofactor of } a_{ij}) \equiv e_{ij} \equiv (-1)^{i+j} m_{ij} .$$

In *Table 5* the cofactor of the element 4 is

$$(-1)^{2+1} \begin{vmatrix} 1 & 5 \\ 0 & 7 \end{vmatrix} = - [7-0] = -7 .$$

In the same table the cofactor of the element 3 is

$$(-1)^{2+3} \begin{vmatrix} 2 & 1 \\ 2 & 0 \end{vmatrix} = - [0-2] = +2 .$$

Hence the absolute values of the first minor of $a_{ij}$ and of its cofactor are identical. They differ only in the manner of determining the sign. If the position sign of the element $a_{ij}$ is positive, the first minor and the cofactor have the same sign. If the position sign of $a_{ij}$ is negative, they have opposite signs.

The numerical value of a determinant can be expressed conveniently for some problems in terms of the cofactors. For example,

$$\begin{vmatrix} a_{11} & a_{12} & a_{13} \\ a_{21} & a_{22} & a_{23} \\ a_{31} & a_{32} & a_{33} \end{vmatrix} = a_{11}e_{11} + a_{21}e_{21} + a_{31}e_{31} .$$

*The numerical value of a determinant is the weighted sum of the elements in any array, each element being weighted by its cofactor.* In the example, the determinant is expressed in terms of the elements of the first column.

As a numerical example, the value of the determinant of *Table 5* can be expressed as follows:

$$\begin{vmatrix} 2 & 1 & 5 \\ 4 & 8 & 3 \\ 2 & 0 & 7 \end{vmatrix} = +2 \begin{vmatrix} 8 & 3 \\ 0 & 7 \end{vmatrix} -4 \begin{vmatrix} 1 & 5 \\ 0 & 7 \end{vmatrix} +2 \begin{vmatrix} 1 & 5 \\ 8 & 3 \end{vmatrix}$$

$$= 2(56-0) - 4(7-0) + 2(3-40)$$

$$= 112 - 28 - 74 = +10 .$$

The numerical value of a determinant can be expressed as the summation:

$$(1) \qquad |a_{ij}| = \sum_{i=1}^{n} a_{ij}e_{ij} = \sum_{j=1}^{n} a_{ij}e_{ij} ,$$

where the weighted sum may be taken over any column or any row. The following is an example of a fourth-order determinant, evaluated by the method of (1):

$$|A| = \begin{vmatrix} 2 & 4 & 1 & 0 \\ 3 & 2 & 4 & 2 \\ 1 & 6 & 1 & 4 \\ 1 & 0 & 2 & 3 \end{vmatrix} = +2 \begin{vmatrix} 2 & 4 & 2 \\ 6 & 1 & 4 \\ 0 & 2 & 3 \end{vmatrix} -3 \begin{vmatrix} 4 & 1 & 0 \\ 6 & 1 & 4 \\ 0 & 2 & 3 \end{vmatrix} +1 \begin{vmatrix} 4 & 1 & 0 \\ 2 & 4 & 2 \\ 0 & 2 & 3 \end{vmatrix} -1 \begin{vmatrix} 4 & 1 & 0 \\ 2 & 4 & 2 \\ 6 & 1 & 4 \end{vmatrix} .$$

$$\begin{vmatrix} 2 & 4 & 2 \\ 6 & 1 & 4 \\ 0 & 2 & 3 \end{vmatrix} = +2 \begin{vmatrix} 1 & 4 \\ 2 & 3 \end{vmatrix} -6 \begin{vmatrix} 4 & 2 \\ 2 & 3 \end{vmatrix} +0 \begin{vmatrix} 4 & 2 \\ 1 & 4 \end{vmatrix}$$

$$= 2(3-8) - 6(12-4) + 0(16-2)$$

$$= -10 - 48 + 0 = -58 .$$

$$\begin{vmatrix} 4 & 1 & 0 \\ 6 & 1 & 4 \\ 0 & 2 & 3 \end{vmatrix} = +4 \begin{vmatrix} 1 & 4 \\ 2 & 3 \end{vmatrix} -6 \begin{vmatrix} 1 & 0 \\ 2 & 3 \end{vmatrix} +0 \begin{vmatrix} 1 & 0 \\ 1 & 4 \end{vmatrix}$$

$$= 4(3-8) - 6(3-0) + 0(4-0)$$

$$= -20 - 18 + 0 = -38 .$$

$$\begin{vmatrix} 4 & 1 & 0 \\ 2 & 4 & 2 \\ 0 & 2 & 3 \end{vmatrix} = +4 \begin{vmatrix} 4 & 2 \\ 2 & 3 \end{vmatrix} -2 \begin{vmatrix} 1 & 0 \\ 2 & 3 \end{vmatrix} +0 \begin{vmatrix} 1 & 0 \\ 4 & 2 \end{vmatrix}$$

$$= 4(12-4) - 2(3-0) + 0(2-0)$$

$$= 32 - 6 + 0 = +26 .$$

$$\begin{vmatrix} 4 & 1 & 0 \\ 2 & 4 & 2 \\ 6 & 1 & 4 \end{vmatrix} = +4 \begin{vmatrix} 4 & 2 \\ 1 & 4 \end{vmatrix} -2 \begin{vmatrix} 1 & 0 \\ 1 & 4 \end{vmatrix} +6 \begin{vmatrix} 1 & 0 \\ 4 & 2 \end{vmatrix}$$

$$= 4(16-2) - 2(4-0) + 6(2-0)$$

$$= +56 - 8 + 12 = +60 .$$

Hence

$$|A| = (+2)(-58) - (3)(-38) + (1)(+26) - (1)(+60) = -36 .$$

For every element $a_{ij}$ in the square matrix $A$ there is a corresponding minor $m_{ij}$ and a corresponding cofactor $e_{ij}$. Let $M$ be the square matrix with elements $m_{ij}$; let $E$ be the square matrix with elements $e_{ij}$; and let $F$ be the transpose of $E$. Then the square matrix $F$ is called the *adjoint* of $A$. Its elements may be denoted $f_{ij} = e_{ji}$.

These definitions are illustrated in the following numerical example:

$$\begin{Vmatrix} 2 & 1 & 5 \\ 4 & 8 & 3 \\ 2 & 0 & 7 \end{Vmatrix} = A \qquad \begin{Vmatrix} 56 & -22 & -16 \\ -7 & 4 & 2 \\ -37 & 14 & 12 \end{Vmatrix} = E$$

$$\begin{Vmatrix} 56 & 22 & -16 \\ 7 & 4 & -2 \\ -37 & -14 & 12 \end{Vmatrix} = M \qquad \begin{Vmatrix} 56 & -7 & -37 \\ -22 & 4 & 14 \\ -16 & 2 & 12 \end{Vmatrix} = F = adjoint\ of\ A .$$

A square matrix $A$ is said to be *symmetric* when $A' = A$. Then we also have $a_{ji} = a_{ij}$. It is symmetric about the principal diagonal.

$$\left\| \begin{array}{ccc} 1 & 4 & 5 \\ 4 & 2 & 8 \\ 5 & 8 & 3 \end{array} \right\| = a\ symmetric\ matrix\ .$$

If $a_{ij} = -a_{ji}$, so that the signs above the principal diagonal are opposite to the signs below the diagonal, then the matrix is said to be *skew symmetric*. A matrix $A$ is skew symmetric if $A' = -A$.

$$\left\| \begin{array}{ccc} 0 & -3 & 4 \\ 3 & 0 & -5 \\ -4 & 5 & 0 \end{array} \right\| = a\ skew\ symmetric\ matrix\ .$$

If all the principal minors of a matrix are greater than or equal to zero, then the matrix is said to be *positive-definite*. If, in addition, it is symmetric, it is a *Gramian* matrix.

$$\left\| \begin{array}{ccc} 2 & 3 & -3 \\ 2 & 4 & 2 \\ 3 & 5 & 6 \end{array} \right\| = a\ positive\text{-}definite\ matrix.$$

$$\left\| \begin{array}{ccc} 5 & 10 & 13 \\ 10 & 20 & 26 \\ 13 & 26 & 36 \end{array} \right\| = a\ Gramian\ matrix.$$

In some problems it is important to know the highest order of the non-vanishing minors. The highest order of the non-vanishing minors is called the *rank* of a matrix. The rank of *Table 5* is equal to its order, namely, 3, because the determinant itself does not vanish. The determinant of *Table 10* does vanish, so that its rank must be less than 3. It contains second-order minors that do not vanish, and the rank of the determinant is therefore 2.

*Table 10*

$$\left| \begin{array}{ccc} 10 & 8 & 1 \\ 8 & 8 & 2 \\ 1 & 2 & 1 \end{array} \right| = 0$$

The third equation (2) is produced by a similar operation on the third row of $A$ and the first column of $y$. The sum of the three products is recorded in the third row and first column of $x$. The equation is

$$(5) \qquad a_{31}y_{11} + a_{32}y_{21} + a_{33}y_{31} = \sum_{j=1}^{3} a_{3j}y_{j1} = x_{31} .$$

The three equations may be written in the more condensed form

$$(6) \qquad \sum_{j=1}^{3} a_{ij}y_{jk} = x_{ik} .$$

This interpretation of two adjacent matrices is called *matrix multiplication*. In the present problem $k=1$, because $y$ has only one column. Since $i$ can take three different values, namely, $i=1, 2, 3$, the equation (6) represents all three of the simultaneous equations in *summational notation*. *Table 11* represents the *rectangular notation*. The three equations (2) may also be represented conveniently in the still more condensed *matrix notation*, namely,

$$(7) \qquad Ay = x ,$$

which is a *matrix equation*. The operation specified by this matrix equation is that if the matrix $A$ is multiplied by the matrix $y$, row-by-column, the matrix product is another matrix, namely, $x$. This is an exceedingly powerful method of handling sets of equations, because many otherwise tedious numerical operations can be shunted, so that the calculations are performed only on a final set of matrices rather than on many intermediate steps. Still more important is the fact that significant relations in a problem are conspicuous in the matrix notation but they may be obscure when the problem is handled in expanded algebraic or numerical form.

*Table 12*

| | $j$ | | | $i$ | | | | $i$ | | |
|---|---|---|---|---|---|---|---|---|---|---|
| $k \parallel y_1$ | $y_2$ | $y_3 \parallel$ | $1$ | $0$ | $2$ | $k \parallel x_1$ | $x_2$ | $x_3 \parallel$ |
| | $y'$ | | $j \quad 2$ | $3$ | $2$ | | $x'$ | |
| | | | $0$ | $1$ | $4 \parallel$ | | | |
| | | | | $A'$ | | | | |

The same set of simultaneous equations (2) may be represented by the matrix multiplication shown in *Table 12*. The multiplication of the first row of $y'$ ($y'$ has only one row) and the first column of $A'$ reproduces the first equation of (2). It should be noted that the matrices of *Table 12* are the transposes of the matrices of *Table 11*. The transpose of a column vector is a row vector with the same elements.

The summational notation for the matrix multiplication of *Table 12* is

$$(8) \qquad \sum_{j=1}^{3} y_{kj} a_{ji} = x_{ki} .$$

The general element of $A$ in *Table 11* is $a_{ij}$. Hence the general element of $A'$ in *Table 12* is $a_{ji}$. The general element of $y$ is $y_{jk}$, so that the general element of $y'$ is $y_{kj}$. The matrix equation for *Table 12* is

$$(9) \qquad y'A' = x' ,$$

which represents the same set of equations as (7).

In order to multiply one matrix by another, the number of columns of the first one must be the same as the number of rows of the second. The columns of $A$ in *Table 11* are represented by the subscript $j$, and this is also the subscript for the rows of $y$. If the subscripts for the first matrix are $i$ and $j$ and the subscripts for the second matrix are $j$ and $k$, then the $j$ subscript is eliminated from the matrix product which has the subscripts $i$ and $k$. The same rule can be verified in the matrix multiplication of *Table 12*, where the subscripts of the first matrix are $k$ and $j$ and those of the second matrix are $j$ and $i$. Eliminating the middle subscript $j$, which is common, the matrix product has the subscripts $k$ and $i$.

The matrix equations (7) and (9) illustrate the following matrix theorem:

Theorem: *The transpose of any product of matrices is the product of their transposes in reverse order.*

Hence, if $AB = C$, it follows that $B'A' = C'$. Applying this theorem to the present example, we have, by *Table 11*, $Ay = x$, and, by the theorem, $y'A' = x'$, which is the matrix equation for *Table 12*.

If the $x$'s are known in (2), then the $y$'s may be found. Let the $y$'s be expressed as linear functions of the $z$'s in (10).

$$(10) \qquad \begin{cases} z_1 & +z_3 & = y_1 , \\ & 2z_2 +z_3 & = y_2 , \\ z_1 +2z_2 & & = y_3 . \end{cases}$$

This set of simultaneous equations is represented in *Table 13*. If the three

*Table 13*

$$
\begin{Vmatrix} 1 & 0 & 1 \\ 0 & 2 & 1 \\ 1 & 2 & 0 \end{Vmatrix} \cdot \begin{Vmatrix} z_1 \\ z_2 \\ z_3 \end{Vmatrix} = \begin{Vmatrix} y_1 \\ y_2 \\ y_3 \end{Vmatrix}
$$

$$\quad B \qquad\qquad z \qquad\quad y$$

matrices of *Table 13* are denoted $B$, $z$, and $y$, we can represent the three equations (10) in the single matrix equation,

$$(11) \qquad\qquad\qquad Bz = y .$$

Since the $y$'s are known, the values of the $z$'s can be determined. Substituting the known values of the $y$'s in (10), we find that

$$z_1 = -\tfrac{8}{14} , \qquad z_2 = \tfrac{7}{14} , \qquad z_3 = -\tfrac{2}{14} .$$

Equation (7) shows that the $x$'s can be expressed linearly in terms of the $y$'s. Equation (11) shows that the $y$'s can be expressed linearly in terms of the $z$'s. It is desired now to express the $x$'s directly in terms of the $z$'s without the intermediate $y$'s. This can be done. From the equations

$$(7) \qquad\qquad\qquad Ay = x ,$$

$$(11) \qquad\qquad\qquad Bz = y ,$$

it follows that

$$A(Bz) = x ,$$

$$ABz = x .$$

Let $AB \equiv C$. Then

$$(12) \qquad\qquad\qquad Cz = x .$$

In order to express the $x$'s in terms of the $z$'s, the matrix product $AB = C$ must be determined numerically. This matrix product is shown graphically in *Table 14*. Consider the first row of $A$ and the first column of $B$. The cross product is

$$(1)(1) + (2)(0) + (0)(1) = +1 .$$

This is therefore the element in the first row and the first column of the matrix product $C$. Consider, as another example, the second row of $A$ and the third column of $B$. The cross product is

$$(0)(1) + (3)(1) + (1)(0) = +3 .$$

This is the element $c_{23}$ in the matrix $C$.

*Table 14*

$$\begin{Vmatrix} 1 & 2 & 0 \\ 0 & 3 & 1 \\ 2 & 2 & 4 \end{Vmatrix} \cdot \begin{Vmatrix} 1 & 0 & 1 \\ 0 & 2 & 1 \\ 1 & 2 & 0 \end{Vmatrix} = \begin{Vmatrix} 1 & 4 & 3 \\ 1 & 8 & 3 \\ 6 & 12 & 4 \end{Vmatrix}$$

$A \qquad\qquad B \qquad\qquad C$

Since the numerical values of the $x$'s, the $y$'s, and the $z$'s are known, the matrix equation (12) may be tested graphically, as shown in *Table 15*. As a

*Table 15*

$$\begin{Vmatrix} 1 & 4 & 3 \\ 1 & 8 & 3 \\ 6 & 12 & 4 \end{Vmatrix} \cdot \begin{Vmatrix} -\frac{8}{14} \\ \frac{7}{14} \\ -\frac{2}{14} \end{Vmatrix} = \begin{Vmatrix} 1 \\ 3 \\ 2 \end{Vmatrix}$$

$C \qquad\qquad z \qquad\qquad x$

sample check, consider the second row of $C$ and the first column of $z$. It should reproduce the value $x_{21}=3$.

$$(1)(-\tfrac{8}{14}) + (8)(\tfrac{7}{14}) + (3)(-\tfrac{2}{14}) = +3 .$$

*Table 14* shows the matrix product $AB=C$. If the order of the matrices $A$ and $B$ is interchanged in this multiplication, a different product is obtained. This is readily verified numerically in *Table 14;* and it illustrates the principle that if $AB=C$, then, in general, $BA \neq C$. Matrix multiplication is not commutative. In matrix algebra it is essential to note the order of the matrix factors because the order is not arbitrary, as in ordinary algebra, where $ab=ba$.

The following is an example of matrix algebra. If, instead of (7) and (11), the transposed forms of these equations were used, we should have

(9) $$y'A' = x' ,$$

(13) $$z'B' = y' .$$

Substituting (13) in (9), we have

$$(14) \qquad\qquad z'B'A' = x' .$$

But

$$(15) \qquad\qquad AB \equiv C .$$

Hence

$$(16) \qquad\qquad B'A' = C' .$$

Substituting (16) in (14), we obtain

$$(17) \qquad\qquad z'C' = x' ,$$

which could also be written directly as the transposed form of (12).

In order that there shall be a unique solution for the simultaneous equations (2), the matrix $A$ of the coefficients must be non-singular, i.e., $|A| \neq 0$. This may be tested by trying to solve a set of non-homogeneous simultaneous equations with coefficients whose determinant does vanish.

The multiplication of matrices is associative. This is illustrated as follows:

$$(AB)C = A(BC) = ABC .$$

The matrix product $(AB)$ may be determined and then *postmultiplied* by $C$, or the matrix product $(BC)$ may be determined and then *premultiplied* by $A$. The product is the same. This principle can be extended to any number of matrix factors. For example,

$$(ABC)D = (AB)(CD) = A(BCD) = ABCD .$$

Note that the order of the matrix factors is retained.

The sum, or difference, of two $m \times n$ matrices is the $m \times n$ matrix each of whose elements is the sum, or difference, of the corresponding elements in the given matrices.

$$\left\| \begin{array}{cc} 1 & 2 \\ 3 & 4 \end{array} \right\| + \left\| \begin{array}{cc} 2 & 3 \\ 4 & 5 \end{array} \right\| = \left\| \begin{array}{cc} 3 & 5 \\ 7 & 9 \end{array} \right\| .$$

The components may be written in any order.

$$A + B = B + A ;$$

$$(A + B) + C = A + (B + C) = A + B + C .$$

If $k$ and $m$ are scalars, then

$$kA + kB = k(A + B) ;$$

$$kA + mA = (k + m)A .$$

The multiplication of matrices is distributive.

$$A(B + C) = AB + AC ;$$

$$(B + C)A = BA + CA .$$

It can be shown that *the rank of a matrix product cannot exceed the lowest rank of any of the factors.* Thus, if the ranks of matrices $A$, $B$, and $C$ are 2, 4, and 3, respectively, then the rank of the matrix product $ABC$ cannot exceed 2.

It is sometimes useful to know that *the determinant of the product of two square matrices is equal to the product of their determinants.* The following is an example:

$$\text{Let } |A| = \begin{vmatrix} 2 & 6 \\ 4 & 7 \end{vmatrix} = -10 , \qquad \text{and let } |B| = \begin{vmatrix} 2 & 1 \\ 3 & 4 \end{vmatrix} = +5 .$$

Then

$$|A| \cdot |B| = |AB| = \begin{vmatrix} 22 & 26 \\ 29 & 32 \end{vmatrix} = -50 = (-10)(+5) .$$

In the matrix product $AB$, the matrix $B$ is said to be *premultiplied* by the matrix $A$, or the matrix $A$ is said to be *postmultiplied* by the matrix $B$.

The operation of multiplying one matrix by another can be summarized for mnemonic purposes in the diagram of *Figure 1*. This diagram shows that rows of the first matrix are associated with columns of the second matrix and that the middle subscript is eliminated in the product. If the $i$th row of $A$ is cross multiplied with the $k$th column of $B$, the cross product is recorded in the cell $ik$ of $C$.

There is nothing magical or profound in the particular rules of matrix multiplication that have become conventional. The *row-by-column* rule is entirely arbitrary. It would have been possible to set up a column-by-row rule provided that the matrices had been so arranged that the rule would have reproduced the original equations which the matrix notation represent-

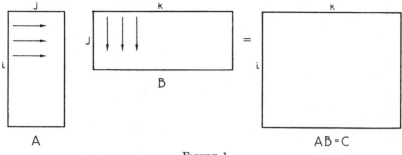

FIGURE 1

ed. It would also have been possible to have a notation which implied that one matrix was on top of another, but this would not have been so convenient for writing habits that go from left to right.

## Diagonal matrices

In the manipulation of systems of equations there occurs frequently a type of matrix in which all of the elements are zero except the diagonal elements. A matrix in which only the elements of the principal diagonal are non-vanishing is called a *diagonal matrix*. The following is a diagonal matrix of order 4:

$$\left\| \begin{array}{cccc} a & 0 & 0 & 0 \\ 0 & b & 0 & 0 \\ 0 & 0 & c & 0 \\ 0 & 0 & 0 & d \end{array} \right\| = D = a \text{ diagonal matrix.}$$

It sometimes happens that all of the elements of a diagonal matrix are identical. Such a matrix is called a *scalar matrix*. The following is an example:

$$\left\| \begin{array}{cccc} k & 0 & 0 & 0 \\ 0 & k & 0 & 0 \\ 0 & 0 & k & 0 \\ 0 & 0 & 0 & k \end{array} \right\| = K = a \text{ scalar matrix.}$$

When a diagonal matrix has unity in each diagonal cell, it is called a *unit matrix* or the *identity matrix*. The following is an identity matrix of order 4:

$$\begin{Vmatrix} 1 & 0 & 0 & 0 \\ 0 & 1 & 0 & 0 \\ 0 & 0 & 1 & 0 \\ 0 & 0 & 0 & 1 \end{Vmatrix} = I = the\ identity\ matrix.$$

The properties of diagonal matrices are very useful in handling sets of linear equations:

1) Premultiplication $DA$ with a diagonal matrix $D$ multiplies each *row* of $A$ by the corresponding element in $D$.

2) Postmultiplication $AD$ with a diagonal matrix $D$ multiplies each *column* of $A$ by the corresponding element in $D$.

$$\underset{D}{\begin{Vmatrix} p & 0 \\ 0 & q \end{Vmatrix}} \cdot \underset{A}{\begin{Vmatrix} a & b \\ c & d \end{Vmatrix}} = \underset{DA}{\begin{Vmatrix} ap & bp \\ cq & dq \end{Vmatrix}} ;$$

$$\underset{A}{\begin{Vmatrix} a & b \\ c & d \end{Vmatrix}} \cdot \underset{D}{\begin{Vmatrix} p & 0 \\ 0 & q \end{Vmatrix}} = \underset{AD}{\begin{Vmatrix} ap & bq \\ cp & dq \end{Vmatrix}}$$

3) Premultiplication or postmultiplication with a scalar matrix $K$ multiplies all elements of $A$ by the constant element of $K$. This is a special case of the first two theorems. The reason why premultiplication with a scalar matrix has the same effect as postmultiplication is that if every row is multiplied by a constant $p$, the effect is the same as if every column is multiplied by the constant $p$. In either case every element of $A$ is multiplied by $p$.

$$\underset{A}{\begin{Vmatrix} a & b \\ c & d \end{Vmatrix}} \cdot \underset{K}{\begin{Vmatrix} p & 0 \\ 0 & p \end{Vmatrix}} = \underset{AK}{\begin{Vmatrix} ap & bp \\ cp & dp \end{Vmatrix}} ;$$

$$\underset{K}{\begin{Vmatrix} p & 0 \\ 0 & p \end{Vmatrix}} \cdot \underset{A}{\begin{Vmatrix} a & b \\ c & d \end{Vmatrix}} = \underset{KA}{\begin{Vmatrix} ap & bp \\ cp & dp \end{Vmatrix}} ;$$

$$\underset{K}{\begin{Vmatrix} p & 0 \\ 0 & p \end{Vmatrix}} \cdot \underset{A}{\begin{Vmatrix} a & b \\ c & d \end{Vmatrix}} = p \underset{pA}{\begin{Vmatrix} a & b \\ c & d \end{Vmatrix}} .$$

Since the effect of a scalar matrix is independent of its position before or after the other matrices in a matrix product, its constant element $p$ can be used in the product instead of the scalar matrix $K$ as shown in the third example. This illustrates the following theorem:

4) If $K$ is a scalar matrix, then its constant element $p$ may be substituted for the scalar matrix in a product.

$$AK = KA = pA = Ap .$$

A multiplier which is independent of the non-commutative rule of matrix algebra is called a *scalar*.

5) To multiply a matrix $A$ by a scalar $p$, in either order, $pA$ or $Ap$, is to multiply each element of $A$ by $p$.

The identity matrix is a special case of the scalar matrix, and hence it is also independent of the non-commutative rule of matrix multiplication.

$$\begin{Vmatrix} 1 & 0 \\ 0 & 1 \end{Vmatrix} \cdot \begin{Vmatrix} a & b \\ c & d \end{Vmatrix} = \begin{Vmatrix} a & b \\ c & d \end{Vmatrix} ;$$
$$\quad I \qquad\qquad A \qquad\qquad IA = A$$

$$\begin{Vmatrix} a & b \\ c & d \end{Vmatrix} \cdot \begin{Vmatrix} 1 & 0 \\ 0 & 1 \end{Vmatrix} = \begin{Vmatrix} a & b \\ c & d \end{Vmatrix} .$$
$$\quad A \qquad\qquad I \qquad\qquad AI = A$$

6) To multiply a matrix $A$ by the identity matrix, in either order, $AI$ or $IA$, is to reproduce the matrix $A$ unaltered.

$$AI = IA = A .$$

The identity matrix $I$ in matrix algebra corresponds to unity in ordinary algebra. Hence the identity matrix is suppressed, just as unity is suppressed in ordinary algebra.

$$1 \times 5 = 5 ,$$

$$1 \times x = x ,$$

$$IA = A .$$

**The inverse**

If a matrix $A$ is non-singular, i.e., $|A| \neq 0$, then there exists another unique matrix such that its multiplication by $A$ produces the identity matrix. This other matrix is called the *inverse* of $A$, and it is denoted $A^{-1}$ Hence, if $A$ is non-singular,

$$AA^{-1} = I .$$

The inverse of $A^{-1}$ is $A$, so that

$$AA^{-1} = I = A^{-1}A .$$

Consider the ordinary algebraic equation,

$$ax = y .$$

If it is desired to state $x$ explicitly, the equation is ordinarily written as

$$x = \frac{1}{a} y .$$

If the given matrix equation is

$$AB = C$$

and if it is desired to write it explicitly for $B$, this cannot be accomplished by ordinary division. A matrix is not a number but a rectangular table of numbers. There is an operation in matrix algebra which corresponds to division in ordinary algebra. If both members of the matrix equation $AB = C$ are premultiplied by $A^{-1}$, we have

$$A^{-1}AB = A^{-1}C .$$

But

$$A^{-1}A = I .$$

Hence

$$IB = A^{-1}C ,$$

or

$$B = A^{-1}C .$$

This is the desired form. This example illustrates the operation in matrix algebra which corresponds to division in ordinary algebra. It consists in moving a premultiplying or postmultiplying factor from one member of the equation to the other member in the same relative position. This operation is illustrated in the following examples:

If

$$ABC = M ,$$

then

$$BC = A^{-1}M ,$$
$$C = B^{-1}A^{-1}M ,$$
$$CM^{-1} = B^{-1}A^{-1} ,$$
$$CM^{-1}A = B^{-1} ,$$
$$M^{-1}A = C^{-1}B^{-1}$$

Since this operation is analogous to ordinary division, the inverse of $A$ is sometimes called the *reciprocal* of $A$.

*The inverse of any product of matrices is the product of their inverses in reverse order.*

Let
$$ABC = M \, ,$$
$$BC = A^{-1}M \, ,$$
$$C = B^{-1}A^{-1}M \, ,$$
$$I = C^{-1}B^{-1}A^{-1}M \, ,$$
$$M^{-1} = C^{-1}B^{-1}A^{-1} \, .$$

But
$$(ABC)^{-1} = M^{-1} \, .$$

Hence
$$(ABC)^{-1} = C^{-1}B^{-1}A^{-1} \, .$$

A method of writing the inverse of a given matrix is as follows: Let the given matrix be $A$ with elements $a_{ij}$.

1) Write the matrix $M$ with elements $m_{ij}$ which are the first minors of the elements $a_{ij}$;

2) Reverse the signs of alternate elements of $M$ so that it becomes the matrix $E$ with elements $e_{ij} = (-1)^{i+j}m_{ij}$;

3) Write the transpose of $E$, namely, $E' = F$, with elements $f_{ij} = e_{ji}$. The matrix $F$ is the adjoint of $A$;

4) Divide each element of $F$ by the value of the determinant $|A|$. This is the inverse $A^{-1}$ with elements

$$g_{ij} = \frac{f_{ij}}{|A|} \, .$$

The writing of an inverse will be illustrated by the numerical example of equations (2). The given matrix equation is

$$Ay = x \, .$$

It is desired to find the inverse of $A$ so that the equation

$$y = A^{-1}x$$

may be written in numerical form.

$$\left\| \begin{matrix} 1 & 2 & 0 \\ 0 & 3 & 1 \\ 2 & 2 & 4 \end{matrix} \right\| = A ; \qquad |A| = +14 .$$

$$\left\| \begin{matrix} 10 & -2 & -6 \\ 8 & 4 & -2 \\ 2 & 1 & 3 \end{matrix} \right\| = M ,$$

$$\left\| \begin{matrix} 10 & 2 & -6 \\ -8 & 4 & 2 \\ 2 & -1 & 3 \end{matrix} \right\| = E ,$$

$$\left\| \begin{matrix} 10 & -8 & 2 \\ 2 & 4 & -1 \\ -6 & 2 & 3 \end{matrix} \right\| = F ,$$

$$\left\| \begin{matrix} \frac{10}{14} & -\frac{8}{14} & \frac{2}{14} \\ \frac{2}{14} & \frac{4}{14} & -\frac{1}{14} \\ -\frac{6}{14} & \frac{2}{14} & \frac{3}{14} \end{matrix} \right\| = A^{-1} ; \qquad |A^{-1}| = +\frac{1}{14} .$$

It is of interest to verify numerically the matrix equation $y = A^{-1}x$. It is written in rectangular notation in *Table 16*.

*Table 16*

$$\left\| \begin{matrix} \frac{10}{14} & -\frac{8}{14} & \frac{2}{14} \\ \frac{2}{14} & \frac{4}{14} & -\frac{1}{14} \\ -\frac{6}{14} & \frac{2}{14} & \frac{3}{14} \end{matrix} \right\| \cdot \left\| \begin{matrix} 1 \\ 3 \\ 2 \end{matrix} \right\| = \left\| \begin{matrix} -\frac{10}{14} \\ \frac{12}{14} \\ \frac{6}{14} \end{matrix} \right\| .$$

$$\qquad A^{-1} \qquad\qquad x \qquad\qquad y$$

In a later section of this Mathematical Introduction will be found a practical computing method for the inverse. The method described above is not suitable for matrices of large order.

## The characteristic equation

The characteristic equation is of considerable theoretical interest in factor analysis, and it appears in several of the fundamental factor problems. For this reason it is described in this introduction. In a more complete didactic presentation of this subject, the characteristic equation should be introduced with some geometric and other interpretation, so that the significance of this equation might be apparent. The relation of the characteristic equation to the problems of factor theory will appear in later chapters.

If a constant $\beta$ is added explicitly to each diagonal element of a square matrix $A$, the resulting matrix is called the *characteristic matrix* of $A$. It is illustrated as follows:

$$
\begin{Vmatrix} a_{11} & a_{12} & a_{13} \\ a_{21} & a_{22} & a_{23} \\ a_{31} & a_{32} & a_{33} \end{Vmatrix} + \beta \begin{Vmatrix} 1 & 0 & 0 \\ 0 & 1 & 0 \\ 0 & 0 & 1 \end{Vmatrix} = \begin{Vmatrix} (a_{11}+\beta) & a_{12} & a_{13} \\ a_{21} & (a_{22}+\beta) & a_{23} \\ a_{31} & a_{32} & (a_{33}+\beta) \end{Vmatrix}
$$

$$
\qquad A \qquad\qquad\qquad \beta I \qquad\qquad\qquad\qquad (A+\beta I)
$$

*Characteristic matrix of A.*

The determinant of the characteristic matrix is the *characteristic determinant* of $A$.

The expansion of a characteristic determinant of order $r$ is a polynomial of degree $r$. When this polynomial is set equal to zero, the equation is called the *characteristic equation* of $A$. An example is the following equation:

$$
\begin{vmatrix} (1+\beta) & 0 & 1 \\ 1 & (2+\beta) & 1 \\ 1 & 0 & (2+\beta) \end{vmatrix} = 0 .
$$

When the determinant is expanded, the characteristic equation becomes

$$
\beta^3 + 5\beta^2 + 7\beta + 2 = 0 .
$$

The coefficients of the expansion of a characteristic determinant can be written in terms of the principal minors without expanding the whole determinant. Let the characteristic equation be as follows:

(18) $$\beta^r + m_1\beta^{r-1} + m_2\beta^{r-2} + \cdots + m_r = 0 .$$

Then the coefficient $m_x$ is the sum of all the $x$-rowed principal minors in $A$. The coefficient $m_1$ is the sum of all the 1-rowed principal minors of $A$. These are 1, 2, 2, and the sum is $+5$. The coefficient $m_2$ is the sum of all the 2-rowed principal minors of $A$. These are

$$
\begin{vmatrix} 1 & 0 \\ 1 & 2 \end{vmatrix} = 2 ; \qquad \begin{vmatrix} 1 & 1 \\ 1 & 2 \end{vmatrix} = 1 ; \qquad \begin{vmatrix} 2 & 1 \\ 0 & 2 \end{vmatrix} = 4 .
$$

The coefficient $m_2 = 2+1+4 = +7$. The coefficient $m_3$ is the sum of all principal minors of order 3. This is the determinant $|A|$ itself, and its value is $+2$. The coefficient of the highest power of $\beta$ is unity. These coefficients can be verified by expanding the determinant.

Another method for finding the coefficients of a characteristic equation has been described by Paul Horst in the *Annals of Mathematical Statistics*, Vol. VI, No. 2 (June, 1935).

## The summational notation

If a set of $n$ numbers is to be summed, the operation may be indicated in the *expanded* form,

$$(19) \qquad x_1 + x_2 + x_3 + \cdots + x_n = y .$$

The same operation may be indicated in the more condensed summational form, namely,

$$(20) \qquad \sum_{i=1}^{n} x_i = y ,$$

in which the subscript $i$ takes the successive integral values from 1 to $n$, inclusive.

In statistical work it is pedantic to indicate the limits, because the summation is over the entire population except in rare cases, which can be specially indicated. It is acceptable practice in statistical work to write $\Sigma x$ without subscripts when the usual form of summation over the population is implied. In factor analysis this simple and convenient notation becomes ambiguous because summation may be over the factors, over the population, or over the variables. It is therefore advisable to adopt the unambiguous double-subscript notation that is conventional in mathematics.

As an example, the sum of the elements in the first row of *Table 2* can be written in the form

$$a_{11} + a_{12} + a_{13} + \cdots + a_{1n} = \sum_{i=1}^{n} a_{1j} .$$

Here it is the second subscript $j$, representing the columns, which is found in the summation sign. This means that the $a$'s are to be summed for all values of $j$ from 1 to $n$. The first subscript is fixed. The summation is thereby confined to one row.

The notation can be generalized to represent any row $i$. It then takes the form

$$a_{i1} + a_{i2} + a_{i3} + \cdots + a_{in} = \sum_{j=1}^{n} a_{ij} .$$

This notation means that the $a$'s are to be summed for a fixed value of $i$, since $i$ does not occur in the summation. The $a$'s are to be summed in one row $i$ for all the column values of $j$ from 1 to $n$.

By analogy, the sum of all the elements in a column $j$ of *Table 2* may be represented as follows:

$$a_{1j} + a_{2j} + a_{3j} + \cdots + a_{mj} = \sum_{i=1}^{m} a_{ij}.$$

Here it is the column $j$ that is fixed because it does not occur in the summation sign. The $a$'s are to be summed in some specified column $j$ for all values of $i$ from 1 to $m$.

If it is desired to designate the sum of all the elements in the matrix, each of the $m$-row sums must be summed. This involves a summation over both $i$ and $j$. We then have

$$\text{Sum of all elements in } A = \sum_{i=1}^{m} \sum_{j=1}^{n} a_{ij}.$$

Since it does not matter whether the rows are summed before the columns, or vice versa, we have

$$\sum_{j=1}^{n} \sum_{i=1}^{m} a_{ij} = \sum_{i=1}^{m} \sum_{j=1}^{n} a_{ij}.$$

A matrix multiplication can also be designated by the summational notation. Consider the matrix multiplication $AB = C$ of *Table 17*.

*Table 17*

|  | $j(n)$ | | | | $k(p)$ | | | | $k(p)$ | | |
|---|---|---|---|---|---|---|---|---|---|---|---|
| $i(m)$ | $a_{11}$ | $a_{12}$ | $a_{13}$ | $j(n)$ | $b_{11}$ | $b_{12}$ | $b_{13}$ | $=i(m)$ | $c_{11}$ | $c_{12}$ | $c_{13}$ |
|  | $a_{21}$ | $a_{22}$ | $a_{23}$ |  | $b_{21}$ | $b_{22}$ | $b_{23}$ |  | $c_{21}$ | $c_{22}$ | $c_{23}$ |
|  | $a_{31}$ | $a_{32}$ | $a_{33}$ |  | $b_{31}$ | $b_{32}$ | $b_{33}$ |  | $c_{31}$ | $c_{32}$ | $c_{33}$ |
|  | $a_{41}$ | $a_{42}$ | $a_{43}$ |  |  |  |  |  | $c_{41}$ | $c_{42}$ | $c_{43}$ |
|  | | $A$ | | | | $B$ | | | | $AB=C$ | |

Let $A$ be a matrix of order $m \times n$ with general element $a_{ij}$. Let $B$ be a matrix of order $n \times p$ with general element $b_{jk}$. Then the product $AB = C$ must be a matrix of order $m \times p$ with the general element $c_{ik}$. The middle subscript $j$ for the general element disappears in the product, and so does the middle dimension $n$ in the product $(mn)(np) = (mp)$. In the example, $m = 4$, $n = 3$, $p = 3$.

The element $c_{11}$ is obtained by the cross multiplication of the first row of $A$ and the first column of $B$. In summational notation,

$$(21) \qquad a_{11}b_{11} + a_{12}b_{21} + a_{13}b_{31} = \sum_{j=1}^{n} a_{1j}b_{j1} = c_{11} .$$

The second row of $A$ and the first column of $B$:

$$(22) \qquad a_{21}b_{11} + a_{22}b_{21} + a_{23}b_{31} = \sum_{j=1}^{n} a_{2j}b_{j1} = c_{21} .$$

The $i$th row of $A$ and the first column of $B$:

$$(23) \qquad a_{i1}b_{11} + a_{i2}b_{21} + a_{i3}b_{31} = \sum_{j=1}^{n} a_{ij}b_{j1} = c_{i1} .$$

The $i$th row of $A$ and the $k$th column of $B$:

$$(24) \qquad a_{i1}b_{1k} + a_{i2}b_{2k} + a_{i3}b_{3k} = \sum_{j=1}^{n} a_{ij}b_{jk} = c_{ik} .$$

The summation of (24) gives a single element in $C$. If it is desired to indicate the sum of all the elements in the $i$th row of $C$, the summation will be over $k$ with a fixed value for $i$. We have then

$$(25) \qquad \sum_{k=1}^{p} \sum_{j=1}^{n} a_{ij}b_{jk} = \sum_{k=1}^{p} c_{ik} .$$

Finally, if the sum of all the elements in $C$ is to be indicated, the summation must also be made for all rows. Then

$$(26) \qquad \sum_{i=1}^{m} \sum_{k=1}^{p} \sum_{j=1}^{n} a_{ij}b_{jk} = \sum_{i=1}^{m} \sum_{k=1}^{p} c_{ik} .$$

The summation of (24) represents the multiplication of two matrices, $a_{ij}$ and $b_{jk}$, whose product is the matrix $c_{ik}$. It can be visualized in *Figure 1*.

As an example of manipulation with the summational notation, consider the first term of equation (12–i). It is

$$\frac{1}{N}\sum_{i=1}^{N}\sum_{m=1}^{r}a_{jm}^{2}x_{mi}^{2} \; ,$$

in which it is desired to substitute

$$\frac{1}{N}\sum_{i=1}^{N}x_{mi}^{2} = 1 \; ,$$

in order to simplify the first term.

Since the order of summation is arbitrary, the order of the summations may be interchanged. Then the first term becomes

$$\frac{1}{N}\sum_{m=1}^{r}\sum_{i=1}^{N}a_{jm}^{2}x_{mi}^{2} \; .$$

Since the subscript $i$ does not occur in $a_{jm}^{2}$, this factor is a constant during the summation over $i$. Hence, it may be placed in front of the summation over $i$ without altering the value of the first term, which then becomes

$$\frac{1}{N}\sum_{m=1}^{r}a_{jm}^{2}\sum_{i=1}^{N}x_{mi}^{2} \; .$$

But the reciprocal of $N$ is a scalar, and so it can be placed anywhere in the summation. Changing its relative position, the first term becomes

$$\sum_{m=1}^{r}a_{jm}^{2}\frac{1}{N}\sum_{i=1}^{N}x_{mi}^{2} \; ,$$

and now the substitution can be made more clearly. Suppressing the part which is equal to unity, the expression simplifies into

$$\sum_{m=1}^{r}a_{jm}^{2} \; .$$

These steps are more explicit than will ordinarily be found necessary, but they illustrate further the manner in which the summational notation can be handled.

## Linear dependence

A matrix of order $m \times n$ may be regarded as $m$ sets of numbers with $n$ numbers in each set. Each row of numbers is then a set. *Table 18* is a matrix

*Table 18*

$$\begin{Vmatrix} 2 & 3 & 5 & 1 & 4 & 2 \\ 4 & 6 & 10 & 2 & 8 & 4 \\ 1 & \frac{3}{2} & \frac{5}{2} & \frac{1}{2} & 2 & 1 \\ 6 & 9 & 15 & 3 & 12 & 6 \end{Vmatrix}$$

of order $4 \times 6$. In this table every row can be expressed linearly in terms of the first row. By this is meant that for any row $i$ there exists a constant $c_i$ such that

$$(27) \qquad\qquad a_{ij} = c_i a_{1j} .$$

For the fourth row the constant $c_i$ is 3, so that each element in the fourth row is three times the corresponding element in the first row. When any row can be so expressed in terms of the first row, the rows are *proportional*, and it can be shown that the columns are then also proportional. If two rows are not proportional, they are said to be *linearly independent*, for one of them cannot be expressed linearly in terms of the other. When each row can be expressed linearly in terms of one row, the rank of the matrix is 1. This means that all second-order minors vanish. This fact is readily verified in *Table 18*.

The idea of proportionality can be generalized to two or more dimensions. An example of rank 2 is shown in *Table 19*. In this matrix any row can be

*Table 19*

$$\begin{Vmatrix} 7 & 5 & 4 & 6 & 7 & 2 \\ 2 & 2 & 0 & 4 & 2 & 4 \\ 5 & 4 & 2 & 6 & 5 & 4 \\ 9 & 7 & 4 & 10 & 9 & 6 \end{Vmatrix}$$

expressed as a linear function of any two rows. In this particular matrix there are no two dependent rows. This requires that two constants $c_1$ and $c_2$ (not both zero) exist such that

$$(28) \qquad\qquad a_{ij} = c_1 a_{1j} + c_2 a_{2j} ,$$

where the elements in the $i$th row are expressed linearly in terms of the first two rows.

In the following example the two constants for the third row of *Table 19* are determined. For the first two entries in the third row,

(29)
$$\begin{cases} 5 = 7c_1 + 2c_2 \, , \\ 4 = 5c_1 + 2c_2 \, . \end{cases}$$

Solving (29) simultaneously, we find that $c_1 = 1/2$ and $c_2 = 3/4$. Testing this on the last column, as an example,

$$(2)(\tfrac{1}{2}) + (4)(\tfrac{3}{4}) = 4 \, .$$

A different set of constants must be determined for each successive independent row.

Since each of the rows in *Table 19* can be expressed linearly in terms of the first two rows, it can be shown that the matrix of *Table 19* is of rank 2. This implies that all third-order minors vanish. As an example, the following third-order minor of *Table 19* vanishes.

$$\begin{vmatrix} 5 & 6 & 7 \\ 4 & 6 & 5 \\ 7 & 10 & 9 \end{vmatrix} = 0$$

It can be shown that if the rank of a matrix is $r$, then there exists a set of $r$ columns, or rows, in terms of which each column, or row, can be linearly expressed.

## Geometric interpretation of linear equations

The most frequent form of equation for a straight line in a plane is probably

(30)
$$y = mx + p \, ,$$

in which $x$ and $y$ are the two variables while $m$ and $p$ are two independent parameters. This agrees with the well-known fact that any two points determine a straight line. The multiplying constant $m$ is the slope, and the additive constant $p$ is the $y$-intercept. In the present context it will be more useful to begin with the equation of a straight line in the more general form:

(31)
$$a_1x_1 + a_2x_2 + k = 0 \, .$$

This equation has two variables, $x_1$ and $x_2$, and three parameters, $a_1$, $a_2$, $k$. Since only two points are needed to determine the line, it follows that the three parameters are not independent.

Equation (31) can evidently be multiplied by any arbitrary constant without affecting its geometrical representation in the plane. Then (31) becomes

$$(32) \qquad\qquad ca_1x_1 + ca_2x_2 + ck = 0 .$$

Let the multiplier $c$ be so chosen that *the sum of the squares of the coefficients of the variables is equal to unity.* Then

$$(33) \qquad\qquad (ca_1)^2 + (ca_2)^2 = 1 ,$$

or

$$(34) \qquad\qquad c = \frac{1}{\sqrt{a_1^2 + a_2^2}}$$

Let $ca_1 = \lambda_1$; $ca_2 = \lambda_2$; $ck = d$. Then

$$(35) \qquad\qquad \lambda_1x_1 + \lambda_2x_2 + d = 0 ,$$

where

$$(36) \qquad\qquad \lambda_1^2 + \lambda_2^2 = 1 .$$

When the equation is written with this adjustment, it is said to be in *normal form.* This definition is applied not only to the equation of a line in a plane, and to the equation of a plane in a space of three dimensions, but also to the equation of a hyperplane of $(n-1)$ dimensions in a space of $n$ dimensions. The number of dimensions of the space defined by equation (35) is $(n-1)$ where $n$ is the number of variables. Hence equation (35) defines a space of one dimension, a line, in a space of $n = 2$ dimensions, a plane.

When a linear equation is in the normal form, the parameters have interesting meaning. The parameters $\lambda_1$ and $\lambda_2$ are the direction cosines of the normal to the linear space which is defined by equation (35); and the parameter $d$ is the distance from the origin to the same linear space. The normal to the line makes $\cos^{-1}\lambda_1$ with the $x_1$-axis and $\cos^{-1}\lambda_2$ with the $x_2$-axis. *The direction cosines of a space are the cosines of the angles that its normal makes with the Cartesian co-ordinate axes.* In the present case the space is a one-dimensional space, namely, that which is defined by equation (35). In order to avoid ambiguity, the normal is taken positive on the side which contains the origin. Equation (35) may be interpreted geometrically as defining a space of one dimension whose normal has the direction cosines $\lambda_1$ and $\lambda_2$ and which is distant $d$ from the origin.

If the parameter $d$ vanishes, then the space which is defined by the equation contains the origin. In equation (35) the line contains the origin if $d$ is zero.

Equation (35) locates a one-dimensional space (a line) in a two-dimensional space (a plane). If a new variable, $x_3$, is added, the equation takes the form

$$(37) \qquad \lambda_1 x_1 + \lambda_2 x_2 + \lambda_3 x_3 + d = 0 \ .$$

It defines a space of two dimensions (a plane) in a space of three dimensions with three orthogonal axes. Here, as before, if the equation is in normal form, then $d$ is the distance of the plane from the origin, and the three coefficients $\lambda_1, \lambda_2, \lambda_3$, are the direction cosines of the normal to the plane. They are the cosines of the angles that the normal makes with intersecting lines that are parallel to the $x_1$, $x_2$, and $x_3$ axes, respectively.

The direction cosines have the property that the sum of their squares is unity. In equation (35) the line is defined if the parameter $d$ and one of the direction cosines are given. In equation (37) the plane is defined by its distance from the origin and any two of its direction cosines. The third direction cosine can be found from the fact that the sum of the squares of the direction cosines equals unity. If $d$ vanishes in (37), the plane contains the origin. A plane through the origin is therefore defined by its direction cosines, which are the direction cosines of its normal.

An equation of the same form in $n$ variables is

$$(38) \qquad \lambda_1 x_1 + \lambda_2 x_2 + \lambda_3 x_3 + \ldots + \lambda_n x_n + d = 0 \ .$$

It defines a hyperplane of $(n-1)$ dimensions in a space of $n$ dimensions. If (38) is in normal form, $d$ is the distance of the hyperplane from the origin. The $\lambda$'s are the direction cosines of the normal to the hyperplane and hence

$$(39) \qquad \sum_{i=1}^{n} \lambda_i^2 = 1 \ .$$

In the present factor analysis the hyperplanes of primary interest contain the origin, so that the parameter $d$ vanishes. Then

$$(40) \qquad \lambda_1 x_1 + \lambda_2 x_2 + \lambda_3 x_3 + \ldots + \lambda_n x_n = 0 \ .$$

The $n$ values of $\lambda_i$ are said to be the direction cosines of the hyperplane $L$ which is defined by its normal $\Lambda$.

A matrix may be given a geometric interpretation. Let the matrix $A$ be of order $m \times n$. Then the $n$ elements of each row may be regarded as the Cartesian co-ordinates of a point in $n$ dimensions. Since there are $m$ rows, the matrix may be thought of as defining the positions of $m$ points, one for each row, in a space of $n$ dimensions. Table 20 is of order $6 \times 3$. It can therefore be regarded as defining the positions of six points in a space of three dimensions.

*Table 20*

$$\begin{Vmatrix} 1 & 2 & -4 \\ -4 & 1 & -11 \\ -2 & -3 & 5 \\ 3 & 5 & -9 \\ 4 & -2 & 14 \\ 0 & 1 & -3 \end{Vmatrix}$$

Let the rank of an $m \times n$ matrix $A$ be $r$. Then it can be shown that the $m$ points are contained in a space of $r$ dimensions which also contains the origin. The rank of the matrix of *Table 20* is 2. Hence the six points should lie in a plane which contains the origin. The equation of such a plane is

$$(41) \qquad \lambda_1 x_1 + \lambda_2 x_2 + \lambda_3 x_3 = 0 ,$$

in which the $x$'s are the three co-ordinates of each of the points in the plane and the $\lambda$'s are the direction cosines of the plane. The $\lambda$'s are not independent parameters because of the conditional equation (39). Hence any two $\lambda$'s define the plane. These may be found by any two of the six points which are not collinear with the origin. Since no two rows of *Table 20* are proportional, no two of the points are collinear with the origin. If two such points were found, then these two points would define a line through the origin and not a plane.

Substituting the $x$'s of the first two points of *Table 20* in (41),

$$(42) \qquad \begin{cases} \lambda_1 + 2\lambda_2 - 4\lambda_3 = 0 , \\ -4\lambda_1 + \lambda_2 - 11\lambda_3 = 0 . \end{cases}$$

Solving for $\lambda_1$ and $\lambda_2$ in terms of $\lambda_3$, we have

$$(43) \qquad \begin{cases} \lambda_1 = -2\lambda_3 , \\ \lambda_2 = 3\lambda_3 . \end{cases}$$

Substituting (43) in (39),

(44) $$4\lambda_3^2 + 9\lambda_3^2 + \lambda_3^2 = 1 ,$$

or

$$\lambda_3 = \frac{1}{\sqrt{14}} ,$$

and hence

$$\lambda_1 = - \frac{2}{\sqrt{14}} ,$$

$$\lambda_2 = \frac{3}{\sqrt{14}} .$$

The equation of the plane in normal form is therefore

(45) $$- \frac{2}{\sqrt{14}} x_1 + \frac{3}{\sqrt{14}} x_2 + \frac{1}{\sqrt{14}} x_3 = 0 .$$

All of the four remaining points must lie in this plane, since the rank of *Table 20* is 2. The three coefficients are the direction cosines of the plane, i.e., the direction cosines of the normal to the plane.

The distance of a point from the origin is $\sqrt{\Sigma x^2}$, where the $x$'s are its co-ordinates. For example, the distance of the fourth point from the origin is $\sqrt{3^2+5^2+(-9)^2}=10.72$. If the sum of the squares of the co-ordinates of a point is equal to unity, then the point is at unit distance from the origin.

Each point may be interpreted as defining the terminus of a vector from the origin. The *scalar product* of any two vectors is $h_1 h_2 \cos \phi$, where $h_1$ and $h_2$ are the lengths of the vectors and $\phi$ is their angular separation. If the two vectors are of unit length, then the scalar product is the cosine of the angular separation. It can be shown that the scalar product of two vectors can be expressed in the form

$$\sum_{j=1}^{n} x_{ij} x_{lj} ,$$

where $i$ and $l$ refer to points (rows) and $j$ refers to co-ordinates (columns). For example, the scalar product of the vectors defined by the second and fourth points of *Table 20* is

$$(-4)(3) + (1)(5) + (-11)(-9) = + 92 .$$

If the sum of the squares of the co-ordinates of each point is equal to unity, so that the points lie at unit distance from the origin, then the scalar product, or cross product, is the cosine of the angular separation of the vectors at the origin.

## Orthogonal transformations

The three simultaneous equations (2) may be regarded as representing the three co-ordinates of a point $x$ ($x_1$, $x_2$, $x_3$), the three co-ordinates of a point $y$ ($y_1$, $y_2$, $y_3$), and the law by which each point $y$ is transformed into a corresponding point $x$. For every point $y$, there exists some other point $x$ whose co-ordinates can be found by (2) when the co-ordinates of $y$ are known. This relation is called a *linear transformation* by which the points $y$ are moved to the corresponding points $x$. Every pair of the corresponding points is related by the linear transformation (2). The transformation is called *linear* when the equations by which the $x$'s can be found from the $y$'s are of the first degree, as is the case in (2).

If the transformation is of such nature that the $x$'s can be obtained from the $y$'s by merely rotating the co-ordinate axes, then the transformation is an *orthogonal transformation* or *rotational transformation*. In order that a transformation shall be orthogonal, it is evidently necessary that the $x$'s be at the same distance from the origin as the corresponding $y$'s because the distance of a point from the origin remains invariant when the co-ordinate axes are rotated. It is also necessary that the angular separations, or scalar products, be invariant, because the configuration of the points is not altered by rotating the co-ordinate axes.

The matrix $A$ of *Table 11* is called the *matrix of the transformation* when it is regarded as the relation by which the points $y$ are changed into the points $x$. A linear transformation is represented in the more general form by the square matrix of *Table 21*. It can be shown that a square matrix is

*Table 21*

$$
\begin{Vmatrix}
a_{11} & a_{12} & a_{13} & \ldots & a_{1n} \\
a_{21} & a_{22} & a_{23} & \ldots & a_{2n} \\
a_{31} & a_{32} & a_{33} & \ldots & a_{3n} \\
\ldots & \ldots & \ldots & a_{ij} & \ldots \\
a_{n1} & a_{n2} & a_{n3} & \ldots & a_{nn}
\end{Vmatrix}
$$

orthogonal, i.e., that it has the effect of rotating a set of points $y$ into a set of points $x$, with the same configuration as the $y$'s, if it satisfies the following conditions:

1) The sum of the squares of the elements in each row is equal to unity, i.e.,

$$(46) \qquad \sum_{j=1}^{n} a_{ij}^2 = 1 ,$$

and

2) The cross product of every pair of rows, $i$ and $l$, is equal to zero, i.e.,

$$(47) \qquad \sum_{j=1}^{n} a_{ij}a_{lj} = 0 ,$$

when $i \neq l$. It is immaterial whether the rotation is conceived as a rotation of the orthogonal co-ordinate axes in a fixed configuration of points or as a rotation of the configuration in a fixed reference frame of the co-ordinate axes. The result is the same.

The two conditions, (46) and (47), are of such frequent occurrence that it is sometimes convenient to combine them in a single statement. This can be done by writing the conditions in the more condensed form

$$(48) \qquad \delta_{il} = \sum_{j=1}^{n} a_{ij}a_{lj} ,$$

where the symbol $\delta_{il}$ is known as *Kronecker's delta*. It is defined as follows:

$$\delta_{il} = + 1 \text{ when } i = l ,$$

$$\delta_{il} = \quad 0 \text{ when } i \neq l .$$

It can be seen that with this definition of $\delta_{il}$, the single statement (48) covers the two statements (46) and (47).

If the matrix of a transformation is square and if it satisfies (48), then the following conditions are also satisfied:

3) The sum of the squares of the elements in each column is unity, i.e.,

$$(49) \qquad \sum_{i=1}^{n} a_{ij}^2 = 1 .$$

4) The cross product of any pair of columns is zero, i.e.,

(50)
$$\sum_{i=1}^{n} a_{ij}a_{ik} = 0, \qquad j \neq k,$$

where $j$ and $k$ refer to columns.

5) The determinant of the transformation is $\pm 1$, i.e.,

(51)
$$|A| = \pm 1.$$

If an orthogonal co-ordinate axis is reversed in direction, then the corresponding co-ordinate for each point is reversed in sign. If an odd number of orthogonal co-ordinate axes are reversed in direction in an orthogonal transformation, then the determinant of the transformation is equal to $-1$. If an even number of axes are reversed, the determinant is equal to $+1$. These two statements can be made with reference to the configuration. If the rotational transformation retains the configuration of the points, the determinant of the transformation is equal to $+1$. If the rotation involves a symmetric distortion of the configuration, the determinant of the orthogonal transformation is equal to $-1$.

Table 22

| | $X_1$ | $X_2$ | | $Y_1$ | $Y_2$ | | | $Y_1$ | $Y_2$ |
|---|---|---|---|---|---|---|---|---|---|
| $a$ | 1 | $-2$ | | .866 | $-.500$ | | $a$ | $-.134$ | $-2.232$ |
| $b$ | 2 | 3 | | .500 | .866 | $=$ | $b$ | 3.232 | 1.598 |
| $c$ | $-1$ | 4 | | | | | $c$ | 1.134 | 3.964 |
| $d$ | 5 | $-2$ | | $G$ | | | $d$ | 3.330 | $-4.232$ |
| $e$ | 4 | 1 | | | | | $e$ | 3.964 | $-1.134$ |
| | $A$ | | | | | | | $AG=B$ | |

Each column of an orthogonal transformation shows the direction cosines of one of the new co-ordinate axes, referred to the given co-ordinate axes.

A rotation of the co-ordinate axes implies that the given configuration and the transformed configuration are contained in the same space. The rows of a transformation correspond to the dimensions of the given configuration, and the columns of a transformation correspond to the dimensions of the new configuration. If the transformation is merely a rotation of axes, it is evident that the matrix of an orthogonal transformation is necessarily square. If the matrix of a transformation is of order $m \times n$ where $m \neq n$, then the transformation cannot be orthogonal, since the number of dimensions of the given configuration and the number of dimensions of the transformed configuration are not the same. However, such a matrix may satisfy condition (47), and it is then said to be *orthogonal by rows*. If the condition is satisfied for columns, as in (50), instead of for rows, then the matrix is said to be *orthogonal by columns*.

*Table 22* is a numerical example of the rotation of five points in a plane. $A$ is a matrix of order $5 \times 2$. The orthogonal transformation $G$ is of order $2 \times 2$. The matrix product $AG = B$ is of order $5 \times 2$, and it shows the co-

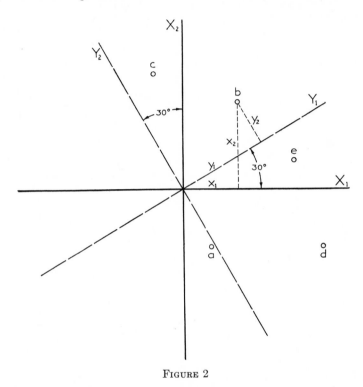

FIGURE 2

ordinates of the same five points with reference to the new rotated co-ordinate axes. In *Figure 2* the five points have been plotted for the given orthogonal co-ordinate axes, $X_1$ and $X_2$, that are implied in $A$.

Let it be desired to rotate these axes through an angle $\phi = 30°$. The usual formulae for rotation of axes* can be written in the form of a $2 \times 2$ transformation as follows:

$$\left\| \begin{array}{cc} \cos \phi & -\sin \phi \\ \sin \phi & \cos \phi \end{array} \right\|$$

* W. F. Osgood and W. C. Graustein, *Plane and Solid Analytic Geometry* (New York: Macmillan Co., 1929), p. 220.

The first condition (46) gives

$$\cos^2 \phi + \sin^2 \phi = + 1 ,$$

and the second condition (47) gives

$$\cos \phi \sin \phi - \cos \phi \sin \phi = 0 .$$

Hence this is an orthogonal transformation in which the other properties may be readily verified.

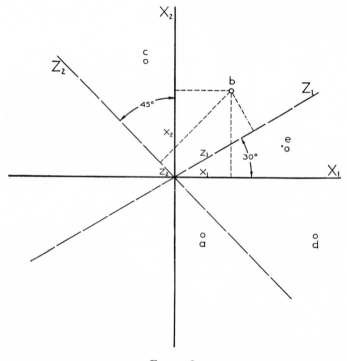

FIGURE 3

Substitution of $\phi = 30°$ in the transformation produces the matrix $G$, and the multiplication $AG$ produces $B$. The numerical values in $B$ may be checked in *Figure 2*, where $Y_1$ and $Y_2$ have been drawn so that $Y_1 O X_1 = \phi$ $= 30°$. For example, the co-ordinates of the second point can be measured on the graph to be 3.23 and 1.60 for the two rotated axes, while they are 2 and 3 for the two original axes. This figure illustrates the geometric interpretation of an orthogonal transformation. The two columns of the transformation $G$ show the direction cosines of the new orthogonal reference vectors $Y_1$ and $Y_2$.

## Oblique transformations

In *Figure 2* the two co-ordinate axes $Y_1$ and $Y_2$ are orthogonal. If it is desired to define the $n$ points with reference to oblique reference axes, the transformation is effected in a similar way. In *Figure 3* the same five points are plotted on the $X_1$ and $X_2$ axes which are implied in the given matrix $A$ of *Table 22*. Here the new axes are oblique; $Z_1$ is rotated $30°$ from $X_1$, and $Z_2$ is rotated $45°$ from $X_2$.

In *Table 23* are shown the numerical values for the corresponding oblique transformation. The matrix $A$ contains the co-ordinates of the given five

*Table 23*

| | $X_1$ | $X_2$ | | $Z_1$ | $Z_2$ | | | $Z_1$ | $Z_2$ |
|---|---|---|---|---|---|---|---|---|---|
| $a$ | 1 | −2 | | .866 | −.707 | | $a$ | −.134 | −2.121 |
| $b$ | 2 | 3 | $\cdot$ | .500 | .707 | $=$ | $b$ | 3.232 | .707 |
| $c$ | −1 | 4 | | | | | $c$ | 1.134 | 3.535 |
| $d$ | 5 | −2 | | $H$ | | | $d$ | 3.330 | −4.949 |
| $e$ | 4 | 1 | | | | | $e$ | 3.964 | −2.121 |
| | | $A$ | | | | | | $AH = C$ | |

points in a space defined by the two orthogonal reference axes $X_1$ and $X_2$. The matrix $H$ is a square matrix of order $2 \times 2$. It is the matrix of the oblique transformation. Its columns show the direction cosines of the new oblique co-ordinate axes $Z_1$ and $Z_2$. These direction cosines may be verified in *Figure 3*.

It should be noted that the sum of the squares of each column of $H$ is equal to unity. Each column of $H$ may be regarded as defining a unit vector in a space of two dimensions. The cross product of the columns of $H$ is

$$\lambda_1 \mu_1 + \lambda_2 \mu_2 ,$$

which is the cosine of the angle between $Z_1$ and $Z_2$.

The product $AH = C$ shows the projection of each of the five points on each of the oblique axes $Z_1$ and $Z_2$. This interpretation can be verified by actual measurement on *Figure 3*.

### A method of finding the roots of a polynomial

Consider a polynomial of the type

(52)          $f(\beta) = c_0\beta^r + c_1\beta^{r-1} + c_2\beta^{r-2} + \cdots c_{r-1}\beta + c_r = 0$ ,

where $r$ is a positive integer, $c_0 \neq 0$, and $c_0, c_1, \ldots, c_r$ are real coefficients. The $r$ roots, $\beta$, of this equation are desired. Determine the upper and lower limits* of the roots of this equation. Let a trial value of $\beta$ within these limits be $\beta'$. If $\beta'$ is a root of the polynomial $f(\beta)$, then by the Remainder Theorem,† $f(\beta') = 0$. The numerical value of $f(\beta')$ may be determined on an electric calculating machine by computing $f(\beta)/(\beta - \beta')$ by the process of synthetic division.‡ Consider the sign of the numerical value of $f(\beta')$ and select a second trial root, designated $\beta''$, which will give $f(\beta'')$ opposite in sign to that of $f(\beta')$. When two such trial values of $\beta$ are found, there is at least one root§ between them. Determine a third trial value, $\beta'''$, by linear interpolation between $f(\beta')$ and $f(\beta'')$. If the value $f(\beta''') = 0$, then $\beta'''$ is one of the $r$ roots of the polynomial. If $f(\beta''') \neq 0$, interpolate for successive trial values until that value of $\beta$ is found for which the remainder, $f(\beta)$, is zero to as many decimals as required.

Repeat this process for each of the $r$ roots of the polynomial by taking trial values in other regions between the upper and lower limits of the roots. In the method of principal axes, a very useful first approximation for each

root, $\beta_m$, of the characteristic equation is $-\sum_{j=1}^{n} a_{jm}^2$ for each column $m$ of $F$,

when $c_0, c_1, \ldots, c_r$ are all positive.

*Table 25* shows the application of the method of synthetic division in calculating one of the roots of the equation:

(53)   $\beta^4 + 6.965369\beta^3 + 10.810494\beta^2 + 5.407203\beta + .840052 = 0$ .

The upper limit of the roots of this equation is any *positive* number; the

lower limit is $-7.965369$. The first trial value $\beta' = -5.011317 = -\sum_{j=1}^{n} a_{j1}^2$,

as found in a principal-axis problem. Since $f(\beta')$ is negative, $\beta'' = -5.020000$ was chosen arbitrarily to secure a positive value of $f(\beta'')$. Linear interpolation between $f(\beta')$ and $f(\beta'')$ gave the third trial value, $\beta''' = -5.019710$.

---

* L. E. Dickson, *First Course in the Theory of Equations* (New York: John Wiley & Sons, 1922), pp. 21–23.

† *Ibid.*, p. 12.          ‡ *Ibid.*, pp. 13–15.          § *Ibid.*, p. 67.

Linear interpolation between $f(\beta''')$ and $f(\beta'')$ gave the fourth trial value, $\beta'''' = -5.019712$, for which the value of the polynomial is $+.000018$. Hence, one root of this equation is $-5.019712$.

The values of $f(\beta)$ in each row of *Table 25* were determined by the equations in their corresponding rows of *Table 24*. In actual application, it is possible to carry out the $r$ calculations in each row on a calculating machine without recording any of the values except the $r$th one in the column headed $f(\beta)$.

*Table 24*

| Trial | $\beta^4$ | $\beta^3$ | $\beta^2$ | $\beta$ | $f(\beta)$ | Trial $\beta$ |
|---|---|---|---|---|---|---|
| | $c_0$ | $c_1$ | $c_2$ | $c_3$ | $c_4$ | |
| 1 | $\ldots\ldots$ | $c_1 + c_0\beta' = c_1'$ | $c_2 + c_1'\beta' = c_2'$ | $c_3 + c_2'\beta' = c_3'$ | $c_4 + c_3'\beta' = c_4'$ | $\beta'$ |
| 2 | $\ldots\ldots$ | $c_1 + c_0\beta'' = c_1''$ | $c_2 + c_1''\beta'' = c_2''$ | $c_3 + c_2''\beta'' = c_3''$ | $c_4 + c_3''\beta'' = c_4''$ | $\beta''$ |
| 3 | $\ldots\ldots$ | $c_1 + c_0\beta''' = c_1'''$ | $c_2 + c_1''\beta''' = c_2'''$ | $c_3 + c_2''\beta''' = c_3'''$ | $c_4 + c_3''\beta''' = c_4'''$ | $\beta'''$ |
| 4 | $\ldots\ldots$ | $c_1 + c_0\beta'''' = c_1''''$ | $c_2 + c_1''''\beta'''' = c_2''''$ | $c_3 + c_2''''\beta'''' = c_3''''$ | $c_4 + c_3'''\beta'''' = c_4''''$ | $\beta''''$ |

*Table 25*

| Trial | $\beta^4$ | $\beta^3$ | $\beta^2$ | $\beta$ | $f(\beta)$ | Trial $\beta$ |
|---|---|---|---|---|---|---|
| | 1.0 | 6.965369 | 10.810494 | 5.407203 | .840052 | |
| 1 | $\ldots\ldots$ | 1.954052 | 1.018120 | .305081 | $-.688806$ | $-5.011317$ |
| 2 | $\ldots\ldots$ | 1.945369 | 1.044742 | .162598 | .023810 | $-5.020000$ |
| 3 | $\ldots\ldots$ | 1.945659 | 1.043850 | .167379 | $-.000142$ | $-5.019710$ |
| 4 | $\ldots\ldots$ | 1.945657 | 1.043856 | .167347 | .000018 | $-5.019712$ |

## A method of computing the square root on a calculating machine

Newton's* iterative method of determining square roots may be used very advantageously on the calculating machine, using Barlow's Tables to determine the first trial value of the square root.

Let $N$ be the number whose square root is desired, and let $x_0$ be the first trial value for the $\sqrt{N}$ derived from Barlow's Tables. Determine $N/x_0$ on the calculating machine, and record it.

Compute a new trial value, $x_1 = .5(x_0 + N/x_0)$ by determining the cumulative sum of the two products, $(.5x_0)$ and $[.5(N/x_0)]$. Determine $N/x_1$. If the two values $x_1$ and $N/x_1$ are the same to as many decimals as desired, then $\sqrt{N} = x_1 = N/x_1$. If these two values differ, this process may be repeated for as many trials as are necessary to find that trial value $x$ which agrees with $N/x$ to the required number of decimals.

---

* E. T. Whittaker and G. Robinson, *The Calculus of Observations* (London: Blackie & Son, 1926), pp. 79–80.

EXAMPLE

| | |
|---|---|
| $N$ | $= 42.072$ . |

$x_0 = \sqrt{42.07}$ in Barlow's Tables $= 6.4861391$ .

$\dfrac{N}{x_0}$ $= 6.48644738$ .

---

$x_1 = .5x_0 + .5\left(\dfrac{N}{x_0}\right)$ $= 6.48629324$ .

$\dfrac{N}{x_1}$ $= 6.48629324$ .

---

### The computation of an inverse

The outline that was described in a previous section for computing an inverse is adequate for small matrices of order $2\times2$ or $3\times3$, but it is not economical for larger matrices. The outline of computations which will be described in this section is applicable to matrices of any order, and the computational labor is not prohibitive even when the order is as large as 10 or 12.*

The method is designed to find the inverse of a symmetric matrix, which may be denoted $M$. If it is desired to find the inverse of a non-symmetric matrix $P$, one can proceed as follows: Compute the matrix $PP' = M$, which is symmetric. Find the inverse $M^{-1}$ of the symmetric matrix $M$ by the method to be described here. Then compute the matrix product $(M^{-1}P)'$. We then have

$$(54) \qquad (M^{-1}P)' = [(PP')^{-1}P]'$$
$$= [(P')^{-1}(P^{-1}P)]'$$
$$= [(P')^{-1}]'$$
$$= P^{-1} .$$

Hence the method can be adapted to find the inverse of a matrix which is either symmetric or non-symmetric.

In *Table 26* we have a numerical example, a symmetric matrix $M$ of order $3\times3$. It is placed in the upper left corner of the table in the first

---

* The method of computing an inverse which is described in this section was designed by Ledyard Tucker. See also his paper, "A Method for Finding the Inverse of a Matrix," *Psychometrika*, III, No. 3 (September, 1938), 189–97.

three rows of *Section A*. The steps in computing the inverse are then as follows, including check columns:

*Table 26*

| | Section A | | | | Section B | | | | Section C | | |
|---|---|---|---|---|---|---|---|---|---|---|---|
| | 1 | 2 | 3 | | I | II | III | | I | II | III |
| 1 | .80 | .48 | .36 | | .80 | 0 | 0 | | 1.00 | 0 | 0 |
| 2 | .48 | .80 | .36 | | .48 | .51 | .01 | | .60 | 1.00 | .02 |
| 3 | .36 | .36 | .86 | | .36 | .14 | .66 | | .45 | .27 | 1.00 |
| | | | | $Ch$ | 1.64 | .66 | .67 | $Ch$ | 2.05 | 1.27 | 1.02 |
| $\Sigma_1$ | 1.64 | 1.64 | 1.58 | $\Sigma_1$ | 1.64 | .65 | .67 | $\Sigma_1$ | 2.05 | 1.27 | 1.02 |
| | 1.00 | 0 | 0 | | 1.00 | − .60 | − .29 | | 1.25 | −1.18 | − .44 |
| | 0 | 1.00 | 0 | | 0 | 1.00 | − .27 | | 0 | 1.96 | − .41 |
| | 0 | 0 | 1.00 | | 0 | 0 | 1.00 | | 0 | 0 | 1.52 |
| | | | | $Ch$ | 1.00 | .40 | .44 | $Ch$ | 1.25 | .78 | .67 |
| $\Sigma_2$ | 1.00 | 1.00 | 1.00 | $\Sigma_2$ | 1.00 | .40 | .44 | $\Sigma_2$ | 1.25 | .78 | .67 |
| | | | | $Ch$ | 2.64 | 1.06 | 1.11 | $Ch$ | 3.30 | 2.06 | 1.69 |
| $\Sigma$ | 2.64 | 2.64 | 2.58 | $\Sigma$ | 2.64 | 1.05 | 1.11 | $\Sigma$ | 3.30 | 2.05 | 1.69 |
| | | | | | 1.25 | 1.96 | 1.52 | | | | |

| | $(b_{qm})$ | | | $(c_{qm})'$ | | | $M^{-1}$ | | |
|---|---|---|---|---|---|---|---|---|---|
| 1.00 | − .60 | − .29 | 1.25 | 0 | 0 | 2.09 | −1.06 | − .44 |
| 0 | 1.00 | − .27 | −1.18 | 1.96 | 0 | −1.06 | 2.07 | − .41 |
| 0 | 0 | 1.00 | − .44 | − .41 | 1.52 | − .44 | − .41 | 1.52 |

1. Record the column sums, $\Sigma_1$, as shown.
2. In the next three rows of $A$ write an identity matrix.
3. Record the column sums, $\Sigma_2$, for these three rows.
4. Record the total column sums, $\Sigma = \Sigma_1 + \Sigma_2$.
5. In column I of *Section B* copy the first column of *Section A*. Here a differentiation is made between the anticipated column sum, $Ch$, and the actual sum, $\Sigma$.
6. Find the reciprocal, $1/b_{11} = 1/.80 = 1.25$. The entry, $b_{11}$, is the first diagonal entry in *Section B*. It is the entry in the first column and in the first row of $B$. Record this reciprocal in the bottom row of $B$ as shown.
7. Compute the values in the first column of *Section C*. These entries are

$$(55) \qquad c_{j1} = b_{j1}\left(\frac{1}{b_{11}}\right).$$

8. Compute the second column of $B$ by the formula

$$(56) \qquad b_{j2} = a_{j2} - (b_{j1}c_{21}) ,$$

where $c_{21} = .60$ is constant for the entire column.

9. Find the reciprocal $1/b_{22} = 1/.51 = 1.96$.

10. Compute the second column of $C$ by the formula

$$(57) \qquad c_{j2} = b_{j2}\left(\frac{1}{b_{22}}\right) .$$

11. Compute the third column of $B$ by the formula

$$(58) \qquad b_{j3} = a_{j3} - b_{j1}c_{31} - b_{j2}c_{32} ,$$

where $c_{31} = .45$ and $c_{32} = .27$ are constants for the entire column.

12. Compute the third column of $C$ by the formula

$$(59) \qquad c_{j3} = b_{j3}\left(\frac{1}{b_{33}}\right) ,$$

where the reciprocal $1/b_{33}$ is a constant multiplier for the whole column.

Continue the process in the same manner so that there will be as many columns in $B$ and in $C$ as there are columns in $A$. The generalized formulae are, then,

$$(60) \qquad c_{jk} = b_{jk}\left(\frac{1}{b_{kk}}\right)$$

and

$$(61) \qquad b_{jk} = a_{jk} - [b_{j1}c_{k1} + b_{j2}c_{k2} + \cdots + b_{j(k-1)}c_{k(k-1)}] .$$

13. When the columns of $B$ and of $C$ have been computed and checked by the column sums, the desired inverse $M^{-1}$ is

$$(62) \qquad M^{-1} = (b_{qm})(c_{qm})' ,$$

where $(b_{qm})$ is the square matrix defined by the columns of $B$ and the rows of the identity matrix in $A$. The square matrix $(c_{qm})$ is defined by the columns of $C$ and the same rows which are defined by the identity matrix in $A$. Note that it is the transpose of the matrix, $(c_{qm})'$, which is used for the final equation for $M^{-1}$. The computed inverse is shown in the table.

### Linear dependence of vectors

Consider two vectors $A$ and $B$ in *Figure 4*. These two vectors define a plane, namely, the plane of the figure. These two vectors are said to *span* the plane of the figure. By this is meant that any vector in that plane can be written as a linear combination of the given vectors $A$ and $B$. Any other vector in that plane, such as $C$, can then be written as the linear combination

$$C = aA + bB \,,$$

where the small letters, $a$ and $b$, represent scalars and the capital letters represent vectors. Any vector $C$ in the plane of the figure is determined entirely by the numerical values of $a$ and $b$. Further, all linear combinations of $A$ and $B$ are confined to the plane of these two vectors. No vector outside of that plane can be described as a linear combination of $A$ and $B$

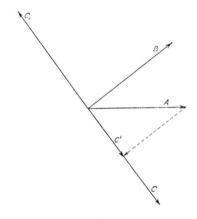

FIGURE 4

This reasoning extends to any number of dimensions. Three vectors span a three-dimensional space if they are linearly independent. The three vectors $A$, $B$, and $C$, in *Figure 4* are not linearly independent because any one of them can be described as a linear combination of the other two. If three vectors are not coplanar, they are linearly independent. Then they span a three-dimensional space. Any vector in those three dimensions can be described as a linear combination of the three independent vectors.

The interpretation of linear dependence of vectors will be illustrated by a numerical example. Let it be required that the vector $C$ shall satisfy three conditions, namely, (1) that it shall lie in the plane of the given vectors $A$ and $B$, (2) that it shall be orthogonal to $B$, and (3) that it shall be of unit length.

The first condition is satisfied if we define $C$ as a linear combination of $A$ and $B$. Then

(63)                           $C = aA + bB \,,$

where $a$ and $b$ are two parameters which are to be determined by the other two conditions. The vector $C$ will be orthogonal to $B$ if the scalar product

$$(64) \qquad\qquad CB = 0 ,$$

and $C$ will be of unit length if

$$(65) \qquad\qquad C^2 = 1 .$$

Substituting (63) in (64), we have the equation

$$(66) \qquad\qquad (aA + bB)B = 0$$

or

$$(67) \qquad\qquad a(AB) + bB^2 = 0$$

Substituting (63) in (65), we have

$$(68) \qquad\qquad a^2A^2 + 2ab(AB) + b^2B^2 = 1 .$$

Equations (67) and (68) can be solved explicitly for $a$ and $b$, but, in computing, it is usually simpler to write, first, a vector $C'$ which is orthogonal to $B$ by satisfying (67) without restriction as to its length. Let $a = 1$. Then $b = -(AB)/B^2$. When such a vector $C'$ has been determined, it can be normalized, and it will then satisfy both conditions.

As a numerical example, consider *Table 27* of direction numbers for $A$ and $B$ in three dimensions. Then $A^2 = 0.69$; $B^2 = 0.83$; and the scalar prod-

*Table 27*

| | I | II | III | |
|---|---|---|---|---|
| $A$ | .7 | .4 | .2 | $A^2 = .69$ |
| $B$ | .5 | .3 | .7 | $B^2 = .83$ |
| $C'$ | .3325 | .1795 | −.3146 | $(AB) = .61$ |
| $C$ | .6763 | .3651 | −.6400 | $\Sigma(c')^2 = .2417$ |
| | | | | $\sqrt{\text{Recip.}} = 2.0341$ |

uct $(AB) = 0.61$. If we set $a = 1.00$, then $b = -(AB)/B^2 = -0.7349$, and then the direction numbers of $C'$ can be written by (63), as shown in the third row of the table. The cross product of rows $B$ and $C'$ vanish, and hence these two vectors are orthogonal. The row $C'$ is next normalized, as shown in row $C$, and then both conditions are satisfied, namely, $CB = 0$ and $C^2 = 1$. If the direction numbers of $C$ were reversed in sign, they would define the vector $C_1$, as shown in *Figure 4*. This vector also satisfies the two conditions imposed. They differ in that the scalar product $CA$ is positive, whereas $C_1A$ is negative.

# CHAPTER I
## THE FACTOR PROBLEM

### On the nature of science

This volume is concerned with methods of discovering and identifying significant categories in psychology and in other sciences. It is therefore of interest to consider some phases of science in general that bear on the problem of finding a methodology for a psychological science.

It is the faith of all science that an unlimited number of phenomena can be comprehended in terms of a limited number of concepts or ideal constructs. Without this faith no science could ever have any motivation. To deny this faith is to affirm the primary chaos of nature and the consequent futility of scientific effort. The constructs in terms of which natural phenomena are comprehended are man-made inventions. To discover a scientific law is merely to discover that a man-made scheme serves to unify, and thereby to simplify, comprehension of a certain class of natural phenomena. A scientific law is not to be thought of as having an independent existence which some scientist is fortunate to stumble upon. A scientific law is not a part of nature. It is only a way of comprehending nature.

A simple example is the concept "force." No one has ever seen a force. Only the movement of objects is seen. The faith of science is that some schematic representation is possible by which complexities of movement can be conceptually unified into an order. The error of a literal interpretation of a force vector as the pictorial representation of a corresponding physical entity is seen in the resolution of forces. If a particle moves with uniform acceleration in a certain direction, it is, of course, possible to describe the movement by one force, or by two, or by three or more coplanar forces. This resolution of a movement into several simultaneous and superimposed movements is frequently done in order that a convenient and habitual reference frame may be retained. While the ideal constructs of science do not imply physical reality, they do not deny the possibility of some degree of correspondence with physical reality. But this is a philosophical problem that is quite outside the domain of science.

Consider, as another example, Coulomb's inverse-square law of electrical attraction. A postulated force is expressed as a function of the linear separation of the charges. Now, if the charges were to be personified, they would probably be much surprised that their actions were being described in terms of their linear separations. No one assumes that there is a string between the charges, but Coulomb's law implies that the length of such a string is to be used in our simplified scheme of comprehending the postulated charges. It is more likely that the whole space surrounding the charges is involved in the phenomena of attraction and that Coulomb's law is a fortunate short cut for representing approximately a part of the phenomena that are called "charges" and "attractions." It is not unlikely that all these entities will eventually vanish as such and become only aspects of an order more involved than Coulomb's law implies but not so chaotic as to individualize completely every moment of nature.

A science of psychology will deal with the activities of people as its central theme. A large class of human activity is that which differentiates individuals as regards their overt accomplishments. Just as it is convenient to postulate physical forces in describing the movements of physical objects, so it is also natural to postulate abilities and their absence as primary causes of the successful completion of a task by some individuals and of the failure of other individuals in the same task.

The criterion by which a new ideal construct in science is accepted or rejected is the degree to which it facilitates the comprehension of a class of phenomena which can be thought of as examples of a single construct rather than as individualized events. It is in this sense that the chief object of science is to minimize mental effort. But in order that this reduction may be accepted as science, it must be demonstrated, either explicitly or by implication, that the number of degrees of freedom of the construct is smaller than the number of degrees of freedom of the phenomena that the reduction is expected to subsume. Consider, as an example, any situation in which a rational equation is proposed as the law governing the relation between two variables. If three observations have been made and if the proposed equation has three independent parameters, then the number of degrees of freedom of the phenomena is the same as the number of degrees of freedom of the equation, and hence the formulation remains undemonstrated. If, on the other hand, one hundred experimentally independent observations are subsumed by a rational equation with three parameters, then the demonstration can be of scientific interest. The convincingness of a hypothesis can be gauged inversely by the ratio of its number of degrees of freedom to that of the phenomena which it has demonstrably covered. It is in the nature of science that no scientific law can ever be proved to be right. It can only be shown to be plausible. The laws of science are not immutable. They are only human efforts toward parsimony in the comprehension of nature.

If abilities are to be postulated as primary causes of individual differences in overt accomplishment, then the widely different achievements of individuals must be demonstrable functions of a limited number of reference abilities. This implies that individuals will be described in terms of a limited number of faculties. This is contrary to the erroneous contention that, since every person is different from every other person in the world, people must not be classified and labeled.

Each generalization in the scientific description of nature results in a loss in the extent to which the ideal constructs of science match the individual events of experience. This is illustrated by simple experiments with a pendulum, in which the mass, the period, and the locus of the center of gravity with reference to a fulcrum are involved in the ideal construct that leads to experimental verification. But the construct matches only incompletely the corresponding experimental situation. The construct says nothing about the rusty setscrew and other extraneous detail. From the viewpoint of immediate experience, scientific description is necessarily incomplete. The scientist always finds his constructs immersed in the irrelevancies of experience. It seems appropriate to acknowledge this characteristic of science, in view of the fact that it is a rather common notion that the scientific description of a person is not valid unless the so-called "total situation" has been engulfed. A study of people does not become scientific because it attempts to be complete, nor is it invalid because it is restricted. The scientific description of a person will be as incomplete from the viewpoint of common sense as the description of other objects in scientific context.

The development of scientific analysis in a new class of phenomena usually meets with resistance. The faith of science that nature can be comprehended in terms of an order acknowledges no limitation whatever as regards classes of phenomena. But scientists are not free from prejudice against the extension of their faith to realms not habitually comprehended in the scientific order. Examples of this resistance are numerous. It is not infrequent for a competent physical scientist to declare his belief that the phenomena of living objects are, at least in some subtle way, beyond the reach of rigorous scientific order.

One of the forms in which this resistance appears is the assertion that, since a scientific construct does not cover all enumerable details of a class of phenomena, it is therefore to be judged inapplicable. Since the analysis of cell growth by mathematical and physical principles does not cover everything that is known about cells, the biologist judges the analysis to be inapplicable. Since no mathematical analysis that can be conceived would cover all the subtle mysteries of personality, this realm is frequently judged to be outside the domain of rigorous science. But physical scientists accept rigorous scientific analyses about physical events that leave fully as much beyond the scientific constructs. Every explosion in the world has been different from every other explosion, and no physicist can write equations to cover all the detail of any explosive event. It is certain that no two thunderstorms have been exactly alike, and yet the constructs of physics are applied in comprehending thunder and lightning, without any demand that the detail of the landscape be covered by the same scientific constructs.

The attitudes of people on a controversial social issue have been appraised by allocating each person to a point on a linear continuum as regards his favorable or his unfavorable affect toward the psychological object. Some social scientists have objected because two individuals may have the same attitude score toward, say, pacifism, and yet be totally different in their backgrounds and in the causes of their similar social views. If such critics were consistent, they would object also to the statement that two men have identical incomes, for one of them earns while the other one steals. They should also object to the statement that two men are of the same height. The comparison should be held invalid because one of the men is fat and the other is thin. This is again the resistance against invading with the generalizing and simplifying constructs of science a realm which is habitually comprehended only in terms of innumerable and individualized detail. Every scientific construct limits itself to specified variables without any pretense of covering those aspects of a class of phenomena about which it has said nothing. As regards this characteristic of science, there is no difference between the scientific study of physical events and the scientific study of biological and psychological events. What is not generally understood, even by many scientists, is that no scientific law is ever intended to represent any event pictorially. The law is only an abstraction from the experimental situation. No experiment is ever completely repeated.

There is an unlimited number of ways in which nature can be comprehended in terms of fundamental scientific concepts. One of the simplest ways in which a class of phenomena can be comprehended in terms of a limited number of concepts is probably that in which a linear attribute of an event is expressed as a linear function of primary causes. Even when the relations are preferably non-linear and mathematically involved, it is frequently possible to use the simple linear forms as first approximations. A well-known example of this type of relation is that in which the chroma of a spectral color is expressed as a linear function of two arbitrarily chosen primaries. If two spectral colors are chosen arbitrarily for use as primaries, it is possible to express any intermediate color as a linear function of the two arbitrarily chosen primaries. The coefficients of the two terms of this linear function represent the angular sizes of the two sectors into which a color rotator is divided. When the rotator is spun, the intermediate color is seen. But here, as elsewhere in science, although the chroma of the resulting color is expressed in terms of the linear function of the arbitrary primaries, it does not follow that the saturation and the gray-values are expressed by the same law. There is still debate about which colors are to be considered primary. This question can be settled only by discovering that a certain set of primaries gives the most parsimonious comprehension of some phase of color vision. A parallel in the delineation of human traits is their description, in first approximation, as linear functions of a limited number of reference traits. The final choice of a set of primary reference traits or faculties must be made in terms of the discovery that a particular set of reference traits renders most parsimonious our comprehension of a great variety of human traits.

## The purpose of factor analysis

A factor problem starts with the hope or conviction that a certain domain is not so chaotic as it looks. The range of phenomena that is represented in any factor analysis will be referred to as its *domain*. If a particular investigation is limited to measurements in visual perception, it is likely that auditory effects will be outside of its domain. The factorial methods were developed primarily for the purpose of identifying the principal dimensions or categories of mentality; but the methods are general, so that they have been found useful for other psychological problems and in other sciences as well. Factor analysis can be regarded as a general scientific method. Since the methods were developed especially for the solution of psychological problems and since the new methods have been used so far mainly on psychological problems, these will be used for most of the examples in this text. Some of the principles can be illustrated to best advantage in terms of simple mechanical or geometrical examples; and these will be used occasionally, especially when it is desired to illustrate a logical principle without involving the distractions of controversial or nebulous subject matter.

The factorial methods were developed for the study of individual differences among people, but the individual differences may be regarded as an avenue of approach to the study of the processes which underlie these differences. If a process is invariant in all its characteristics in an experimental population of individuals, then there exist no individual differences as regards such a process, and it cannot be investigated by factorial means.

Thus, if we select an experimental population of individuals who are all equally good or equally bad in some form of visual perception, then we cannot expect to identify or differentiate such processes by factorial methods. It is only to the extent that the individuals of an experimental population exhibit individual differences in a process and its effects that these effects can become accessible to investigation by factorial methods.

When a particular domain is to be investigated by means of individual differences, one can proceed in one of two ways. One can invent a hypothesis regarding the processes that underlie the individual differences, and one can then set up a factorial experiment, or a more direct laboratory experiment, to test the hypothesis. If no promising hypothesis is available, one can represent the domain as adequately as possible in terms of a set of measurements or numerical indices and proceed with a factorial experiment. The analysis might reveal an underlying order which would be of great assistance in formulating the scientific concepts covering the particular domain. In the first case we start with a hypothesis that determines the nature of the measurements that enter into the factorial analysis. In the second case we start with no hypothesis, but we proceed, instead, with a set of measurements or indices that cover the domain, hoping to discover in the factorial analysis the nature of the underlying order. It is this latter application of the factorial methods that is sometimes referred to as an attempt to lift ourselves by our own boot straps, because the underlying order in a domain can be discovered without first postulating it in the form of a hypothesis. This is probably the characteristic of factor analysis that gives it some interest as a general scientific method.

Factor analysis is not restricted by assumptions regarding the nature of the factors, whether they be physiological or social, elemental or complex, correlated or uncorrelated. For example, some of the factors may turn out to be defined by endocrinological effects. Others may be defined in biochemical or biophysical parameters of the body fluids or of the central nervous system. Other factors may be defined by neurological or vascular relations in some anatomical locus; still other factors may involve parameters in the dynamics of the autonomic nervous system; still others may be defined in terms of experience and schooling. Factor analysis assumes that a variety of phenomena within a domain are related and that they are determined, at least in part, by a relatively small number of functional unities or factors. The factors may be called by different names, such as "causes," "faculties," "parameters," "functional unities," "abilities," or "independent measurements." The name for a factor depends on the context, on one's philosophical preferences and manner of speech, and on how much one already knows about the domain to be investigated. The factors in psychological investigations are not ordinarily to be thought of as elemental things which are present or absent, like heads or tails in the tossing of coins.

The exploratory nature of factor analysis is often not understood. Factor analysis has its principal usefulness at the border line of science. It is naturally superseded by rational formulations in terms of the science involved. Factor analysis is useful, especially in those domains where basic and fruitful concepts are essentially lacking and where crucial experiments have been difficult to conceive. The new methods have a humble role. They enable us to make only the crudest first map of a new domain. But if we have scientific intuition and sufficient ingenuity, the rough factorial map of a new domain will enable us to proceed beyond the exploratory factorial stage to the more direct forms of psychological experimentation in the laboratory.

In a domain where fundamental and fruitful concepts are already well formulated and tested, it would be absurd to use the factorial methods except for didactic purposes to illustrate factorial logic. In such situations there are available more direct methods of investigating rival hypotheses. In the relatively young sciences and in the new domains of the older sciences, the factorial experiments will be useful. It seems quite likely that the new methods will be applied with profit in the field of meteorology, but it is not likely that they will ever be used in classical mechanics.

In factorial investigations of mentality we proceed on the assumption that mind is structured somehow, that mind is not a patternless mosaic of an infinite number of elements without functional groupings. The extreme, opposite view would be to hold that mind has no structure at all. *In the interpretation of mind we assume that mental phenomena can be identified in terms of distinguishable functions, which do not all participate equally in everything that mind does.* It is these functional unities that we are looking for with the aid of factorial methods. It is our scientific faith that such distinguishable mental functions can be identified and that they will be verified in different types of experimental study. No assumption is made about the nature of these functions, whether they are native or acquired or whether they have a cortical locus.

In order to illustrate the method, let us consider a set of gymnastic stunts that might be given to a group of several hundred boys of comparable age. A factor analysis starts with a table of intercorrelations of the variables. If there were twenty different stunts, we should have a square $20 \times 20$ table showing the correlation of every performance with every other performance. Our question now is to determine whether these relations can be comprehended in terms of some underlying order, which is simpler than the whole table of several hundred experimentally determined coefficients of correlation. Let us suppose that some of the stunts require principally strength of the right arm, that others require principally a good sense of balance, that still others require speed of bodily movement. Several tests that require good sense of balance might not require arm strength, while those which require a strong arm might require very little bodily balance. We might then find that the correlations can be comprehended in terms of a small number of functional unities, such as sense of balance, arm strength, or speed of bodily movement. Each of the gymnastic tests might require one or several of these functional unities; but it is not likely that every test will require every one of the functional unities that are represented by the whole set of gymnastic tests. A factorial analysis would reveal these functional unities, and we would say that each of them is a primary factor in the battery of tests. Now, if we should take any one of these functional unities, such as sense of balance, and represent it in a new set of twenty tests of great variety which all required bodily balance, we might find that there are really several primary factors involved in this domain. For example, there might conceivably be a separate balancing factor for each of the semicircular canals, or there might be some other breakdown of the balancing factors that would be revealed in an extensive study of balancing tests.* A new set of more refined primary factors might be found within the domain of bodily balance. This process might continue with the factorial investigation of more and more restricted domains, as long as the functional unities continued to be difficult to conceive in direct experimentation. Eventually, the factorial methods, which are essentially exploratory, would yield to the reformulation of a problem in terms of the fundamental rational constructs of the science involved. It is not unlikely that factorial analyses will point the way in the work of inventing significant and fundamental scientific concepts.

Let us consider, next, an example in the sensory and perceptual fields. Let us start with a set of twenty perceptual tests involving several of the modalities. Some of the tests might require visual acuity; others would require keen discrimination of rhythm; still others might require speed of perception. Each of the perceptual tests might involve one or more of these functional unities; but few would require all these functions. Some of the tests, for example, might not depend on visual acuity. In this simple case we should not be surprised to find factorially the primary functional unities that are obvious at the start.

If we turn to the more central functions that are involved in the intellectual and temperamental differences among people, it seems reasonable to suppose that here also we may expect to find functional unities that will some day be as obvious as the sensory and perceptual unities are obvious to us now.

Our work in the factorial study of the human mind rests on the assumption that mind represents a dynamical system which can eventually be understood in terms of a finite number of parameters. We have assumed, further, that all these parameters, or groups of parameters, are not involved in the individual differences of every kind of mental task. Just as we take it for granted that the individual differences in visual acuity are not involved in pitch discrimination, so we assume that in intellectual tasks some mental or cortical functions are not involved in every task. This is the principle of "simple structure" or "simple configuration" in the underlying order for any given set of attributes.

Observation and educational experience lend plausibility to the conception that the mental abilities are determined by a great multiplicity of causes or determiners and that these determiners are more or less structured or linked in groups. This multiplicity of determiners can be thought of as a field of elements in which all are not equally closely linked. Some elements may be quite independent in their actions, while others may be rather closely associated. The factors are probably functional groupings, and it would be a distortion to assume that they must be elemental. We know precious

---

* Several such factors might appear in the place of specific variance and uninterpreted common-factor variance in the earlier studies.

little about the determiners of human talent and temperament, and we should not impose upon our thinking an unnecessarily rigid causal frame.

If we grant that men are not all equal in intellectual endowment and in temperament and if we have the faith that this domain can be investigated as science, then we must make the plausible and inevitable assumption that individual differences among men can be conceived in terms of a finite number of traits, parameters, or factors. Some of the factors may be found to be anatomically determined; others will be physiological; while others will be defined, at first, in experiential, educational, and social terms. As scientists, we must believe that a set of categories can be found for the understanding of mentality, which have, by their simplicity, a prior claim on our conceptual formulations.

### Factor analysis and empirical prediction

Factor analysis involves a number of well-known statistical procedures, and it is only natural for the student to begin his study of factor theory with a statistical point of view. In some respects this point of view is legitimate and useful, but there are some fundamental differences between the objectives of factor analysis and the customary objectives in statistical work that might as well be made explicit at the start. Some of the controversial questions in factor theory have their source in misunderstandings about the objectives for which factor theory was developed.

Many statistical problems take a form in which a certain number of indices are available for each member of a statistical population, and it is desired to predict some new index in terms of the known or given indices for each member of the population. A familiar example in psychological work is the prediction of student scholarship in terms of indices that are available at the time of college entrance. Prediction problems of this type are resolved by writing a regression equation, in which the dependent variable which is to be predicted is expressed as a linear function of the independent variables. The weight given to each independent variable is called its "regression coefficient," and the weights are so determined as to minimize the sum of the squares of the residual errors. The multiple correlation coefficient is the correlation between the predicted values of the dependent variable and the actually observed values. When the residual errors are small, the multiple correlation is high. Factor analysis differs from these statistical problems in that there is no distinction between independent and dependent variables. In factor analysis one does not select some one variable which is to be predicted or determined by the other variables. All the variables in factor analysis are treated alike in this sense. Whenever the investigator pivots his attention on one of the given variables which is central in importance and which is to be predicted by a set of independent variables, he is not talking about a factor problem. He is then talking about a customary statistical problem, involving a regression equation and multiple correlation. If he looks upon the whole set of variables as representing a domain that is to be explored and if his object is to discover whether there is some underlying order among these variables, then he is talking about a factor problem. Of course, it is possible to treat the same set of data successively by the two points of view. In the first case we are concerned about the prediction of one of the variables from the others, while in the second case we try to discover some underlying order in the whole system of traits.

It might be noted, in passing, that the distinction between independent and dependent variables is not intrinsic in the phenomena themselves. The differentiation between independent and dependent variables reflects only the attitude or purpose of the investigator. What is an independent variable for one investigator can be a dependent one for another investigator working with the same data. Sometimes an author reveals his bias unwittingly in the way he plots diagrams. What he plots as a base line is likely to be his independent variable. What he plots as ordinates is likely to be his dependent variable. In this way we may show that a depression is caused by unemployment or that unemployment is caused by a depression.

In the factor problem as well as in the statistical prediction problem, one is concerned about residuals and how to minimize them. This is practically universal in problems that involve observational data. In the statistical prediction problem, one's attention is centered on the one variable which is to be predicted and on how to minimize the residual errors in that prediction. In the factor problem, one is concerned about how to account for the observed correlations among all the variables in terms of the smallest number of factors and with the smallest possible residual errors. Here we have the practical problem that, as we postulate more and more factors to account for the observed correlations, the residuals get smaller and smaller. Hence, every factor problem must deal with the practical question of determining when the addition of a new factor causes only a negligible reduction in the residuals. The mathematical theory of this problem has not yet been adequately solved, but there have been developed practical methods of dealing with it. There seems to be some question as to whether the nature of the problem is such that a rigorous solution exists; but that is for later discussion.

There are problems in which the distinction between multiple correlation and factor theory is not sharply drawn, and we shall describe one example here. If a set of twenty independent variables is to be used for the prediction of a certain criterion, one's first impulse might be to write a regression equation of twenty terms in which each of the twenty given variables is weighted so as to give the best possible prediction of the dependent variable. In many situations such a solution would give regression coefficients which are so grossly in error that their absurdity can be seen by inspection. This result happens if the supposedly independent variables are not linearly independent. If the intercorrelations of those twenty variables can be accounted for in terms of, say, six factors, then we should be justified in using only six terms in the regression equation. Any additional terms in that equation would be likely to give absurd results, since they would imply that we rely on more factors than are really present in the supposedly independent variables. The intercorrelations of the twenty variables might then be analyzed factorially in order to determine six groups, each of which would give an average or composite. These six composites could then be weighted in a regression equation of six terms for as many independent variables. Such a problem is, however, only a prediction problem, and the prediction might be accomplished as well by different groupings of the twenty given variables or indices. In the more fundamental factorial problem the object is to discover whether the variables can be made to exhibit some underlying order that may throw light on the processes that produce the individual differences shown in all the variables.

In statistical prediction, the independent variables are given, and the problem is to predict some one dependent variable. The weights that are given to the independent variables do not ordinarily have any direct physical interpretation, because they depend on the number of given variables, their dispersions, and their correlations among themselves and with the variable that is to be predicted. The weights or regression coefficients are ordinarily treated merely as numerical coefficients which happen to maximize the multiple correlation. Their use is justified, not because of the meaning that can be attributed to their numerical values, but rather to the mere fact that a prediction can be made with the minimum residual.

In factor analysis, all the given variables are treated as co-ordinate as regards independence or dependence. The object of a factor problem is to account for the tests, or their intercorrelations, in terms of a small number of derived variables, the smallest possible number that is consistent with acceptable residual errors. The weights that are given to these derived variables are given more direct physical interpretation than is usually the case with regression coefficients. The derived variables are of scientific interest only in so far as they represent processes or parameters that involve the fundamental concepts of the science involved. Whereas the statistical prediction problem demands merely that a good prediction shall be made, the factorial problem demands that there shall be a meaningful interpretation of the small number of derived variables in terms of which the whole set of given variables can be comprehended.

Since it is the derived variables, or factors, that are the objective of a factorial analysis, one might regard them as dependent variables. This interpretation would agree with the usual meaning of the terms, "independent" and "dependent," if the factors had previously been isolated and if we had started out to determine which tests constitute the best appraisal of a given factor. Such a problem would be similar to the familiar problem in test construction when the object is to determine the relative validities of several tests for a given criterion. In the exploratory type of problem for which the factorial methods were developed, the object is to discover the underlying order in a system of variables and to identify their nature. In this use of the factorial methods there is no distinction between independent and dependent variables.

### Psychological postulates and definitions

The factorial methods have been developed primarily for the purpose of analyzing the relations of human traits. These are defined as follows:

Definition 1. A **trait** *is any attribute of an individual.*

The factorial methods are applicable also in the analysis of attributes of inanimate members of a group. The members of a statistical population may be moments in time or regions in space or any other entities, each of which has a set of attributes. This generalization will not be made explicitly, but it is implied in the following chapters. Since the methods have been developed primarily with psychological categories in mind, these will be explicitly discussed, even though the same methods are applicable to problems which involve the attributes of inanimate members of a statistical group.

It is useful to distinguish between those traits which are descriptive of the individual as he appears to others and those traits which are exemplified primarily in the things that he can do. This distinction is involved in the definition of "ability."

Definition 2. An **ability** *is a trait which is defined by what an individual can do.*

This definition implies that there are as many abilities as there are enumerable things that individuals can do. Each ability is therefore objectively defined in terms of a specified task and of a specified method of appraising it.

Definition 3. *The task, together with the method of appraising it, which defines an ability, is called a* **test**.

Definition 4. *The numerical evaluation of a test performance is called a* **score**.

It is implied in these definitions that an index of ability is covariant with the score in the test which defines the ability and that a true index of ability is covariant with the true score in the test.

It is desirable to develop the factorial methods in such a manner that they are independent of the assumption of normality of ability in any particular experimental population. *In the present theoretical development of the factorial methods it will not be assumed that any of the distributions of ability are normal.*

The application of the factorial methods in science rests on a fundamental postulate.

Postulate. *The standard scores of all individuals in an unlimited number of abilities can be expressed, in first approximation, as linear functions of their standard scores in a limited number of abilities.*

The correlation between the true scores in two tests will be referred to as the correlation between the two abilities which are defined by the tests. In statistical work it is customary to refer to two variables as "independent" when their correlation is zero. The term *independence* will be used with three different meanings. They will be designated by appropriate adjectives unless the context makes the designation unnecessary.

Definition 5. *A set of* n *abilities are* **linearly independent** *if the rank of the matrix of their true intercorrelations is* n.

Definition 6. *Two abilities are* **statistically independent** *in a population if their correlation is zero in that population.*

Definition 7. *Two observations are* **experimentally independent** *if they are experimentally distinct, so that one is not derived from the other by a constraint either of the experimental situation or of the computations.*

In one sense, no two observations can ever be experimentally independent. The term can be used only with reference to the state of knowledge at the time that the observations are made.

It is clarifying to interpret geometrically the relations of abilities. In such a context, two abilities that are uncorrelated in a population will be called *orthogonal* in that population. Two abilities that are correlated in a population will be called *oblique* in that population.

There is special interest in the limited number of abilities in terms of which all other abilities can be defined, since these are landmarks in terms of which all abilities can be comprehended.

### The reduction of raw scores to standard scores

A factor analysis starts, ordinarily, with a table of intercorrelations between the variables that are to be analyzed. These correlations are computed from the individual test scores for the experimental population. It is of interest, therefore, to consider the reduction of the raw scores to derived scores, such as standard scores, and the effect of such reductions on the correlation coefficients and on the resulting factorial structure.

It will be useful to recall that the coefficient of correlation between two variables $x$ and $y$ is unaffected if an arbitrary constant is added to the $x$'s and if some arbitrary constant is added to the $y$'s. Furthermore, the coefficient of correlation between the two variables is unaffected if the $x$'s are multiplied by some arbitrary multiplier and if the $y$'s are similarly subjected to some arbitrary stretching factor. These properties of the correlation coefficient can be summarized in the statement that the correlation coefficient for two variables $x$ and $y$ is the same as the correlation between any linear functions of $x$ and $y$. Stated in symbols, we have

$$(1) \qquad r_{xy} = r_{(ax+b)(cy+d)} \; ,$$

where $a$, $b$, $c$, $d$, are arbitrary constants.

Two ways of reducing the given raw scores to standard form will be considered here. They give numerically different values for the standard scores and different intercorrelations.

*Case 1, assuming that the distribution of ability is not necessarily Gaussian:* Let the given distribution of raw scores be represented by the skewed frequency curve at $A$ in *Figure 1*, with mean at $m_j$, which is the mean of the raw scores in test $j$. Let $X_{ji}$ denote the raw score of individual $i$ in test $j$. The frequency distribution $A$ of the raw scores $X_{ji}$ will be subjected to two changes, namely, (1) a translation to the position $B$ without change in shape, so that the new mean will be at the origin $O$, and (2) a stretching factor, by which the distribution $B$ is changed to the form $C$, which has unit standard deviation and mean at the origin. The frequency distribution $A$ of the raw scores $X_{ji}$ is changed by the translation to the frequency distribution of scores $(X_{ji}-m_j)$, as shown at $B$. This distribution is changed by the stretching factor to the distribution of standard scores,

$$s_{ji} = \frac{1}{\sigma_j} (X_{ji} - m_j) \; ,$$

as shown at $C$. The translation is over the distance $m_j$, and the stretching factor is $1/\sigma_j$. The new distribution at $C$ has its mean at the origin, and it has unit standard deviation. The shape of the distribution $C$ is exactly the same as the shape of the distribution at $A$ as regards degree of skewness. The correlation of any variable with the raw scores $X_{ji}$ is the same as the correlation with the corresponding standard scores $s_{ji}$. The important feature of this reduction to standard scores is that the degree of skewness is unaltered and the correlation coefficients are unaltered.

*Case 2, assuming that the distribution of true scores in ability* j *is Gaussian:* If the investigator wants to make this assumption, the reduction of the raw scores $X_{ji}$ to standard scores involves an additional change in the frequency distribution, namely, to the normal distribution form. The numerical values of the standard scores are not the same as in the first case, and the correlation coefficients between the variables are not the same. The procedure is simply to regard the raw scores as placing the individuals in rank order according to the ability represented by the test. If the percentile rank of each

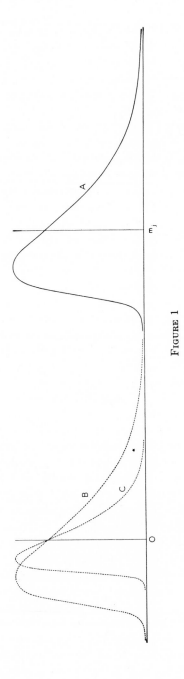

FIGURE 1

individual is determined from his raw score, the corresponding normalized standard score can be found directly and without further computation from the Kelley-Wood tables of the probability curve or from similar tables. This reduction to normalized standard scores gives a distribution that is normal with mean at the origin and with unit standard deviation. The only function served by the raw scores in this case is to arrange the individuals in rank order, and no attention is then given to the actual numerical values of the scores beyond their rank order.

These two ways of reducing the raw scores to standard form raise the question as to which of the two ways should be adopted. Psychological considerations enter into this choice, but fortunately the factorial results do not seem to be seriously affected in those problems which are otherwise determinate. In dealing with the raw scores on psychological tests, it must be recognized that the scoring methods are, on the whole, quite arbitrary. So many points are allowed for this, and so many points are deducted for something else. The resulting raw scores in tests are as arbitrary as the scoring formulae adopted by the intuitions of the investigator. The editorial composition of a paper-and-pencil test also has an effect on this problem. If a large number of relatively easy tasks is included, the raw scores will rise. The dispersion of the scores and the shape of the distribution are markedly affected by the more or less arbitrary time limits that are adopted for a test. If the distribution is positively skewed, it can ordinarily be made to approach the normal shape by merely increasing the time limit for the test. It takes very little experience in test construction to realize that the distribution of raw scores has relatively little fundamental significance, and consequently it seems proper to regard them as essentially not much more than a set of indices that place the subjects in rank order according to their ability to do the kind of task that is involved in the test. If the intuitions of the psychologist in assembling a new test and in adopting a scoring formula are not too seriously in error, he will obtain an approximate rank order of his subjects that will remain essentially unaltered with reasonable shifts in editorial composition and in some changes of scoring formulae, even though the raw scores and the shape of their distribution might be subject to considerable alteration by such changes.

If the factorial methods were seriously dependent on the investigator's luck in hitting some sort of "right" scoring formula and time limit for each test, the new methods would not be able to produce meaningful results. The factorial methods are sufficiently powerful that one can take considerable liberties with the raw scores without seriously affecting the results. If we take a factor analysis in which several fundamental and meaningful factors have been clearly identified, it would be instructive to subject the factor methods to a severe test by radical changes in the original raw scores and then make a new factor analysis with the altered scores. We might change the scores in one test by writing their reciprocals instead; the scores in another test might be altered by writing their square roots; the scores for another test might be altered by writing their logarithms; still another test might be altered by using the squares of the original scores instead of the scores themselves; and so on with a new monotonic function for each test. The rank orders of the subjects in a test would be either the same or completely reversed. We might use case 1 in reducing the scores to standard form so as to retain for the correlations all the distorted distribution shapes. The correlation coefficients to be analyzed would then be markedly different from those used in the original analysis, but it seems quite likely that the same basic factors would be identified. This demonstration has not been made,* but it probably would be successful in showing the power of the factorial methods in isolating the underlying order among the test variables and the basic factors that determine the individual differences.

* Since this chapter was written, the demonstration has been made, and it is described in *chap. xv.*

# CHAPTER II

## FUNDAMENTAL EQUATIONS

### Reference abilities

In a multiple correlation problem one writes a regression equation to express a dependent variable as a linear combination of a set of independent variables. Applied to psychological tests, the regression equation is an attempt to predict a criterion—the dependent variable—as a linear combination of a set of tests—the independent variables. The observation equation which is the starting-point for multiple-factor theory is analogous to the familiar regression equation in certain respects. The score in a test is expressed as a linear function of the scores in a set of postulated reference abilities. Here the standard score $s_{ji}$ of individual $i$ in test $j$ corresponds to the

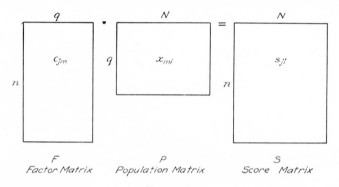

F
Factor Matrix            Population Matrix            Score Matrix

FIGURE 1

dependent variable which is to be accounted for; but in the factor problem all the individual test scores are dependent variables, in this sense, that are to be accounted for.

If an experimental population of $N$ individuals has been given a set of $n$ tests, the resulting tabulation of scores will be an $n \times N$-score matrix $S$, whose elements are the standard scores $s_{ji}$, where the subscript $j$ refers to the test and $i$ refers to the individual (see *Figure 1*). If the test battery has a fairly large number of tests, $n$, and if these cover a fairly restricted range, one might attempt to account for the scores $s_{ji}$ in terms of a smaller number of factors than the number of tests. This assumption is represented in the following equation:

$$(1) \qquad s_{ji} = c_{j1}x_{1i} + c_{j2}x_{2i} + c_{j3}x_{3i} + \cdots + c_{jq}x_{qi} \,,$$

where $s_{ji}$ is the standard score of individual $i$ in test $j$, the $x$'s are standard scores of individual $i$ in each of the uncorrelated reference abilities, and the

68

$c$'s are the weights assigned to the standard scores in the reference abilities for the determination of the observed standard score $s_{ji}$. The equation is written to represent $q$ terms in the right-hand member, and it is hoped that this number of reference abilities will be relatively small compared with the number of tests, $n$, in the whole battery.

The psychological interpretation of equation (1) is that a subject's performance, $s_{ji}$, on a test is determined in part by the abilities that are called for by the test and in part by the degrees to which the subject possesses these abilities. It should be noted that the $x$'s in equation (1) contain the subscript $i$ but not $j$. Hence the $x$'s are descriptive of the individuals but not of the tests. The $c$'s in the same equation have subscript $j$ but not $i$. Hence the $c$'s are descriptive of the tests but not of the individual subjects. The first term represents the contribution of the first reference ability to the score, the second term represents the contribution of the second reference ability, and so on, for $q$ reference abilities. If the first reference ability is involved in the test $j$, then the coefficient $c_{j1}$ will be large and positive. If the individual $i$ possesses this reference ability to a marked extent, then his standard score in that ability, $x_{1i}$, will be large and positive. The product will be an appreciable contribution toward a good score in the test. If the second reference ability is not involved in test $j$, then the coefficient $c_{j2}$ will be zero; and if the individual $i$ has this second reference ability to a marked degree, his standard score $x_{2i}$ will be large and positive, but it will not contribute toward the score in the test because the test does not involve this second ability. For this individual subject and test, the second term vanishes. Similar interpretation can be made for high and low test coefficients and for high and low standard scores in the reference abilities.

*If the standard scores of N individuals in n abilities are expressed as linear functions of their scores in r linearly independent abilities, where r < n, then the r abilities will be called* **reference abilities.**

It will be shown that if a battery of tests can be described with reference to $r$ orthogonal abilities, there exists an infinite number of sets of $r$ orthogonal abilities in terms of which the description can be made with equal accuracy. An arbitrary set of $r$ orthogonal abilities may be chosen for purposes of description. These are the statistically independent or orthogonal reference abilities. If a battery of tests can be described in terms of $r$ orthogonal reference abilities, the tests can also be described by a set of $r$ oblique reference abilities. It is not necessary that a reference ability be represented by a test in which it is involved exclusively. While each of the tests used in experimental work defines an ability, it may happen that the reference abilities in terms of which tests and individuals are described are not represented by actual tests but by linear combinations of several tests. A linear combination of tests may be thought of as a *composite test.*

It should be noted that, even if each individual can be described in terms of a limited number of independent reference abilities, it is still possible for every person to be different from every other person in the world. Each person might be described in terms of his standard scores in a limited number of independent abilities. The number of permutations of these scores would probably be sufficient to guarantee the retention of individualities.

With a limited number of abilities not only does this formulation allow every person to be different from every other person, but it also allows the widest possible differences between several individuals who attain the same objective performance in a test. This may be readily seen by considering a hypothetical example. Assume that a test calls for two abilities, such as ability in abstraction and ability in the manipulation of numbers. Several individuals try the test and attain the same score. One of them may possess a high degree of ability in making the abstractions involved in the test, but he may be slow in numerical manipulation. Another may be slow in formulating the abstract part of the problem, but he may make up for this deficiency by superior numerical speed. The objective result might be the same. The purpose of factor analysis is to obtain a quantitative description of each fundamental ability in each individual by means of tasks that require these abilities in different amounts. Since every task is probably composite in the abilities required, it is necessary to make the appraisal of the abilities of individuals by analytical methods. This is exactly the object of the multiple-factor methods as applied to the problem of describing the abilities of people.

Factor analysis is reminiscent of faculty psychology. It is true that the object of factor analysis is to discover the mental faculties. But the severe restrictions that are imposed by the logic of factor analysis make it an arduous task to isolate each new mental faculty, because it is necessary to prove that it is called for by the experimental observations. Factor analysis does not allow that a new faculty be added as soon as a new name can be found for the things that people can do. In order to prove that reasoning and abstraction are two different faculties, for example, it will be necessary to show that the tasks which call for such activities really do involve two factors, and not one.

In the psychology of the future it may be found useful to postulate a different form of ideal construct for the description of mental endowment than the simple one that is implied in equation (1). The ideal constructs of the future may involve elements with location in a space frame with spatial, dynamic, and temporal constraints analogous to the ideal constructs of genetics. It would be unfortunate if some initial success with the analytical methods to be described here should lead us to commit ourselves to them with such force of habit as to disregard the development of entirely different constructs that may be indicated by improvements in measurement and by inconsistencies between theory and experiment.

## The factor matrix and the population matrix

Equation (1) can be represented in rectangular form, as shown in *Figure 1*. The factor matrix $F$ contains the elements $c_{jm}$, which are descriptive of tests $j$ in terms of reference factors $m$. The population matrix $P$ contains the elements $x_{mi}$, which are descriptive of individuals $i$ in terms of reference factors $m$. The cross product of a row of $F$ and a column of $P$ is represented in equation (1). If the factor matrix $F$ is multiplied by the population matrix $P$, the product is the score matrix $S$ with elements $s_{ji}$, as shown in equation (1) and in *Figure 1*. The observation equation (1) can be written in the matrix form

$$(2) \qquad\qquad S = FP \,,$$

or in the summational notation

$$(3) \qquad\qquad s_{ji} = \sum_{m=1}^{q} c_{jm} x_{mi} \,,$$

or in the rectangular form of *Figure 1*. It will be assumed in our use of this equation that the reference abilities represented by columns of $F$ are orthogonal. In a later chapter the equation will be generalized for the case of oblique or correlated reference factors.

This observation equation is the starting-point for the development of factorial theory. It should be noted that all the $c$'s and all the $x$'s are unknown and that we know only the individual scores $s_{ji}$ in each test at the start of a factorial analysis.

## Interpretation of the test coefficients

The entries $c_{jm}$ of the factor matrix $F$ describe the tests $j$ in terms of the factors $m$, and they are called the *test coefficients* or *factor loadings*. Their interpretation can be found in terms of the variance of the tests.

Since $s_{ji}$ and $x_{mi}$ are standard scores, their sums for the experimental population are identically zero. Then, by (3),

$$(4) \qquad\qquad \sum_{i=1}^{N} s_{ji} = \sum_{i=1}^{N} \sum_{m=1}^{q} c_{jm} x_{mi} = 0 \,,$$

and

$$(5) \qquad\qquad \sum_{i=1}^{N} x_{mi} = 0 \,.$$

The standard deviations of $s_{ji}$ and of $x_{mi}$ are both unity by definition. Hence

(6)
$$\frac{1}{N} \sum_{i=1}^{N} s_{ji}^2 = 1 ,$$

and

(7)
$$\frac{1}{N} \sum_{i=1}^{N} x_{mi}^2 = 1 .$$

The square of the standard score, $s_{ji}$, is

(8)
$$s_{ji}^2 = \sum_{m=1}^{q} c_{jm}x_{mi} \sum_{M=1}^{q} c_{jM}x_{Mi} + \sum_{m=1}^{q} c_{jm}^2 x_{mi}^2 \qquad (m \neq M),$$

where $m$ and $M$ are subscripts denoting the reference factors and where $m \neq M$. Summing the squares of the standard scores over the experimental population and dividing by $N$, we have

(9)
$$\sigma^2 = \frac{1}{N} \sum_{i=1}^{N} s_{ji}^2 = \frac{1}{N} \sum_{i=1}^{N} \sum_{m=1}^{q} c_{jm}x_{mi} \sum_{M=1}^{q} c_{jM}x_{Mi} + \frac{1}{N} \sum_{i=1}^{N} \sum_{m=1}^{q} c_{jm}^2 x_{mi}^2 .$$

Rearranging the summations, we have

(10)
$$\sigma_j^2 = \sum_{m=1}^{q} \sum_{M=1}^{q} c_{jm}c_{jM} \frac{1}{N} \sum_{i=1}^{N} x_{mi}x_{Mi} + \sum_{m=1}^{q} c_{jm}^2 \frac{1}{N} \sum_{i=1}^{N} x_{mi}^2 = 1 .$$

But the correlation between each pair of orthogonal reference abilities $m$ and $M$ vanishes by definition, so that

(11)
$$r_{mM} = \frac{1}{N} \sum_{i=1}^{N} x_{mi}x_{Mi} = 0 ,$$

and the $x$'s are standard scores by definition, so that they have unit standard deviation. Hence,

(12)
$$\sigma_m^2 = \frac{1}{N} \sum_{i=1}^{N} x_{mi}^2 = 1 ,$$

so that

(13)
$$\sigma_j^2 = \sum_{m=1}^{q} c_{jm}^2 = 1 .$$

This equation can be stated in the theorem that *the sum of the squares of the test coefficients of a test for all orthogonal factors is equal to unity.*

It should be recalled that this theorem concerning the test coefficients assumes a set of uncorrelated reference abilities. Each test is here represented as having unit variance, since the test scores are assumed to be reduced to standard form. The square of each test coefficient, $c_{jm}^2$, is that part of the total variance of test $j$ which is attributable to the reference ability $m$. The sum of these variances is the total unit variance of the test.

The entries in a factor matrix are sometimes called *factor loadings.* The square of any cell entry in $F$, such as $a_{jm}^2$, $b_{jj}^2$, $e_{jj}^2$, $u_j^2$, represents the fractional part of the total variance of a test attributable to a given factor. We have, then, the theorem that *each factor loading or test coefficient* $c_{jm}$ *for orthogonal factors is the square root of the variance of test* j *attributable to the factor* m.

### Common factors and unique factors

The square of each test coefficient $c_{jm}$ in *Figure 1* can be interpreted as the fractional part of the variance of test $j$ which is attributable to the reference ability or factor $m$. Psychological knowledge about tests enables us to postulate different kinds of factors in $F$. Some of the factors represent abilities that are involved in two or more tests of a battery. These are called *common factors.* Another kind of factor is an ability which is involved in only a single test of a battery. These are called *specific factors.* These two types of factors can be illustrated with a psychological example. In a battery of tests there might be only one test whose score depends in part on writing speed. For that battery and for that test the ability to write fast would be a specific factor. Performance in another test might depend in part on acuity of hearing, and that ability might not be involved in any other test of the battery. It would be a factor specific to one test in the battery. Other factors, such as word fluency or number facility or visualizing, might be in two or more tests of the battery so that they would be common factors.

The common factors and the specific factors are thought of as bona fide abilities, whose isolation and description are of psychological interest. But, in addition to these cognitive factors, it is well known that we must deal also with fortuitous errors in test scores. If we knew the true scores in a particular test for a given population, the addition of fortuitous chance errors to the true scores would increase the dispersions so that the true score variance would be some fraction of the observed variance. This error part of the total variance of each test should be represented by an error factor in the factor matrix $F$. Since the fortuitous variable errors in one test are, in general, uncorrelated with the variable errors in each other test, we must provide in the factor matrix $F$ one error factor for each test of the battery.

In *Figure 2* we have represented six tests with three kinds of factors—

the common factors, the specific factors, and the error factors. Sampling errors will be discussed in a later section. In *Figure 2* we have shown three common factors in the first three columns. The letters $a$, $b$, and $e$ represent non-vanishing cell entries. The blank cells represent zero entries. The common factors, I, II, III, are here shown as if each common factor were present in each test. Later we shall consider the situation in which the common factors are not all present in each of the tests. The next block of the factor matrix of *Figure 2* shows eight specific factors. Two of them occur only in the first test. We have labeled them *4* and *5*. The third test is also shown with two specifics, and each of the other tests is represented with one specific factor. Each test is assigned a variable error factor $e_{jj}$ in the third block of the factor matrix.

| | common | | | specific | | | | | | | | error | | | | | |
| | I | II | III | 4 | 5 | 6 | 7 | 8 | 9 | 10 | 11 | I | 2 | 3 | 4 | 5 | 6 |
|---|---|---|---|---|---|---|---|---|---|---|---|---|---|---|---|---|---|
| 1 | $a_{11}$ | $a_{12}$ | $a_{13}$ | $b_{14}$ | $b_{15}$ | | | | | | | $e_{11}$ | | | | | |
| 2 | $a_{21}$ | $a_{22}$ | $a_{23}$ | | | $b_{26}$ | | | | | | | $e_{22}$ | | | | |
| 3 | $a_{31}$ | $a_{32}$ | $a_{33}$ | | | | $b_{37}$ | $b_{38}$ | | | | | | $e_{33}$ | | | |
| 4 | $a_{41}$ | $a_{42}$ | $a_{43}$ | | | | | | $b_{49}$ | | | | | | $e_{44}$ | | |
| 5 | $a_{51}$ | $a_{52}$ | $a_{53}$ | | | | | | | $b_{5\,10}$ | | | | | | $e_{55}$ | |
| 6 | $a_{61}$ | $a_{62}$ | $a_{63}$ | | | | | | | | $b_{6\,11}$ | | | | | | $e_{66}$ |

*Complete Factor Matrix* $F_1$

FIGURE 2

The total variance of the first test in this fictitious example can be expressed in the summation

$$(14) \qquad (a_{11}^2 + a_{12}^2 + a_{13}^2) + (b_{14}^2 + b_{15}^2) + e_{11}^2 = 1 \,,$$

on the assumption that all the factors involved in the test can be divided into three types—common, specific, and error. Only the common factors are shared with any of the other tests in the battery. Each of the other factors is unique for one test.

The total variance of the test can be divided into two parts, namely, that part which it shares with other tests in a particular battery and that part which is unique. We then have

$$(15) \qquad \sum_{m=1}^{r} a_{jm}^2 \equiv h_j^2 \equiv communality \text{ of test } j \,,$$

where the $a$'s refer only to common factors and $r$ is the number of common factors. The notation $h_j^2$ will be used to denote that part of the total variance of a test which is attributable to the common factors.

Definition: *The **communality** of a test is its common-factor variance.*

The specific factors are those abilities which are involved in only one test of a battery. Their variance can be written

$$(16) \qquad \sum_{m=1}^{q} b_{jm}^2 \equiv \textit{specificity of test } j ,$$

where the $b$'s refer only to specific abilities.

Definition: *The **specificity** of a test is that part of its total variance which is attributable to abilities that are unique for the test in a given battery.*

The specific factors and the variable error factor are all unique for each particular test. The fractional part of the total variance of a test which it does not share with any other tests of the battery can be written

$$(17) \qquad \sum_{m=1}^{t} b_{jm}^2 + e_{jj}^2 \equiv u_j^2 \equiv \textit{uniqueness of test } j .$$

Definition: *The **uniqueness** of a test is that part of its total variance which is not shared with any other tests in a battery.*

It will be seen that *the uniqueness is the complement of the communality*, so that

$$(18) \qquad h_j^2 + u_j^2 = 1 .$$

A factor that is specific for a test in one battery may become a common factor when the test is moved into another battery. Auditory acuity might be specific in one battery, but it might become a common factor if a test were moved into a new battery, where two or more tests depended on auditory acuity.

All the unique factors of a test may be combined into a single unique factor for each test. As an example, the unique-factor entry for the first test in *Figure 2* would be

$$\sqrt{b_{14}^2 + b_{15}^2 + e_{11}^2} = u_1 ,$$

as is also shown in equation (17). It will be useful to re-write the factor matrix $F$ with two blocks instead of three. These two blocks are the common factors and the unique factors. This has been done in *Figure 3*.

The pattern of the non-vanishing entries in $F$ should be noted. We have shown the common-factor block in $F$ as filled, whereas the unique-factor block is a diagonal pattern with zeros in the side entries. This pattern follows from the definition according to which each of the six factors occurs in only one of the six tests.

Definition: *A factor matrix which represents the total unit variance of each test is called a* **complete factor matrix**.

The complete factorial matrix is denoted $F_1$. The factorial matrices of *Figures 2* and *3* are complete factorial matrices. In factor analysis it is useful to identify by a special name that part of the factorial matrix which represents only the common factors. The common-factor block is a matrix of order $n \times r$ for $n$ tests and $r$ common factors. In *Figure 3* this matrix is of order $6 \times 3$ with elements $a_{jm}$.

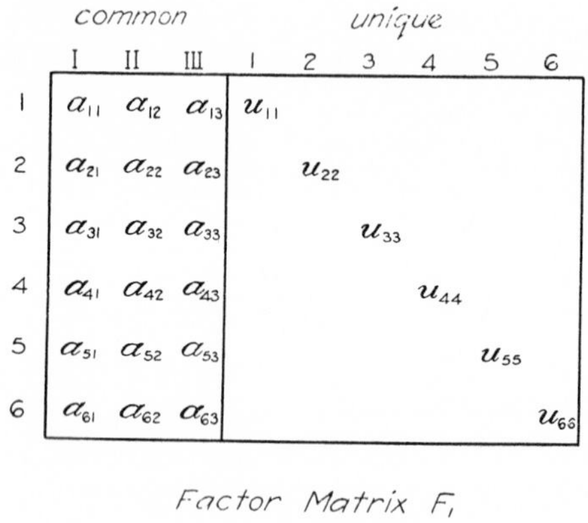

Factor Matrix $F_1$

FIGURE 3

Definition: *A factor matrix which represents only the common-factor variance of each test is called a* **reduced factorial matrix**.

The reduced factorial matrix is denoted $F$.

From this definition and equation (15) we have the theorem that *the sum of the squares of each row* j *of the reduced factorial matrix* F *is the communality* $h_j^2$ *of test* j

If we postulate a unique factor for each test, as shown in *Figure 3*, the total number of linearly independent factors in $F_1$ is $(n+r)$, where $r$ is the number of common factors. But this formulation of the problem involves more factors than tests, a situation that would seem to make the problem insoluble. Before a stable solution can be expected by any method of analysis, the factor problem must be so formulated that the number of observations exceeds the number of independent parameters to be determined.

### The intercorrelations

The square table of intercorrelations of $n$ tests is called the *correlation matrix*. Such a matrix is illustrated in *Figure 4*. The correlation matrix is square, and it is symmetric because $r_{jk} = r_{kj}$. When the correlation matrix is written with unity in the diagonal cells, it is called a *complete correlation matrix*, and it is denoted $R_1$. The correlation matrix can be expressed in terms of the matrices that have been defined in previous sections. The correlation between the standard scores $s_{ji}$ and $s_{ki}$, where the subscripts $j$ and $k$ both refer to tests, is

$$(19) \qquad r_{jk} = \frac{1}{N} \sum_{i=1}^{N} s_{ji} s_{ki} ,$$

since the standard scores have unit standard deviation. If we write it in the form

$$(19a) \qquad r_{jk} = \frac{1}{N} \sum_{i=1}^{N} s_{ji} s_{ik} ,$$

we imply the multiplication of two score matrices, namely, $s_{ji}$ and $s_{ik}$. The score matrix with elements $s_{ji}$ is of order $n \times N$ and it is denoted $S$. The

$$n$$

$$n \left\|
\begin{array}{ccccc}
r_{11} & r_{12} & r_{13} \ldots & & r_{1n} \\
r_{12} & r_{22} & r_{23} \ldots & & r_{2n} \\
r_{13} & r_{23} & r_{33} \ldots & & r_{3n} \\
\cdots & \cdots & \cdots & (r_{kj} = r_{jk}) \ldots & \\
r_{1n} & r_{2n} & r_{3n} \ldots & & r_{nn}
\end{array}
\right\|$$

Correlation Matrix R

FIGURE 4

score matrix with elements $s_{ik}$ is the transpose of $S$ and is of order $N \times n$. Hence we have

$$(20) \qquad R_1 = \frac{1}{N} SS' ,$$

where the diagonal entries of $R_1$ are unity, i.e.,

$$(21) \qquad r_{jj} = \frac{1}{N} \sum_{i=1}^{N} s_{ji}^2 = 1 .$$

By (20) and (2) we have

$$(22) \qquad R_1 = \frac{1}{N} (F_1 P)(F_1 P)'$$

or

$$(23) \qquad R_1 = \frac{1}{N} F_1 P P' F_1' .$$

The product $PP'$ in (23) represents the cross products of rows of $P$. These can be written in the form

$$(24) \qquad PP' = \sum_{i=1}^{N} x_{mi} x_{iM}$$

or

$$(25) \qquad PP' = N r_{mM} ,$$

where $r_{mM}$ is the correlation between the two factors or reference abilities $m$

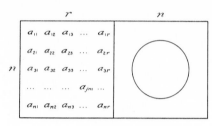

Factor Matrix $F_r$

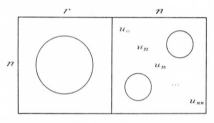

Factor Matrix $F_u$

FIGURE 5

and $M$. These correlations are zero, except the diagonal self-correlations, which are unity. Hence

$$(26) \qquad PP' = NI ,$$

where $I$ is the identity matrix. Substituting in (23), we have

$$(27) \qquad R_1 = F_1 F_1' .$$

This equation is fundamental in factor analysis. It can be stated as a fundamental theorem, namely, that *the product of the complete factorial matrix by its transpose is the complete correlation matrix.*

The complete factorial matrix $F_1$ of *Figure 3* can be expressed as a sum of the two matrices shown in *Figure 5*. The matrix $F_r$ is of order $n$ by $(n+r)$, where the unique factor loadings have been omitted. The matrix $F_u$ is also of order $n$ by $(n+r)$, where the common factor loadings have been omitted. If we superimpose these two matrices, we get a matrix sum of the type shown in *Figure 3*. Hence we write

$$(28) \qquad\qquad F_r + F_u = F_1 .$$

Substituting in (27), we have

$$(29) \qquad\qquad R_1 = (F_r + F_u)(F_r + F_u)'$$

or

$$(29a) \qquad\qquad R_1 = (F_r + F_u)(F_r' + F_u') .$$

This becomes

$$(30) \qquad\qquad R_1 = F_r F_r' + F_r F_u' + F_u F_r' + F_u F_u ,$$

in which $F_r$ and $F_u$ are both of order $n$ by $(n+r)$. These four separate products in (30) are shown in rectangular notation in *Figure 6*. In order to simplify *Figure 6*, it has been particularized to the case of $n=4$ and $r=2$. The products $F_r F_u'$ and $F_u F_r'$ both vanish. Hence we have

$$(31) \qquad\qquad R_1 = F_r F_r' + F_u F_u' .$$

The product $F_u F_u'$ is shown in rectangular notation in *Figure 6*. The product $F_u F_u'$ is a square matrix of order $n \times n$ with diagonal entries $u_{jj}^2$. It is that part of the correlation matrix which shows the contribution of the unique factors to the correlation matrix $R_1$.

The product $F_r F_r'$ in (31) is shown in rectangular notation in *Figure 6*. This product is that part of the correlational matrix $R_1$ which is contributed by the common factors. It will be denoted $R$ without subscript. Note that $R$ contains the intercorrelations of the tests and that the diagonal elements are the communalities instead of unity as in $R_1$. It is of significance that *the unique factors contribute only to the diagonal cells in the correlation matrix*, as illustrated in *Figure 6*. The matrix $R$ will be called the *reduced correlation matrix* because its diagonal elements have been depressed from unity to the communalities.

The product $F_r F_r'$, where $F_r$ is of order $n$ by $(n+r)$, as illustrated in *Figure 6*, is the same as the product $FF'$, where $F$ is a reduced factor matrix of order $n \times r$, as shown in *Figure 7*. We have, therefore, the important equation

$$(32) \qquad\qquad FF' = R ,$$

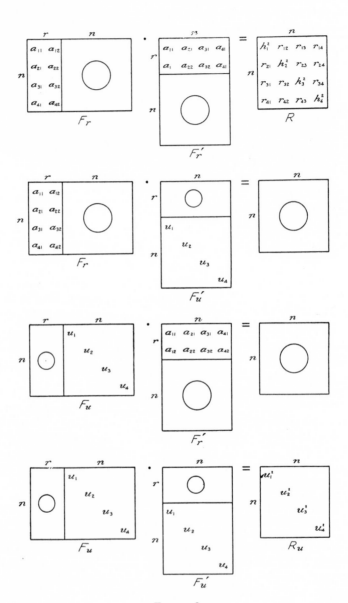

FIGURE 6

which can be stated as the fundamental factor theorem: *The product of the reduced factor matrix by its transpose is the reduced correlation matrix.* This fundamental relation between $F$ and $R$ is shown in rectangular notation in *Figure 7*.

The complete correlation matrix $R_1$ has now been divided into two parts, namely, $R$ and $R_u$,

$$(33) \qquad\qquad R_1 = R + R_u ,$$

where $R_u$ is a diagonal matrix. This summation is shown in rectangular notation in *Figure 8*. Since each diagonal element $u_j^2$ of $R_u$ shows the unique

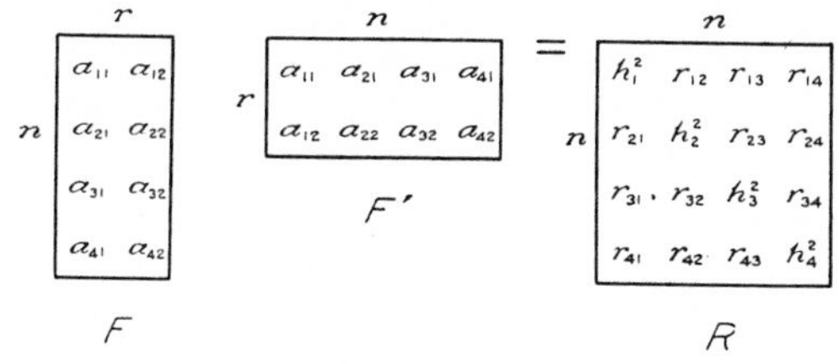

FIGURE 7

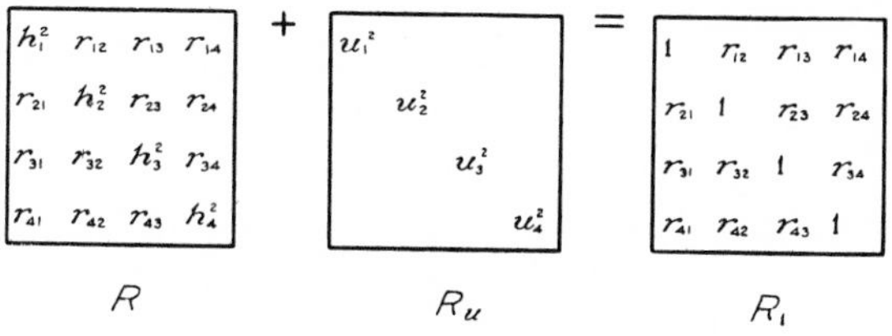

FIGURE 8

variance of test $j$, the complete correlation matrix $R_1$ and the reduced correlation matrix $R$ differ only in the diagonal cells. The diagonals of $R$ contain the communalities.

If we regard the correlation coefficients as the given data and the factor matrix $F$ as the desired objective in a factorial analysis, we have $n(n-1)/2$ experimentally given coefficients which must exceed the number of linearly independent parameters in $F$. It will be seen that, by limiting ourselves to the common factors of $F$ and the corresponding intercorrelations, the factor problem becomes determinate, even though we admit the existence of unique variance, which is known to exist in all psychological tests. This restriction of the factor problem to the common factors with no attempt to account for the total variance of each test is one of the turning-points in finding a determinate solution in factor analysis as a scientific method.

In general, the rank of the complete correlation matrix is equal to its order, namely, $n$. Since the reduced correlation matrix $R$ is the product $FF'$, it follows that the rank of $R$ cannot exceed the rank of $F$. The reduced factor matrix $F$ is of order $n \times r$, where $r < n$. Since the columns of $F$ represent linearly independent factors, the rank of $F$ is equal to the number of common factors $r$. Hence we have the important theorem: *The number of common factors represented in a reduced correlation matrix is equal to the rank of the matrix.* Experimentally obtained correlation coefficients are subject to sampling errors, which constitute a fortuitous element in each coefficient. In the strict sense of the term, the rank of a correlation matrix for experimental data is always equal to its order, namely, $n$. The scientific problem is to account for as much as possible of the relations between tests by the smallest possible number of common factors. This leads necessarily to a problem of determining when the residuals are negligible for any given number of common factors. The computational problem is made more difficult because the communalities in the diagonal cells of $R$ are unknown. These diagonal elements must be estimated at the start of an analysis in finding the factor matrix $F$ for a given set of correlations in $R$.

In the mathematical sense, the number of linearly independent factors involved in the correlations between $n$ tests is the rank of the correlation matrix, irrespective of what the diagonal elements may be. In general, one would limit this reduction of correlations into factors by considering only correlation matrices whose diagonal elements do not destroy the Gramian properties of the correlation matrix. In stating the theorem concerning the number of factors in a correlation matrix explicitly for the reduced correlation matrix, we have in mind the scientific problem of discovering physically identifiable factors as distinguished from numerical artifacts which might be permissible as mathematical solutions but are not allowable as scientifically significant solutions in a factor problem.

The correlation matrix for psychological tests with unity in the diagonal cells has, in general, a rank that is equal to its order, namely, $n$. Since we have for the complete correlation matrix the relation $R_1 = F_1 F_1'$, we should expect $n$ linearly independent factors in $F_1$. But by psychological considerations we expect $(n+r) = q$ factors in $F_1$. Hence the columns of $F_1$ are not linearly independent. It will be shown that $R_1$, which is of rank $n$ and order $n$, can be factored into a factor matrix with as many factors as there are tests; but such a numerical solution is not ordinarily of much interest or value, since it represents a condensation of $(n+r)$ factors into $n$ linearly independent columns of numbers in $F_1$, which rarely correspond to the $r$ linearly independent psychological common factors of the intercorrelations. This numerical solution with as many factors as there are tests will be described in detail in a later section.

## The reliability coefficient

The correlation between two administrations of the same test or between two tests that are designed to be parallel is called the *reliability coefficient* of the test. An example is the correlation between the scores in two spelling tests of one hundred words each, when the two lists have been drawn as random samples from a longer vocabulary. If the two tests are truly parallel, they must involve the same abilities, common and specific, but the variable chance errors in the two tests are independent. This situation is represented in *Figure 9*.

It is customary in psychological work to write the reliability coefficient in the diagonal cells of a correlation matrix. By the present analysis it is seen that the diagonal entries of $R_1$ are unity, while the diagonal entries of

|  | $r$ common factors | | | | | | Two specific factors | | Four error factors | | | |
|---|---|---|---|---|---|---|---|---|---|---|---|---|
| $j$ | $a_{j1}$ | $a_{j2}$ | $a_{j3}$ | ... | $a_{jr}$ | $b_j$ | O | $e_j$ | O | O | O |
| $j'$ | $a_{j1}$ | $a_{j2}$ | $a_{j3}$ | ... | $a_{jr}$ | $b_j$ | O | O | $e_{j'}$ | O | O |
| $k$ | $a_{k1}$ | $a_{k2}$ | $a_{k3}$ | ... | $a_{kr}$ | O | $b_k$ | O | O | $e_k$ | O |
| $k'$ | $a_{k1}$ | $a_{k2}$ | $a_{k3}$ | ... | $a_{kr}$ | O | $b_k$ | O | O | O | $e_{k'}$ |

FIGURE 9

$R$ are the communalities $h_j^2$. The relation between the reliability and the communality of a test may be shown by considering in detail the factorial matrix for a test $j$, a parallel test $j'$, another test $k$, and its parallel test $k'$. The factorial matrix for these four tests is shown in *Figure 9*.

Let there be $r$ common factors in the four tests. Let $b_j^2$ be the specific variance in test $j$. Since $j$ and $j'$ are parallel tests, it is evident that they must require the same common abilities and the same specific ability. Hence $b_j$ is recorded in the same column of $F_1$ in *Figure 9* for both $j$ and $j'$. For the same reason, $b_k$ must be common to tests $k$ and $k'$, which are parallel. But the variable errors are uncorrelated by definition, even for parallel tests. Hence $F_1$ shows a separate error factor for each of the four tests.

The correlation between the tests $j$ and $j'$ is the reliability coefficient of test $j$, and it will be denoted $r_{jj}$. Since $R_1 = F_1 F_1'$, the reliability of $j$ can be found in *Figure 9* as the cross product of the first two rows of the matrix. We then have

(34) $$r_{jj} = \sum_{m=1}^{r} a_{jm}^2 + b_j^2,$$

and the reliability of test $k$ is

$$(35) \qquad r_{kk} = \sum_{m=1}^{r} a_{km}^2 + b_k^2 .$$

By (34) we have

$$(36) \qquad r_{jj} = h_j^2 + b_j^2 .$$

Since the total variance of $j$ is unity, we have

$$(37) \qquad r_{jj} = 1 - e_j^2 .$$

This equation states the theorem: *The reliability of a test is the complement of its error variance.*

Since

$$(38) \qquad h_j^2 = 1 - u_j^2$$

and

$$(39) \qquad u_j^2 = b_j^2 + e_j^2 ,$$

we have

$$(40) \qquad h_j^2 = 1 - b_j^2 - e_j^2$$

or

$$(41) \qquad h_j^2 = r_{jj} - b_j^2 ,$$

and hence

$$(42) \qquad h_j^2 \leqq r_{jj} .$$

This inequality states the theorem: *The communality of a test is always smaller than the reliability except in the limiting case where the specific factor is absent, in which case the communality and the reliability are equal.*

It is of interest to note that the factorial methods effect a separation between the communality and the uniqueness of each test in a battery but that the uniqueness cannot be separated into its two principal parts—specificity and error—by factorial methods. In order to estimate the specific variance of a test or its reliability coefficient, a separate experiment must be made with a repetition of the test or with parallel forms of it. If the reliability coefficient is determined by independent experiment, the specific variance can be estimated as the difference between the reliability and the communality.

An object of psychological inquiry is to isolate an increasing number of abilities until the specific variance of each important test is reduced to a minimum. It is not likely that any single test will be completely described in terms of the factors which it has in common with those of one battery. In order to isolate all the abilities that are called for by a test, it will probably be necessary to insert it in several test batteries in succession. The specific variance of a test should be regarded as a challenge; it is that part of the total variance of a test which is unique in a particular battery, and hence its factorial composition is unknown. In order to test a hypothesis concerning the abilities which are involved in the specific variance of a test, the test should be combined with others which involve the hypothetical abilities. If the specific variance is reduced, the hypothesis is sustained.

For the next few years it will probably be more interesting to isolate new abilities than to reduce the specificity in particular tests. Increased knowledge of the primary mental abilities will facilitate the type of experiment by which the specificities of particular tests may be reduced. It will probably be found that a considerable fraction of the total variance of each test is attributable to factors of such limited social significance that the complete elimination of the specificity of each test will not be essential in the early stages of the scientific study of human abilities.

## Summary of terminology and notation

The terminology for the different parts of the variance of a test is summarized as follows:

$$
\begin{aligned}
Total\ variance &= 1 &&= h_j^2 + b_j^2 + e_j^2 = h_j^2 + u_j^2\ ; \\
Reliability &= r_{jj} = h_j^2 + b_j^2 &&= 1 - e_j^2\ ; \\
Communality &= h_j^2 = h_j^2 &&= 1 - u_j^2\ ; \\
Specificity &= b_j^2 = && b_j^2\ ; \\
Uniqueness &= u_j^2 = && b_j^2 + e_j^2\ ; \\
Error\ variance &= e_j^2 = && e_j^2 = 1 - r_{jj}\ .
\end{aligned}
$$

The notation for scores, matrices, and matrix elements is as follows:

$N$ = number of individuals in experimental population;

$j, k$ = two subscripts for tests;

$s_{ji}$ = standard score of individual $i$ in test $j$;

$i$ = subscript for individual in experimental population;

$m, M$ = two subscripts for arbitrary orthogonal reference abilities or factors;

$x_{mi}$ = standard score of individual $i$ in reference ability $m$;

$c_{jm}$ = test coefficient of test $j$ for the factor $m$;

$r$ = number of common factors in correlation matrix;

$n$ $\quad$ = number of tests in the battery;

$r_{jk}$ $\quad$ = correlation between tests $j$ and $k$;

$r_{jj}$ $\quad$ = reliability of test $j$;

$a_{jm}$ $\quad$ = test coefficient of test $j$ in the common factor $m$;

$F_1$ $\quad$ = complete factor matrix for total variance of each test;

$F$ $\quad$ = reduced factor matrix for common-factor variance in each test;

$P$ $\quad$ = population matrix with elements $x_{mi}$;

$b_j$ $\quad$ = specific factor loading in test $j$;

$e_j$ $\quad$ = error factor loading in test $j$;

$u_j$ $\quad$ = unique factor loading in test $j$;

$S$ $\quad$ = score matrix with elements $s_{ji}$;

$\sigma_j^2$ $\quad$ = total variance of test $j = 1$;

$\sigma_m^2$ $\quad$ = variance of scores $x_{mi} = 1$;

$R_1$ $\quad$ = complete correlation matrix with unity in diagonal cells;

$R$ $\quad$ = reduced correlation matrix with communalities in diagonal cells.

# CHAPTER III

# GEOMETRICAL MODELS

## Geometrical representation in factor analysis

In understanding the relation between the factor matrix $F$ and the correlation matrix $R$, it will be helpful to consider a set of geometrical models. The algebraic development of factor theory could be represented by several different geometrical analogies, but we have selected one that seems to be the simplest and most direct, and it will be used throughout this text. In this chapter we shall consider the geometrical representation of problems that involve only two common factors. These problems can all be represented by two-dimensional diagrams. In later chapters we shall extend the same kind of geometrical interpretation to problems involving three common factors which can be represented by three-dimensional models. The same geometrical interpretations will then be extended to the $n$-dimensional methods of multiple-factor analysis. Most students find it very helpful to visualize the problems of factor analysis by geometrical representations.

## Factorial structure

In *Figure 1* we have represented a problem that involves eight tests with two common factors. The correlational matrix $R$ is shown at *1e* in the figure and the factor matrix $F$ is shown at *1b*.

The factor matrix $F$ will now be given a simple geometrical interpretation. Let the entries in each row represent the co-ordinates of a point in the diagram at *1a* in the figure. The first row gives the factor loadings .70 and .30 for test 1. These two numerical values are interpreted as the co-ordinates of a point which is plotted in the diagram *1a*. This point is the terminus of the test vector 1. The test is now represented by a *test vector*. Each of the eight tests in the factor matrix $F$ is represented in a similar manner in the diagram at *1a*, and we then have as many test vectors in the diagram as there are rows in the factor matrix $F$. In addition, we have the two unit reference vectors $A$ and $B$, which represent the factors that are shown by the columns of $F$. *The combination of the test vectors and the reference vectors for a test battery is called a **factorial structure**.** The factorial structure for the present illustrative example is shown in the diagram at *1a*.

In the factor matrix there are four tests, namely, 1, 3, 4, 7, which have non-vanishing entries in both columns of $F$. These are represented in the middle of the first quadrant of *Figure 1a*. Two of the tests—2 and 5—have

---

* These definitions of structure and related concepts are the same as in the writer's original publications on multiple-factor analysis (1931–35).

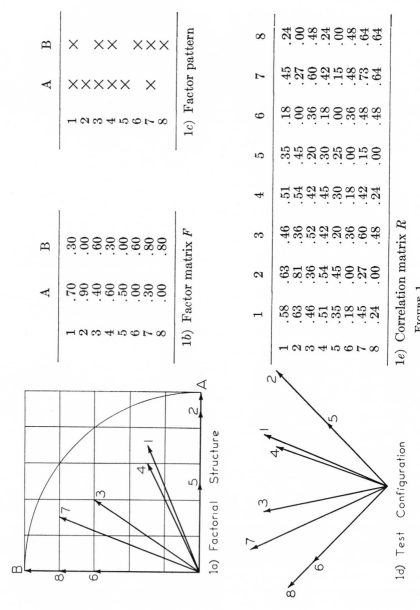

**1a) Factorial Structure**

### 1b) Factor matrix $F$

|   | A | B |
|---|---|---|
| 1 | .70 | .30 |
| 2 | .90 | .00 |
| 3 | .40 | .60 |
| 4 | .60 | .30 |
| 5 | .50 | .00 |
| 6 | .00 | .60 |
| 7 | .30 | .80 |
| 8 | .00 | .80 |

### 1c) Factor pattern

|   | A | B |
|---|---|---|
| 1 | × | × |
| 2 | × |   |
| 3 | × | × |
| 4 | × | × |
| 5 |   |   |
| 6 |   | × |
| 7 | × | × |
| 8 |   | × |

### 1e) Correlation matrix $R$

|   | 1 | 2 | 3 | 4 | 5 | 6 | 7 | 8 |
|---|---|---|---|---|---|---|---|---|
| 1 | .58 | .63 | .46 | .51 | .35 | .18 | .45 | .24 |
| 2 | .63 | .81 | .36 | .54 | .45 | .00 | .27 | .00 |
| 3 | .46 | .36 | .52 | .42 | .20 | .36 | .60 | .48 |
| 4 | .51 | .54 | .42 | .45 | .30 | .18 | .42 | .24 |
| 5 | .35 | .45 | .20 | .30 | .25 | .00 | .15 | .00 |
| 6 | .18 | .00 | .36 | .18 | .00 | .36 | .48 | .48 |
| 7 | .45 | .27 | .60 | .42 | .15 | .48 | .73 | .64 |
| 8 | .24 | .00 | .48 | .24 | .00 | .48 | .64 | .64 |

**1d) Test Configuration**

FIGURE 1

non-vanishing entries only in column $A$. These two tests have corresponding test vectors that are collinear with the reference vector $A$. Two other tests —6 and 8—have non-vanishing entries only in column $B$ of $F$. These are represented in the corresponding structure by test vectors that are collinear with the reference vector $B$.

The geometrical representation of the test battery can be generalized in the statement that *each factor loading* $a_{jm}$ *in F is represented as a projection of the test vector* j *on the reference axis* m. The first test vector has a projection of .70 on the reference vector $A$ and a projection of .30 on the reference vector $B$. The second test vector has a projection of .90 on the reference vector $A$ and zero on the reference vector $B$. This means that the second test vector is orthogonal to the reference vector $B$. *If a factor loading* $a_{jm}$ *in F is zero,*

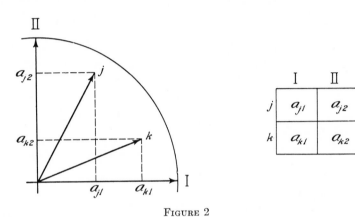

FIGURE 2

*the geometrical interpretation is that the corresponding test vector* j *is orthogonal to the reference vector* m.

### Correlations as scalar products

The intercorrelations can also be represented geometrically in a very useful way. Each of the tests is represented in *Figure 1a* as a test vector. It will be shown that the correlation between any two tests is the scalar product of their test vectors. The scalar product of two vectors $j$ and $k$ is $h_j h_k \cos \phi_{jk}$, where $h_j$ and $h_k$ denote the lengths of the vectors and $\phi_{jk}$ is their angular separation.

In *Figure 2* we have represented two test vectors $j$ and $k$, whose lengths are $h_j$ and $h_k$, respectively. Adjacent to the figure is also the factor matrix for the two tests $j$ and $k$ in their own plane with orthogonal axes I and II. The factor loadings, $a_{j1}$ and $a_{j2}$, are the projections of the test $j$ on the two orthogonal axes, as shown in the figure, and a similar interpretation applies to the factor loadings, $a_{k1}$ and $a_{k2}$ of test $k$.

The correlation $r_{jk}$ between the two tests can be determined by the product of the factor matrix and its transpose. The intercorrelation is then the cross product of the two rows of the factor matrix, namely,

$$(1) \qquad r_{jk} = a_{j1}a_{k1} + a_{j2}a_{k2} .$$

Dividing by $h_j h_k$, we obtain

$$(2) \qquad \frac{r_{jk}}{h_j h_k} = \frac{a_{j1}}{h_j} \cdot \frac{a_{k1}}{h_k} + \frac{a_{j2}}{h_j} \cdot \frac{a_{k2}}{h_k} ;$$

but

$$(3) \qquad \frac{a_{j1}}{h_j} = \cos \phi_{j1} ,$$

$$(4) \qquad \frac{a_{k1}}{h_k} = \cos \phi_{k1} ,$$

$$(5) \qquad \frac{a_{j2}}{h_j} = \sin \phi_{j1} ,$$

$$(6) \qquad \frac{a_{k2}}{h_k} = \sin \phi_{k1} ,$$

where $\phi_{j1}$ and $\phi_{k1}$ are the angular separations between the test vectors $j$ and $k$ from the first reference axis. We have, therefore,

$$(7) \qquad \frac{r_{jk}}{h_j h_k} = \cos \phi_{j1} \cos \phi_{k1} + \sin \phi_{j1} \sin \phi_{k1} .$$

The angle $\phi_{jk}$ can be expressed as the difference between $\phi_{j1}$ and $\phi_{k1}$, so that

$$(8) \qquad \phi_{jk} = \phi_{j1} - \phi_{k1} ;$$

but the right-hand member of equation (7) is the expression for the cosine of the difference between the angles $\phi_{j1}$ and $\phi_{k1}$. Hence we have

$$(9) \qquad \frac{r_{jk}}{h_j h_k} = \cos \phi_{jk} ,$$

or

$$(10) \qquad r_{jk} = h_j h_k \cos \phi_{jk} .$$

*The correlation between any two tests is equal to the scalar product of their test vectors.*

An important fact about this theorem is its independence of the reference axes. It should be noted that equation (10) does not involve the reference axes. Since the scalar product is determined only by the lengths of the vectors and by their angular separation, *the scalar product of a pair of vectors is invariant under rotation of the reference frame.* We can now make an inference which involves one of the central ideas in factorial theory, namely, that *the correlation matrix determines the test vectors as to their lengths and angular relations, but the correlation matrix does not define the location of the reference axes.*

With the scalar-product interpretation of the correlation coefficient, it follows that a negative coefficient is always represented by an obtuse angular separation of the test vectors, the lengths $h_j$ and $h_k$ being taken as positive. Also, with non-vanishing lengths of the vectors, a zero correlation is represented geometrically by a right angle. *A pair of tests with zero correlation have orthogonal test vectors.*

If two vectors are each of unit length, then the numerical values of $h_j$ and $h_k$ are both unity, and their scalar product is the cosine of their angular separation. But cos $\phi_{jk}$ is also the projection of either unit vector on the other. Hence we have the theorem that *the scalar product of a pair of unit vectors is equal to the projection of either vector on the other.*

If the entries in the correlation matrix are all positive, as is the case with tests of the cognitive or intellective functions, then all pairs of test vectors are separated by acute angles. It follows that *if all the correlations are positive, the configuration of test vectors lies inside a cone of 45° generating angle.*

### The configuration

The correlation matrix of *Figure 1e* contains all the correlations for the eight-test battery. Since only two common factors are involved in these correlations, the rank is 2, and it is possible to represent the test relations by a set of eight test vectors in two dimensions. The lengths of the test vectors are determined by the diagonal entries in the correlation matrix. Each diagonal entry $h_j^2$ is the communality of a test $j$, and the length of the corresponding test vector is $h_j$. The angular separations between the test vectors are determined by the side entries of the correlational matrix in such a way that the scalar products of all pairs of vectors are equal to the corresponding correlations. The number of the dimensions that are required to represent the given correlations is the same as the rank of $R$, and this is the same as the number of common factors in the test battery.

If we consider only the arrangement of the test vectors among themselves as determined by the correlation coefficients and without regard to any reference frame, we call the arrangement or grouping a *configuration* of test vectors. The configuration of test vectors for the present example is shown in *Figure 1d*. The configuration at *1d* is identical with that at *1a*. The only difference is that the *configuration* and the *reference axes* are combined to form a *structure* at *1a,* whereas the configuration alone is shown at *1d* without any reference frame. The configuration has been drawn intentionally in different positions at *1a* and *1d.*

There is an exact relation between the test configuration at *1d* and the correlation matrix at *1e.* A model or diagram of the configuration can be constructed from the correlations, and the reverse is also possible, in that the correlations can be computed from the configuration. We lose no information in going from the correlations to the configuration or vice versa because they are merely two different ways of stating the same facts. It should be noted especially that *neither the correlations nor the configuration has any reference frame.*

Just as there is a direct correspondence between the *correlation matrix* and the *test configuration,* neither of which involves a reference frame, so there is a direct correspondence between the *factor matrix* and the *factorial structure,* both of which do involve a reference frame. The pairs have been placed adjacent to each other in *Figure 1* to emphasize these relations. The test structure cannot be defined until the reference axes have been located in the configuration, as shown in *Figure 1a.* In the same manner, the factor matrix at *1b* cannot be defined except in terms of a particular set of reference axes which are implied by the two columns of that matrix.

A factor problem usually starts with a table of intercorrelations, as shown in *Figure 1e.* If it were determined that the rank of that matrix is 2, then we should know that the intercorrelations of the eight tests are produced by two common factors even before we could have any idea what these two factors are. We would also know that the configuration of test vectors would be contained within two dimensions, so that they could be represented as a plane diagram, as shown at *1d.* When the correlational matrix is given, including the diagonal entries, then the configuration can be drawn. It should be especially noted that the correlation matrix and the test configuration have no reference axes.

The object of a factorial problem is to write a factor matrix $F$ that will reproduce the correlations $R$ by the fundamental theorem $FF' = R$. This problem can be represented geometrically. It consists in determining the rank of $R$, which is also the number of dimensions in the test configuration, and the rank is also the number of columns of the factor matrix $F$. The configuration can then be drawn uniquely. A set of reference axes can then be inserted into the configuration to form the structure at *1a.* When the reference axes have been inserted into the configuration, it is possible to determine the projection of each test vector on each one of the reference axes. These projections constitute the cell entries $a_{jm}$ of the factor matrix $F$. It should be clear, then, that the factor matrix cannot be written until a set of reference axes has been inserted into the configuration which is defined by the intercorrelations.

Certain features of the test configuration can be inferred by mere inspection of the correlation coefficients. If all the correlations are positive or zero, we can infer that all the test vectors are separated by acute angles. The largest angular separation would then be a right angle. It follows that the whole test configuration must be contained within a cone of 45° generating angle when the correlation matrix has no negative entries. This is the situation with psychological tests of the cognitive or intellective functions, which seem never to show any significant negative correlations.

## The arbitrary reference frame

Since the object of factor analysis is to find a factor matrix $F$ from a given correlation matrix $R_1$ so that the fundamental factor theorem $FF' = R$ is satisfied, it is of interest to note that every correlation matrix can be factored into a factor matrix. In fact, the correlation matrix is, by definition, a product of two score matrices, as has already been shown in (20–ii),

$$(20\text{–ii}) \qquad\qquad R_1 = \frac{1}{N}\, SS' \,.$$

Since the correlation matrix is obtained computationally as a product of two matrices, it is evident that every correlation matrix can be factored. We have, therefore, the theorem that *for every correlation matrix* R *there exists a corresponding factorial matrix* F *such that* FF′ = R.

We have seen that a given correlation matrix can be interpreted as showing the scalar products of pairs of test vectors. We have also seen that the factor matrix can be interpreted as showing the projections of each test vector on each of the co-ordinate axes. The numerical values of the projections of the test vectors are, of course, dependent on where we put the factorial reference frame. Hence we have the important theorem that *an infinite number of factor matrices* F *can be written which reproduce any given correlation matrix* R. This theorem makes it evident that when we have factored a given correlation matrix $R$ into a factor matrix $F$ we do not have a unique solution. Further restrictions must be imposed on the solution $F$, so as to make it in some sense unique before we can hope to interpret the test coefficients. On this question there has been much controversy, which we shall have occasion to consider in a later chapter.

In order to demonstrate the arbitrary location of the reference frame, we have drawn in *Figure 3* several positions of the co-ordinate axes for one test configuration. The configuration of *Figure 1d* is reproduced in three different positions in *Figure 3* as regards the co-ordinate axes. Below each diagram in the figure we have the corresponding factor matrix. Although the numerical values are different in these three factor matrices, they all reproduce the same correlations, namely, those of *Figure 1e*.

Since the correlation matrix $R$ consists of scalar products of test vectors, while the factor matrix $F$ shows the projections of the test vectors on the co-ordinate axes, we have several other theorems that are useful in understanding the relations between these matrices, $R$ and $F$. Consider the test vector $k$ and the unit vector $X$ in *Figure 4*. The scalar product of these two vectors is $h_k h_x \cos \phi_{kx}$, which becomes $h_k \cos \phi_{kx}$, since $X$ is a unit vector. Let $Z$ be a unit vector collinear with $k$. Then the projection of $Z$ on $X$ is $\cos \phi_{kx}$. But the projection of $k$ on $X$ is proportional to the length $h_k$ of $k$. Hence the projection of $k$ on $X$ is $h_k \cos \phi_{kx}$. We then have the theorem that

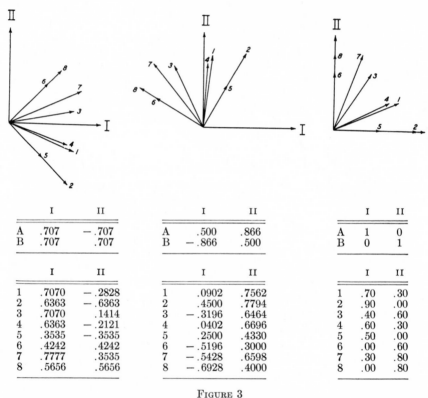

| | I | II |
|---|---|---|
| A | .707 | − .707 |
| B | .707 | .707 |

| | I | II |
|---|---|---|
| A | .500 | .866 |
| B | − .866 | .500 |

| | I | II |
|---|---|---|
| A | 1 | 0 |
| B | 0 | 1 |

| | I | II |
|---|---|---|
| 1 | .7070 | − .2828 |
| 2 | .6363 | − .6363 |
| 3 | .7070 | .1414 |
| 4 | .6363 | − .2121 |
| 5 | .3535 | − .3535 |
| 6 | .4242 | .4242 |
| 7 | .7777 | .3535 |
| 8 | .5656 | .5656 |

| | I | II |
|---|---|---|
| 1 | .0902 | .7562 |
| 2 | .4500 | .7794 |
| 3 | − .3196 | .6464 |
| 4 | .0402 | .6696 |
| 5 | .2500 | .4330 |
| 6 | − .5196 | .3000 |
| 7 | − .5428 | .6598 |
| 8 | − .6928 | .4000 |

| | I | II |
|---|---|---|
| 1 | .70 | .30 |
| 2 | .90 | .00 |
| 3 | .40 | .60 |
| 4 | .60 | .30 |
| 5 | .50 | .00 |
| 6 | .00 | .60 |
| 7 | .30 | .80 |
| 8 | .00 | .80 |

FIGURE 3

*the projection of a test vector on any given axis is the scalar product of the test vector and a unit vector collinear with the axis.*

Consider a set of test vectors $k$ and a particular test vector $j$. We have seen that the projection of a test vector $k$ on $X$ is $h_k \cos \phi_{kx}$. This is the same as $h_k \cos \phi_{jk}$, since $\phi_{kx}$ and $\phi_{jk}$ are the same angle. But the correlation $r_{jk} = h_j h_k \cos \phi_{jk}$. Hence the projection of the test vector $k$ on a particular test vector $j$ is

$$(11) \qquad P_{kj} = \frac{r_{jk}}{h_j} .$$

Hence *the correlations between a set of tests* k *and a particular test* j *are proportional to the projections of the test vectors* k *on an axis collinear with the test vector* j. This theorem can be applied in the geometrical interpretation of a column, or row, $j$, of the correlation matrix. Such a row shows the correlations between a set of tests, $k$, and a particular test $j$. The configuration of test vectors corresponding to the correlation matrix satisfies the theorem that *the correlations in any particular row or column,* j, *of the correlation matrix are proportional to the projections of the test vectors on an axis through the test vector* j. This is merely a restatement of the previous theorem. The proportionality factor is $1/h_j$, so that, if the length of a particular test vector $j$ is known or assumed, then one column of the factor matrix can be immediately written by (11) if we decide to locate one of the co-ordinate axes

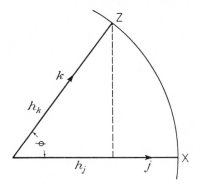

through one of the test vectors $j$. The projections $P_{kj}$ are then, in fact, the entries of one of the columns of the factor matrix.

The same theorem can be restated in still another form that is important for factorial analysis, namely, that, *for any given correlation matrix with an implied common-factor space, there exists in that space an axis through the origin on which the test vectors have projections that are proportional to the correlations of any given column, or row, of the correlation matrix.* If the correlation matrix is of order $n$, there exist $n$ such axes in its common-factor space.

If the co-ordinate axes are located elsewhere in the common-factor space, the projections of the test vectors on these co-ordinate axes will be linear combinations of the projections on the axes through the test vectors. We infer a fundamental theorem in factorial theory, namely, that *every column of factor loadings in the factorial matrix is a linear combination of columns of the correlational matrix.* We shall make use of this theorem in designing different methods of factoring the correlational matrix.

It should be clear that any interpretation of the factor matrix must be made in relation to the principles that are chosen for locating the co-ordinate axes in the configuration defined by the correlations. In general, the numerical entries of the factor matrix are as arbitrary as the location of the reference frame. It is only to the extent that the reference frame can be in some sense unique that the numerical entries of the factor matrix can be given any scientific interpretation.

### Sign reversals in the factor matrix

When a reference frame has been inserted into the configuration and the projections of the test vectors computed as shown in *Figure 1a* and *1b*, it should be noted that the sense in which a co-ordinate vector such as $A$ in *Figure 1a* is taken determines the signs of the projections in column $A$ of *1b*. If the direction of the co-ordinate vector $A$ is reversed, then all the signs in column $A$ of the factor matrix are also reversed. If the reference vector $A$ represented some fundamental human trait, such as cheerfulness, then the reversal of direction of the reference vector would represent the direct opposite, such as grouchiness. Since the scalar products of the test vectors are independent of the location of the reference frame, we have the computationally useful theorem that *the signs of all the entries in a column of the factor matrix may be changed without altering the corresponding correlation matrix.* Computationally, this theorem becomes evident also if we consider the correlation coefficient as a cross product of a pair of rows of the factor matrix, such as *Figure 1b*. If we reverse the signs in both $a_{jm}$ and $a_{km}$ for a fixed column $m$, their product remains unchanged in sign so that the correlation coefficient $r_{jk}$ remains unchanged. The psychological interpretation of this reversal in direction of a reference vector can be shown in terms of the example given. The correlation between two traits remains unaffected by the arbitrary decision to call one of the component reference traits "plus cheerfulness" or "minus grouchiness."

Now consider the reversal of all the signs in a row $j$ of the factor matrix. This has the effect of reversing the direction of the corresponding test vector $j$. Its scalar remains the same, while its angular separation $\phi_{jk}$ from any other test vector $k$ is changed to the supplement of $\phi_{jk}$. Hence the absolute values of the correlations of this test with the other tests remain unaltered, but their signs are reversed. The psychological interpretation can be shown by an example, namely, that if one variable correlates positively with "plus tactfulness," then it will correlate negatively with "minus tactfulness," which might be defined as "plus tactlessness."

We have, therefore, another useful theorem that *if all the signs are reversed in a row of the factor matrix, then all the signs are reversed in the corresponding row and in the corresponding column of the correlation matrix.* To reverse the signs of all entries in a row $j$ of the factor matrix does not change the positive sign of the self-correlation of test $j$, since, by the theorem, the signs are reversed in the row $j$ and also in the column $j$ of the correlation matrix. These two sign changes in the diagonal cell keep the sign of the self-correlation unaltered. This theorem can also be inferred from the factor matrix. If all the signs in a row of that matrix are reversed, then all the terms in a cross product of row $j$ with any other row $k$ are similarly reversed in sign so that the correlation $r_{jk}$ is reversed in sign except the self-correlation of test $j$, which remains the sum of the squares of the entries in the row $j$. We can also infer from these relations that *the self-correlation of a test remains positive for all possible reversals of sign of tests and factors.*

### The restriction that $r$ be less than $n$

In the illustrative example of *Figure 1* we have eight tests and two common factors, so that $n = 8$ and $r = 2$. There are certain inequalities relating $r$ and $n$ which must be satisfied in order that a determinate factor solution shall be possible. To introduce these restrictions, consider the case in which $r > n$. This case is illustrated in *Figure 5*, which shows a factor pattern of

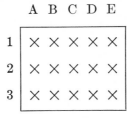

FIGURE 5

five common factors and three tests. The crosses represent non-vanishing factor loadings in the factor matrix. Assume that the five common factors are uncorrelated. The correlations between the three tests determine the correlation matrix, which is of order 3. The rank of that matrix cannot exceed 3, but we have set up the problem to represent more than three common factors. If such a correlation matrix were factored, it would give a factor matrix of not more than three columns or factors. The numerical entries in such a factor matrix would determine the correlations exactly, but the three factors would probably be artifacts as far as any scientific problem is concerned. The relations might have some statistical interest, and they might be useful for constructing various empirical prediction formulae, but they would not reveal the five factors that were operative in the test variances. *Factor analysis is built on the postulate that the number of common factors does not exceed the number of tests in the battery.* As far as a numerical solution is concerned, every correlation matrix can be factored routinely if we are willing to accept as many factors as there are tests. The scientific interpretation and validity of the factors is another matter.

The geometrical interpretation of the postulate that $r \leqq n$ can be seen if we consider the configuration of $n$ test vectors. If these vectors are defined in terms of their components in more than $n$ dimensions, the $n$ vectors can also be described in an $n$-dimensional subspace which is spanned by the $n$ vectors. That is the space defined by the factor matrix, from which it would not be possible to identify the larger number of factors that produced the test correlations.

These considerations raise the question of how one can be sure that any particular battery of $n$ variables really does involve less than $n$ common factors. *There is no guarantee beforehand that any proposed battery of* n *measurements will involve less than* n *common factors that have significant interpretation.* To produce such a situation is as much dependent on scientific intuition as other scientific experiments are subject to intuition for success and significance. One can, of course, factor any given correlation matrix to determine its rank. If the rank of the correlation matrix turns out to be comparable with its order, one has merely made a bad guess, and one must start over again with a revised test battery in the same domain.

### The test space and the common-factor space

The relation between the correlation matrix and the configuration is very markedly dependent on whether we insert unity or the communalities in the diagonal cells of the correlation matrix. The principles involved here can be illustrated in terms of the correlation between two tests, $j$ and $k$. The correlation matrix would be of order 2. If we write unity in the diagonal cells, there will be only one correlation coefficient to determine, namely, $r_{jk}$. The corresponding configuration is a pair of unit vectors, which are separated by an angle whose cosine is the given correlation coefficient. If we consider the tests of a battery as represented by unit vectors to cover the total variance of each test, then we have a configuration of $n$ unit vectors in a space of $(n+r)$ dimensions, which represent the common factors and the unique factors. Such a space is called the *test space* to distinguish it from the space that is defined by the common factors, which is called the *common-factor space*. Since the test space represents usually more factors or parameters than there are tests, we shall not use it except in special problems where the total test space is indicated. The total test space is of $n$ dimensions if we disregard the factorial composition of the tests.

### Summary of geometrical concepts

The geometrical representations described in this chapter will be summarized here. These theorems and definitions are all applicable to factor problems with any determinate number of factors or dimensions.

*The factor matrix and the configuration*

1) A reference frame must be inserted into the configuration before any factor matrix can be written.

2) Since the co-ordinate axes are not determined by the experimentally obtained correlation matrix, every factor matrix is in the nature of a factorial interpretation of the given correlations.

3) Each row of the factor matrix can be interpreted as showing the rectangular components of a test vector.

4) Each column of the factor matrix identifies a factorial axis in the structure.

5) Each reference factor is represented by a unit reference vector.

6) The graphs on which are plotted pairs of columns of the factor matrix show the factorial structure which combines the test vectors and the reference frame.

7) If the components of an orthogonal factor matrix are all positive or zero, the structure has all test vectors in the first quadrant or octant.

*The correlation matrix and the configuration*

8) The correlation matrix can be interpreted as showing the scalar products of all pairs of test vectors.

9) The length of each test vector is equal to the positive square root of its communality.

10) The correlation matrix with known diagonal entries determines a unique configuration of test vectors that can be represented as a physical model if the rank of the matrix is less than 4.

11) The correlation matrix does not determine any reference frame.

12) If the dimensionality or rank is less than 4, a physical model can be constructed to show the configuration alone or the factorial structure which includes the configuration and the reference axes.

13) No information is lost in representing the correlation matrix as a configuration, or vice versa.

14) A correlation matrix with coefficients that are all positive or zero determines uniquely a configuration of test vectors in which there are no obtuse angular separations.

15) The scalar product of a pair of vectors is invariant under rotation of axes.

16) The scalar product of a pair of unit vectors is equal to the projection of either vector on the other.

17) A positive correlation coefficient represents a pair of test vectors with acute angular separation. A negative correlation represents a pair of test vectors with obtuse angular separation.

18) The projection of a test vector on any given axis is the scalar product of the test vector and a unit vector collinear with the axis.

19) The correlations between a set of tests $k$ and a particular test $j$ are proportional to the projections of the set of test vectors $k$ on an axis collinear with the test vector $j$.

20) Given a correlation matrix with an implied common-factor space, there exists in that space an axis through the origin on which the test vectors have projections that are proportional to the correlations of any column, or row, of the correlation matrix.

21) Every column of factor loadings in the factor matrix is a linear combination of columns of the correlation matrix.

*Sign reversals in the factor matrix*

22) The signs of all the entries in a column of the factor matrix may be reversed without altering the corresponding correlation matrix.

23) Reversing the signs in a column of the factor matrix reverses the direction of the corresponding reference factor and reference vector.

24) If all the signs are reversed in a row of the factor matrix, then all the signs are reversed in the corresponding row and in the corresponding column of the correlation matrix.

25) To reverse the signs in a row of the factor matrix reverses the direction of the corresponding test vector.

26) The self-correlation of a test remains positive for all possible reversals of sign of tests and factors.

# CHAPTER IV

## A FACTOR PROBLEM IN TWO DIMENSIONS

### Introduction

So far we have considered the assumptions of factor analysis, the fundamental equations, and some of the geometrical concepts of factor theory. In discussing the sections of *Figure 1* in chapter iii we have seen the relations between the factor matrix, the factorial structure, the test configuration, and the correlation matrix. We shall now consider the illustrative problem of that chapter as if it were a factor problem to be solved. The problem starts with the given correlation matrix, which is ordinarily determined from experimental data. The problem now is to analyze the correlation matrix so as to discover the factor matrix $F$ and the structure as shown. The correlation matrix of the previous chapter will be used now as the given data, and we shall determine from it the factor matrix. It is a simple matter to construct a correlation matrix from a given factor matrix, but it is usually more difficult to extract the factor matrix from a given correlation matrix. It is the latter which constitutes factor analysis, where the experimental data are in the form of correlation coefficients from which a factor matrix is to be found.

The solution of a factorial problem consists usually of two steps, namely, (1) to factor the given correlations into a factor matrix with arbitrary reference frame and (2) to rotate the arbitrary reference frame into a preferred or simplifying position. The first is known as *the factoring problem*, and the second is known as *the rotational problem*. We shall describe both steps for the present example. There are several methods of factoring a correlation matrix, and there are several methods of solving the rotational problem. In fact, most of the theory and computational methods of factor analysis are concerned with these two main problems. Here we shall start with perhaps the simplest of the factoring methods, namely, *the diagonal method*.

### The diagonal method of factoring

Before proceeding to the factorial solution of the correlation matrix of the previous chapter, we shall describe the diagonal method of factoring by a small five-variable matrix in *Table 1*. This method of factoring is not well suited to large problems involving fallible data, but it is a simple routine method that can be used on a correlation matrix of any order and any rank.

The correlation matrix of *Table 1* will be used to illustrate the diagonal method of factoring. The total number of independent correlation coeffi-

101

cients is $\frac{1}{2}n(n+1)$ if the diagonal entries are included. Since the correlation matrix of *Table 1* is of order 5, there are fifteen correlation coefficients

Table 1

*Correlation Matrix*

|   | 1 | 2 | 3 | 4 | 5 |
|---|---|---|---|---|---|
| 1 | .85 | .28 | .36 | .82 | .18 |
| 2 | .28 | .80 | .40 | .16 | .56 |
| 3 | .36 | .40 | .61 | .54 | .53 |
| 4 | .82 | .16 | .54 | .97 | .27 |
| 5 | .18 | .56 | .53 | .27 | .58 |

$R$

available for determining the factorial matrix.

The corresponding factor matrix is shown in literal form in *Table 2* and in numerical form in *Table 3*. In *Table 2* all the entries above the principal

Table 2

*Factor Matrix*

|   | I | II | III | IV | V |
|---|---|----|-----|----|---|
| 1 | $a_{11}$ | 0 | 0 | 0 | 0 |
| 2 | $a_{21}$ | $a_{22}$ | 0 | 0 | 0 |
| 3 | $a_{31}$ | $a_{32}$ | $a_{33}$ | 0 | 0 |
| 4 | $a_{41}$ | $a_{42}$ | $a_{43}$ | $a_{44}$ | 0 |
| 5 | $a_{51}$ | $a_{52}$ | $a_{53}$ | $a_{54}$ | $a_{55}$ |

$F$

Table 3

*Factor Matrix*

|   | I | II | III | IV | V |
|---|---|----|-----|----|---|
| 1 | .922 | 0 | 0 | 0 | 0 |
| 2 | .304 | .841 | 0 | 0 | 0 |
| 3 | .390 | .335 | .588 | 0 | 0 |
| 4 | .889 | −.131 | .403 | .000 | 0 |
| 5 | .195 | .595 | .433 | .000 | .000 |

$F$

diagonal are zeros. This circumstance will be explained in two ways, namely, geometrically in terms of the arbitrary location of a reference frame and algebraically in terms of the correlations expressed as cross products of rows of $F$. It should be noted that the number of coefficients to be determined in *Table 2* is exactly equal to the number of correlation coefficients in *Table 1*. It will be shown that each correlation coefficient in $R$ determines one of the factor loadings in $F$, so that the method can be extended to the case where the rank of $R$ is equal to its order, in which case the number of factors in $F$ is equal to the number of variables in $R$. When the rank of $R$ is less than its order, it will be found that a smaller number of columns will be required in $F$. In the present example the rank of $R$ is 3, and hence the last two columns of *Table 3* contain only zeros.

The zero entries in *Table 2* can be explained in terms of the arbitrary reference frame. Let the first axis be collinear with the first test vector.

Then this vector will have a projection on the first axis equal to the length of the vector, namely, the square root of its communality. The test vector will have zero projections on all other possible axes that are orthogonal to the first axis. Hence the remaining entries in the first row of $F$ are all zeros.

The second axis may be placed orthogonal to the first axis and in the plane that is spanned by the first two test vectors. Then the second test vector will have projections on the first two axes but not on any others. Hence all but the first two entries in the second row of $F$ will be zeros. The third axis may be placed in the space spanned by the first three test vectors and orthogonal to the first two axes. The third test vector will then have projections on the first three axes but not on any of the other axes. We are assuming that the successive tests that are used for the location of the reference frame are so chosen by inspection that they are linearly independent. The manner of doing this will be shown in the numerical example. The fourth axis is placed orthogonal to the first three axes and in the four-dimensional subspace that is spanned by the first four test vectors. Hence the fourth test vector will have projections on the first four orthogonal axes but not on any of the other axes. This process is continued until a sufficient number of dimensions has been defined to account for the scalar products of the correlation matrix. This location of the reference frame produces a set of zero entries in the upper half of the factor matrix, as shown in *Table 2*. The zero entries of this table can be inserted at the start of the factoring.

The triangular arrangement of zeros in *Table 2* can also be explained algebraically in terms of the cross products of $F$ that must reproduce the correlations in $R$. The sum of the squares of the first row of *Table 2* is equal to the communality of test 1. Since there is only one entry in the first row of $F$, we have

$$a_{11} = \sqrt{.85} = .922 ,$$

and this is recorded in *Table 3*.

The cross product of the first two rows of $F$ must reproduce the correlation $r_{21} = .28$. Hence we have

$$a_{11}a_{21} = .28 ,$$
$$.922a_{21} = .28 ,$$
$$a_{21} = .304 .$$

The correlation between the first test and any other test $j$ becomes

(1) $$a_{11}a_{j1} = r_{j1} ,$$

or

(2)
$$a_{j1} = \frac{r_{j1}}{a_{11}} = \frac{1}{.922} r_{j1} .$$

The entries in the first column of *Table 3* are therefore proportional to the first column of correlation coefficients in $R$, as shown in equation (2).

When the first column of the factor matrix has been recorded, we turn to the communality of the second test, which is the sum of the squares of the entries in the second row of $F$. Hence

$$a_{21}^2 + a_{22}^2 = .80 ,$$

in which $a_{22}$ is the only unknown. It can therefore be determined, and it is recorded as .841 in *Table 3*.

The correlations of the second test with any other test $j$ can be written in the form

$$a_{21}a_{j1} + a_{22}a_{j2} = r_{j2} ,$$

in which $a_{j2}$ is the only unknown. The second column of *Table 3* is thus numerically determined.

The communality of the third test is, similarly,

$$\sum_{m=1}^{3} a_{3m}^2 = r_{33} ,$$

in which $a_{33}$ is the only unknown. It is recorded as .588 in *Table 3*.

The correlation of test 3 with any other test $j$ can be written

$$\sum_{m=1}^{3} a_{3m}a_{jm} = r_{j3} ,$$

in which $a_{j3}$ is the only unknown. Hence the third column of *Table 3* becomes numerically determined.

In this numerical example, the rank of $R$ is 3, and hence, if this process is continued, the remaining factor loadings in *Table 3* will be found to vanish. Three columns of $F$ represent three arbitrary reference factors, which account for the correlations in $R$.

In the diagonal method of factoring, the selection of each successive test should be made on the basis of the residual variances of the tests. For example, when two columns of *Table 3* have been numerically determined, one might compute the sum of the squares of each row of $F$ and compare these sums with the communalities as shown in $R$. That test might be taken for determining the third axis, which shows the largest residual variance; but any test can be used as a pivot for the next factor if it has an appreciable diagonal entry.

The practical limitation of the diagonal method of factoring for fallible data is that the method pivots on one test at a time. The choice of a diagonal entry which is estimated with practical data determines the factor loadings in a manner which is very sensitive to errors in the estimations for the diagonal cells. In general, computing methods are preferred in which all the data contribute to the determination of each parameter by summations. However, the diagonal method is theoretically correct, and it can be used as a routine computational method of factoring where the given correlational entries can be regarded as exact.

### A two-dimensional example

The correlation matrix in *Figure 1-iii* has been reproduced here as *Table 4*, and it will be factored by the diagonal method. We choose arbi-

*Table 4*

*Correlation Matrix*

|   | 1 | 2 | 3 | 4 | 5 | 6 | 7 | 8 |
|---|------|------|------|------|------|------|------|------|
| 1 | .58 | .63 | .46 | .51 | .35 | .18 | .45 | .24 |
| 2 | .63 | .81 | .36 | .54 | .45 | .00 | .27 | .00 |
| 3 | .46 | .36 | .52 | .42 | .20 | .36 | .60 | .48 |
| 4 | .51 | .54 | .42 | .45 | .30 | .18 | .42 | .24 |
| 5 | .35 | .45 | .20 | .30 | .25 | .00 | .15 | .00 |
| 6 | .18 | .00 | .36 | .18 | .00 | .36 | .48 | .48 |
| 7 | .45 | .27 | .60 | .42 | .15 | .48 | .73 | .64 |
| 8 | .24 | .00 | .48 | .24 | .00 | .48 | .64 | .64 |
| Σ | 3.40 | 3.06 | 3.40 | 3.06 | 1.70 | 2.04 | 3.74 | 2.72 |

trarily the first test to determine the first reference axis. The communality of test 1 is .58, and hence the desired multiplier is $1/\sqrt{.58} = 1.313064$. Applying this stretching factor on the first column of correlations in *Table 4*, we obtain the first column of factor loadings which are entered in *Table 8*.

The computational checks have been included in this example. First, we sum the columns of *Table 4*, as shown in row Σ. The sum for the first column, 3.40, is treated as an additional entry in this column. Applying the stretching factor to it, as for the correlation coefficients in the first column, we have 4.464, which is recorded in *Table 8*, row *Ch*. The actual sum of that column of *Table 8* is 4.465. Since the predicted check sum (*Ch*) agrees with the actual sum (Σ) in *Table 8*, we assume that the computations and the copying into the table are correct. We shall not specifically mention each check sum, since the principle is essentially the same for the rest of the computations. Almost every novice in computing minimizes the importance of formal computational checks. After he has wasted some days hunting for his errors, he learns that it saves both time and annoyance to proceed with formal explicit checks at every step in computing. In the publication of computational results it is not customary to distract the reader with the computational checks.

When the first column of the factor matrix in *Table 8* has been numerically determined, the cross products of this column are listed as shown in *Table 5*. The summation in *Table 8* is here again treated as an additional entry, which gives row *Ch* in *Table 5*. This table shows the contributions made by the first reference factor to the given correlations.

Table 5

First-Factor Products $a_{j1}a_{k1}$

|    | 1 | 2 | 3 | 4 | 5 | 6 | 7 | 8 |
|----|------|------|------|------|------|------|------|------|
| 1 | .581 | .630 | .460 | .511 | .351 | .180 | .450 | .240 |
| 2 | .630 | .684 | .500 | .554 | .380 | .195 | .489 | .261 |
| 3 | .460 | .500 | .365 | .405 | .278 | .143 | .357 | .190 |
| 4 | .511 | .554 | .405 | .449 | .308 | .158 | .396 | .211 |
| 5 | .351 | .380 | .278 | .308 | .212 | .109 | .272 | .145 |
| 6 | .180 | .195 | .143 | .158 | .109 | .056 | .139 | .074 |
| 7 | .450 | .489 | .357 | .396 | .272 | .139 | .349 | .186 |
| 8 | .240 | .261 | .190 | .211 | .145 | .074 | .186 | .099 |
| *Ch* | 3.402 | 3.693 | 2.697 | 2.992 | 2.054 | 1.054 | 2.639 | 1.406 |
| Σ | 3.403 | 3.693 | 2.698 | 2.992 | 2.055 | 1.054 | 2.638 | 1.406 |

Table 6

First-Factor Residuals $r_{2.jk} = r_{jk} - a_{j1}a_{k1}$

|    | 1 | 2 | 3 | 4 | 5 | 6 | 7 | 8 |
|----|-------|-------|-------|-------|-------|-------|-------|-------|
| 1 | −.001 | .000 | .000 | −.001 | −.001 | .000 | .000 | .000 |
| 2 | .000 | .126 | −.140 | −.014 | .070 | −.195 | −.219 | −.261 |
| 3 | .000 | −.140 | .155 | .015 | −.078 | .217 | .243 | .290 |
| 4 | −.001 | −.014 | .015 | .001 | −.008 | .022 | .024 | .029 |
| 5 | −.001 | .070 | −.078 | −.008 | .038 | −.109 | −.122 | −.145 |
| 6 | .000 | −.195 | .217 | .022 | −.109 | .304 | .341 | .406 |
| 7 | .000 | −.219 | .243 | .024 | −.122 | .341 | .381 | .454 |
| 8 | .000 | −.261 | .290 | .029 | −.145 | .406 | .454 | .541 |
| *Ch* | −.003 | −.633 | .702 | .068 | −.355 | .986 | 1.102 | 1.314 |
| Σ | −.003 | −.633 | .702 | .068 | −.355 | .986 | 1.102 | 1.314 |

The cross products shown in *Table 5* are subtracted from the correlations in *Table 4*. These are denoted

(3) $$r_{jk} - a_{j1}a_{k1} = r_{2.jk} ,$$

which are shown in *Table 6*. The subscript 2 in $r_{2.jk}$ refers to the fact that these are residual correlations from which the second factor loadings are to be determined.* *Table 6* can now be treated just like *Table 4*, in order to determine the next column of factor loadings.

* In some of our previous work we have used the notation $r_{2.jk}$ to represent second-factor residuals instead of first-factor residuals, as in this problem.

Column 8 in *Table 6* shows the highest diagonal entry, and we therefore choose it as the second pivot test. The residual communality for test 8 is .541, so that the multiplying factor is now $1/\sqrt{.541} = 1.359569$. Applying this stretching factor to column 8 of *Table 6*, we get the second column of the factor matrix in *Table 8*.

Table 7

Second-Factor Products $a_{j2}a_{k2}$

|    | 1 | 2 | 3 | 4 | 5 | 6 | 7 | 8 |
|----|------|-------|------|-------|-------|-------|-------|-------|
| 1 | .000 | .000 | .000 | .000 | .000 | .000 | .000 | .000 |
| 2 | .000 | .126 | −.140 | −.014 | .070 | −.196 | −.219 | −.261 |
| 3 | .000 | −.140 | .155 | .015 | −.078 | .217 | .243 | .290 |
| 4 | .000 | −.014 | .015 | .002 | −.008 | .022 | .024 | .029 |
| 5 | .000 | .070 | −.078 | −.008 | .039 | −.109 | −.122 | −.145 |
| 6 | .000 | −.196 | .217 | .022 | −.109 | .305 | .341 | .406 |
| 7 | .000 | −.219 | .243 | .024 | −.122 | .341 | .381 | .454 |
| 8 | .000 | −.261 | .290 | .029 | −.145 | .406 | .454 | .542 |
| Ch | .000 | −.634 | .704 | .070 | −.352 | .986 | 1.102 | 1.314 |
| Σ | .000 | −.634 | .702 | .070 | −.353 | .986 | 1.102 | 1.315 |

Table 8

Factor Matrix F

|    | I | II |
|----|------|-------|
| 1 | .762 | .000 |
| 2 | .827 | −.355 |
| 3 | .604 | .394 |
| 4 | .670 | .039 |
| 5 | .460 | −.197 |
| 6 | .236 | .552 |
| 7 | .591 | .617 |
| 8 | .315 | .736 |
| Ch | 4.464 | 1.786 |
| Σ | 4.465 | 1.786 |
| d | .58 | .541 |
| $\sqrt{d}$ | .761577 | .735527 |
| $1/\sqrt{d}$ | 1.313065 | 1.359569 |

Table 9

| Given Factor Matrix | | Transformation Matrix | | Rotated Factor Matrix | |
|---|---|---|---|---|---|
| I | II | A | B | A | B |
| 1 | .762 | .000 | I | $\lambda_{1a}$ | $\lambda_{1b}$ | 1 | .70 | .30 |

Given Factor Matrix

|    | I | II |
|----|------|-------|
| 1 | .762 | .000 |
| 2 | .827 | −.355 |
| 3 | .604 | .394 |
| 4 | .670 | .039 |
| 5 | .460 | −.197 |
| 6 | .236 | .552 |
| 7 | .591 | .617 |
| 8 | .315 | .736 |

$F_1$

Transformation Matrix

|    | A | B |
|----|------|------|
| I | $\lambda_{1a}$ | $\lambda_{1b}$ |
| II | $\lambda_{2a}$ | $\lambda_{2b}$ |

|    | A | B |
|----|------|------|
| I | .917 | .400 |
| II | −.400 | .917 |

$\Lambda$

Rotated Factor Matrix

|    | A | B |
|----|------|------|
| 1 | .70 | .30 |
| 2 | .90 | .00 |
| 3 | .40 | .60 |
| 4 | .60 | .30 |
| 5 | .50 | .00 |
| 6 | .00 | .60 |
| 7 | .30 | .80 |
| 8 | .00 | .80 |

$F_2$

The cross products of the second column of the factor matrix give $(a_{j2}a_{k2})$, which are shown in *Table 7*. These are the contributions of the second reference factor to the correlations in *Table 4*. Subtracting the entries of *Table 7* from the first-factor residuals $r_{2.jk}$ in *Table 6*, we find that they vanish, showing that the two factors in *Table 8* are sufficient to account for the given correlations.

### Rotation in two dimensions

The factor matrix of *Table 8* has been plotted in *Figure 1*, where we see the two-dimensional configuration and the arbitrary reference axes $I$ and $II$. In choosing a reference frame for the interpretation of the variables in terms of factors, we must decide on some criterion by which to make the choice. The first axis might be passed through the centroid of the eight points in *Figure 1*, or the first axis might be so placed as to maximize the sum of the squares of the projections of the eight test vectors. We might place the axes in such positions that the negative projections will be eliminated or

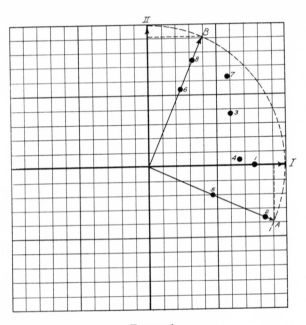

FIGURE 1

minimized as far as possible. Another criterion which can sometimes be used is to place the axes so as to minimize what we have called the "complexities" of the tests. When this criterion is applicable, the axes are so placed that a large number of zero entries appear in the factor matrix. The rotational problem is one of the most important in factor analysis.

In the present example we see in *Figure 1* that the angular span of the configuration is a right angle, so that a frame can be chosen which eliminates all negative factor loadings and which reduces the complexities of four tests to one instead of two. The two axes chosen by these criteria are denoted $A$ and $B$ in the figure.

The numerical problem now is to write a factor matrix which will represent the two orthogonal factors $A$ and $B$ instead of the arbitrary orthogonal factors $I$ and $II$, which appeared in the factoring of the correlation matrix. In *Table 9* we have the factor matrix $F_1$ for the axes $I$ and $II$ (from *Table 8*), and we want to find an orthogonal transformation matrix $\Lambda$ so that $F_1\Lambda = F_2$, where $F_2$ will be a factor matrix for the axes $A$ and $B$.* The notation $F_1, F_2, F_3, \ldots$, will henceforth be used to represent successive rotations of the reference frame.

Since the present configuration of test vectors is contained in two dimensions, the orthogonal transformation $\Lambda$ will be of order $2\times2$. It will be useful to make a geometrical interpretation of the cell entries in the matrix $\Lambda$ of the transformation. The cell entries in the first column $A$ of this matrix are denoted $\lambda_{1a}$ and $\lambda_{2a}$. These are the direction cosines of the unit vector $A$ referred to the frame $I$–$II$. Another way of saying the same idea is that the unit vector $A$ in *Figure 1* can be expressed as a vector sum of its projections on the axes $I$ and $II$. We have, then, for the vector $A$,

(4) $$A = \lambda_{1a}I + \lambda_{2a}II \ .$$

The first column $A$ of the orthogonal matrix $\Lambda$ in *Table 9* states that the vector $A$ is $\lambda_{1a}$ of the unit vector $I$ plus $\lambda_{2a}$ of the unit vector $II$. In *Figure 1* these coefficients of equation (4) can be determined graphically. Since $A$ is a unit vector, we shall expect that

(5) $$\lambda_{1a}^2 + \lambda_{2a}^2 = 1 \ .$$

By inspection of *Figure 1*, and normalizing, we have

(6) $$A = .917\,I - .400\,II \ ,$$

and these coefficients are entered in the numerical form of the transformation matrix $\Lambda$ in *Table 9*.

A similar interpretation applies to the second column $B$ of the transformation matrix. From the figure we obtain close estimates of the projections of $B$ on $I$ and $II$, namely, $\lambda_{1b}$ and $\lambda_{2b}$, which, when normalized, give the unit vector $B$ as the vector sum,

(7) $$B = .400\,I + .917\,II \ .$$

In *Table 9* it should be noted that the rows of the transformation matrix refer to the axes $I$ and $II$, while the columns refer to the axes $A$ and $B$. If we perform the matrix multiplication

(8) $$F_1\Lambda = F_2 \ ,$$

---

* For theorems related to rotation of axes see "Mathematical Introduction" and theorems in *chap. iii*.

the product is of order $n \times 2$, and the columns are denoted $A$ and $B$. This has been done in *Table 9*, where $F_2$ is the desired factor matrix for the factorial axes $A$ and $B$. This matrix is identical with the factor matrix with which we started in *chapter iii*.

In writing this factorial solution, we might have labeled the two axes $A$ and $B$ in reverse order in the figure, or we might have reversed the order of the two columns of the transformation matrix $\Lambda$. The effect would have been merely that the columns of $F_2$ would appear in a different order. It should be evident that the order in which the columns of $F_2$ are written would have no effect on the interpretation of the factors in terms of the tests.

The extension of the reasoning illustrated here to three or more dimensions involves essentially no new ideas, although the higher-dimensional problems are more complex. In problems involving more common factors it is more difficult, for example, to identify the nature of the configuration, which is obvious in a single diagram in two dimensions.

## CHAPTER V

## THE GROUPING METHOD OF FACTORING

The diagonal method of factoring a correlation matrix has been described in *chapter iv*. While that method is simple in principle, it has a serious disadvantage when dealing with fallible data, namely, that it pivots successively on single tests and on single correlation coefficients. If any of these individual coefficients is in error, the calculations that are based on them are similarly in error, so that the residuals become larger than when some summational procedure is used. For this reason the centroid method was developed. The grouping method to be described here is a variant of the centroid method.

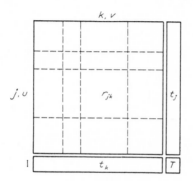

FIGURE 1

Consider the correlation matrix $r_{jk}$ in *Figure 1*. Instead of summing over all the variables, which is the starting-point for the centroid method, we shall sum here over a group of tests. The group should contain at least three or four tests. The successive groups to be used should be so selected that the intercorrelations of the tests within one group are large, relative to the magnitudes of the coefficients in the table. Detailed routine for selecting the groups will be shown in the numerical example. Let there be $s$ tests in the selected group. Let the rows of the selected group be denoted by the subscript $u$, and let the corresponding columns be denoted by the subscript $v$. Let the rank of the correlation matrix be $r$.

Let us augment the correlation matrix by a row, as shown in *Figure 1*, of which each element, $t_k$, is the sum of the coefficients in the $u$-rows for column $k$. These elements are

$$(1) \qquad\qquad t_k = \sum_{u=1}^{s} r_{uk} ,$$

111

where $r_{uk}$ represents the correlation coefficients in the selected rows. The augmented matrix is now of order $(n+1)$ by $n$. It should be noted that the rank of the matrix is unaltered because the new row is a linear combination of the rows of the given matrix $r_{jk}$.

Next we augment the matrix by a column, as shown in the figure. Each element $t_j$ of the new column is the sum of the coefficients in the $v$ columns of the row $j$. These elements are

$$(2) \qquad \sum_{v=1}^{s} r_{jv} = t_j ,$$

where $r_{jv}$ represents the correlation coefficients in the selected columns. The augmented matrix is now a square matrix of order $(n+1)$. Its rank is still unaltered because the new column is a linear combination of the columns of the previous matrix.

The diagonal entry at the intersection of the new column and the new row is denoted $T$. Let $t_u$ and $t_v$ denote the sums $t_j$ and $t_k$ in the rows and columns of the selected group. Then $T$ can be written

$$(3) \qquad T = \sum_{v=1}^{s} t_v = \sum_{u=1}^{s} t_u ,$$

because the transpose of the row $t_k$ is the column $t_j$.

Let a multiplying factor be defined by

$$(4) \qquad m \equiv \frac{1}{\sqrt{T}} .$$

Then a new matrix may be written as in *Figure 2*, which contains the square matrix $r_{jk}$ with a new row $a_k$ and a new column $a_j$ and their intersection. The entries, $a$, in the new row are determined by the relation

$$(5) \qquad a_k = mt_k ,$$

and the diagonal entry then becomes $\sqrt{T}$. The entries in the column $a_j$ are determined by the relation

$$(6) \qquad a_j = mt_j ,$$

after which the diagonal entry becomes 1. The rank of the matrix is unaffected by the application of the stretching factor $m$. The column $a_j$ is the transpose of the row $a_k$, since $a_j = a_k$ when $j = k$.

The new row and column can now be regarded as showing the projections of the $n$ tests of the matrix $r_{jk}$ on a unit reference vector $I$, as shown in *Figure 2*. The entries $a_j$ can therefore be taken as the first column of the factor matrix. A table of first-factor residuals is then prepared, and a new group of relatively well-correlated tests selected for a repetition of the same process. This procedure is continued until the residuals disappear or become small enough to be ignored.

As a numerical example for factoring we shall take the correlation matrix of *Figure 1* in *chapter iii*. That matrix is reproduced here in *Table 2*. We select a test that has the largest number of relatively high coefficients. Such is No. 7, which has three coefficients of .60 or higher. We arrange the

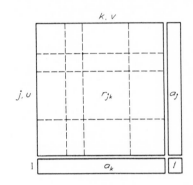

FIGURE 2

*Table 1*

*First Group*

|   | 7 | 8 | 3 | 6 | 1 | 4 |
|---|---|---|---|---|---|---|
| 7 | .73 |  |  |  |  |  |
| 8 | .64 | .64 |  |  |  |  |
| 3 | .60 | .48 | .52 |  |  |  |
| 6 | .48 | .48 |  |  |  |  |
| 1 | .45 |  | .46 |  |  |  |
| 4 | .42 |  | .42 |  | .51 |  |

coefficients for No. 7 in descending order by absolute value and tabulate the intercorrelations of a group of tests as shown in *Table 1*. In this table are shown only the coefficients above .40. What is to be regarded as a high coefficient depends on the order of magnitude of the coefficients in the whole table. The grouping method does not give a unique solution, and there is no absolute rule for determining the size of the group of tests to be used for computing each successive column of the factor matrix. In *Table 1* we selected three tests to constitute the first group, namely, 7, 8, and 3. We might have included test 6.

The three tests selected to constitute the first group are marked in columns and rows of *Table 2*. The summations $t_k$ are shown for each column, as well as the sum $T$. Applying the multiplying factor $m$, we have the bottom row of the table, which shows the first-factor loadings. These are copied as the first column of the factor matrix in *Table 6*.

In *Table 4* are shown the first-factor residuals. These are $(r_{jk} - a_{j1}a_{k1})$. These entries are obtained by subtracting elements of *Table 3* from the corresponding elements of *Table 2*.

### Table 2

#### Correlation Matrix

|   | 1 | 2 | ×3 | 4 | 5 | 6 | ×7 | ×8 | |
|---|---|---|---|---|---|---|---|---|---|
| 1 | .58 | .63 | .46 | .51 | .35 | .18 | .45 | .24 | |
| 2 | .63 | .81 | .36 | .54 | .45 | .00 | .27 | .00 | |
| ×3 | .46 | .36 | .52 | .42 | .20 | .36 | .60 | .48 | |
| 4 | .51 | .54 | .42 | .45 | .30 | .18 | .42 | .24 | |
| 5 | .35 | .45 | .20 | .30 | .25 | .00 | .15 | .00 | |
| 6 | .18 | .00 | .36 | .18 | .00 | .36 | .48 | .48 | |
| ×7 | .45 | .27 | .60 | .42 | .15 | .48 | .73 | .64 | |
| ×8 | .24 | .00 | .48 | .24 | .00 | .48 | .64 | .64 | |
| $t$ | 1.15 | .63 | 1.60 | 1.08 | .35 | 1.32 | 1.97 | 1.76 | 5.33 $= T$ |
| $I$ | .498 | .273 | .693 | .468 | .152 | .572 | .853 | .762 | .4331 $= m$ |

### Table 3

#### First-Factor Products

|   | 1 | 2 | 3 | 4 | 5 | 6 | 7 | 8 |
|---|---|---|---|---|---|---|---|---|
| 1 | .248 | .136 | .345 | .233 | .076 | .285 | .425 | .379 |
| 2 | .136 | .075 | .189 | .128 | .041 | .156 | .233 | .208 |
| 3 | .345 | .189 | .480 | .324 | .105 | .396 | .591 | .528 |
| 4 | .233 | .128 | .324 | .219 | .071 | .268 | .399 | .357 |
| 5 | .076 | .041 | .105 | .071 | .023 | .087 | .130 | .116 |
| 6 | .285 | .156 | .396 | .268 | .087 | .327 | .488 | .436 |
| 7 | .425 | .233 | .591 | .399 | .130 | .488 | .728 | .650 |
| 8 | .379 | .208 | .528 | .357 | .116 | .436 | .650 | .581 |

In order to compute second-factor loadings, a column is chosen which has a relatively large number of the higher coefficients. Test 2 is so selected, and its coefficients are arranged in descending order of absolute values in the first column of *Table 5*. The lower coefficients are ignored. The intercorrelations are recorded as shown. Test 8 has a negative correlation with test 2, so that test 8 is recorded here with negative sign ($-8$). The correlation between tests ($+2$) and ($-8$) is $+.208$. A similar interpretation applies to the other coefficients in this table. A group of tests is to be selected in which the signs of the intercorrelations within the group are all positive. According to this criterion, all the tests in *Table 5* could be included in the group, with tests 6 and 8 taken as negative. The coefficients of several tests are rather low, so we retain only four tests for the second group, namely 2, 1, 4, 5. These are marked in rows and columns of *Table 4*.

The row $t_k$ is determined by summation of four coefficients in each column, and the value of $T$ is computed as shown. Applying the multiplying factor $m$, we obtain the second-factor loadings in the bottom row, II. These are copied as the second column of the factor matrix of *Table 6*.

*Table 4*

*First-Factor Residuals*

|  | $\underset{1}{\times}$ | $\underset{2}{\times}$ | 3 | $\underset{4}{\times}$ | $\underset{5}{\times}$ | 6 | 7 | 8 | |
|---|---|---|---|---|---|---|---|---|---|
| × 1 | .332 | .494 | .115 | .277 | .274 | −.105 | .025 | −.139 | |
| × 2 | .494 | .735 | .171 | .412 | .409 | −.156 | .037 | −.208 | |
| 3 | .115 | .171 | .040 | .096 | .095 | −.036 | .009 | −.048 | |
| × 4 | .277 | .412 | .096 | .231 | .229 | −.088 | .021 | −.117 | |
| × 5 | .274 | .409 | .095 | .229 | .227 | −.087 | .020 | −.116 | |
| 6 | −.105 | −.156 | −.036 | −.088 | −.087 | .033 | −.008 | .044 | |
| 7 | .025 | .037 | .009 | .021 | .020 | −.008 | .002 | −.010 | |
| 8 | −.139 | −.208 | −.048 | −.117 | −.116 | .044 | −.010 | .059 | |
| $t$ | 1.377 | 2.050 | .477 | 1.149 | 1.139 | −.436 | .103 | −.580 | $5.715 = T$ |
| II | .576 | .858 | .200 | .481 | .476 | −.182 | .043 | −.243 | $.4183 = m$ |

*Table 5*

*Second Group*

|  | +2 | +1 | +4 | +5 | −8 | +3 | −6 |
|---|---|---|---|---|---|---|---|
| +2 | .735 | | | | | | |
| +1 | .494 | .332 | | | | | |
| +4 | .412 | .277 | .231 | | | | |
| +5 | .409 | .274 | .229 | .227 | | | |
| −8 | .208 | .139 | .117 | .116 | .059 | | |
| +3 | .171 | .115 | .096 | .095 | .048 | .040 | |
| −6 | .156 | .105 | .088 | .087 | .044 | .036 | .033 |

*Table 6*

*Factor Matrix*

|  | I | II |
|---|---|---|
| 1 | .498 | .576 |
| 2 | .273 | .858 |
| 3 | .693 | .200 |
| 4 | .468 | .481 |
| 5 | .152 | .476 |
| 6 | .572 | −.182 |
| 7 | .853 | .043 |
| 8 | .762 | −.243 |

When the second-factor products $(a_{j2}a_{k2})$ are subtracted from the first-factor residuals in *Table 4*, it is found that the second-factor residuals all vanish. The reason for this is that the given matrix of *Table 2* is of rank 2. The grouping method is exact in the sense that if the given correlation matrix is of rank $r$, then the extraction of $r$ factors by this method will give residuals that all vanish identically. This is also true of the centroid method to be described later.

In *Figure 3* we have plotted the factor loadings of *Table 6*. The configuration here is the same as that of *Figure 1a* in *chapter iii*. The apparent dif-

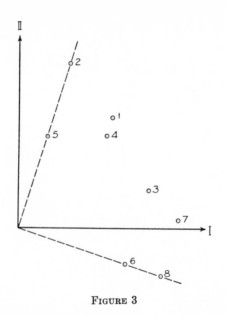

FIGURE 3

ference is due to the interchange of abscissae and ordinates. This is associated with the fact that in multiple-factor analysis there is no distinction between independent and dependent variables. The arrangement of the columns in the factor matrix is of no significance, and, in plotting two-dimensional sections of a configuration, it is of no consequence whether any particular factor is plotted as abscissa or as ordinate. An orthogonal transformation of order 2 can be written, as previously described, by which *Table 6* is carried back to the factor matrix of *Figure 1b* in *chapter iii*.

The grouping method has been used on large factor studies. It is comparable with the centroid method. Each has certain advantages that will be discussed in a later chapter. The check rows and columns were omitted from the present chapter in order that the principles of the method might be described without the distractions of computational detail.

# CHAPTER VI

## FACTORS AS EXPLANATORY CONCEPTS

Factor analysis was developed as a scientific method of investigating related measurements that are not well understood. In order to illustrate the method we shall apply it to a problem in which the relations between the measurements are simple and well known. Instead of dealing with human beings and their test scores or other measurements, we shall consider a set of simple physical objects. In *Table 1* we have listed twenty-seven cylin-

*Table 1*

*Twenty-seven Cylinders*

| Cylin- der | $d$ | $l$ | $s$ | Cylin- der | $d$ | $l$ | $s$ | Cylin- der | $d$ | $l$ | $s$ |
|---|---|---|---|---|---|---|---|---|---|---|---|
| 1 | 1 | 2 | 1 | 10 | 1 | 2 | 2 | 19 | 1 | 2 | 3 |
| 2 | 2 | 2 | 1 | 11 | 2 | 2 | 2 | 20 | 2 | 2 | 3 |
| 3 | 3 | 2 | 1 | 12 | 3 | 2 | 2 | 21 | 3 | 2 | 3 |
| 4 | 1 | 3 | 1 | 13 | 1 | 3 | 2 | 22 | 1 | 3 | 3 |
| 5 | 2 | 3 | 1 | 14 | 2 | 3 | 2 | 23 | 2 | 3 | 3 |
| 6 | 3 | 3 | 1 | 15 | 3 | 3 | 2 | 24 | 3 | 3 | 3 |
| 7 | 1 | 4 | 1 | 16 | 1 | 4 | 2 | 25 | 1 | 4 | 3 |
| 8 | 2 | 4 | 1 | 17 | 2 | 4 | 2 | 26 | 2 | 4 | 3 |
| 9 | 3 | 4 | 1 | 18 | 3 | 4 | 2 | 27 | 3 | 4 | 3 |

ders. The shape of each cylinder is completely determined by two parameters, namely, the diameter $d$ and the length $l$. For each cylinder is also listed the specific gravity $s$.

With these given measures we can compute for each cylinder the following seven measures:

1) diameter $d$ ,

2) length $l$

$$a = \frac{\pi d^2}{4} \; ;$$

3) base area $a$ ,

$$c = \pi dl \; ;$$

4) side area $c$ ,

5) volume $v$ ,

$$v = \frac{\pi d^2 l}{4} \; ;$$

6) diagonal $t$ ,

$$t = \sqrt{d^2 + l^2} \; ;$$

7) weight $w$ .

$$w = sv \; .$$

The computed values of these measures were correlated. The result is shown in the correlation matrix of *Table 2* for the seven measures on the population of twenty-seven cylinders. The diagonal entries were computed

117

as the best-fitting values for rank 2 by methods to be described in later chapters. The correlation matrix of *Table 2* will now be regarded as the starting-point for a factor analysis in which we shall try to extract as much information as possible about these seven measures *solely from the intercorrelations.*

We shall consider this problem as if the actual cylinders were available, each one identified by its number and by its seven scores. But we shall assume that we know nothing about how each of the measurements was taken and that we know nothing about how the measurements happen to be correlated. For the purposes of this illustrative example, this situation corresponds to that in which each member of an experimental population is available and is identified as to his several test scores or other measurements but in which we do not understand what the measurements mean or why the measurements happen to be correlated.

*Table 2*

*Correlation Matrix*

|   | 1 | 2 | 3 | 4 | 5 | 6 | 7 |
|---|------|-------|------|------|------|------|------|
| 1 | .978 | .000 | .990 | .812 | .895 | .556 | .746 |
| 2 | .000 | 1.000 | .000 | .541 | .348 | .823 | .290 |
| 3 | .990 | .000 | .987 | .803 | .905 | .558 | .754 |
| 4 | .812 | .541 | .803 | .968 | .969 | .874 | .807 |
| 5 | .895 | .348 | .905 | .969 | .962 | .767 | .834 |
| 6 | .556 | .823 | .558 | .874 | .767 | .968 | .639 |
| 7 | .746 | .290 | .754 | .807 | .834 | .639 | .672 |

Before starting the factoring, we inspect the intercorrelations that have been given to us for analysis. Perhaps the first thing to be noticed is that all the intercorrelations in this problem are positive or zero. This means that the configuration of test vectors does not spread over more than a right angle and that all the test vectors are contained within a cone of 45° generating angle. This is also the situation actually found experimentally with tests of the cognitive functions.

Inspection of the diagonal cells shows remarkably high communalities except for variable No. 7, whose communality is .672. In most experimental studies one does not find communalities of .96 and higher unless the domain has been explored so completely that most of the variance of each test is fairly well known. Variable 7, whose communality is .672, has only two-thirds of its variance in common with the other tests of this battery. Hence one-third of its variance is unique. In this example it is easily seen why this should happen; but, in factorial studies generally, the nature of unique variance is usually unknown. Variable 7 is the weight of the cylinder, which is determined by the volume and the specific gravity. The volume is a function of diameter $d$ and length $l$, and hence the variance in this characteristic is shared with the other measurements, which are also functions of $d$ and $l$. But the specific gravity $s$ enters into only one variable of the battery, namely, the weight $w$, and hence the individual differences among the cylinders as regards specific gravity produce unique variance in $w$. That part of the variance of $w$ which is due to volume is common-factor variance, while that part of the variance of $w$ which is due to specific gravity is unique variance. The common-factor variance of $w$ is its communality, while the unique variance is the complement of the communality.

The correlation matrix of *Table 2* was factored by the grouping method that was described in *chapter v*. Tests 1, 3, 4, 5, were used for the first group, and tests $-1$, $+2$, $-3$, $+4$, $+5$, $+6$, were used for the second factor. The resulting factor matrix is shown in *Table 3, a*. This factor matrix was plotted in *Figure 1*, with the orthogonal axes $I$ and $II$ as shown.

*Table 3*

*Factor Matrices*

| | $a$ | | | $b$ | | | $c$ | |
|---|---|---|---|---|---|---|---|---|
| | I | II | | $A_1$ | $A_2$ | | $B_1$ | $B_2$ |
| 1 | .960 | −.234 | 1 | .989 | .000 | 1 | .821 | −.551 |
| 2 | .232 | .972 | 2 | .000 | 1.000 | 2 | .554 | .835 |
| 3 | .963 | −.238 | 3 | .992 | −.004 | 3 | .822 | −.556 |
| 4 | .928 | .341 | 4 | .821 | .551 | 4 | .989 | .000 |
| 5 | .975 | .132 | 5 | .916 | .359 | 5 | .961 | −.213 |
| 6 | .720 | .643 | 6 | .547 | .796 | 6 | .898 | .355 |
| 7 | .821 | .119 | 7 | .770 | .310 | 7 | .812 | −.172 |

With the factoring completed, we have before us the factor matrix of *Table 3, a*, and the configuration of *Figure 1*. We also have the twenty-seven cylinders, each identified with its seven measures or scores; but we have, supposedly, no knowledge of what the measurements mean. In this simple geometrical example we hope to show the fundamental nature of factorial analysis as a scientific method. If the principles can be seen in a simple case in which the underlying relations are definite and well known, perhaps the application of the method to more complex problems can be undertaken with more confidence and with a better understanding of its possibilities and limitations.

It has been shown that the location of the reference frame $I-II$ that is obtained in factoring is essentially arbitrary. Its location in the configuration depends on the method of factoring. In the present case the axes $I$ and $II$ were determined when the successive groups of tests were chosen. The method of choosing the groups is not unique. Hence we should not be misled in assuming some simple physical interpretation of factors $I$ and $II$. They may have physical meaning if each group constitutes a cluster with some trait in common. In the present case there is no definite cluster about axis *I*, and there is no cluster at all near axis *II*.

The seven test vectors in *Figure 1* spread in a fan from tests 1 and 3 to test 2, with the other test vectors between them. It can be seen by inspection that the fan covers a right angle. This fact is associated with the fact that test 2 correlates zero with 1 and 3 as shown in *Table 2*. Tests 1 and 3 are practically collinear, and this is associated with the fact that their correlation is practically unity.

One alternative is to locate the reference frame at $A_1$ and $A_2$ because this orthogonal pair of reference vectors incloses the whole configuration. If we put the reference frame in this position, the factor loadings will be all

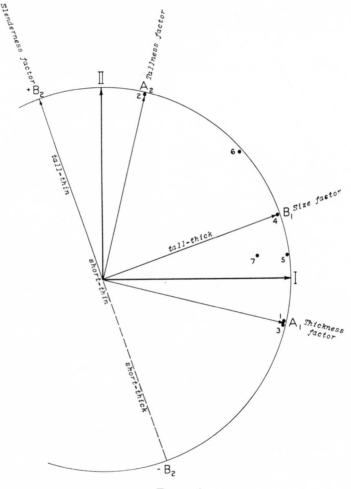

FIGURE 1

positive or zero, as shown in the factor matrix of *Table 3, b.* A factor matrix of this type and of rank 2 is associated with the fact that all the intercorrelations are positive or zero. The extension of this relation to 3 and higher dimensions will be discussed later. An interpretation can often be found for factors, such as $A_1$ and $A_2$, which inclose a whole configuration.

Another alternative location of the reference frame is to put the first axis in the middle of the configuration. Such an axis can be located in the middle of the span between $A_1$ and $A_2$, or it can be so located that it will pass through the centroid of all the test-vector termini, or it can be located so as to maximize the sum of the squares of the projections of the test vectors on the axis. The two latter methods would give nearly the same factor axis in *Figure 1.* As an example of the location of a first axis in the middle of the configuration, we have drawn the factor axis $B_1$ through test 4. The resulting factor loadings are shown in the first column of *Table 3, c.* It will be seen that the factor loadings are all positive and of appreciable magnitude. *A common factor which has appreciable loadings on all the tests in a battery is called a* **general factor** *for that battery.* Strictly speaking, a general factor might be one that has non-vanishing loadings in all tests, even though some are positive and some negative. But, as the term is ordinarily used, a general factor is one that has appreciable positive loadings in all tests of a battery. In the present problem the location of a general-factor axis is not unique because it can be moved over a considerable range and still give appreciable positive loadings for all tests. If a general-factor axis $B_1$ is placed somewhere in the middle of the configuration, the second orthogonal factor axis $B_2$ can be placed as shown or in the opposite direction. One of these directions is chosen as positive $(+B_2)$ and the other as negative $(-B_2)$. The same could have been done for the first axis—if there had been any test vectors with negative projections. The factor loadings on $B_2$ are shown in *Table 3, c.* It will be seen that some tests have positive loadings and that some tests have negative loadings on the factor $B_2$. *A factor which has both positive and negative saturations is called a* **bipolar factor.**

It should also be noted that *whenever a factor axis is placed in the middle of a configuration, then each of the subsequent factors in the analysis will be bipolar factors.* This theorem is clearly seen in the configuration of *Figure 1,* and it is true for a test configuration in any number of dimensions or factors. Since this relation follows as a geometrical necessity from the location of the first axis in the middle of the configuration of test vectors, we should be cautious in attempting to impose a physical interpretation on the bipolarity of factors. This type of bipolarity may have physical significance, but it may also be merely a geometric consequence of the location of the first axis in the middle of the test configuration.

We have considered several of the principles by which a frame of reference factors can be located in the configuration. We shall now proceed to analyze two of these reference frames to illustrate the manner in which one attempts to find an interpretation for each reference factor.

The frame $A_1 A_2$ is represented by two unit vectors, $A_1$ and $A_2$. Each of these unit vectors may be thought of as a test vector for a perfect test of a factor. Such a test would have unit communality. The factor $A_1$ is of a nature such that it determines the intercorrelations of measures *1* and *3* completely, since these two measures have zero loadings on the factor $A_2$. The factor $A_1$ is entirely absent in the variance of test 2, since the factor loading is zero. The factor $A_1$ is involved in the variance of all the measures to an appreciable extent except No. 2, but it is represented in almost pure form in tests 1 and 3.

If we know something about the measures that are involved, we turn to them to see if some hypothesis can be formulated for the factor that would seem plausible for all the tests that are high in the factor and which would also be absent in tests that are low in the factor. In psychological work one can sometimes make a plausible hypothesis by examining the tests, but more often it is necessary to use introspection for each test to ascertain the nature of the common factor. This is the method that has been used for identifying most of the primary abilities.

In the present example it is assumed that we have no knowledge about the nature of the measurements. This is even more of a handicap than we ordinarily have in factorial studies, because experimental measurements are usually based on some knowledge of their implications, even if their underlying order is not understood. If we arrange the nine different cylindrical forms in order, from the lowest to the highest in accordance with factor $A_1$, we have the arrangement shown in *Figure 2*. This arrangement reveals that the factor is associated with the thickness of the cylinders, and we might call it the "thickness" factor. The diameter (*1*) and the cross-sectional area (*3*) are both determined by this factor, as is shown by the fact that these two measurements have no projection on the only other common factor in this battery. The fact that the communalities are near unity reveals that there is hardly any residual or unique variance left in these two measurements after the factor $A_1$ has been determined.

We proceed next in the same manner with the factor $A_2$ by arranging the nine different cylindrical forms in order, as shown in the figure. These cylinders are evidently arranged in the order of their height, and we might therefore call this the "height" factor. This factor is involved in all the measures except *1* and *3*. It should be noted that, when we name these factors either by examining the nature of the measurements in some way or by examining the individual members of the experimental population, we have only a hypothesis concerning the nature of the factor. Sometimes two or more hypotheses appear to be equally plausible for the interpretation of a factor. Then a new factorial experiment should be set up, with additional measurements so selected that they represent the two hypotheses with the least possible overlapping. The resulting factorial experiment might sustain one of the hypotheses, or it might show that neither of the hypotheses is correct. In the present case we have identified one factor that is associated with thickness. It has two scores or measurements completely determined by this factor, namely, *1* and *3* (diameter and base area). Another factor is associated with the height of the cylinder. We have found that all the measurements involve these two parameters or factors and that only one of the measurements (*7*) involves some additional factor.

We turn next to the alternative reference frame represented by the unit reference vectors, $B_1$ and $B_2$. The factor $B_1$ was placed so as to be collinear

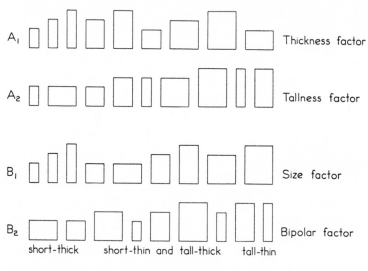

FIGURE 2

with the test vector *4*, which is in the middle of the range of test vectors. All the factor loadings are positive and of appreciable magnitude, so that this is a general factor. In *Figure 2* we have the nine cylindrical forms arranged in order according to this factor, from the lowest to the highest. Inspection reveals that the cylinders are arranged in order of size, irrespective of shape. We might call this characteristic a "general-size" factor. It can be seen in the figure that the cylinders are in order according to longitudinal-section area. This happens to be proportional to the measure actually taken for the factor $B_1$, namely, the side area. We might choose a neighboring vector as an index of size, such as the volume vector *5*. The location of this factor in the configuration is not unique.

We turn next to the factor $B_2$, according to which the nine cylindrical forms were arranged in the last row of *Figure 2*. The plot of *Figure 1* reveals this as a bipolar factor, and we therefore look for some characteristic which can have either positive or negative values, or we look for a bipolar factor that can be thought of as a composite. For negative values of the factor $B_2$ we find the short-thick cylinders, while at the positive end of the distribution we find the tall-thin cylinders. This might be called by a single name, such as a "slenderness" factor. Negative values for this factor would refer to short and thick cylinders. In the middle of the distribution, where the factor loadings are near zero, we should then expect to find those cylinders which are neither tall-thin nor short-thick. Here we find those that can be classified as short-thin and as tall-thick. The two descriptions, "short-thin" and "tall-thick," would both have zero saturation on the slenderness factor, but tall-thick would have positive saturation on the size factor. For some purposes of classification or interpretation it might be meaningful to describe these objects in terms of their general size, such as volume, and their degree of slenderness; but for most purposes this classification would probably seem artificial. In most situations in which a configuration represents correlations that are positive or zero, we should probably find the simplest explanatory concepts to be represented by factorial axes that border or inclose the configuration rather than those in which a dominant factor is an average of all the measures of the battery by going through the middle of the configuration. As far as adequacy of description is concerned, any reference frame might be used which can gain acceptance as to the interpretation of the factors. All three of the frames that have been discussed here are equally accurate in the description of the correlation coefficients.

We have seen that the reference frame that is found in the factoring is ordinarily arbitrary. We have considered two alternative sets of orthogonal reference factors, both of which can be given some physical interpretation. The location of a meaningful reference frame is not unique, but there sometimes exists a preferred reference frame that is more readily interpreted than the others. In the nature of the case one cannot prove that the frame chosen is in any sense the correct one. Nor can one demonstrate that some other frame would not also be meaningful. The best that one can do is to discover a set of reference factors that can be given plausible interpretation to aid in understanding the underlying order among the variables in the battery. Such findings can be followed by other experiments in the exploration of the factors that are revealed by the factorial analysis. It should be recognized that a factorial study is successful to the extent that meaningful factors can be identified by a proper choice of reference axes.

# CHAPTER VII

## THE SPHERICAL MODEL

**The vector model**

In previous chapters we have considered factor problems in two dimensions. The same concepts will now be extended to problems of three common factors. The correlation matrix can be represented by a set of vectors whose scalar products are the correlation coefficients. If the rank of the correlation matrix is 3, then there must be postulated three common factors. The

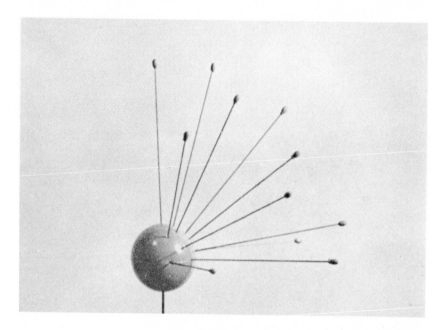

FIGURE 1

vector model for such a correlation matrix would extend to three dimensions. In *Figure 1* we have such a model, in which the test vectors are represented by long pins or wires that are stuck into a central cork. Each of the pins represents a test vector. The correlation between any two tests is equal to $h_1 h_2 \cos \phi_{12}$, where $h_1$ and $h_2$ are the lengths of the pins and $\phi_{12}$ is the angle between them. If such a model were given to us, we should be able to reconstruct the correlation matrix from which the model was built. No information is lost in going from the correlation matrix to the model or vice versa. They give the same information.

In the vector model of the figure we see that the entire configuration of test vectors spans not more than a right angle. This means that the intercorrelations are all positive. If two vectors in the model were at right angles, the corresponding correlation coefficient would be zero. The scalar product of a test vector with itself is $h_1^2$, the angle $\phi_{11}$ being zero, and $\cos \phi_{11}$, unity. Hence the square of the length of a test vector $j$ is equal to its communality $h_j^2$.

In *Figure 1* the test vectors are arranged more or less at random, except for the restriction that there are no obtuse angular relations. Such a con-

FIGURE 2

figuration would be produced if we were to write a correlation matrix at random with positive or zero coefficients and subject to the restriction that it be of rank 3 to correspond with the three dimensions of the model. In *Figure 2* we have a configuration of test vectors showing three clusters. The tests within a cluster would have high intercorrelations, while pairs of tests from different clusters would have low correlations. If the three clusters were at right angles, the tests from different clusters would have correlations of zero or near zero. If such a configuration were found, it would be natural to suspect that the tests represented three different kinds of traits which are statistically independent. The clusters would be apparent by inspection of the correlation matrix because the tests could be so grouped that the tests within a given group would be highly correlated, while tests from different groups would show low correlations.

*Figure 3* shows a different type of configuration, in that the test vectors are arranged in three planes. The configuration could be described as a three-sided cone with test vectors in each side of the cone and with apex at the center of the cork. If such a configuration of test vectors were found, it would be natural to suspect that three parameters or factors had determined the correlations and that the parameters could be represented in the simplest way at the corners of the configuration. Each test vector that lies in one of

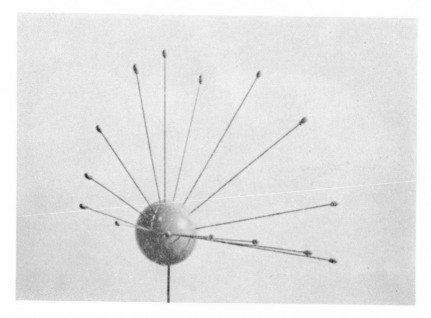

FIGURE 3

the co-ordinate planes could then be described as a linear combination of two primary or co-ordinate vectors.

The same kind of configuration with the test vectors in the three sides of a cone could also be represented in the model of *Figure 4*, in which the three sides are represented by cardboards on which have been drawn the vectors of the test configuration.

## The spherical model

Three-dimensional test configurations can be represented by models of the kind that have been illustrated, but it has been found more convenient to represent them on the surface of a sphere, as shown in *Figure 5*. In order to represent a test configuration on the surface of a sphere, the test vectors are first extended to unit length. The termini of the vectors can then be represented as points on the surface of a unit sphere. For the purpose of showing a test configuration graphically in three dimensions, one can use to advantage a blackboard sphere of the kind used in teaching spherical trigonometry. On the sphere of *Figure 5* we have the same type of test configuration as in *Figure 2*, where the tests are arranged in three clusters. In *Figure 6* we have the same type of configuration as in the vector model of *Figure 3*, where the test vectors lie in three planes.

If we should find that the configuration of a test battery looked like *Figure 6*, then the simplest description of the test vectors would be in terms of

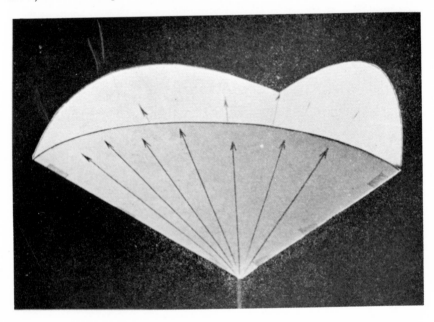

FIGURE 4

the vectors $A$, $B$, and $C$ at the corners of the configuration. All the tests on the side $AB$ could be described in terms of the two vectors $A$ and $B$; the test vectors on the side $BC$ could be described in terms of the vectors $B$ and $C$; and similarly for the test vectors on the side $AC$ in terms of the vectors $A$ and $C$. We should then make the hypothesis that the vectors $A$, $B$, and $C$ at the corners of the configuration represent underlying properties or simplifying parameters in terms of which the correlations of the whole test battery can be understood. A test vector near the middle of the side $AB$ would then be described as a linear combination of $A$ and $B$ with equal weights for $A$ and $B$. A test vector near $A$ on the side $AB$ would also be described as a linear combination of $A$ and $B$, but the weight would be relatively larger

FIGURE 5

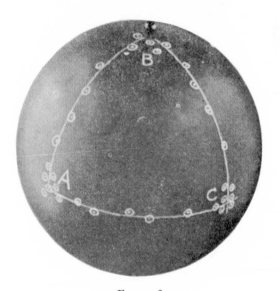

FIGURE 6

for $A$ and smaller for $B$. In a configuration of this kind each test vector could be described in terms of less than three factors, even though the battery as a whole required three factors. This is the principal characteristic of a *simple structure*, which is the combination of a test configuration and a set of co-ordinate axes in which each test vector lies in one or more of the co-ordinate planes, as in *Figure 6*. If there should be a test in the battery that involved all three of the factors $A$, $B$, and $C$, then it would lie inside the spherical triangle, and it would not contribute toward the location of the co-ordinate planes.

In *Figure 7* we have a model of test vectors in three dimensions in which the triangular configuration is incomplete. Here we have no tests which con-

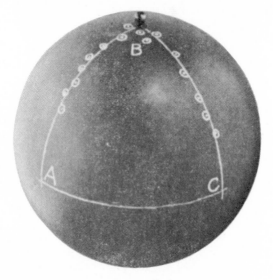

FIGURE 7

tain only the common factor $A$ or the common factor $C$. The tests near $B$ contain only one of the three common factors, namely, $B$. Furthermore, we see that all the tests in the battery have some saturation on the factor $B$ because the tests on the side $AB$ are linear combinations of $A$ and $B$, while the tests on the side $BC$ are linear combinations of $B$ and $C$. Hence the factor $B$ would here be a general common factor which is present in all the tests of the battery. In a configuration of this kind the location of the plane $AC$ is indeterminate, and so are also the co-ordinate vectors $A$ and $C$ as far as the configuration is concerned. The only vector that is here determinate is the general common factor $B$.*

* This common factor must not be confused with the kind of general common factor that is sometimes obtained for a factor matrix by locating the factor in the center of the configuration as a whole. Such an axis will necessarily be inside the spherical triangle,

## Plotting the spherical configuration

In order to study a configuration of test vectors in three dimensions, it is useful to extend them to unit length so that the configuration can be easily plotted on the surface of a sphere. When that has been done, we can see the whole three-dimensional configuration, as shown in the examples of *Figures 5, 6, 7, 10,* and *11.* The process of extending the test vectors to unit length will be called *normalizing the test vectors.*

In *Table 1* we have a given factor matrix of twenty measures or tests and three orthogonal factors, I, II, and III. The first step in normalizing the

*Table 1*

*Normalizing of Test Vectors*

| TEST | FACTOR MATRIX $F$ | | | | | | NORMALIZED FACTOR MATRIX $F_n$ | | |
|---|---|---|---|---|---|---|---|---|---|
| | I | II | III | $h_j^2$ | $h_j$ | $1/h_j$ | I | II | III |
| 1 | .659 | −.736 | .138 | .9950 | .997497 | 1.002509 | .661 | −.738 | .138 |
| 2 | .725 | .180 | −.656 | .9884 | .994183 | 1.005851 | .729 | .181 | −.660 |
| 3 | .665 | .537 | .500 | .9806 | .990252 | 1.009844 | .672 | .542 | .505 |
| 4 | .869 | −.209 | −.443 | .9951 | .997547 | 1.002459 | .871 | −.210 | −.444 |
| 5 | .834 | .182 | .508 | .9867 | .993328 | 1.006717 | .840 | .183 | .511 |
| 6 | .836 | .519 | .152 | .9914 | .995691 | 1.004328 | .840 | .521 | .153 |
| 7 | .856 | −.452 | −.269 | 1.0094 | 1.004670 | .995691 | .852 | −.450 | −.268 |
| 8 | .848 | −.426 | .320 | 1.0030 | 1.001500 | .998502 | .847 | −.425 | .320 |
| 9 | .861 | .416 | −.299 | 1.0038 | 1.001898 | .998106 | .859 | .415 | −.298 |
| 10 | .880 | −.341 | −.354 | 1.0160 | 1.007968 | .992095 | .873 | −.338 | −.351 |
| 11 | .889 | −.147 | .436 | 1.0020 | 1.001000 | .999001 | .888 | −.147 | .436 |
| 12 | .875 | .485 | −.093 | 1.0095 | 1.004788 | .995235 | .871 | .483 | −.093 |
| 13 | .667 | −.725 | .109 | .9824 | .991161 | 1.008918 | .673 | −.731 | .110 |
| 14 | .717 | .246 | −.619 | .9578 | .978673 | 1.021792 | .733 | .251 | −.632 |
| 15 | .634 | .501 | .522 | .9254 | .961977 | 1.039526 | .659 | .521 | .543 |
| 16 | .936 | .257 | .165 | .9694 | .984581 | 1.015660 | .951 | .261 | .168 |
| 17 | .966 | −.239 | −.083 | .9972 | .998599 | 1.001403 | .967 | −.239 | −.083 |
| 18 | .625 | −.720 | .166 | .9366 | .967781 | 1.033292 | .646 | −.744 | .172 |
| 19 | .702 | .112 | −.650 | .9278 | .963224 | 1.038180 | .729 | .116 | −.675 |
| 20 | .664 | .536 | .488 | .9663 | .983006 | 1.017288 | .675 | .545 | .496 |

vectors is to determine the communalities $h_j^2$ as shown. The length of each vector $h_j$ is then determined, as well as its reciprocal $1/h_j = d_j$, which becomes a multiplier for each row of the given factor matrix. The augmented factor loadings $A_{jm}$ of the normalized factor matrix are shown in the last three columns of *Table 1.* The data are then ready to be plotted on a sphere.

The three entries in any row of the normalized factor matrix $F_n$ give the projections of the normalized test vector $J$ on the three orthogonal axes.

and its location will be determined entirely by the particular collection of tests that happens to be used as a battery in the factor analysis. This problem is discussed in later chapters.

Each projection $A_{jm}$ is the cosine of the angle between the normalized test vector $J$ and the reference vector $M$. The relation between the given factor matrix $F$ and the normalized factor matrix $F_n$ can be stated formally in the matrix equation

$$(1) \qquad\qquad DF = F_n ,$$

where $D$ is a diagonal matrix with the stretching factor $d_j$, or, by the elements,

$$(2) \qquad\qquad d_j a_{jm} = A_{jm} .$$

Before plotting the spherical configuration, we first draw on the sphere three mutually orthogonal great circles. If the sphere is to be used repeated-

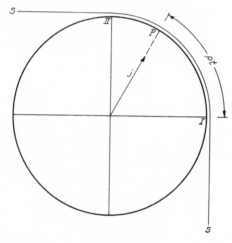

FIGURE 8

ly for factorial problems, it is best to paint or scratch the three great circles, so that they will not be erased for each problem. One of the octants is chosen as positive for all three co-ordinate axes $I, II, III$, as shown in *Figure 10*, and the three co-ordinate axes are labeled.

In plotting the test vector termini on the surface of the sphere it is convenient to use a strip of paper of length about twice the diameter of the sphere. On this strip are marked the surface distances corresponding to the cosines $A_{jm}$. In *Figure 8* we have represented the strip $S$, which has also been drawn in *Figure 9*. The point 1.00 on the scale is placed at the reference axis $I$ on the sphere. The point on the scale at axis $II$ is marked zero. The surface distance from $I$ to $II$ is then

$$(3) \qquad\qquad \frac{\pi d}{4} = 0.7584\, d \equiv t .$$

The intermediate points on the scale are labeled directly in terms of the corresponding cosines, which are the entries in the normalized factor matrix $F_n$. For the projection $A_{j1}$ in $F_n$ we have the corresponding angle

$$(4) \qquad\qquad \phi_{j1} = \cos^{-1}A_{j1}$$

and the corresponding surface distance

$$(5) \qquad\qquad pt = \frac{t \cos^{-1}A_{j1}}{90}.$$

For any given sphere the scale will be proportional to that of *Figure 9*. The measuring strip should be made twice as long as the scale indicated in *Fig-*

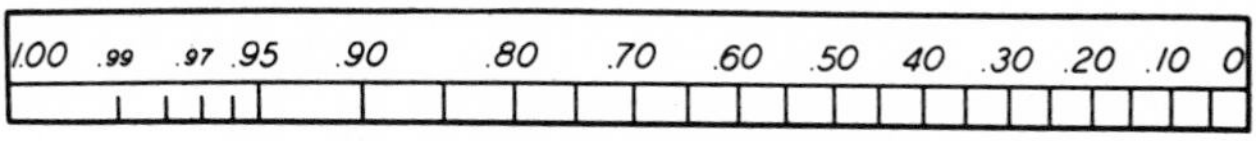

FIGURE 9

*ure 9*, so that measurements can be made of both positive and negative cosines.

In locating the terminus of a test vector on the sphere, we find a point which has the required surface distances from the three orthogonal axes. The third measurement checks the location inferred from the first two

*Table 2*

*Values of* p *for Given Values of* $A_{jm} = \cos \phi_{jm}$

| a | p | a | p | a | p | a | p | a | p |
|---|---|---|---|---|---|---|---|---|---|
| 1.00 | .00 | .95 | .20 | .70 | .51 | .45 | .70 | .20 | .87 |
| .99 | .09 | .90 | .29 | .65 | .55 | .40 | .74 | .15 | .90 |
| .98 | .13 | .85 | .35 | .60 | .59 | .35 | .77 | .10 | .94 |
| .97 | .16 | .80 | .41 | .55 | .63 | .30 | .81 | .05 | .97 |
| .96 | .18 | .75 | .46 | .50 | .67 | .25 | .84 | .00 | 1.00 |

measurements. When the scale has been prepared on a strip of paper or cardboard, any three-dimensional configuration is readily plotted on the sphere, so that the whole configuration can be seen directly.

In *Table 2* we have listed the values of $p$ for different given values of the normalized factor loadings $A_{jm}$. These values of $p$ can be used for making a scale to fit a sphere of any given diameter $d$.

The present battery of twenty measures or tests has been plotted on the sphere of *Figure 10*. Each point has been numbered to identify the corresponding test vector. The three great circles are indicated, as well as the three co-ordinate axes *I, II,* and *III.* Inspection of the configuration on the sphere shows that the points are arranged in the form of a triangle and that all but two of the test vectors lie in the sides of the spherical triangle. Instead of using the arbitrary reference frame *I*, *II*, *III*, which was obtained by the factoring method, we draw a new reference frame, as shown in *Figure 11*. By using these new reference axes, we should be able to describe each of the test vectors that lie in the sides of the spherical triangle in terms of one or two reference axes instead of three, as required in the frame of *Figure 10*. The three great circles are so drawn as to pass through or near groups of vectors, as shown in *Figure 11*. The new reference vectors are the normals to the three great circles, and the primary factors are determined by the three intersections of the new great circles.

FIGURE 10

With the model as shown in *Figure 11* we are ready to put the factorial solution into numerical form. Consider the great circle drawn through or near the points *19, 2, 14, 9, 12, 6, 20, 3, 15*. By means of the measuring strip locate a point on the surface of the sphere which is orthogonal to this circle. It represents one of the unit reference vectors, which may be denoted $\Lambda_x$. In the same manner locate the other two reference vectors orthogonal to the other two planes. One of the reference vectors is shown in *Figure 11*, namely, $\Lambda_z$.

By means of the measuring strip, measure the three direction cosines for each of the reference vectors and record them in columns of the transformation matrix $\Lambda$, as shown in *Table 3*. In determining the direction cosines of a reference vector, measure its surface distance from each of the three orthogonal axes *I*, *II*, *III*, on the sphere. In the first section of the table we have the given factor matrix $F$, and in the last section we have the desired factor matrix $V$, which describes the twenty test vectors in terms of the three new reference vectors $\Lambda_p$, where the subscript $p$ refers to the new axes. When the measurements have been taken from the sphere, it is advisable to adjust them in the second or third decimal, so that the sum of their squares is equal to unity. This step insures that each of the reference vectors is of unit length.

When the transformation matrix $\Lambda$ has been written as in *Table 3*, we can carry out the matrix multiplication

$$(6) \qquad\qquad F\Lambda = V .$$

The entries in this matrix show the projection of each test vector on each of the three new reference vectors. The point *20*, for example, is on or near two of the new co-ordinate planes, as shown in *Figure 11*, and hence it should have two factor loadings that are zero or near zero, as shown in *Table 3*.

The new reference vectors are not orthogonal. The cosines of their angular separations can be determined by the measuring strip and recorded in the matrix $C$ of *Table 3*. The numerical values of these cosines can also be determined without direct measurement by the equation

$$(7) \qquad\qquad \Lambda'\Lambda = C ,$$

or, in terms of the elements,

$$(8) \qquad\qquad \lambda_{pm}\lambda_{mq} = c_{pq} ,$$

where the subscripts $p$ and $q$ refer to the new axes. The transformation matrix $\Lambda$ is not an orthogonal matrix, because the three new reference vectors are not orthogonal. The columns are normalized to correspond to the fact that the reference vectors are unit vectors. The cross products of pairs of columns of the transformation matrix $\Lambda$ give the cosines of their angular separations, as in equations (7) and (8). In an orthogonal matrix these co-

*Table 3*

*The Transformation Matrix $\Lambda$*

| Given Factor Matrix F | | | | Transformation $\Lambda$ | | | | Rotated Factor Matrix V | | |
|---|---|---|---|---|---|---|---|---|---|---|
| Test | I | II | III | | $\Lambda_x$ | $\Lambda_y$ | $\Lambda_z$ | Test | $\Lambda_x$ | $\Lambda_y$ | $\Lambda_z$ |
| 1 | .659 | −.736 | .138 | I | .483 | .466 | .479 | 1 | .969 | .003 | −.003 |
| 2 | .725 | .180 | −.656 | II | −.834 | .254 | .560 | 2 | .025 | .939 | .005 |
| 3 | .665 | .537 | .500 | III | .267 | −.847 | .675 | 3 | .007 | .023 | .957 |
| 4 | .869 | −.209 | −.443 | | | | | 4 | .476 | .727 | .000 |
| 5 | .834 | .182 | .508 | | | | | 5 | .387 | .005 | .844 |
| 6 | .836 | .519 | .152 | | | | | 6 | .012 | .393 | .794 |
| 7 | .856 | −.452 | −.269 | | | | | 7 | .719 | .512 | −.025 |
| 8 | .848 | −.426 | .320 | | | | | 8 | .850 | .016 | .384 |
| 9 | .861 | .416 | −.299 | | | | | 9 | −.011 | .760 | .444 |
| 10 | .880 | −.341 | −.354 | | | | | 10 | .615 | .623 | −.008 |
| 11 | .889 | −.147 | .436 | | | | | 11 | .668 | .008 | .638 |
| 12 | .875 | .485 | −.093 | | | | | 12 | −.007 | .610 | .628 |
| 13 | .667 | −.725 | .109 | | | | | 13 | .956 | .034 | −.013 |
| 14 | .717 | .246 | −.619 | | | | | 14 | −.024 | .921 | .063 |
| 15 | .634 | .501 | .522 | | | | | 15 | .028 | −.019 | .937 |
| 16 | .936 | .257 | .165 | | | | | 16 | .282 | .362 | .704 |
| 17 | .966 | −.239 | −.083 | | | | | 17 | .644 | .460 | .273 |
| 18 | .625 | −.720 | .166 | | | | | 18 | .947 | −.032 | .008 |
| 19 | .702 | .112 | −.650 | | | | | 19 | .072 | .906 | −.040 |
| 20 | .664 | .536 | .488 | | | | | 20 | .004 | .032 | .948 |

| Primary Vectors T | | | | $T\Lambda = D$ | | | |
|---|---|---|---|---|---|---|---|
| $T_x$ | .661 | −.736 | .144 | $T_x$ | .972 | 0 | 0 |
| $T_y$ | .713 | .199 | −.671 | $T_y$ | 0 | .951 | 0 |
| $T_z$ | .654 | .545 | .524 | $T_z$ | 0 | 0 | .972 |

| Correlation of Primaries | | | | Cosines of Reference Vectors | | | |
|---|---|---|---|---|---|---|---|
| | $T_x$ | $T_y$ | $T_z$ | | $\Lambda_x$ | $\Lambda_y$ | $\Lambda_z$ |
| $T_x$ | 1.000 | .229 | .105 | $\Lambda_x$ | 1.000 | −.213 | −.055 |
| $T_y$ | .229 | 1.000 | .224 | $\Lambda_y$ | −.213 | 1.000 | −.206 |
| $T_z$ | .105 | .224 | 1.000 | $\Lambda_z$ | −.055 | −.206 | 1.000 |

$$TT' = R_{pq}$$

$$\Lambda'\Lambda = C$$

sines are zero because such a transformation represents the rotation of a rigid orthogonal reference frame.

The primary vectors which represent the three underlying factors or parameters in pure form are unit vectors at the corners of the configuration. A unit vector at the corner near the test vectors *3*, *15*, and *20* represents one of these primary factors. It is defined by the intersection of two of the co-ordinate planes. Let the primary test vectors be denoted $T_x$, $T_y$, and $T_z$. The direction cosines of each of these unit vectors may be determined by the measuring strip and recorded in the rows of the factor matrix, as shown in *Table 3*. Here we are treating the three primary vectors as if they were additions to the given factor matrix. If we had three perfect tests of these primary factors with no unique variance, they would appear in the factor matrix, as shown in the rows $T_x$, $T_y$, and $T_z$.

If we add the three primary vectors to the given factor matrix and carry out the transformation,

(9) $$F\Lambda = V,$$

for the last three rows of the factor matrix, we have the corresponding equation,

(10) $$T\Lambda = D,$$

where the product must be a diagonal matrix, as shown in *Table 3*. By defi-nition each primary vector lies in two of the co-ordinate planes, and hence it must have zero projections on two of the reference axes. The result is a diagonal matrix. If the reference vectors were orthogonal, they would coin-cide with the primary vectors; but, when the reference vectors are oblique, as in the present case, the product is a diagonal matrix, in which the diago-nal entries deviate from unity. The diagonal entries are, in fact, the cosines of the angles between the primary vectors $T_p$ and the corresponding refer-ence vectors $\Lambda_p$, as can be verified on the spherical model.

The matrix $T$, which shows the direction cosines of the primary vectors, can be determined from the transformation matrix $\Lambda$ without direct meas-urement on the sphere. By (10) we have

(11) $$T = D\Lambda^{-1}.$$

We find the inverse of the transformation matrix $\Lambda$ and normalize the rows of that matrix. Normalizing the rows of $\Lambda^{-1}$ is represented in equation (11) by the premultiplication with the diagonal matrix $D$. The result is the matrix $T$, which shows the direction cosines of the primary vectors.

The correlations between the primary factors can be determined by di-rect measurement on the surface of the sphere. The same correlations can be determined from the transformation matrix $\Lambda$ without direct measurement. Just as the correlations between the tests are given by the fundamental factor theorem,

$$(12) \qquad\qquad FF' = R_{jk} = R \,,$$

so for the last three rows of the factor matrix we also have the corresponding equation,

$$(13) \qquad\qquad TT' = R_{pq} \,.$$

Substituting (11) in (13), we obtain

$$(14) \qquad\qquad R_{pq} = (D\Lambda^{-1})(D\Lambda^{-1})'$$

or

$$(15) \qquad\qquad R_{pq} = D(\Lambda'\Lambda)^{-1}D \,.$$

By this equation the correlations between the primary factors can be determined. When the product $(\Lambda'\Lambda)^{-1}$ has been computed, the diagonal matrix $D$ is so written that the diagonal entries of the correlation matrix $R_{pq}$ are unity, since the scalar product of a unit vector and itself is, of course, unity. The diagonal matrix in (15) is the same as the diagonal matrix shown in in the lower section of the oblique factor matrix $V$. Each entry in $D$ is the cosine of the angle between a primary vector $T_p$ and the corresponding reference vector $\Lambda_p$.

For some purposes it is useful to designate explicitly the general elements of the several matrices of *Table 3*. In the given orthogonal factor matrix we have the elements $a_{jm}$, and in the transformation matrix we have $\lambda_{mp}$, where the subscript $p$ refers to primary factors. The product is

$$(16) \qquad\qquad a_{jm}\, \lambda_{mp} = v_{jp} \,,$$

where the elements $v_{jp}$ of $V$ show the projections of the test vectors $j$ on the reference vectors $\Lambda_p$. The elements of the matrix $T$ are denoted $t_{pm}$. The correlation matrix for the primary factors is denoted $R_{pq}$, to distinguish it from the correlation matrix for the tests, which is written $R_{jk}$, or simply $R$ without subscript. Let the elements of $(\Lambda'\Lambda)^{-1}$ be denoted $b_{pq}$. Then the diagonal elements are $b_{pp}$. The diagonal elements of $D$ are, then, $d_p$, or

$$d_p = \frac{1}{\sqrt{b_{pp}}} \,.$$

The present example has been discussed in detail for the three-dimensional case to show the relation between the computational work and the geometrical interpretation. In the interpretation of primary factors we inspect each column of the oblique factor matrix $V$ to discover, if possible, the nature of the trait which is present in the tests with significant factor loadings and absent in the tests with negligible loadings on the factor. There is no guarantee beforehand that a simple configuration like *Figure 11* can be found in any given problem, and there is no guarantee that a clarifying description of the factors can be obtained. That is determined by the intuitions of the investigator in setting up his factorial experiments so that meaningful and significant results can be obtained.

### Correlated factors

In the previous discussion, examples of both orthogonal and oblique reference vectors have been given. A set of orthogonal reference vectors is a geometrical representation of factors which are uncorrelated, and correlated factors are shown by an oblique reference frame. Among statisticians and psychologists there is a rather general belief that if human traits are to be accounted for by any kind of factors, then these factors must be uncorrelated. This belief has its origin in the statistical and mathematical convenience of uncorrelated factors and also in our ignorance of the nature of the underlying structure of mental traits. The reason for using uncorrelated reference traits can be understood, but it cannot be justified. Height and weight are two useful measures of body size, even though they are correlated. If we should use, instead, two linear combinations of height and weight which are uncorrelated in the general population, we might find such measures more convenient in statistical theory, in that the cross products would vanish and we could find a certain satisfaction in that the two measures are independent; but they would be awkward to think about.

We might as well make use of the freedom of factor analysis as regards orthogonality by allowing the primary factors or parameters to be correlated. In the physical and biological sciences we have the exact counterpart of this situation. There we deal with parameters that usually have some physical meaning, such as momentum, acceleration, blood pressure, the liminal stimulus, and thousands of other parameters that have meaning in conceptual representation. Scientists seldom worry about the fact that parameters are correlated in a random group of people who might be the subjects in a scientific study, unless such covariance is itself the object of study in relation to underlying theory. If two parameters should be found to be nearly perfectly correlated, the fact would surely be noticed, and we would then try to reduce the corresponding concepts to an identity by reformulating fundamental ideas about the phenomena.

The restriction that parameters be uncorrelated appears only in those investigations in which we start with no ideas. The correlation coefficient is a symbol of complete ignorance. It is rarely, if ever, used in those problems which are well understood. Let us take an example to show how unnecessary it would be to insist on zero correlation between parameters when the relations are well understood. Let us suppose that nothing is known about the nature of rectangles except that we can take measurements on them. We might measure five hundred rectangles and discover that there is a correlation of $+.70$ between the lengths and the widths in our collection of rectangles. Such a finding would be determined by the fact that big rectangles tend to have long sides and to be wider than small rectangles. We might have the conviction that the principal properties of rectangles could be determined from their lengths and widths, but we should have to meet the restriction that the two parameters must be uncorrelated in the particular set of rectangles that we collected for measurement. That could be done if, for instance, we took the length as one measurement and, say, $(W - \frac{1}{2}L)$ as the other measurement, where $L$ and $W$ are the length and width, respectively. The linear combination would depend on the particular set of rectangles in the experiment. Two measures could easily be found which were uncorrelated in our particular collection of rectangles, but the result would not be very useful in thinking about rectangles. As another example, in taking physical measurements of men, it is customary to record height and weight. If we were forbidden to use these two measures because they are correlated, the absurdity of such a restriction would be self-evident. On the other hand, it should be recognized that if we deal with a group of measures that are highly correlated, we are likely to be confining ourselves to one domain, and it is then useful to look for other significant measures that cover additional features of the things that are being measured. In general, measures that cover different aspects of an individual are likely to show lower correlation than those which represent the same domain; but it does not follow that our fundamental concepts should be in any sense restricted to those which show zero correlation in a random group of people. In developing the factorial methods we have insisted that the methods must not impose orthogonality on the fundamental parameters that are chosen for factorial description, even though the equations are thereby simplified in that the cross products vanish. In the methods that we have developed, each author is still free to impose orthogonality on the factors if he so chooses or if the nature of his problem is such that this restriction is indicated.

### The box problem

The box problem is an example involving three parameters or factors that are represented in the spherical model of *Figure 11*.* A physical ex-

---

* The numerical problem that is used in this chapter is the so-called "box problem," which was designed to correct some current misconceptions about factor analysis. Sections from the original publication of the box problem will be used here to illustrate by a physical example the interpretation of primary factors as simplifying parameters that are not necessarily unique (see "Current Issues in Factor Analysis," *Psychological Bulletin*, XXXVII, No. 4 [April, 1940], 189–236).

ample of two parameters or factors—the cylinder problem—was used in *chapter vi*.

A random collection of boxes constitutes the population in this example. Let us imagine a collection of boxes and a set of twenty measurements for each box. Let us assume, as is really the case in most psychological problems, that we have no idea what these measurements represent and that we believe some underlying order may exist in the twenty measurements for each box. In this fictitious example the boxes constitute the individuals in a statistical population, and the measurements correspond to twenty test scores for each individual. In *Table 4* we have the three dimensions, $x$, $y$, $z$, for each box.

*Table 4*

| Boxes | Dimensions | | |
|:-:|:-:|:-:|:-:|
| | $x$ | $y$ | $z$ |
| 1 | 3 | 2 | 1 |
| 2 | 3 | 2 | 2 |
| 3 | 3 | 3 | 1 |
| 4 | 3 | 3 | 2 |
| 5 | 3 | 3 | 3 |
| 6 | 4 | 2 | 1 |
| 7 | 4 | 2 | 2 |
| 8 | 4 | 3 | 1 |
| 9 | 4 | 3 | 2 |
| 10 | 4 | 3 | 3 |
| 11 | 4 | 4 | 1 |
| 12 | 4 | 4 | 2 |
| 13 | 4 | 4 | 3 |
| 14 | 5 | 2 | 1 |
| 15 | 5 | 2 | 2 |
| 16 | 5 | 3 | 2 |
| 17 | 5 | 3 | 3 |
| 18 | 5 | 4 | 1 |
| 19 | 5 | 4 | 2 |
| 20 | 5 | 4 | 3 |

The box population is here defined in terms of twenty different rectangular box shapes, and it is assumed that these twenty shapes occur with equal frequency in the population of boxes. For example, if the population consists of two hundred boxes, there are ten of each kind. Any other arrangement could have been taken. In *Table 5* we have a list of the twenty measurements (tests) that were taken for each box. These measurements consist of various non-linear functions of the three dimensions, $x, y, z$; but in the factor analysis the number of basic factors and their combination in the twenty measurements are assumed to be entirely unknown.

It will be seen in the formulae of *Table 5* that each of the tests 1, 2, and 3 represents the square of an edge of the box; 4, 5, and 6 represent the area of a side; 7, 8, and 9 represent the diagonal of a side; 10, 11, and 12 represent the perimeter of a side; and the other tests are similar arbitrary functions of the three box measurements. In dealing with the twenty measurements for each box, we treat them merely as if they were twenty test scores for each box. We correlate them and factor them as if we knew nothing about the manner in which the scores became correlated. Our object is to discover by factor analysis whether or not the twenty measurements for each box reveal some underlying physical order. Actually, we have set up the measurements so that three factors are involved—namely, the three dimensions of a box—but we deal with the problem factorially as if we did not even know how many factors were involved in the twenty test scores for each

*Table 5*

| Tests | Structure | | | Test Formulae |
|---|---|---|---|---|
| | $x$ | $y$ | $z$ | |
| 1 | $+$ | | | $x^2$ |
| 2 | | $+$ | | $y^2$ |
| 3 | | | $+$ | $z^2$ |
| 4 | $+$ | $+$ | | $xy$ |
| 5 | $+$ | | $+$ | $xz$ |
| 6 | | $+$ | $+$ | $yz$ |
| 7 | $+$ | $+$ | | $\sqrt{x^2+y^2}$ |
| 8 | $+$ | | $+$ | $\sqrt{x^2+z^2}$ |
| 9 | | $+$ | $+$ | $\sqrt{y^2+z^2}$ |
| 10 | $+$ | $+$ | | $2x+2y$ |
| 11 | $+$ | | $+$ | $2x+2z$ |
| 12 | | $+$ | $+$ | $2y+2z$ |
| 13 | $+$ | | | $\log x$ |
| 14 | | $+$ | | $\log y$ |
| 15 | | | $+$ | $\log z$ |
| 16 | $+$ | $+$ | $+$ | $xyz$ |
| 17 | $+$ | $+$ | $+$ | $\sqrt{x^2+y^2+z^2}$ |
| 18 | $+$ | | | $e^x$ |
| 19 | | $+$ | | $e^y$ |
| 20 | | | $+$ | $e^z$ |

box. In order to simplify the problem, errors of measurement and sampling errors are here omitted. The correlations are therefore unaffected by the number of multiples of the twenty different box shapes that constitute the statistical box population. The correlations were determined from the box measurements listed in *Table 4* and the test formulae of *Table 5*. In *Table 3* we have the centroid matrix for three factors. The mean of the absolute residuals (disregarding sign) after three factors had been extracted was .008, which does not warrant the extraction of more factors. At this point we would know that only three factors were involved in the twenty fictitious box scores.

In the interpretation of the rotated factor matrix $V$ of *Table 3* we look for the tests which have the high saturations in the first column. These are tests 1, 13, and 18; and we conclude that the first primary factor is very heavily represented in these tests. In this fictitious problem we can actually turn back to *Table 5* to find the formulae for these tests in terms of the primary factors. These are, of course, not known in psychological problems. We find that tests 1, 13, and 18 are the only three tests which depend exclusively on the $x$-dimension of the boxes.

In the third column of the factor matrix $V$ of *Table 3* we find three tests with high saturations, namely, 3, 15, 20. These three tests are therefore judged to have most of their variance on one of the underlying factors. In *Figure 11* we find these three tests at one corner of the configuration, and we conclude, therefore, that they involve only one of the three common factors, whatever they may be. Turning back to *Table 5*, as we can do in this fictitious example, we see that the three test scores are the only ones that are functions of the parameter $z$.

Consider the bottom row of tests in *Figure 11*. These tests are 19, 2, 14, 9, 12, 6, 20, 3, 15. Since these test vectors lie in one of the co-ordinate planes, we infer that there is one factor that is absent in all these tests and that the factor is conspicuous in 1, 13, and 18, which lie at the opposite corner of the configuration. Turning to *Table 5*, we see that this factor is $x$.

The same kind of comparison can be made for each of the three primary factors $x$, $y$, and $z$. Those tests which depend on only one of the primary factors are in the corresponding corner of the diagram, and they are represented in the factor matrix $V$ with large factor loadings in the proper column. Those tests which are functions of two primary factors are represented as points on the sides of the triangle, and the points are consistent throughout as to the pairs of primary factors involved. Finally, the two tests 16 and 17, which have formulae containing all three of the primary factors, are inside the triangle. They are the volume and the principal diagonal, respectively. It is interesting that the linear approximations which are assumed in factor analysis reveal a simple configuration, even though the twenty measurements were nonlinear functions of the primaries. The discrepancies are represented by the small entries in the factor matrix $V$, which would be zero if the factor methods did not depend on the assumption of linearity as a first approximation.

Next we note that the three primary factors in this population of boxes are correlated. The correlations among the primary factors as determined by the factor analysis are shown in *Table 3*. The actual correlations between the primaries in the original data are shown in *Table 6*, and the agreement is self-evident. In setting up this example we assumed that a random collection of boxes would show correlation between the three dimensions. A box that is tall is likely to be thick and wide, probably to a greater extent than the correlations which we assumed in the fictitious problem.

It would be possible to set up an example with twenty measurements so that every measurement would involve all three of the box dimensions.

A factor analysis of such a system of measurements would not reveal a simple structure, so that no clear bounding planes could be determined. In psychological experiments we must recognize this possibility. Some factor experiments will fail to reveal primary factors. This will necessarily happen if each variable involves as many factors as there are factors in the whole set of variables. There is no guarantee beforehand that this will not happen. On the other hand, it is extremely unlikely that a simple structure will appear with the same identifiable primaries in several independent factor analyses of different test batteries that are given to different populations, unless the structure is valid.

The interpretation of the primary factors in the factor matrix $V$ would consist in studying the several test variables that show high saturation on

*Table 6*

*Correlation Matrix*

|  | $X$ | $Y$ | $Z$ |
|---|---|---|---|
| $X$ | 1.00 | | |
| $Y$ | .25 | 1.00 | |
| $Z$ | .10 | .25 | 1.00 |

each primary factor. One would try to find what it is that is common to these variables or measures. One might discover that, in general, tallness is a common characteristic of one primary and that the best measurements available for tallness are those which show highest saturation on the factor. We might name it a "tallness" factor. That would merely imply that the twenty measurements are functions of three linearly independent parameters and that one of them is tentatively named "tallness." A box which measures high on that factor would stand higher from the floor than boxes that are low in that factor. Now this identification of the linearly independent parameters in the twenty box measurements would not imply that the tallness factor has some sort of locus in each box or that the factor is a separate organ or gadget in each box or that it is some sort of isolated, abstract, statistical box-element that has nothing in common with the rest of the box. It is an independent parameter that is involved in the box measurements. Exactly the same procedure is followed in dealing with psychological data. The identification of a primary factor in psychological test experiments is merely a challenge for us to find out what sort of process or attribute it is in terms of known concepts or else to invent new concepts that fit the experimentally determined primary categories.

The attempts to interpret the primary factors have often been criticized because they are not sufficiently objective. Let us be clear about two distinct problems that are involved here. It is one problem to isolate a primary factor and to determine by repeated experiments that it has some functional uniqueness. That is factor analysis proper. It is another problem to find the psychological or physiological meaning of a functional uniqueness when it has been determined. That is a matter of interpretation, and consequently it is necessarily subject to debate, with conflicting interpretations. We must remember that the interpretation of every scientific experiment is subjective. There is no kind of scientific experiment in which the interpretation rolls out "objectively." If there is such a factor as auditory imagery, for example, just how should the auditory character of the factor produce itself objectively in the statistical analysis and without the subjective interpretation of the investigator? Or just how could tallness in the box population appear objectively in the data? Factor analysis is no exception to other kinds of scientific experimentation. It is a fortunate circumstance, however, that different interpretations of a primary factor can usually be resolved as questions of fact. New factorial experiments can be made to determine which interpretation is the more plausible.

In naming the primary factors it is a better policy to name the factors in terms of well-known concepts, such as Number, Space, Verbal, and Memory factors than to name them in some noncommittal way, such as $x_1$, $x_2$, and so on. If we name a factor "Number," it will provoke experimentation with number tests and with nonnumerical tests, and the experiments are likely to be made in terms of psychological hypotheses that can be sustained or disproved experimentally. In this way we shall advance faster than if the primary factors are left as interesting statistical curiosities. They should be recognized as psychologically challenging experimental effects. We cannot expect to be correct in all interpretations of primary factors, and we shall probably have occasion to revise interpretations repeatedly as more experimental information becomes available. Again, this policy is consistent with the desire to make factor analysis a useful psychological tool instead of a mere statistical routine for condensing test scores and correlations.

Those who criticize factor analysis as faculty psychology talk in the next breath about verbal and nonverbal intelligence, special aptitudes for music and for art, mechanical aptitudes, and disabilities in reading and arithmetic, without realizing that they are implying factor analysis and the interpretation of factors. Conversationally, we can talk about musical ability in the singular; but, as psychologists, we believe that different abilities are probably involved in a good voice, absolute pitch, originality in harmony, counterpoint, orchestration, melodic memory, ease in memorizing at the piano, ability in musical interpretation, and so on. How many important functional unities might there be in this domain? They are surely not all completely independent. They are correlated, and they probably represent a smaller number of abilities than the infinite number of musical tasks that could be given to a music student. To find these functional unities is the problem of factor analysis. If that is faculty psychology, then so is most investigation of individual differences and most of the work on special aptitudes and defects. And so also are many of the chapter headings in the textbooks of psychology which the same critics are teaching.

### Correction for uniqueness

The correlation between two experimentally obtained measures is sometimes called a "fallible" coefficient in the sense that the correlation is somewhat depressed by the experimental errors in the measures. If the two measures are the best available for two traits $x$ and $y$ and if it is desired to estimate the true correlation between the traits themselves as it would be expressed by perfect tests of the two traits, then the obtained or fallible coefficient is *corrected for attenuation*. The correction for attenuation is an estimate of what the correlation between two tests would be if the error variances were eliminated. The estimate is made in terms of experimentally determined reliability coefficients for both tests. If a factor matrix is available showing the loadings on common factors, specific factors, and error factors, then the correction for attenuation can be obtained by eliminating the error factor loadings and then normalizing the remaining common factors and specific factors for each test, so that the sum of their squares is equal to unity. The correlation between two tests corrected for attenuation would then be the cross product of their respective rows in the normalized factor matrix for common and specific factors. The same numerical result is obtained by the usual formula for this correction, namely,

$$(17) \qquad r'_{xy} = \frac{r_{xy}}{\sqrt{r_{xx} r_{yy}}},$$

where $r'_{xy}$ is the augmented coefficient, corrected for attenuation, and $r_{xx}$ and $r_{yy}$ are the reliability coefficients.

The *correction for uniqueness* is analogous to the correction for attenuation. Instead of eliminating the error variance, we can imagine the test so modified as to eliminate both error variance and specific variance. The result would be a measure containing only the common factors normalized so that the sum of the squares of their loadings is unity. That is what *Table 1* represents. The correlation between two tests as determined by the normalized common factor matrix is

$$(18) \qquad R_{xy} = \frac{r_{xy}}{\sqrt{h_x^2 h_y^2}} = \frac{r_{xy}}{h_x h_y},$$

in which communalities are substituted for reliabilities. The correlations corrected for uniqueness are the scalar products of pairs of unit test vectors as represented on the spherical model. These corrections are useful in some theoretical problems, and they are represented in the illustrative problem of this chapter by the cosines of the angles between the normalized test vectors. In the present case the principal interest is in studying the configuration of test vectors and not in estimating what the correlations would be if the tests were in any way altered. In studying the configuration of test vectors by the methods described here, it is best not to include in the configuration any tests whose communalities are small. Such test vectors are short, and, when they are much extended, their projected location on the surface of the sphere is unstable. If they are used in plotting the configuration, they should be specially marked so that less weight is given to them than to the test vectors which are not very much extended in normalizing.

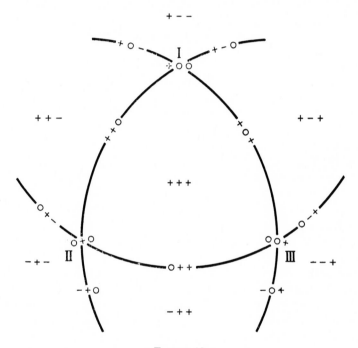

FIGURE 12

## The octants

In *Figure 12* we have represented diagrammatically the right spherical triangle shown in the photograph of *Figure 11*. This diagram will be used frequently to represent the positive octant for three-dimensional factor problems, and it can be used to advantage in discussing factorial principles extending to more than three dimensions. The three orthogonal axes *I*, *II*, *III*, are shown at the corners of the co-ordinate triangle in *Figure 12*.

A test vector that is collinear with one of the co-ordinate axes would have zero loadings on all but one of the factors. A test vector that is a linear combination of two reference vectors lies in the plane that is spanned by the two reference vectors. The test vector can then be defined by a vector equation, such as

$$(19) \qquad w_{j1}X_1 + w_{j2}X_2 = J \, ,$$

in which $w_{j1}$ and $w_{j2}$ are the weights assigned to the test vector $J$ for the two reference vectors $X_1$ and $X_2$. If the two weights are equal, then the test vector $J$ lies midway between the two reference vectors in the plane $I$–$II$ of *Figure 12*. If the weight $w_{j1}$ is the larger, then the test vector $J$ lies close to the first reference vector. If we write the equation of a test vector $J$ for the three dimensions of *Figure 12*, we have

$$(20) \qquad w_{j1}X_1 + w_{j2}X_2 + w_{j3}X_3 = J \, ,$$

in which the weight $w_{j3}$ is zero when the test vector $J$ lies in the plane $I$–$II$.

The signs of the three weights determine the region in which the test vector $J$ is located. If all three of the weights are positive, the test vector $J$ is located inside the positive octant, as indicated by the signs $+ + +$ in the positive octant of *Figure 12*. If the third weight is zero and the other two are positive, we have the weights $+ + 0$, and the test vector then lies in the arc $I$–$II$ of *Figure 12*. If the weights are $0 + 0$, the vector $J$ is collinear with the second reference vector, as shown in the figure. Similarly, if the weights are $+ 0 \, 0$, the vector $J$ is collinear with the first reference vector. If the first weight is negative, we have the weights $- + 0$, and the vector $J$ then lies in the plane spanned by the first and second reference vectors, as shown in the figure. Similar relations hold for the weight combination $+ - 0$ as shown.

There are twenty-six sign combinations of the weights in equation (2) which define the region in which the test vector can be located in three dimensions, the combination $0\,0\,0$ being eliminated because it represents a null vector. If one of the signs is zero, the test vector lies in one of the co-ordinate planes. If two of the signs are zero, the test vector is at the intersection of two of the co-ordinate planes. The same reasoning can be extended to $n$ dimensions. The fact that the weights of the equation are all positive does not imply that the configuration can be inclosed within a right spherical triangle unless the reference vectors are separated by right angles or acute angles. If the saturations of the tests in the several factors are all positive and if the factors are not negatively correlated, then the configuration can be inclosed in a right spherical triangle which becomes the positive octant. This is a special case of considerable psychological interest because of the fact that mental abilities do not seem to show any negative correlations and psychological tests are positively correlated, even when they represent the most diverse tasks.

# CHAPTER VIII

# THE CENTROID METHOD OF FACTORING

In factoring a correlation matrix the purpose is usually to account for the correlations with fewer factors than there are tests, so that $r < n$, where $r$ is the number of factors and $n$ is the number of tests. With fallible data there will always be residual correlation coefficients after the extraction of $r$ factors unless $r = n$, in which case the residuals can be made to vanish exactly. The reason is that the rank of a correlation matrix for fallible data is always equal to its order. The factoring should be done so as to make the residuals as small as possible after each factor has been determined. The least-squares solution for this problem minimizes the residuals and maximizes the factor loadings on each successive factor. The resulting factorial axes are the principal axes. These would be determined routinely in factor analysis, except for the computational labor that is involved for large test batteries of twenty or thirty or more tests. The centroid method, like the grouping-method, is a computational compromise. The main centroid axis for any given table of correlation coefficients, or residual coefficients, can be regarded as a first approximation to the major principal axis. The main centroid axis for any given correlation matrix, or residual matrix, is obtained by simple summational procedures after appropriate reflections of the test vectors with corresponding sign changes, and the results are often fairly close to the statistically ideal least-squares axes. In large problems it is sometimes desirable to determine an additional factor by the centroid method beyond what is required by the principal axes to obtain the same average magnitude of residuals. The subsequent rotation of axes from either method of factoring usually shows one or more residual factors that do not contain enough variance for dependable interpretation.

Several theorems will be derived which involve the centroid of the test vector termini. These will be followed by numerical and geometrical examples. The theoretical examples in this chapter are exact, in that all correlational elements are assumed to be known and the rank $r$ is less than $n$, so that the $r$th-factor residuals vanish identically. An example will also be given showing computational methods that are suitable for experimental data.

## Centroid theorems

Consider, first, the fundamental equation of multiple-factor analysis, namely,

$$(1) \qquad r_{jk} = a_{j1}a_{k1} + a_{j2}a_{k2} + \cdots + a_{jr}a_{kr},$$

in which the correlation between two tests, $j$ and $k$, is expressed in terms of the factor loadings of these tests in $r$ orthogonal factors. Summing each column of the correlation matrix, we have

$$(2) \qquad \sum_j r_{jk} = a_{k1} \sum_j a_{j1} + a_{k2} \sum_j a_{j2} + \cdots + a_{kr} \sum_j a_{jr}.$$

Summing for all columns, we have

$$(3) \qquad \sum_k \sum_j r_{jk} = \sum_k a_{k1} \sum_j a_{j1} + \sum_k a_{k2} \sum_j a_{j2} + \cdots + \sum_k a_{kr} \sum_j a_{jr}.$$

But

$$(4) \qquad \sum_k a_{km} = \sum_j a_{jm},$$

so that

$$(5) \qquad \sum_k \sum_j r_{jk} = \left[\sum_j a_{j1}\right]^2 + \left[\sum_j a_{j2}\right]^2 + \cdots + \left[\sum_j a_{jr}\right]^2.$$

Let the sum of all the correlation coefficients (or residual coefficients) be denoted $r_t$, then

$$(6) \qquad \sum_k \sum_j r_{jk} = r_t,$$

so that

$$(7) \qquad r_t = \sum_m \left[\sum_j a_{jm}\right]^2.$$

We then have the interesting theorem that *the sum of all the coefficients in a correlation matrix is equal to the sum of the squares of the column sums in any corresponding orthogonal factor matrix.*

For the purpose of illustrating the theorems of this chapter, a small fictitious example was written, as shown in *Table 1*, for five variables and two factors. The intercorrelations are shown in *Table 2*. The sum of the correlations is $+.29$. Applying the theorem to the sums of the factor matrix, we have $(-.2)^2+(+.5)^2=+.29$, which is also the sum of the correlations. In *Figure 1* we have the corresponding configuration of five test vectors, which are drawn without reference frame.

Table 1

Fictitious Factor
Matrix

| | I | II |
|---|---|---|
| 1 | −.9 | −.1 |
| 2 | −.6 | −.6 |
| 3 | .4 | −.3 |
| 4 | .7 | .1 |
| 5 | .6 | .4 |
| Σ | −.2 | .5 |

Table 2

Correlation Matrix

| | +1 | +2 | +3 | +4 | +5 |
|---|---|---|---|---|---|
| +1 | .82 | .60 | − .33 | − .64 | − .58 |
| +2 | .60 | .72 | − .06 | − .48 | − .60 |
| +3 | − .33 | − .06 | .25 | .25 | .12 |
| +4 | − .64 | − .48 | .25 | .50 | .46 |
| +5 | − .58 | − .60 | .12 | .46 | .52 |
| Σ | − .13 | .18 | .23 | .09 | − .08 |
| \|Σ\| | 2.97 | 2.46 | 1.01 | 2.33 | 2.28 |

$r_t = .29$

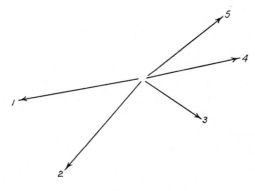

FIGURE 1

The centroid of a set of points is the center of gravity of equal weights at the points. The centroid of the test vector termini has the co-ordinates

$$\frac{1}{n} \sum_j a_{j1}, \frac{1}{n} \sum_j a_{j2}, \ldots, \frac{1}{n} \sum_j a_{jr} .$$

If the axes are so placed that the centroid lies in the first axis of reference, then the centroid has zero projections on all the remaining $(r-1)$ co-ordinate axes. Hence,

(8) $$\sum_j a_{j2} = \sum_j a_{j3} = \cdots = \sum_j a_{jr} = 0 ,$$

so that the $r$ co-ordinates of the centroid are

$$\frac{1}{n} \sum_j a_{j1}, 0, 0, \ldots, 0$$

Substituting (8) in (7), we have

$$(9) \qquad r_t = \left[ \sum_j a_{j1} \right]^2 ,$$

where the first axis contains the centroid. We then have the theorem that *the sum of the coefficients in the correlation matrix is equal to the square of the sum of the first centroid factor loadings.*

The first co-ordinate of the centroid of the test vector termini is also its distance from the origin, since the remaining $(r-1)$ co-ordinates vanish. Hence the distance of the centroid from the origin is

$$(10) \qquad d = \frac{1}{n} \sum_j a_{j1} .$$

By (9) we have

$$(11) \qquad d = \frac{1}{n} \sqrt{r_t} ,$$

in which *the distance of the centroid from the origin is expressed in terms of the coefficients in the correlation matrix.*

In order to determine the loadings $a_{j1}$ on the centroid factor, substitute (8) in (2). Then we have

$$(12) \qquad \sum_j r_{jk} = a_{k1} \sum a_{j1} ;$$

and from (9) we get

$$(13) \qquad \sum_j r_{jk} = a_{k1} \sqrt{r_t} .$$

For convenience, let the column sums of the correlation matrix be denoted

$$(14) \qquad \sum r_{jk} \equiv r_k .$$

Then

$$(15) \qquad r_k = a_{k1} \sqrt{r_t} ,$$

so that

$$(16) \qquad a_{k1} = \frac{r_k}{\sqrt{r_t}} .$$

For computing, determine a multiplier $m = \dfrac{1}{\sqrt{r_t}}$. Then

(17)
$$a_{k1} = mr_k ,$$

by which the first-factor loadings are proportional to the corresponding column sums of the correlation matrix. By (17) the first-factor loadings are numerically determined.

By equation (9) we have a useful check on the computations, namely,

(9a)
$$\sum_j a_{j1} = \sqrt{r_t} .$$

### Reflection of test vectors

The correlation matrix of *Table 2* represents a configuration which is shown in *Figure 1*. The fact that no reference frame has been drawn in this figure corresponds to the fact that no reference frame is implied in the correlation matrix. A first axis in the configuration of five vectors evidently should be in the general direction of the vectors *1, 2, 4, 5*, since an axis in this direction through the configuration would make the projections the largest possible. It is of secondary consequence whether the positive sense of this first reference axis is in the direction of the test vectors *1, 2*, or in the direction of *4, 5*.

Since the configuration is not immediately given by the correlation matrix and since it cannot be physically constructed or seen when the correlations involve more than three dimensions, it is a practical problem to determine the general direction of the longest dimension of the configuration by inspection of the correlation coefficients. When that can be determined by inspection of the correlation matrix, several of the test vectors can be reflected so as to move the centroid as far away from the origin as possible. Then the first centroid axis can be located so as to account for a large part of the correlation coefficients, leaving their residuals as small as possible.

Several criteria can be used to ascertain which test vectors lie in or near the longest dimension of the configuration. These criteria are not always consistent, since a configuration has extension in several directions. One criterion is to determine the absolute sum of the correlation coefficients, or residual coefficients, in each column. That test vector which has the highest absolute sum is likely to be in or near the longest dimension of the test configuration. Another criterion is to find that column which has the largest absolute sum, ignoring the diagonals. One simple method is to select for reflection that test vector which has the largest number of negative coefficients. This process can be continued until each column has a majority of positive coefficients. Another method is to select for reflection that test vector which has the highest communality. Inspection of the correlation matrix of *Table 2* indicates that test vectors 1 and 2 should be reflected. When these columns and rows have been reversed in sign, the resulting correlation matrix is shown in *Table 3*, and the configuration, after reflection, is shown in *Figure 2*. The centroid of the reflected configuration is shown at point *c* in *Figure 2*.

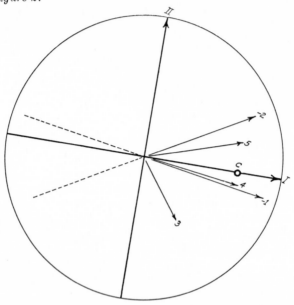

FIGURE 2

The computation of the first-factor loadings is shown in *Table 3*. Sum the columns to find $r_k$ for each column. Find the total sum $r_t$ and the multiplier $m$. Apply the multiplier $m$ to find the first-factor loadings $a_{j1}$ as shown. These loadings correspond to the variables with signs, as shown in *Table 3*. The same factor loadings are recorded in the factor matrix of *Table 4* for all variables with positive sign.

*Table 3*

*Correlations after Sign Changes*

|        | $-1$ | $-2$ | $+3$ | $+4$ | $+5$ |
|--------|------|------|------|------|------|
| $-1$   | .82  | .60  | .33  | .64  | .58  |
| $-2$   | .60  | .72  | .06  | .48  | .60  |
| $+3$   | .33  | .06  | .25  | .25  | .12  |
| $+4$   | .64  | .48  | .25  | .50  | .46  |
| $+5$   | .58  | .60  | .12  | .46  | .52  |
| $r_k$  | 2.97 | 2.46 | 1.01 | 2.33 | 2.28 |
| $a_{j1}$ | .893 | .740 | .304 | .701 | .686 |

$r_t = 11.05$
$\sum_j a_{j1} = 3.324$

*Table 4*

*Factor Matrix*

|   | I     | II    |
|---|-------|-------|
| 1 | $-.893$ | $-.149$ |
| 2 | $-.740$ | .414  |
| 3 | .304  | .397  |
| 4 | .701  | .094  |
| 5 | .686  | $-.223$ |
| $\Sigma$ | .058 | .533 |

$m = .300828$

The theorem of equation (9) can be verified in *Table 3*. The sum of the first-factor loadings, with variables 1 and 2 reversed, is 3.324, and $(3.324)^2 =$ 11.05, which is the sum of the coefficients in this table. The first-factor loadings in *Table 4* represent all variables with positive sign as originally given.

The first-factor residual coefficients can be written by equation (1), in the form

$$(18) \qquad r_{2.jk} = r_{jk} - a_{j1}a_{k1} = \sum_{m=2}^{r} a_{jm}a_{km} .$$

The first-factor residuals are shown in *Table 5*. They were computed from the given coefficients in *Table 2* and the first-factor loadings, first column,

*Table 5*

*First-Factor Residuals*

|     | +1 | +2 | +3 | +4 | +5 |
|-----|------|------|------|------|------|
| +1 | .023 | −.061 | −.059 | −.015 | .032 |
| +2 | −.061 | .172 | .164 | .038 | −.093 |
| +3 | −.059 | .164 | .158 | .037 | −.089 |
| +4 | −.015 | .038 | .037 | .009 | −.021 |
| +5 | .032 | −.093 | −.089 | −.021 | .049 |
| *Ch* | −.079 | .222 | .212 | .049 | −.120 |
| Σ | −.080 | .220 | .211 | .048 | −.122 |
| \|Σ\| | .190 | .528 | .507 | .120 | .284 |
| Σ$r_s$ | −.103 | .048 | .053 | .039 | −.171 |
| Neg. | 3 | 2 | 2 | 2 | 3 |

of *Table 4*. The check sums, *Ch*, of *Table 5* were obtained from the column sums Σ of *Table 2* and the first column of *Table 4*. *Example:* $-.13 - (-.893)$ $(+.058) = -.079$. The algebraic column sums are shown in row Σ and the absolute column sums in row \|Σ\| of *Table 5*. The sums, omitting diagonals, are shown in row Σ$r_s$, and the last row shows the number of negative coefficients in each column. Ordinarily, all these rows are not computed. They are shown here to illustrate different methods of determining which variables to reflect. By the absolute sums we could reflect test 2. By the sums, omitting the diagonal, we could start by reflecting test 5; and, by counting the number of negative signs, we could reflect either test 1 or test 5.

In *Figure 3* we have the original configuration of five points and the first and second centroid axes. The correlation matrix in *Table 5* is of rank 1, and its configuration is therefore of dimensionality 1. The one-dimensional residual configuration is shown in *Figure 3*, where the five test vectors are indicated by as many collinear arrows in the second centroid axis. These

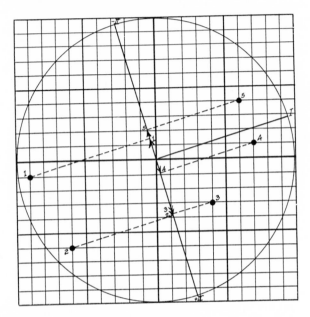

FIGURE 3

residual vectors are seen to be the projections of the five original test vectors on a one-dimensional subspace (axis *II*) orthogonal to the first axis. When the residual vectors *1* and *5* are reflected, the resulting five vectors are unidirectional, and the second-factor loadings are then equal to the residual vector lengths. The computation of the second-factor loadings is shown in *Table 6*, and they are recorded with proper sign in the second column of *Table 4*. The second-factor residuals vanish, since the given correlation matrix

Table 6

*First-Factor Residuals after Sign Changes*

|      | $-1$  | $+2$  | $+3$  | $+4$  | $-5$  |
|------|-------|-------|-------|-------|-------|
| $-1$ | .023  | .061  | .059  | .015  | .032  |
| $+2$ | .061  | .172  | .164  | .038  | .093  |
| $+3$ | .059  | .164  | .158  | .037  | .089  |
| $+4$ | .015  | .038  | .037  | .009  | .021  |
| $-5$ | .032  | .093  | .089  | .021  | .049  |
| $r_k$    | .190  | .528  | .507  | .120  | .284  |
| $a_{j2}$ | .149  | .414  | .397  | .094  | .223  |

$r_t = 1.629$

$\sum_j a_{j2} = 1.277$

$m = .7835$

of *Table 2* is of rank 2 and the rank of each residual matrix is one less than the previous correlation matrix.

## The group centroid method

The procedure to be described here is one of the simplest forms of the centroid method.

In *Table 7* we have an eight-variable correlation matrix. The last column shows the algebraic sum of each row, and it will be used for check purposes. The check column is vacant in the given correlation matrix. The first summation row shows the absolute sum of each column. The highest absolute sum is 4.06, so that test 8 is chosen as a pivot test. In this column we choose several tests, in this case three, which have the highest correlations with

*Table 7*

*First Factor Determined by Group Centroid Method*

|   | 1 | 2 | 3 | 4 | 5 | 6 | 7 | 8 | Ch | Σ |
|---|---|---|---|---|---|---|---|---|---|---|
| 1 | .50 | .27 | .19 | − .53 | .15 | .03 | .09 | − .24 | | .460 |
| 2 | .27 | .94 | − .38 | .10 | .48 | − .17 | − .51 | .03 | | .560 |
| 3 | .19 | − .38 | .57 | − .41 | − .54 | .52 | .06 | − .57 | | − .560 |
| 4 | − .53 | − .10 | − .41 | .65 | .10 | − .26 | − .08 | .47 | | − .160 |
| 5 | .15 | .48 | − .54 | .10 | .86 | − .77 | .29 | .67 | | 1.240 |
| 6 | .03 | − .17 | .52 | − .26 | − .77 | .81 | − .47 | − .79 | | −1.100 |
| 7 | .09 | − .51 | .06 | − .08 | .29 | − .47 | .89 | .43 | | .700 |
| 8 | − .24 | .03 | − .57 | .47 | .67 | − .79 | .43 | .86 | | .860 |
| Σ\|r_{jk}\| | 2.00 | 2.88 | 3.24 | 2.60 | 3.86 | 3.82 | 2.82 | 4.06 | | |
| s | 0 | 0 | 0 | 0 | +1 | −1 | 0 | +1 | | |
| Σr_{sk} | − .12 | .68 | −1.63 | .83 | 2.30 | −2.37 | 1.19 | 2.32 | 3.20 | 3.20 |
| u | 0 | 0 | −1 | +1 | +1 | −1 | +1 | +1 | | |
| Σr_{uk} | − .75 | .45 | −2.55 | 1.81 | 3.23 | −3.62 | 1.94 | 3.79 | 4.30 | 4.30 |
| a_{j1} | − .182 | .109 | − .620 | .440 | .785 | − .880 | .471 | .921 | 1.045 | 1.044 |

$$T = 16.94 \quad \sqrt{T} = 4.115823 \quad m = .242965$$
$$\Sigma a_{u1} = 4.117 \quad (4.117)^2 = 16.95$$

test 8, disregarding sign. These correlations are $r_{58} = +.67$, $r_{68} = -.79$, and $r_{88} = +.86$. In practice these subgroups may contain three to five tests or more, provided that only those tests are included in the subgroup which have significant correlations with the pivot test.

The three tests in the subgroup are 5, 6, and 8, and the signs of their correlations with test 8 are +, −, and +, respectively. In row *s* we record unit weight with these signs for columns 5, 6, and 8, and zeros for the rest, as shown.

In the next row we record the column sums for these three rows with signs. The first entry in row $\Sigma r_{sk}$ is obtained from the first column, namely, $(+.15) - (+.03) + (-.24) = -.12$. The other entries are obtained in a similar manner. The check sum is obtained from the Σ column, namely, $+(+1.240) - (-1.100) + (+.860) = +3.200$, which is the expected sum. The actual sum of the row is the same, and it is recorded in the Σ column.

Note, next, the highest absolute sum in this row, which is −2.37. As a practical, but somewhat arbitrary, rule, we note that one-third of this sum,

## Table 8
### Second Factor Determined by Group Centroid Method

|  | 1 | 2 | 3 | 4 | 5 | 6 | 7 | 8 | Ch | Σ |
|---|---|---|---|---|---|---|---|---|---|---|
| 1 | .467 | .290 | .077 | − .450 | .293 | − .130 | .176 | − .072 | .650 | .651 |
| 2 | .290 | .928 | − .312 | − .148 | .394 | − .074 | − .561 | − .070 | .446 | .447 |
| 3 | .077 | − .312 | .186 | − .137 | − .053 | − .026 | .352 | .001 | .087 | .088 |
| 4 | − .450 | − .148 | − .137 | .456 | − .245 | .127 | − .287 | .065 | − .619 | − .619 |
| 5 | .293 | .394 | − .053 | − .245 | .244 | − .079 | − .080 | − .053 | .420 | .421 |
| 6 | − .130 | − .074 | .026 | .127 | − .079 | .036 | − .056 | .020 | − .181 | − .182 |
| 7 | .176 | − .561 | .352 | − .287 | − .080 | − .056 | .668 | − .004 | .208 | .208 |
| 8 | − .072 | − .070 | .001 | .065 | − .053 | .020 | − .004 | .012 | − .102 | − .101 |
| $\Sigma\|r_{jk}\|$ | 1.955 | 2.777 | 1.144 | 1.915 | 1.441 | .548 | 2.184 | .297 |  |  |
| $s$ | 0 | +1 | −1 | 0 | +1 | 0 | −1 | 0 |  |  |
| $\Sigma r_{sk}$ | .330 | 2.195 | − .903 | .031 | .771 | − .071 | −1.661 | − .120 | .572 | .572 |
| $u$ | +1 | +1 | −1 | 0 | +1 | 0 | −1 | 0 |  |  |
| $\Sigma r_{uk}$ | .797 | 2.485 | − .826 | − .419 | 1.064 | − .201 | −1.485 | − .192 | 1.222 | 1.223 |
| $a_{j2}$ | .309 | .963 | − .320 | − .162 | .412 | − .078 | − .576 | − .074 | .473 | .474 |

$$T = 6.657 \qquad \sqrt{T} = 2.580116 \qquad m = .387579$$
$$\Sigma a_{u2} = 2.580 \qquad (2.580)^2 = 6.656$$

## Table 9
### Third Factor Determined by Group Centroid Method

|  | 1 | 2 | 3 | 4 | 5 | 6 | 7 | 8 | Ch | Σ |
|---|---|---|---|---|---|---|---|---|---|---|
| 1 | .372 | − .008 | .176 | − .400 | .166 | − .106 | .354 | − .049 | .505 | .505 |
| 2 | − .008 | .001 | − .004 | .008 | − .003 | .001 | − .006 | .001 | − .009 | − .010 |
| 3 | .176 | − .004 | .084 | − .189 | .079 | − .051 | .168 | − .023 | .240 | .240 |
| 4 | − .400 | .008 | − .189 | .430 | − .178 | .114 | − .380 | .053 | .542 | .542 |
| 5 | .166 | − .003 | .079 | − .178 | .074 | − .047 | .157 | − .023 | .226 | .225 |
| 6 | − .106 | .001 | − .051 | .114 | − .047 | .030 | − .101 | .014 | − .145 | − .146 |
| 7 | .354 | − .006 | .168 | − .380 | .157 | − .101 | .336 | − .047 | .481 | .481 |
| 8 | − .049 | .001 | − .023 | .053 | − .023 | .014 | − .047 | .007 | − .066 | − .067 |
| $\Sigma\|r_{jk}\|$ | 1.631 | .032 | .774 | 1.752 | .727 | .464 | 1.549 | .217 |  |  |
| $s$ | −1 | 0 | 0 | +1 | 0 | 0 | −1 | 0 |  |  |
| $\Sigma r_{sk}$ | −1.126 | .022 | − .533 | 1.210 | .501 | .321 | −1.070 | .149 | −1.528 | −1.528 |
| $u$ | −1 | 0 | −1 | +1 | −1 | +1 | −1 | 0 |  |  |
| $\Sigma r_{uk}$ | −1.574 | .030 | − .747 | 1.691 | − .701 | .449 | −1.496 | .209 | −2.139 | −2.140 |
| $a_{k3}$ | − .610 | .012 | − .289 | .655 | − .272 | .174 | − .580 | .081 | − .829 | − .829 |

$$T = 6.658 \qquad \sqrt{T} = 2.580310 \qquad m = .387550$$
$$\Sigma a_{u3} = 2.580 \qquad (2.580)^2 = 6.656$$

## Table 10
### Factor Matrix by Group Centroid Method

|  | I | II | III | $h^2$ |
|---|---|---|---|---|
| 1 | − .182 | .309 | − .610 | .501 |
| 2 | .109 | .963 | .012 | .939 |
| 3 | − .620 | − .320 | − .289 | .570 |
| 4 | .440 | − .162 | .655 | .649 |
| 5 | .785 | .412 | − .272 | .860 |
| 6 | − .880 | − .078 | .174 | .811 |
| 7 | .471 | − .576 | − .580 | .890 |
| 8 | .921 | − .074 | .081 | .860 |

which is about .80, and all columns whose sums are less than this number are given a weight of zero in the next row, $u$, as shown. The other columns are given weights of $+1$ or $-1$ according to the signs of $\Sigma r_{sk}$ as shown.

With the weights $u$ we find the column sums $\Sigma r_{uk}$, which are recorded in the next row. The first entry in this row is obtained from the first column with the weights given in the row $u$. It is $-(+.19)+(-.53)+(+.15)-(+.03)+(+.09)+(-.24)=-.75$. The check sum, $+4.30$, is obtained with similar weights from the $\Sigma$ column, and it agrees with the actual sum of the entries in this row.

Summing the entries in the row and applying again the same weights, we have

$$+ 2.55 + 1.81 + 3.23 + 3.62 + 1.94 + 3.79 = 16.94 = T,$$

from which we obtain the multiplier $m=\dfrac{1}{\sqrt{T}}=.242965$. Applying this multiplier to row $\Sigma r_{uk}$ and to its sum 4.30, we have the factor loadings $a_{j1}$ with proper signs and their expected sum, 1.045. The actual sum of the row is 1.044, and it is recorded in the $\Sigma$ column. Finally, the algebraic sum of the row with weights $u$ is $\Sigma a_{u1}=4.117$, and the square of this sum is equal to the value of $T$ or $r_t$ of equation (9a). The factor loadings in row $a_{j1}$ are copied directly in the first column of the factor matrix in *Table 10*.

*Table 8* shows similar computations for the second-factor loadings. The check column is obtained from the $\Sigma$ column of *Table 7*, the first-factor loadings, and their sum, 1.045. The check sum in the first row of *Table 8* is obtained thus: $+.460-(-.182)(1.045)=+.650$. The actual sum of the residuals in the first row of *Table 8* is $+.651$, as recorded. The second-factor loadings, $a_{j2}$, are recorded in the second column of *Table 10*.

*Table 9* shows the corresponding computations for the third-factor loadings. The third-factor residuals computed from *Tables 7* and *10* vanish in the range $\pm.001$.

The computational routine for what we have called the "group centroid method" is so simple that a clerk can easily learn it. Attention should be called to the fact that the subgroup $s$ should include three or more tests. If only one pivot test were used and if the weights $u$ were made $+1$ or $-1$, omitting the zero weight, then this method would reduce to what was called the "simplified centroid method," which was published in 1933.* That method was defective, in that the communalities of the pivot tests were too high, sometimes even exceeding unity. Moreover, the method did not properly separate the common factors from the unique factors. The method which has been described here and which has been called the "group centroid method" avoids these difficulties by using the subgroups $s$ and by using the three weights for $u$. However, the group centroid method is probably

* A *Simplified Multiple Factor Method* (University of Chicago Bookstore, 1933).

**Table 11**

| Test | 1 | 2 | 3 | 4 | 5 | 6 | 7 | 8 | 9 | 10 | 11 | 12 | Σ | Ch |
|---|---|---|---|---|---|---|---|---|---|---|---|---|---|---|
| 1 |  | .17 | .49 | .51 | .64 | .30 | .36 | .60 | .22 | .65 | .52 | .48 | 4.94 | ✓ |
| 2 | .17 |  | .46 | .63 | .46 | .71 | .71 | .41 | .69 | .29 | .68 | .63 | 5.84 | ✓ |
| 3 | .49 | .46 |  | .75 | .62 | .61 | .55 | .73 | .48 | .61 | .67 | .78 | 6.75 | ✓ |
| 4 | .51 | .63 | .75 |  | .70 | .73 | .71 | .73 | .63 | .62 | .80 | .83 | 7.64 | ✓ |
| 5 | .64 | .46 | .62 | .70 |  | .56 | .60 | .68 | .48 | .66 | .72 | .68 | 6.80 | ✓ |
| 6 | .30 | .71 | .61 | .73 | .56 |  | .72 | .56 | .68 | .43 | .74 | .74 | 6.78 | ✓ |
| 7 | .36 | .71 | .55 | .71 | .60 | .72 |  | .54 | .68 | .45 | .76 | .70 | 6.78 | ✓ |
| 8 | .60 | .41 | .73 | .73 | .68 | .56 | .54 |  | .44 | .67 | .68 | .74 | 6.78 | ✓ |
| 9 | .22 | .69 | .48 | .63 | .48 | .68 | .68 | .44 |  | .33 | .67 | .63 | 5.93 | ✓ |
| 10 | .65 | .29 | .61 | .62 | .66 | .43 | .45 | .67 | .33 |  | .60 | .61 | 5.92 | ✓ |
| 11 | .52 | .68 | .67 | .80 | .72 | .74 | .76 | .68 | .67 | .60 |  | .79 | 7.63 | ✓ |
| 12 | .48 | .63 | .78 | .83 | .68 | .74 | .70 | .74 | .63 | .61 | .79 |  | 7.61 | ✓ |
| $\Sigma r = s$ | 4.94 | 5.84 | 6.75 | 7.64 | 6.80 | 6.78 | 6.78 | 6.78 | 5.93 | 5.92 | 7.63 | 7.61 | 79.40 | ✓ |
| $-2B = C$ | 4.94 | 5.84 | 6.75 | 7.64 | 6.80 | 6.78 | 6.78 | 6.78 | 5.93 | 5.92 | 7.63 | 7.61 | 79.40 | ✓ |
| $d$ | .65 | .71 | .78 | .83 | .72 | .74 | .76 | .74 | .69 | .67 | .80 | .83 | 8.92 | ✓ |
| $\mu d = D$ | .65 | .71 | .78 | .83 | .72 | .74 | .76 | .74 | .69 | .67 | .80 | .83 | 8.92 | ✓ |
| $C + D = E$ | 5.59 | 6.55 | 7.53 | 8.47 | 7.52 | 7.52 | 7.54 | 7.52 | 6.62 | 6.59 | 8.43 | 8.44 | 88.32 | ✓ |
| $mE = a_i$ | .59 | .70 | .80 | .90 | .80 | .80 | .80 | .80 | .70 | .70 | .90 | .90 | 9.39 | 9.40 |

$$T = \Sigma |E| = 88.32$$
$$\sqrt{T} = 9.397872$$
$$1/\sqrt{T} = m = .106407$$
$$mT = 9.40 = \sqrt{T}\ (\checkmark)$$
$$\Sigma |a| = 9.39 = mT\ (\checkmark)$$
$$m\Sigma E = \Sigma a\ (\checkmark)$$

not so effective as the complete centroid method in separating the common-factor space from the unique test space.

## The complete centroid method

The complete centroid method which has been in use in the Psychometric Laboratory for a number of years will be described here. This description will be given in terms of the computations on a standardized data sheet, which is illustrated in *Tables 11–13* inclusive. The complete centroid method will be described with a numerical example of twelve variables, and we shall include here a description of all the numerical checks which constitute a part of our computational routine. The computational checks are explicitly shown on the data sheets.

By the complete centroid method we mean the successive reflection of variables, one at a time, until all the column sums in the correlation matrix, or the residual matrix, are positive or zero. These column sums include the diagonal entries. No matter what the signs may be in a given correlation matrix, one can always reflect some of the variables so that all the column sums become positive or zero. In the complete centroid method this work is done systematically by reflecting one variable at a time. While it is always possible to make all the column sums positive or zero by reflecting some of the variables, the factorial solution is, in general, not unique. If simple structure exists in the test configuration, the rotated factor matrix is unique. It is independent of the factor matrix that is obtained by the centroid method. The lack of uniqueness of the centroid method of factoring constitutes, then, no problem because the rotated factor matrix is unique and the structure is unambiguous.

The following paragraphs are numbered to show the successive computational steps in the complete centroid method with successive adjustment of the communalities:

1. A given correlation matrix with twelve variables is recorded in *Table 11*. The diagonal entries are left blank, as shown. This example is intended to show the computational routine that is used on experimental data for the particular case in which it is decided to adjust the diagonals after each factor has been extracted.
2. The column sums are recorded in row $s$, and the row sums are recorded in the column $\Sigma$. The sum of all the entries in the correlation matrix is 79.40, which is recorded at the intersection of row $s$ and column $\Sigma$.
3. Since all the given correlation coefficients are positive in this example, we omit several steps that are required for subsequent factors. Row $s$ is copied into row $C$, as shown.
4. The communalities are recorded in row $d$. Here the computer decides how to treat the unknown communalities. He may use one of the

# Table 12

| $b=-a$ | $-.59$ | $-.70$ | $-.80$ | $-.90$ | $-.80$ | $-.80$ | $-.80$ | $-.80$ | $-.70$ | $-.70$ | $-.90$ | $-.90$ | $-v=-9.39$ | |
|---|---|---|---|---|---|---|---|---|---|---|---|---|---|---|
| $+a$ / Test | 1 | 2 | 3 | 4 | 5 | 6 | 7 | 8 | 9 | 10 | 11 | 12 | $\Sigma$ | $Ch$ |
| .59 — 1 | −.24 | −.24 | | | −.17 | −.17 | −.11 | −.13 | | −.19 | −.01 | −.05 | −.23 | ⌄ |
| .70 — 2 | −.02 | −.10 | −.12 | −.02 | −.10 | −.15 | −.15 | −.15 | −.20 | −.20 | −.05 | −.00 | −.24 | ⌄ |
| .80 — 3 | −.02 | | −.03 | −.03 | −.02 | −.03 | −.09 | −.09 | −.08 | −.05 | −.05 | −.06 | −.12 | ⌄ |
| .90 — 4 | −.17 | −.10 | | | −.02 | −.01 | | −.01 | | −.01 | −.01 | −.04 | −.00 | ⌄ |
| .80 — 5 | −.17 | −.15 | −.09 | | −.08 | −.08 | −.08 | −.04 | −.08 | −.10 | −.00 | −.02 | −.07 | ⌄ |
| .80 — 6 | −.11 | −.15 | −.09 | −.01 | −.04 | | −.10 | −.08 | −.12 | −.13 | −.02 | −.02 | −.09 | ⌄ |
| .80 — 7 | −.13 | −.15 | −.08 | −.00 | −.04 | −.12 | −.12 | −.10 | −.12 | −.11 | −.04 | −.02 | −.09 | ⌄ |
| .80 — 8 | −.11 | −.15 | −.08 | −.01 | −.08 | −.13 | | | −.16 | −.16 | −.04 | −.00 | −.09 | ⌄ |
| .70 — 9 | −.13 | −.20 | −.05 | −.00 | −.10 | −.02 | −.11 | −.11 | | | −.04 | −.02 | −.15 | ⌄ |
| .70 — 10 | −.19 | −.20 | −.05 | −.01 | −.08 | −.12 | | | −.16 | −.03 | −.04 | −.00 | −.16 | ⌄ |
| .90 — 11 | −.24 | −.05 | −.05 | −.01 | −.10 | −.02 | −.04 | −.04 | −.16 | −.03 | −.36 | −.07 | −.01 | ⌄ |
| .90 — 12 | −.01 | −.00 | −.06 | −.02 | −.00 | −.02 | −.02 | −.02 | −.00 | −.02 | −.11 | −.02 | −.03 | ⌄ |

$9.39=v=\Sigma a$

| | 1 | 2 | 3 | 4 | 5 | 6 | 7 | 8 | 9 | 10 | 11 | 12 | $\Sigma$ | $Ch$ |
|---|---|---|---|---|---|---|---|---|---|---|---|---|---|---|
| $s+vb+\beta^2=Ch$ | −.25 | −.24 | −.12 | .00 | −.07 | .09 | .09 | .09 | .15 | .16 | −.01 | −.03 | −1.32 | ⌄ |
| $\Sigma r=s$ | −.23 | −.24 | −.12 | .00 | −.07 | .09 | .09 | .09 | .15 | .16 | −.01 | −.03 | −1.30 | ⌄ |
| $-\tfrac{1}{3}s=A$ | −.115 | (.120) | .060 | .000 | −.035 | .045 | .045 | .045 | .075 | .080 | .005 | .015 | −1.28 | ⌄ |
| $++(2)$ | −.125 | (.120) | .040 | .000 | −.065 | .195 | .195 | .105 | .275 | .120 | .055 | .015 | .640 | ⌄ |
| $++(9)$ | −.315 | (.320) | .120 | .010 | −.145 | .315 | .315 | .225 | .275 | .280 | .095 | .015 | .400 | ⌄ |
| $++(6)$ | −.485 | (.470) | .150 | .010 | −.225 | .315 | .395 | .305 | .395 | .410 | .115 | .035 | .250 | ⌄ |
| $++(7)$ | −.595 | (.620) | .240 | .000 | −.265 | .395 | .395 | .405 | .515 | .520 | (.155) | .015 | .160 | ⌄ |
| $B+(11)$ | −.605 | (.670) | .290 | −.010 | .265 | .415 | .435 | .445 | .555 | .550 | (.155) | −.005 | .070 | ⌄ |
| $-2B=C$ | 1.21 | −1.34 | .58 | .02 | .53 | .83 | .87 | .89 | −1.11 | 1.10 | .31 | .01 | .060 | ⌄ |
| $d$ | −.24 | .24 | .10 | .03 | .17 | .17 | .15 | .15 | .20 | .24 | .05 | .06 | .12 | ⌄ |
| $\mu d=D$ | −.24 | .24 | .10 | .03 | .17 | .17 | .15 | .15 | .20 | .24 | .05 | .07 | 1.80 | ⌄ |
| $C+D=E$ | 1.45 | −1.58 | .68 | .05 | .70 | 1.00 | −1.02 | 1.04 | −1.31 | 1.34 | −.36 | .07 | .18 | ⌄ |
| $mE=a_j$ | .45 | −.49 | .21 | .02 | .22 | .31 | .31 | .32 | .40 | .41 | −.11 | .02 | .03 | .02 |

$$T=\Sigma|E|=10.60$$
$$1/\sqrt{T}=m=3.255764$$
$$mT=m=.307148$$

$$\frac{\Sigma s-v^2+\Sigma b^2}{\cdot} \;\div\; \Sigma Ch\,(\surd) \;\div\; \Sigma\Sigma r\,(\surd)$$

$$mT=3.26 \;=\;\sqrt{T}\,(\surd)$$
$$\Sigma|a|=3.27 \;=\;mT\,(\surd)$$
$$m\Sigma E=\Sigma a\,(\surd)$$

estimation formulae for the communalities and record the estimates in this row. Several such formulae are described in *chapter xiii*. If he decides to use unit communalities, these may be recorded in row *d*. The simplest estimation formula is to take the highest coefficient in each column as the estimated communality, and this is the method used in the present numerical example. The data sheet is designed so that it is applicable for any method of estimating or computing the diagonal values. Since there have been no sign changes in this table, row *d* is copied into row *D*, as shown in *Table 11*.

5. Row *E* gives the sum of $C + D$.

6. The entry 88.32 in row *E* is the sum of the entries *C* and *D* immediately above it. Row *E* is then summed. If the sum agrees with the already recorded sum, this fact is indicated by a check mark, as shown.

7. The first entry in the small table at the lower right corner is 88.32, which is obtained from row *E*. It is denoted *T*.

8. The value $\sqrt{T}$ is next recorded, as shown.

9. The reciprocal *m* is recorded in the next space.

10. The product $mT$ is equivalent to 9.40 and is recorded in the next space.

11. Next, it is verified that this value checks with $\sqrt{T}$. This verification is indicated by the check mark, as shown.

12. The last row of the table shows the factor loadings, which are the products $mE$, as shown. Applying the same multiplier to the check sum gives $m\Sigma E = 9.40$, as shown.

13. The algebraic sum of the last row is 9.39, as recorded in the $\Sigma$ column. The fact that these two sums agree, namely, 9.39 and 9.40, is indicated by a check mark.

14. The sum of the absolute values of the entries in the last row (9.39) is recorded in the small table. The fact that it agrees with the value of $mT$ is shown by a check mark.

15. The first-factor loadings are recorded in the first column of the factor matrix *F* in *Table 15*.

*The calculation of residuals*

The computations for the first-factor residuals and for the second-factor loadings are carried out on a new data sheet, as shown in *Table 12*. The successive steps in these computations are as follows:

1. The first-factor loadings are recorded in column $+a$, as shown. The sum of this column (9.39) is also recorded.

2. In the top row $(b = -a)$ the same factor loadings are recorded with reversed sign. The sum of the top row is $-v = -9.39$, as recorded.

3. The first-factor residuals $(\rho_{jk})$ are ordinarily expressed in the form

$$\rho_{jk} = r_{jk} - a_{j1}a_{k1} \, .$$

Since the first-factor loadings, $a_{j1}$ and $a_{k1}$, may be positive or negative and since their product is preceded by a minus sign, the computer is ordinarily required to keep in mind these three signs. The computational routine is simplified by expressing the residual in the form

$$\rho_{jk} = r_{jk} + (a_{j1})(-a_{k1}) \, .$$

The factor loading $(a_{j1})$ is represented in the column $(+a)$ and the factor loading $(-a_{k1})$ is represented by the top row $(b)$ on the data sheet. The actual computation of residuals will be illustrated for the first correlation coefficient, namely, $r_{21} = +.17$ in *Table 11*. The residual $\rho_{21}$ is to be recorded in the cell entry (21) in *Table 12*. The factor loadings .70 and $-.59$ are found in column $a$ and row $b$ directly opposite the cell entry (21). The actual computation for this residual then is

$$.17 + (.70)(-.59) = -.24 \, .$$

The residuals in the rest of the column for the first variable are computed in the same manner. The diagonal cells are left blank in the residual table.

4. The check sum $(-.25)$ for this column of residuals is next recorded. The value $s$ is obtained from the previous data sheet. In detail the computation for this entry is

$$4.94 + (9.39)(-.59) + (-.59)^2 = -.25 \, .$$

5. The sum $(-.23)$ of the first column of residuals is recorded in row $s$.
6. If this sum $s$ agrees closely with the check sum $Ch$, as in the present case, it is assumed that the computations were done correctly. The slight discrepancy is to be expected from rounding. When the agreement of the sum and the check sum has been noted, the first column of residuals is copied into the first row of the table. The sum $(s = -.23)$ is copied into column $\Sigma$.
7. The transcription in the first row is verified by actually summing that row. The agreement of the actual sum with the recorded sum is indicated by the check mark.
8. The residuals for the second variable are next computed, beginning in cell (32). When the residuals in the second column have been computed, they are verified in the rows $Ch$ and $s$ as before. The second

column of residuals is then copied into the second row and verified by adding the second row. The rest of the residuals are computed in the same manner. It should be noted that the number of residuals to be computed is reduced in the successive columns. When the computer reaches column 11, he has only one residual to compute. When the computer reaches column 12, there are no new residuals to compute. The last column is verified by the check sums.

9. The final check for the whole table of residuals is obtained in the form

$$\Sigma s - v^2 + \Sigma b^2 .$$

Its numerical value ($-1.32$) is recorded as shown.

10. The sum ($-1.30$) of the row $Ch$ is next recorded. The fact that this sum ($-1.30$) agrees closely with the previously recorded sum ($-1.32$) is represented by a check mark in the small square.* This verifies the computations in the row $Ch$.

11. The sum ($-1.28$) of the row $s$ is next recorded. The fact that this sum agrees closely with the two sums just recorded is represented by a check mark, as shown in the second small square.

12. The entries in column $\Sigma$ are summed. The fact that this sum agrees with the already recorded sum ($-1.28$) is represented by a check mark adjacent to this sum.

*The sign changes*

1. If all the entries in row $s$ are positive, then no reflections are necessary. This was the case in *Table 11*. However, in *Table 12* row $s$ contains negative entries. Hence we proceed by recording the entries in row $A$. The entries in row $A$ are recorded to three decimals. The previous calculations have been recorded to two decimals. The anticipated sum (.640) is recorded, as shown. Row $A$ is next summed. The fact that the sum agrees with the expected sum is represented by a check mark.

2. The highest positive number in row $A$ is .120. This number is written in parentheses, and it occurs in the second column. This fact is represented by writing $+(2)$ at the beginning of the next row.

3. Each entry in this row is the sum of the corresponding cell entry of row $A$ and the second row of residuals. For example, the first entry is

$$(.115) + (-.24) = -.125 .$$

In the sign-change calculations the diagonal entries are treated as zeros. Thus the second entry in row $+(2)$ is the same as the second

---

* The boxes in the printed data sheet are represented here as parentheses.

entry in row $A$. Each entry in this row is written in parentheses if the corresponding entry in row $A$ is in parentheses.

4. The anticipated sum (.400) is obtained from the corresponding entries in column $\Sigma$, namely, .640 and $-.24$. The sum of the new row agrees with the anticipated sum, .400. This fact is represented by the check mark.

5. The highest positive sum in this row is .275, and hence this number is written in parentheses. This number is in column 9, and therefore the next row is denoted $+(9)$ as shown. Each entry in row $+(9)$ is the sum of the corresponding entries in row $+(2)$ and in the ninth row of residuals. For example, the first entry is

$$(-.125) + (-.19) = -.315 .$$

The sums in row $+(9)$ are written in parentheses if the corresponding entries in the previous rows are in parentheses. It will be seen that the entries in these columns are written in parentheses after the sign change for that column. The entries in row $+(9)$ are summed and checked as before. This procedure continues until all the entries in a row are negative, zero, or positive in parentheses.

It happens occasionally, especially with a large test battery, that a test vector is reflected twice. In determining the next variable which is to be reversed, we choose either the largest positive number without parentheses or the largest negative number in parentheses, whichever has the larger absolute value. The same result is obtained if we regard the parentheses as the equivalent of a negative sign and if the rule is adopted of reversing that variable which has the largest positive value. If, according to the rule, a variable must be reversed which has previously been reversed, this can be accomplished by subtracting the corresponding row of residuals instead of adding, as in the regular procedure.

6. When all the entries in a row are zero or negative, counting parentheses as the equivalent of a negative sign, this row is denoted $B$, as shown in *Table 12*.

7. The entries in row $C$ are recorded to two decimals.

8. The weighted sum of the twelve entries in column $\Sigma$ is recorded in row $C$. Each weight is either $+1$ or $-1$. The weight is $+1$ if the variable has not been reversed, and it is $-1$ if the variable has been reversed. The weighted sum of the twelve entries in column $\Sigma$ is then $-.12$, as shown.

9. The entries in row $C$ are summed. The sum must equal the anticipated sum, which here is $-.12$. This agreement is represented by the check mark.

*The communalities*

1. In row $d$ are recorded the estimated diagonals. Each entry in row $d$ is the largest absolute value of the residuals. For example, in the second column the residual with largest absolute value is $-.24$. It is recorded in row $d$ with positive sign.

2. In row $D$ the same values are recorded with the signs indicated in row $C$. The weight, $\mu$, is $+1$ for unreflected test vectors and $-1$ for reflected vectors. The sum (.18) of row $D$ is recorded as shown.

*Calculation of factor loadings*

1. Row $E$ is the sum of entries in rows $C$ and $D$. The anticipated sum (.06) is, similarly, the sum of $\Sigma$-entries of rows $C$ and $D$. Row $E$ is summed. The fact that the sum of row $E$ is equal to the anticipated sum (.06) is indicated by the check mark.

2. The sum of the absolute values in row $E$ is 10.60, which is recorded in the small table. It will be noted that $\Sigma|E| = \Sigma\mu E$.

3. The value of $\sqrt{T}$ is next recorded in the small table.

4. The reciprocal $m$ is recorded in the next space in the small table.

5. The product $mT$ is recorded in the next space of the small table. It is recorded to two decimals. Its agreement with $\sqrt{T}$ is indicated by the check mark.

6. The factor loadings are recorded in the last row of *Table 12*. The anticipated sum, $m\Sigma E = .02$, is recorded in the check column.

7. The sum of the factor loadings (.03) is recorded in the $\Sigma$ column. The fact that these two sums agree closely, namely, .03 and .02, is indicated by a check mark in the small square.

8. The sum of the absolute values (3.27) of the factor loadings is recorded in the last space of the small table. The fact that this sum agrees closely with $mT$ is indicated by a check mark in the small square.

The same routine is followed in computing the second-factor residuals, which are shown in *Table 13*. The third-factor residuals are shown in *Table 14*. These residuals are too small to justify further factoring.

The factor loadings are assembled in the factor matrix $F$ of *Table 15*. The fourth column of this matrix shows the communalities as determined by the centroid method, with successive adjustment in the diagonal cells. The last column of this table shows the true communalities, which are consistent with the side correlations of the given correlation matrix, which is of rank 3.

When the true communalities are known, as in the present fictitious example, the same data sheets can be used for the centroid method in such a way that the third-factor residuals vanish identically. The obtained communalities are then exactly equal to the true communalities. The procedure is then to record the true communalities in row $d$ of *Table 11*. In computing the residuals for *Table 12* the communalities are treated in the same way as

## Table 13

| +a | b = -a / Test | - .45 / 1 | .49 / 2 | - .21 / 3 | - .02 / 4 | - .22 / 5 | .31 / 6 | .31 / 7 | - .32 / 8 | .40 / 9 | - .41 / 10 | .11 / 11 | - .02 / 12 | - v = - .03 / Σ | Ch |
|---|---|---|---|---|---|---|---|---|---|---|---|---|---|---|---|
| .45 | 1 | - .02 | - .02 | - .07 | - .03 | .07 | .03 | .03 | - .01 | - .01 | .06 | .04 | - .06 | - .03 | ✓ |
| .49 | 2 | - .07 | .00 | .00 | .01 | .01 | .00 | .00 | .01 | .00 | .06 | .00 | .01 | - .02 | ✓ |
| - .21 | 3 | - .03 | .01 | .03 | .03 | - .07 | .04 | .02 | .01 | .01 | .04 | .03 | .06 | .08 | ✓ |
| - .02 | 4 | - .07 | .00 | .07 | .02 | .02 | .02 | .03 | .00 | .01 | .01 | .01 | .02 | .01 | ✓ |
| - .22 | 5 | - .03 | .01 | .04 | .00 | .01 | .01 | .02 | .02 | .00 | .00 | .01 | .04 | - .04 | ✓ |
| - .31 | 6 | - .03 | .00 | .02 | .00 | .03 | .00 | .03 | .00 | .00 | .02 | .00 | .03 | .04 | ✓ |
| - .31 | 7 | - .01 | .00 | .02 | .01 | .01 | .02 | .02 | .02 | .00 | .02 | .00 | .01 | .01 | ✓ |
| - .32 | 8 | - .01 | .00 | .00 | .02 | .03 | .00 | .00 | .02 | .01 | .02 | .00 | .01 | .03 | ✓ |
| .40 | 9 | - .03 | .00 | .00 | .00 | .01 | .00 | .02 | .00 | .00 | .02 | .00 | .01 | .00 | ✓ |
| - .41 | 10 | - .01 | .00 | .04 | .01 | .02 | .01 | .01 | .00 | .00 | .03 | .02 | .03 | .02 | ✓ |
| .11 | 11 | - .06 | .00 | .03 | .01 | .02 | .03 | .01 | .01 | .02 | .00 | .02 | - .03 | .00 | ✓ |
| - .02 | 12 | - .06 | .01 | .06 | .02 | .04 | .03 | .01 | .01 | .01 | .03 | .02 | .02 | .02 | ✓ |

.03 = v = Σa

| | - .45 / 1 | .49 / 2 | - .21 / 3 | - .02 / 4 | - .22 / 5 | .31 / 6 | .31 / 7 | - .32 / 8 | .40 / 9 | - .41 / 10 | .11 / 11 | - .02 / 12 | Σ |
|---|---|---|---|---|---|---|---|---|---|---|---|---|---|
| s + vb + b² = Ch | - .04 | .01 | - .08 | .00 | - .03 | .02 | .02 | .00 | .02 | .00 | .01 | - .03 | - .10 |
| Σr = s | - .03 | .02 | - .08 | .01 | - .02 | .04 | .04 | .00 | .03 | .00 | .00 | - .02 | - .02 |
| - ½s = A | - .015 | - .010 | (.040) | - .005 | - .010 | .020 | .020 | - .005 | - .015 | .000 | .010 | .010 | - .010 |
| +(3) | - .055 | .000 | (.100) | .025 | - .060 | .020 | .040 | .015 | - .005 | .040 | .040 | .070 | - .090 |
| +(12) | - .115 | - .010 | (.140) | .045 | - .110 | .050 | .050 | .045 | - .005 | .070 | .060 | .100 | - .110 |
| +(6) | - .145 | .000 | (.170) | (.065) | - .130 | (.050) | .070 | (.045) | .005 | .070 | .070 | (.120) | - .070 |
| +(4) | - .175 | .010 | (.190) | (.065) | - .160 | (.070) | .070 | (.045) | .015 | .090 | .080 | (.130) | - .060 |
| +(8) | - .185 | (.020) | (.190) | (.075) | - .150 | (.090) | .070 | (.055) | (.015) | .110 | .080 | (.140) | - .050 |
| +(2) | - .205 | (.020) | (.190) | (.085) | - .140 | (.090) | .070 | (.065) | (.015) | .110 | .080 | (.150) | - .030 |
| B + (9) | - .215 | (.020) | (.190) | .17 | .28 | .18 | .14 | .13 | .03 | .11 | .08 | .30 | - .000 |
| - 2B = C | .43 | .04 | .38 | .03 | .07 | .04 | .03 | .03 | .01 | .22 | .16 | .06 | .53 |
| ud = D   d | .07 | .02 | .07 | .03 | .07 | .04 | .03 | .03 | .01 | .06 | .04 | .06 | - .01 |
| C + D = E | .50 | .06 | .45 | .20 | .35 | .22 | .17 | .16 | .04 | .28 | .20 | .36 | - .01 |
| mE = $a_i$ | .29 | .03 | .26 | .12 | .20 | .13 | .10 | .09 | .02 | .16 | .12 | .21 | - .01 |

$$- .11 = \frac{\Sigma s - v^2 + \Sigma b^2}{\div \Sigma Ch} \ (\checkmark) = \Sigma r \ (\checkmark)$$

$$T = \Sigma |E| = 2.99$$
$$1/\sqrt{T} = m = .578315 \qquad \sqrt{T} = 1.729162$$
$$mT = m = 1.73 = \sqrt{T} \ (\checkmark)$$
$$\Sigma |a| = 1.73 = mT \ (\checkmark)$$

$$.01 = m\Sigma E = \Sigma a \ (\checkmark)$$

168

Table 14

| b = −a | | −.29 | .03 | .26 | .12 | −.20 | .13 | −.10 | .09 | .02 | −.16 | −.12 | .21 | −v = −.01 | |
|---|---|---|---|---|---|---|---|---|---|---|---|---|---|---|---|
| +a | Test | 1 | 2 | 3 | 4 | 5 | 6 | 7 | 8 | 9 | 10 | 11 | 12 | Σ | Ch |
| .29 | 1 | −.01 | −.01 | .01 | .00 | .01 | .01 | .00 | .02 | .00 | .01 | .01 | .00 | .06 | ˅ |
| −.03 | 2 | −.01 | −.01 | −.01 | .01 | .02 | .00 | .00 | .01 | .00 | .00 | .00 | .00 | .02 | ˅ |
| .26 | 3 | .00 | −.01 | .00 | .00 | .02 | .01 | .01 | .00 | −.01 | .00 | .00 | .01 | .00 | ˅ |
| −.12 | 4 | .01 | .01 | −.02 | .00 | .00 | .02 | .01 | −.01 | .01 | .02 | .00 | −.01 | .01 | ˅ |
| .20 | 5 | .01 | .02 | .01 | .01 | .02 | −.01 | .01 | −.01 | .01 | .02 | .01 | .00 | .02 | ˅ |
| −.13 | 6 | .01 | .00 | .00 | .01 | .01 | .00 | .01 | .01 | .00 | .00 | .01 | −.01 | .07 | ˅ |
| −.10 | 7 | .02 | .01 | −.01 | .01 | .01 | .02 | −.00 | .01 | .01 | .01 | .00 | .01 | .14 | ˅ |
| −.09 | 8 | .00 | .00 | .00 | .01 | −.01 | −.00 | .00 | −.01 | .00 | −.01 | .00 | −.01 | .03 | ˅ |
| −.02 | 9 | .01 | .00 | .01 | .00 | .02 | −.01 | .00 | .01 | .00 | .00 | .01 | −.01 | .03 | ˅ |
| .16 | 10 | .00 | .00 | .00 | .00 | .00 | .01 | .00 | −.01 | .00 | .00 | .00 | .00 | .00 | ˅ |
| .12 | 11 | .01 | .00 | .01 | .00 | .00 | .01 | .01 | −.01 | .01 | .00 | .01 | .01 | .04 | ˅ |
| −.21 | 12 | .00 | .00 | .01 | −.01 | .00 | .01 | .01 | −.01 | .01 | .00 | .01 | −.01 | .02 | ˅ |

.01 = v = Σa

| s + vb + b² = Ch / Σr = s | .05 / .06 | .02 / .02 | −.01 / .00 | .03 / .01 | .02 / .02 | .06 / .07 | .05 / .04 | .02 / .03 | .03 / .03 | .02 / .00 | .03 / .02 | .03 / .02 | .35 / .34 | .35 |

$$.35 = \Sigma s - v^2 + \Sigma b^2$$
$$\doteq \Sigma Ch \; (\surd) \doteq \Sigma\Sigma r \; (\surd)$$

169

the correlation coefficients. The residual communalities are then recorded in row $d$ of *Table 12* without any adjustment. When this procedure is followed, the third-factor residuals vanish identically, including the communality residuals, and the obtained communalities are equal to the true communalities. This procedure would be used with experimental data except for the fact that the true communalities are unknown and hence must be estimated. In dealing with experimental data the residual communalities are adjusted after each factor has been extracted in the manner which has been described. The computer may prefer some other method of adjusting

*Table 15*

| | I | II | III | Obtained Values $h_j^2$ | True Values $h_j^2$ |
|---|---|---|---|---|---|
| 1 | .59 | .45 | .29 | .6347 | .70 |
| 2 | .70 | −.49 | −.03 | .7310 | .74 |
| 3 | .80 | .21 | −.26 | .7517 | .77 |
| 4 | .90 | .02 | −.12 | .8248 | .82 |
| 5 | .80 | .22 | .20 | .7284 | .72 |
| 6 | .80 | −.31 | −.13 | .7530 | .74 |
| 7 | .80 | −.31 | .10 | .7461 | .74 |
| 8 | .80 | .32 | −.09 | .7505 | .74 |
| 9 | .70 | −.40 | −.02 | .6504 | .65 |
| 10 | .70 | .41 | .16 | .6837 | .66 |
| 11 | .90 | −.11 | .12 | .8365 | .83 |
| 12 | .90 | .02 | −.21 | .8545 | .85 |
| Σ | 9.39 | .03 | .01 | | |

the estimate of the communalities for each residual table by using one of the estimation formulae in *chapter xiii.*

## A multiple group method of factoring the correlation matrix

Most of the methods of factoring the correlation matrix require the calculation of residuals after each factor has been extracted. This is perhaps the most laborious part of factoring. The method to be described here avoids the computation of residuals after each factor has been computed. Since the method turns on the selection of groups of test vectors, it will be called *a multiple group method of factoring.* * The method can be used for extracting one factor at a time if that is desired; but it will be considered here for the more interesting case in which several groups of tests are selected from the correlation matrix at the start. The result of this method of factoring is a factor matrix $F$ which satisfies the fundamental relation $FF' = R$.

The multiple group method of factoring is general, in that it can be used

* L. L. Thurstone, "A Multiple Group Method of Factoring the Correlation Matrix," *Psychometrika*, X (June, 1945), 73–78.

on a correlation matrix of any rank, any order, and any configuration of test vectors, and the method is successful for any arbitrary grouping of the tests, provided that the several groups of tests are linearly independent.* This method of factoring has a limitation, in that the communalities are assumed to be known at the start. This is not a serious hardship, because the factoring can be repeated with the communalities that are found in the first trial and the convergence toward the correct communalities can be expected to be rapid.

This method of factoring is based on the well-known principle that a common-factor space of $r$ dimensions is spanned by any set of $r$ linearly independent vectors in that space. The group centroid vectors are used for this purpose.

The method of selecting the groups of tests is not crucial for the multiple group method of factoring, since the only requirement is that the centroid vectors for the several groups shall be linearly independent. This condition is nearly always satisfied without taking any special precautions about it. With experimental data it would be a rare case in which this condition would not be satisfied. If, by chance, the centroid vectors for the several groups should happen to be linearly dependent, then this fact would become apparent in a later step of the calculations in which an inverse is computed.

In selecting the several groups of tests for the purpose of factoring, the computer will naturally put together the tests that have high intercorrelations. He will select, for each group, those tests which are nearly collinear, if such groups can be found in the correlation matrix. If such groups are not readily seen by inspection, then the grouping can be carried out by some other routine. One such routine is as follows: Select, as the first pivot, a test which has one or more significant correlations and which also has an appreciable number of low coefficients, if these can be found. Arrange as a group those tests that have significant correlations with the first pivot test, either positive or negative. Retain, as the first group, those tests which, by reflection if necessary, produce a subgroup in which all correlations are positive or zero. Choose the next pivot test from the remaining tests in the same manner. Proceed in this way until all the tests with significant correlations are represented in the several groups. The grouping of the tests can

---

* Holzinger has described a factoring method which anticipated the first two parts of the multiple group method of factoring, namely, the computation of an oblique factor matrix $V$ by summations and the computation of the correlations between the group centroid axes ("A Simple Method of Factor Analysis," *Psychometrika*, Vol. IX [December, 1944]). The multiple group method adds a third step, namely, the computation of an orthogonal factor matrix $F$, which is the starting-point for the rotational problem. In describing his factoring method, Holzinger limits the method to correlation matrices which can be divided into sections of unit rank. However, his method is general, and it can be used on correlation matrices of any order, rank, and configuration. His method is algebraically equivalent to the first two steps in the multiple group method.

# Table 16

## Correlation Matrix $R_{jk}$

|   | 1 | 2 | 3 | 4 | 5 | 6 | 7 | 8 |
|---|------|------|------|------|------|------|------|------|
| 1 | .64 | .48 | .16 | −.16 | −.32 | .48 | .00 | .32 |
| 2 | .48 | .72 | .66 | .42 | .12 | .72 | −.48 | .00 |
| 3 | .16 | .66 | .85 | .77 | .46 | .66 | −.72 | −.28 |
| 4 | −.16 | .42 | .77 | .85 | .62 | .42 | −.72 | −.44 |
| 5 | −.32 | .12 | .46 | .62 | .52 | .12 | −.48 | −.40 |
| 6 | .48 | .72 | .66 | .42 | .12 | .72 | −.48 | .00 |
| 7 | .00 | −.48 | −.72 | −.72 | −.48 | −.48 | .64 | .32 |
| 8 | .32 | .00 | −.28 | −.44 | −.40 | .00 | .32 | .32 |

## Matrix S

|       | 1 | 2 | 3 | 4 | 5 | 6 | 7 | 8 |
|-------|-----|------|------|------|------|-------|-------|------|
| $S_1$ | .64 | .00 | −.56 | −.88 | −.80 | .00 | .64 | .64 |
| $S_2$ | .00 | 1.20 | 1.80 | 1.80 | 1.20 | −1.20 | −1.60 | −.80 |

## Oblique Factor Matrix V'

|       | 1 | 2 | 3 | 4 | 5 | 6 | 7 | 8 |
|-------|-------|-------|--------|--------|--------|-------|--------|--------|
| $p_1$ | .5657 | .0000 | −.4950 | −.7778 | −.7071 | .0000 | .5657 | .5657 |
| $p_2$ | .0000 | .6000 | .9000 | .9000 | .6000 | .6000 | −.8000 | −.4000 |

Group 1 = Tests 1, 2, 6, 7
Group 2 = Tests 3, 4, 5, 8

## Factor Matrix F

|   | I | II |
|---|--------|--------|
| 1 | .5657 | .5657 |
| 2 | .0000 | .8485 |
| 3 | −.4950 | .7778 |
| 4 | −.7778 | .4950 |
| 5 | −.7071 | −.1414 |
| 6 | .0000 | .8485 |
| 7 | .5657 | −.5657 |
| 8 | .5657 | .0000 |

$W_1 = .883883$
$W_2 = .500000$

### Matrix T

$$\begin{matrix} 1.28 & −1.60 \\ −1.60 & 4.00 \end{matrix}$$

### Matrix U

$$\begin{matrix} 1.1314 & −1.4142 \\ −.8000 & 2.0000 \end{matrix}$$

$$\begin{matrix} 1.0000 & −.7071 \\ −.7071 & 1.0000 \end{matrix} = R_{pq} = F_{pm}F'_{pm}$$

$$\begin{matrix} 1.0000 & .0000 \\ −.7071 & .7071 \end{matrix} = F_{pm} = \Lambda_{mp}$$

$$\begin{matrix} 1.0000 & 1.0000 \\ .0000 & 1.4142 \end{matrix} = (F'_{pm})^{-1} = \Lambda^{-1}_{mp}$$

be carried out in any one of several ways for the multiple group method of factoring.

In *Table 16* we have a numerical example which illustrates the multiple group method. The given correlation matrix has eight variables with intercorrelations as shown. The communalities were known in this case. With experimental data the communalities must be estimated. In the present example, the grouping of the tests was quite arbitrary, with little reference to the correlations. Tests 1, 2, 6, and 7 were placed in group 1, and tests 3, 4, 5, and 8 were placed in group 2. Only two groups were used in this example. The natural procedure is to group the tests into correlated clusters as far as possible. The multiple group method is not dependent on the grouping, and hence the groups were selected arbitrarily for this numerical example.

In row $S_1$ we have the sums of columns for rows 1, 2, 6, and 7. In row $S_2$ we have the corresponding sums for rows 3, 4, 5, and 8. The correlation matrix has now been augmented by two rows, but the rank is unchanged because these two rows are linear combinations of the given eight rows. If two similar columns were added to the right of the correlation matrix, we should have an augmented correlation matrix of the same rank. This has not been done in *Table 16* because it would simply be the transpose of the two rows of matrix $S$, which are already computed and recorded in the table.

The sum of the corresponding entries in each row of the matrix $S$ are then computed and recorded, as shown in matrix $T$. For example, the entry 1.28 is the sum of columns 1, 2, 6, and 7, of the first row of $S$. The other sums are computed in the same manner. The square matrix $T$ is of order $2 \times 2$, and it represents the lower right corner of the augmented correlation matrix in which the rank is unaltered.

The next step is to compute the reciprocals of the square roots of the diagonal elements of the matrix $T$. These are the weights $w_1$ and $w_2$, which are shown to the right of the matrix $T$.

The matrix $V'$ is computed by applying the weight $w_1$ to the first row of $S$, and the weight $w_2$ to the second row of $S$. Similarly, the same weights on the rows of $T$ give the square matrix $U$, as shown. The matrices $V'$ and $U$ may be thought of as two rows by which the correlation matrix could be augmented instead of the rows of $S$ and $T$. The matrix $U$ would then be the lower right corner of the augmented correlation matrix, in which the rank is still unaltered.

The two weights, $w_1$ and $w_2$, are applied to the columns of the matrix $U$, and we then have the matrix $R_{pq}$ with unit diagonals. The calculations are in part checked by the unit diagonals of this matrix. This matrix shows the cosine of the angular separation of the two unit reference vectors that have been chosen. Each one of them contains the centroid of a group of test vectors.

If we write the transpose of the matrix $V'$, we have an oblique factor matrix $V$, as in previous methods of rotation from the orthogonal factor matrix $F$, but we have obtained here the oblique matrix directly and without computing the orthogonal factor matrix $F$, which is usually obtained first by the various factoring methods.

Since we have here an oblique factor matrix $V$, as well as the cosines of the angular separations of the unit reference vectors for the factor matrix $V$, we can determine the transformation which should carry the oblique factor matrix $V$ into an orthogonal factor matrix $F$. Since the location of an orthogonal frame in the system defined by $V$ and $U$ is not unique, we must first define in some convenient way the location of the desired orthogonal reference axes of $F$. We shall do this by locating the first of the orthogonal references axes collinear with the first of the oblique axes. Then the first column of $F$ will be the same as the first column of $V$. The next orthogonal reference axis will be located in the plane of the first two oblique axes and orthogonal to the first one. This process is, in fact, the diagonal method of factoring applied to the correlation matrix $R_{pq}$. When this is carried out routinely, we have the factor matrix $F_{pm}$, in which the two oblique reference axes $p$ are defined in the orthogonal frame $m$.

The inverse of the transpose of this matrix gives $\Lambda_{mp}^{-1} = (F'_{pm})^{-1}$. We can now write the transformation by which the orthogonal factor matrix $F$ can be written for the whole test battery. The matrix $F_{pm}$ then is the additional two rows of $F$ which describe the oblique reference axes $p$. This transformation is

$$(19) \qquad\qquad V\Lambda^{-1} = F ,$$

from which we have

$$(20) \qquad\qquad F\Lambda = V ,$$

where $\Lambda$ is already numerically given.

Applying this transformation to the matrix $V$ by equation (19), we obtain the factor matrix $F$, which is shown in the upper right corner of *Table 16.*

When this factor matrix has been written, a residual table can be computed for the two factors, to determine whether additional factors need to be extracted. In the present example, which is exact, the residuals vanish identically. In a practical problem with experimental data, the residual table should be computed and inspected to determine whether additional factors should be extracted. If that is desirable, one proceeds with the residual table as with the original correlation matrix in the present example. Groups are then listed from the residual correlation matrix until the tests with significant residuals seem to be represented. The process is repeated so as to add one or more columns to the factor matrix $F$.

In the present case we have one set of residuals to compute for the entire factor matrix $F$ instead of several sets of residuals, as would have been required in most of the current methods of factoring the correlation matrix. It will also be seen that the order of the inverse to be computed is equal to that of the number of factors determined by this process. For example, if seven factors are to be determined and if the process starts with seven linearly independent clusters, then there is an inverse of order $7 \times 7$ to be computed. If the factoring proceeds with, say, only four groups, then there is an inverse of order $4 \times 4$ to be computed, and the fourth factor residuals should then reveal three additional groups, resulting in three columns to be added to the factor matrix $F$. The computational labor is probably minimized by finding as many groups in the given correlation matrix as there are common-factor dimensions, so that only one table of correlational residuals needs to be computed. However, if the first estimate of the number of clusters is too small, one merely repeats the process until the residuals vanish. If the factoring is done in several steps, the inverses are, of course, of smaller order.

The grouping was chosen quite arbitrarily in this example in order to illustrate in a numerical example that the multiple group method of factoring is independent of the method of grouping the variables. The only requirement is that the centroid vectors of the several groups must be linearly independent.

It is not necessary to select the same number of tests in each group, but there should be at least three or four tests in each group. This requirement is associated with the separation of the common factors from the unique factors. A limiting case is that in which each group contains only one test. The multiple group method then degenerates into the diagonal method of factoring.* The multiple group method is not quite foolproof. A computer might assemble a group of tests whose sum would give a null vector. It would then be necessary merely to alter the grouping.

* L. L. Thurstone, *Theory of Multiple Factors* (Ann Arbor, Mich.: Edwards Bros., January, 1933), pp. 13–16.

# CHAPTER IX

## CONFIGURATIONS AND FACTOR PATTERNS

### Interpretation of factorial structure

We have seen that every correlation matrix implies a configuration of test vectors and that the number of dimensions of the configuration is the rank of the correlation matrix. It has also been shown that a reference frame must be inserted in the configuration before a factor matrix can be written. The combination of the configuration and the reference frame is called a "structure." The problem to be considered now is how to locate the reference axes in relation to the configuration so as to give the most plausible interpretation for the reference frame. All students of the multiple-factor problem agree that the reference axes should be placed in some relation to the configuration, but they differ on the criteria by which this should be accomplished. These differences, which are the subject of considerable controversy, are due principally to the different purposes of factor analysis which the several writers have had in mind. What is correct and acceptable for one purpose may be irrelevant for another purpose.

At the outset of a factor analysis, the investigator must decide whether he will write a factor matrix to account for the complete variance of each test or only the common-factor variance. His choice will depend on his purpose. If he decides to account factorially for the complete variance of each test, then he writes unity in the diagonal cells of the correlation matrix. The several methods of factoring are applicable in this case, just as well as in the case where communalities are inserted in the diagonal cells. The factor matrix will then represent a set of $n$ unit test vectors, which define the *total test space*. This is a subspace of the *total factor space*, which involves, in general, $(n+r)$ factors or dimensions. The configuration will not involve any more dimensions or factors than there are tests in the battery, and it will reproduce the intercorrelations exactly, as well as the diagonal unit self-correlations. If the object is merely to write a factor matrix which reproduces the correlations, then the task is easily done by any one of several factoring methods. The reservation about this solution is that it is difficult to identify the factors, common and unique, from such a factor matrix; but that may not be the purpose of the investigator who proceeds in this way.

If the purpose of a factorial analysis is to identify the functions or parameters that produce the intercorrelations, then the problem can sometimes be solved by limiting the analysis to the common factors which are determined by the reduced correlation matrix. If this is the purpose of the analysis, the communalities are inserted in the diagonal cells of the correlation matrix. If there is reason to suspect that there is no unique variance in the measurements, then unity can be used in the diagonal; but such situations are rare in those fields in which factor analysis is likely to be most useful. With the communalities in the diagonal, we have the possibility that the number of common factors is considerably less than the number of measurements, so that the problem becomes soluble, at least as far as the number of unknown common factors is concerned.

The purpose of a factor analysis also determines how the data are to be treated, even after a decision has been made concerning the self-correlations. The two conflicting purposes that are largely responsible for controversy in this field are (1) the statistical condensation of the correlations into a factor matrix with maximum effectiveness and (2) the interpretation of the factors which represent distinguishable functions or parameters. Ever since multiple-factor analysis was introduced, it has been known that these variant solutions are mathematically equivalent. The debate is concerned with the choice of reference frame for the factor matrix, which is the end-product of the computational work and the starting-point for interpretation. These two purposes may overlap when an investigator tries to accomplish both the maximum statistical condensation of the correlation coefficients into a factor matrix and also a physical interpretation of the factors as representing fundamental concepts or functions. Some students of factor analysis deny that meaningful factors exist in psychological measurements or performances, at least when they are revealed factorially. In other contexts the same authors speak confidently about "auditory acuity," "mechanical aptitude," "fluency," "visualizing," and many other components of abilities and disabilities; but, when these same functions appear in a factor analysis, they promptly discard the psychological interpretations as foolish. For such authors an attempt factorially to identify abilities is supposed to be a forbidden faculty psychology.

### Statistical criteria for the reference frame

If the principal purpose of a factorial study is to condense the intercorrelations into a factor matrix with a set of numbers that will account for the correlations, then we have a legitimate statistical problem that can be solved. In general, the factorial solution would be considered the more successful, the smaller the number of factors that account for the correlations with negligible residuals. The statistical condensation is judged to be successful if the number of independent parameters in the factor matrix is very much smaller than the number of independent correlation coefficients. By the usual statistical considerations the most acceptable factor matrix would then represent a reference frame that is called the *principal axes* of the configuration of test vectors. It is located by a *maximum variance criterion*. Some of the characteristics of the principal-axes solution will be mentioned here. The first axis is so placed in the configuration that the sum of the squares of the projections of the test vectors on the first axis is maximized. There usually exists a unique solution for a given test battery. When the first axis is so placed, the first-factor products account for more of the variances of the $n$ tests than can be accounted for by any other axis in the configuration. When the same criterion is applied to the first-factor residual coefficients, the second principal axis is so placed that it accounts for more of the residuals than any other axis in the residual configuration. The first two factors, then, account for more of the test variances than any other pair of axes in the test configuration. For any given number of factors so extracted from the correlation matrix, the residuals are minimized. This is an interesting and important feature of the principal axes of a test configuration. This reasoning may be applied to a correlation matrix with unity or with communalities in the diagonal cells.

When the correlation matrix is large, say forty or fifty tests, the principal-axes solution is quite laborious, and it is usually advisable to make some compromise. Another statistical principle that can be used for locating the reference frame is to place the first axis through the centroid of the termini of the test vectors for the whole battery. This axis is usually nearly the same as the first principal axis when the correlation matrix has coefficients that are all positive or zero. This type of solution can also be made either for the total test space or for the common-factor space. With some modifications, the subsequent axes can be placed so as to accomplish essentially the same purpose for the residual coefficients after the extraction of each factor. This principle does not lead to a unique solution for any given test battery. Its purpose is essentially similar to that of the principal-axes solution, in that one attempts to account for as much as possible of the test variances by each successive factor; but the centroid solution is not unique for any given test battery, and the solution does not have the interesting mathematical properties of the principal-axes solution. The centroid method of factoring and the centroid solution for the location of the reference axes are to be regarded as a computational compromise, in that they have been found to involve much less labor than the principal-axes solution. The residuals after the extraction of a given number of factors are somewhat larger than the residuals remaining after the same number of factors determined by the principal axes.

The two principles that have been described for locating the reference frame are both dependent on the whole configuration. Each successive factor is determined by some criterion that is applied to the whole test configuration. These criteria we have called "statistical" in contrast with the configurational criteria for locating the reference frame which depend on the nature of the test configuration as determined by its distinguishable parts.

When we apply statistical criteria for locating the reference frame, our principal interest is in the size of the residuals, which are made as small as possible. Less interest is then ordinarily given to the factor loadings themselves, although some writers make attempts to interpret the factorial axes located by these criteria. When the successive factorial axes have been located with the purpose of minimizing the residuals, the factor loadings are regarded more or less as regression coefficients, whose principal usefulness is that they account for the dependent variable with the smallest possible residuals. In most cases when a regression equation is written the principal concern is to predict the dependent variable with the smallest possible error, and little attention is then given to the interpretation of the regression coefficients themselves. They serve ordinarily as a set of useful, but otherwise meaningless, numbers that do predict the dependent variable. In factor analysis we have no differentiation between independent and dependent variables, but we can apply statistical criteria to ascertain whether the several factors do account for the intercorrelations with minimum residuals. If this is the principal purpose of a factorial study, then it seems reasonable to expect the writer to show that he gains something which is not available in the classical statistical methods involving multiple correlation and regression equations.

The statistical and the configurational criteria for locating a reference frame in the configuration of test vectors can be combined in what seems to be the ideal factorial study. If we disregard computational labor, which may be reduced by improvements in computational methods, the ideal solution for a factor problem seems to be, first, to determine a set of $r$ factors for the given correlation matrix which are so determined that the $r$th residual coefficients satisfy two requirements, namely, (1) that the residuals are the smallest possible for $r$ orthogonal factors and (2) that they are small enough to be ignored. This implies the first $r$ principal axes of the test configuration. When the solution has arrived at this point, we can be certain that the $r$ factors account for more of the common-factor variances than can be accounted for by any other set of $r$ orthogonal factors. The factoring should be made with communalities in the diagonal cells of the correlation matrix. The next step in the solution is to find a reference frame in the $r$-dimensional configuration which will represent the distinguishable functions or parameters of the tests and their correlations. When such a reference frame can be found, it represents primary factors in the test variances. There is no guarantee beforehand that such a reference frame can be found. If the test battery is a hodgepodge of complex tests, there may not exist in the configuration any clues as to what the underlying functions may be; but this possibility is dependent on the intuitions of the experimenter in assembling a significant set of measurements rather than on factorial theory and method as such.

In this text it is assumed that the principal purpose of factor analysis is to identify one or more underlying factors, functional unities, or parameters that produce the differential performances or other individual differences, even if the discovery of such a factor or factors should account for only a part of the test variances in any particular test battery, leaving considerable parts of the variances still unaccounted for and to be identified by future investigation.

If it should be found, for example, that the ability for serial learning is distinct from the ability to memorize paired associates, then such a finding would be an important addition to our knowledge about the faculty or faculties of memory, even if the serial-learning factor should account for only a part of the variances of the memory tests involved. If it should be found that serial learning and paired associates do not separate factorially, then we should conclude that, as far as we can ascertain now, these two forms of recall are mediated by the same cortical functions. The question of whether these factors account for all, or only a part, of the variances of the particular tests that we happen to use is, then, a secondary matter for the scientific problem. At the same time, we should regard any unknown residual variance as a challenge to further exploration either by factorial or by other experimental means.

The parameters or functions in terms of which a domain is described are probably never unique, and this corresponds to the fact that no one has ever demonstrated any factorial description to be unique. The best that can be said for any factorial description of a domain is that it reveals some aspects of an underlying order; but, in so far as this is successfully done, it is likely to reveal alternative sets of parameters or functions that might be chosen for the scientific description. In the simple two-dimensional example of the cylinders in *chapter ii*, this lack of uniqueness of the factorial resolution is easily seen, but it does not invalidate either of the factorial descriptions. The choice of fundamental axes would depend on the context, but it will be seen in the higher-dimensional problems that the common practice of taking a central or average factor for all the measurements in any particular factorial experiment as one of the basic parameters for the domain tends usually to blur rather than to clarify the underlying order. The lack of uniqueness of factorial resolutions is in agreement with the principle that a scientific hypothesis can never be demonstrated to be correct; it can only be shown to be plausible for the data at hand or inconsistent with them.

In the development of multiple-factor analysis one naturally raises the question as to whether the object is to account factorially for the original raw test scores or the intercorrelations. These two objectives are not the same. One might reproduce the intercorrelations with communalities by a factor matrix which would not enable us to reproduce the raw scores. Sometimes this question is discussed as an issue in which we might make a choice. To analyze a set of raw scores so that they are reproduced factorially involves more factors than can be solved for by present methods. Limiting the analysis to the common factors sometimes makes the problem soluble. By identifying one factor at a time and by building new test batteries for the exploration of unknown factors, we hope eventually to know enough about the factors involved so that the actual test performances themselves may be accounted for to an acceptable degree of approximation. That is the ultimate objective. Limiting ourselves to the common factors in each study is a means of eventually attaining the interpretation of the individual test performances.

Considering factor analysis as a scientific method rather than as an efficient method of statistical condensation, we shall discuss different types of factors, configurations, and factor patterns to determine how they may be used in the discovery of an underlying order in the complexities of human traits or in other fields, where basic concepts may be formulated in terms of exploratory factorial investigation.

### Simple structure

One of the turning-points in the solution of the multiple-factor problem is the concept of "simple structure." It will be shown that this concept enables us to obtain an invariance of factorial description that has not, so far, been available by other means. The combination of a test configuration and the co-ordinate axes is called a *structure*. The co-ordinate axes determine the co-ordinate planes. If each test vector is in one or more of the co-ordinate planes, then the combination of the configuration and the co-ordinate axes is called a *simple structure*. The corresponding factor pattern will then have one or more zero entries in each row. If a test vector lies in one of the co-ordinate planes in a three-dimensional configuration, then it can be described as a linear combination of two co-ordinate vectors, so that one of its factor loadings is zero. If a test vector lies in two of the co-ordinate planes in a three-dimensional problem, then it is collinear with one of the co-ordinate axes, and it will have two zero factor loadings. If a test vector lies in all three co-ordinate planes in a three-dimensional problem, then it is a null vector with three zero factor loadings, and it is of no scientific interest.

When a factor matrix reveals one or more zeros in each row, we can infer that each of the tests does not involve all the common factors that are required to account for the intercorrelations of the battery as a whole. This is the principal characteristic of a simple structure. A simple structure and its corresponding factor pattern reveal that the complexities of the individual tests are lower than the complexity of the battery as a whole. When a configuration reveals that the test vectors lie in restricted subspaces, such as the co-ordinate planes, and in their intersections of still lower dimensionality, this circumstance can be used for the location of a reference frame that will generally give a simpler interpretation for the individual tests than if each test is supposed to involve all the factors of the whole battery. Most of the configurations and factor patterns in the following section are examples of simple structure, in that generally the rows of the factor matrices have one or more zeros. The degrees of convincingness and overdetermination of simple structure and the algebraic relations will be discussed in separate sections.

## Types of factors

Factors are classified in several types according to the manner in which they enter into the test variances of a battery. A factor which is of a given type in one battery may be of another type when it enters into the tests of another battery. The classification refers, then, to the manner in which a factor is involved in a given test battery.

A factor which is involved in the variances of two or more tests of a battery is called a *common factor* in that battery. Our use of the term "common factor" in this text implies that the factor is determined by the side correlations. We distinguish between common factors so determined and the unique factors determined by the diagonal self-correlations. Exceptions to this use of the term will be explicitly noted.

A factor which is involved in the variance of only one test of a battery is a *unique factor* in that battery.

A common factor which is involved in the variances of all tests in a battery is a *general factor* in that battery.

A common factor which is involved in the variances of two or more, but not in all, of the tests of a battery is sometimes called a *group factor* in that battery.

A common factor which is involved in the variances of only two tests in a battery is called a *doublet*.

A common factor which is involved in the variances of only three tests in a battery is called a *triplet*.

A factor which enters into the test variances of a battery with both positive and negative signs is a *bipolar factor*.

## Types of configurations

All the configurations discussed in this section are three-dimensional. The principles illustrated here can be generalized to configurations in $n$ dimensions.

### Random configuration

In *Figure 1* we have three orthogonal axes, *I, II*, and *III*, which determine the right spherical triangle shown. The points represent normalized test vectors. The test vectors in this figure show a *random configuration*, which gives no clue as to factorial composition. Hence the cells in the corresponding factor pattern are, in general, all filled. Both positive and negative factor loadings are then found in the factor matrix. This is illustrated in factor pattern 1.

*Cone configuration*

In *Figure 2* we have a *cone configuration,* in which the normalized test vectors all lie in a cone with a 45° generating angle. The intercorrelations for a cone configuration are all positive or zero. So far, the cone configuration

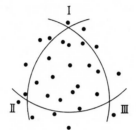

*Random Configuration*

| I | II | III |
|---|----|-----|
| × | × | × |
| × | × | × |
| × | × | × |
| × | × | × |
| × | × | × |
| × | × | × |
| × | × | × |
| × | × | × |
| × | × | × |

Factor pattern 1

FIGURE 1

has been of only theoretical interest, and it is included here to bring out the fact that, although the correlations are all positive or zero, the loadings for orthogonal factors cannot all be positive or zero. This is illustrated in the figure in which the cone configuration cannot be inclosed within the three orthogonal co-ordinate planes. If the rank of the correlation matrix is 2 or 1 and if the correlations are all positive or zero, then a factor matrix can be written in which all the loadings are positive or zero. When the rank of the correlation matrix is 3 or higher, then a positive factor matrix does not necessarily exist. However, in practice it is usually possible to write a positive factor matrix when the correlations are positive or zero because the test configuration is rarely, if ever, cone-shaped.

*Isolated constellations*

In *Figure 3* we have a set of three constellations or clusters of test vectors. In *Figure 3a* the clusters are shown at the co-ordinate axes, *I*, *II*, and *III*. When the clusters are separated by acute angles, the clusters are correlated, and the co-ordinate axes would then be oblique if they were passed through the center of each cluster. The factor matrix *3a* shows a simple structure with complexity 1 for each test; but, if the factors are correlated, this circumstance is interpreted to mean that the three factors themselves have some second-order factor in common. For example, visual and auditory acuity might be two factors in terms of which tests may be described, but these two factors might themselves be correlated by some second-order factor, such as general physical fitness or age.

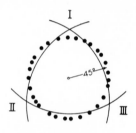

FIGURE 2

*Cone configuration*

In *Figure 3b* we have a different structure and consequently a different factor pattern for the same configuration of three clusters. Here axis *I* is placed in the middle of the configuration, and one of the clusters has been placed in the plane *I–II*. The other two clusters are then necessarily one positive on *III* and the other equally negative on *III*. One cluster is a function of only two factors, namely, *I* and *II*, while the other clusters involve all three factors. Factor pattern *3b* is not likely to reveal so much about the underlying functions as is pattern *3a*.

The isolated constellations or clusters constitute one of the most easily recognized of all the types of simple structure. It can usually be seen by inspection of the correlation matrix when such a configuration is present. The tests within a cluster have relatively high intercorrelations, while tests from different clusters have much lower intercorrelations. The differentiation of constellations was the first type of multiple-factor pattern to be investigated, and it is the simplest form of configuration, since each test then has unit complexity.

*Complete triangular configuration*

A three-dimensional configuration sometimes shows the test vectors to lie in three distinct planes, as shown in *Figures 4a* and *4b*. In the simple structure and factor pattern of *Figure 4a* there are both positive and negative factor loadings because the configuration extends beyond the triangle *I–II–III* of the three co-ordinate axes. In the simple structure of *Figure 4b* there are only positive factor loadings because the test vectors are confined to the positive right spherical triangle. The test vectors in the plane *I–II* are described as linear combinations of two factors, and the third-factor loadings are then zero. It will be noticed that all the tests in the triangular configuration have a complexity of 2, except those which lie at the corners of the configuration, which have unit complexity.

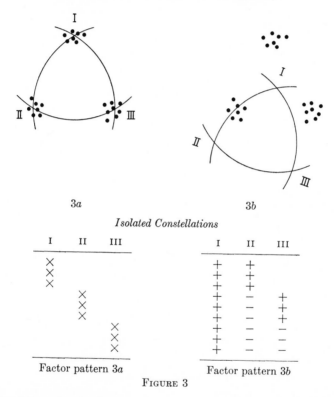

3a                              3b

*Isolated Constellations*

| I | II | III |   | I | II | III |
|---|----|-----|---|---|----|-----|
| × |    |     |   | + | + |     |
| × |    |     |   | + | + |     |
| × |    |     |   | + | + |     |
|   | ×  |     |   | + | − | + |
|   | ×  |     |   | + | − | + |
|   | ×  |     |   | + | − | + |
|   |    | ×   |   | + | − | − |
|   |    | ×   |   | + | − | − |
|   |    | ×   |   | + | − | − |

Factor pattern 3a            Factor pattern 3b

FIGURE 3

*Incomplete triangular configuration*

It does not usually happen in exploratory studies that all the co-ordinate planes are defined by the configuration. In the three-dimensional case of *Figure 5* we have a simple structure in which only two of the co-ordinate planes are defined by the configuration. These are the co-ordinate planes *I–II* and *I–III*. If the fans of test vectors in the planes *I–II* and *I–III* extend over right angles and if the dihedral angle at *I* is a right angle, the location of the three orthogonal axes as shown would be fairly convincing, even though the plane *II–III* was not defined by the configuration. In such a situation one would try to find an interpretation for the factors *II* and *III* to determine whether there is some good reason why they should not have combined in some of the tests so as also to produce a fan in the plane *II–III*. New tests might be constructed in which these two factors are involved and a new factor study made to ascertain whether the interpretation of factors *II* and *III* can be sustained by the appearance of a fan of test vectors in that plane. The present example includes only positive

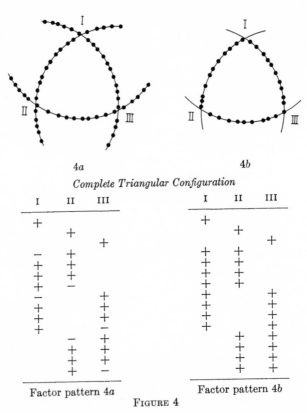

4a                 4b

*Complete Triangular Configuration*

| I | II | III | | I | II | III |
|---|----|-----|---|---|----|-----|
| + |   |   | | + |   |   |
|   | + |   | |   | + |   |
|   |   | + | |   |   | + |
| − | + |   | | + | + |   |
| + | + |   | | + | + |   |
| + | + |   | | + | + |   |
| + | − |   | | + | + |   |
| − |   | + | | + |   | + |
| + |   | + | | + |   | + |
| + |   | + | | + |   | + |
| + |   | − | | + |   | + |
|   | − | + | |   | + | + |
|   | + | + | |   | + | + |
|   | + | + | |   | + | + |
|   | + | − | |   | + | + |

Factor pattern 4a          Factor pattern 4b

FIGURE 4

factor loadings, but the same general type of reasoning can be extended to simple structure with negative factor loadings, as will be shown in other examples.

If the dihedral angle at *I* is not a right angle, the inference is made that factors *II* and *III* are probably correlated, either positively or negatively, depending on their exact locations. If the fans of test vectors from the first axis do not extend to a full right angle, as shown in *Figure 5b*, then the location of the co-ordinate plane *II–III* is indeterminate. It might be assumed to be orthogonal to *I*, or it might be placed in the oblique position *II'–III'*, as indicated by the test vectors in the two planes. But such a situation may have arisen because the test battery did not happen to contain any test measurements that were functions of *I* and *II* near *II*, or of *I* and *III* near *III*. This is a frequent type of ambiguity in the factorial resolution of test batteries. It is not profitable to insist that factorial method as such should identify the locations of *II* and *III* in the configuration if these factors are not involved either separately or in some combinations in the battery. It is better to make some interpretation of what *II* and *III* might represent

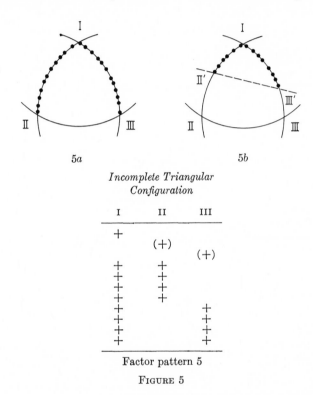

5a                              5b

*Incomplete Triangular*
*Configuration*

| I | II | III |
|---|----|-----|
| + |    |     |
|   | (+) |    |
|   |    | (+) |
| + | +  |     |
| + | +  |     |
| + | +  |     |
| + | +  |     |
| + |    | +   |
| + |    | +   |
| + |    | +   |
| + |    | +   |

Factor pattern 5

FIGURE 5

and then construct new test batteries involving these factors in the purest possible form as well as in combination. If the predicted factorial compositions are sustained by their location in a defined plane *II–III*, the hypothesis can be accepted; but, if the new tests scatter in a different manner, the hypothesis concerning the nature of *II* and *III* must be discarded. Factorial analysis then becomes a scientific method whereby proposed factorial interpretations become questions of fact to be determined experimentally.

It should be noticed that in the interpretation of factorial results we speak of a hypothesis being *sustained*. We do not say that it is proved to be correct. No matter how convincing any experiment may seem to be as regards some scientific hypothesis, it is always possible that future experiments may show us to be wrong, as the fundamental ideas of a science are modified or replaced by more embracing conceptions. What is a discovery of interest and importance in one generation becomes inadequate or even wrong in the next generation. There is little use in belaboring this limitation, which is universal for all science. These reservations will be taken for granted throughout our discussion of factor analysis as an aid in scientific exploration.

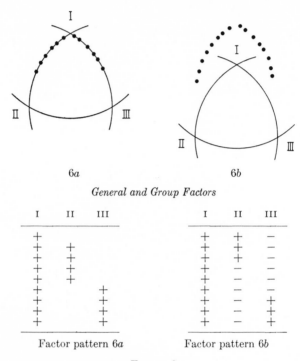

6a                              6b

*General and Group Factors*

| I | II | III |   | I | II | III |
|---|----|-----|---|---|----|-----|
| + |    |     |   | + | +  | −   |
| + | +  |     |   | + | +  | −   |
| + | +  |     |   | + | +  | −   |
| + | +  |     |   | + | −  | −   |
| + | +  |     |   | + | −  | −   |
| + |    | +   |   | + | −  | −   |
| + |    | +   |   | + | −  | +   |
| + |    | +   |   | + | −  | +   |
| + |    | +   |   | + | −  | +   |

Factor pattern 6a            Factor pattern 6b

FIGURE 6

### General and group factors

Since factor analysis was dominated for a quarter of a century by the central theme of a single general intellective factor with other factors regarded as "disturbers" of secondary importance, it is of interest to see perhaps the simplest form of general factor in a configuration. One type of configuration involving a general factor in a battery is shown in the structure of *Figure 6*. The simple structure is incomplete in that only two of the co-ordinate planes are defined by the configuration, namely, *I–II* and *I–III*. Note also that all the test vectors have positive projections on the first axis, so that the first column of the factor pattern is filled. All the correlations would be significantly positive. The rank of the correlation matrix would be 3.

The plane *II–III* is not defined by the configuration in the structure of *Figure 6a*. Some students of factor analysis prefer to locate the reference frame for a configuration of this type as shown in *Figure 6b*. They place the first axis centrally in the configuration, so as to maximize the projections of the first factor, as shown. The location of orthogonal axes *II* and *III* can then be made by one of several statistical criteria. The corresponding factor pattern is then, in general, filled as shown, the second and third factors being both bipolar. The resolution of *Figure 6a* is the simpler and more readily interpreted, but the first-factor saturations are not maximized.

When a configuration is found such as that of the two figures, *6a* and *6b*, there is some uncertainty in the interpretation of all three of the factors. The second and third factors may not exist in the absence of the first, or they may be correlated with the first factor, in which case the structure would be oblique. The first factor is defined by its presence in all tests of the battery; but it would be interpreted more clearly if we could predict with assurance the tests in which it is absent, as well as the tests in which it is present. A new factor experiment should then be made with a variety of tests, in which it is predicted that the first factor should be absent but in which one or both of the other two factors should be present. The simplest and clearest result would be to find a complete triangular structure with a group of tests in which the first factor is absent. If the predicted configuration is obtained, one has more assurance in the interpretation of the factors than if the factorial result is left as in *Figure 6*. Whatever the general factor is in a particular battery, its nature is better understood if we can predict with confidence the tests in which it is absent, as well as the tests in which it is present. Since factor analysis was for so many years primarily concerned with the single general factor and with correlation matrices of rank 1, the procedure here suggested is still avoided by some investigators, even though it is indicated when the problem is regarded from the point of view of multiple-factor analysis.

*Bipolar simple structure*

The concept of simple structure implies that the test vectors lie in the coordinate planes, or hyperplanes; but it does not imply that the factor loadings are all positive, as this concept is often misstated. By way of example, *Figure 7* has been drawn to show one bipolar factor and two positive factors, whose saturations are all positive or zero. It is factor *I*, which here is bipolar. A configuration such as that of *Figure 7* would be interpreted as showing that factor *I* combines either positively or negatively with *III* but that it combines only positively with *II*. The figure shows only one of a great variety of configurations in which positive and bipolar factors can be combined.

*Dependent composite factor*

Occasionally, but not often, it happens in analyzing experimental data that the trait vectors define a secondary plane or hyperplane, as shown at *II–A* in *Figure 8* for a three-dimensional configuration. When a secondary plane like this appears in the configuration, the interpretation is likely to be

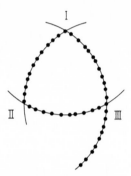

*Bipolar Simple Structure*

| I | II | III |
|---|---|---|
| + | + | |
| + | + | |
| + | + | |
| + | | + |
| + | | + |
| + | | + |
| − | | + |
| − | | + |
| − | | + |
| | + | + |
| | + | + |
| | + | + |

Factor pattern 7

FIGURE 7

of special interest. The test vectors in the secondary plane *II–A* can be described as linear combinations of *I*, *II*, and *III*, where *I* and *III* always enter into the tests in the same ratio. The configuration of the figure would mean that whenever *I* and *III* combine with *II*, then *I* and *III* enter the measurement in some fixed ratio. The test vectors in the three bounding co-ordinate planes are all linear combinations of only two of the factors. A situation like this should not be ignored when it is found in experimental data. It may be suggestive for some fundamental concepts in the domain that is being investigated.

*The factor pattern*

The factor pattern has been defined as a factor matrix in which are recorded the non-vanishing cell entries denoted $X$ and the vanishing entries which are left blank. When a differentiation is to be made between positive and negative factor loadings, the non-vanishing entries are denoted $+$ or $-$, while the vanishing entries are blank. For the interpretation of factorial results the factor pattern is sometimes of greater importance than the numerical values of the factor loadings. It is sometimes important to know about an unknown factor or function that it is present in certain tests and absent in certain others, or that it enters positively (as in a numerator) in some tests and negatively (as in a denominator) in certain other tests. In fact, it is more significant to know the factor pattern in this way than it is to know the actual numerical values of the factor loadings, because the numerical values

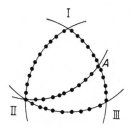

FIGURE 8

*Dependent composite factor*

are determined by such irrelevant matters as the metric, the numerical scales in terms of which the measurements were made, and the decision of the investigator to reduce the measurements to correlations or to leave them in the form of covariances. It will be shown that certain fundamental forms of invariance in factor analysis relate to the invariance of the factor pattern. Not all these forms of invariance are applicable to the numerical values of the factor loadings.

The factor pattern can be regarded in two different ways during a factor analysis. It can be set up as a hypothesis at the beginning of an analysis, and the factoring may be carried out with a specified pattern in mind, or the factor pattern can be inferred from the configuration when the factoring has been completed. Some writers postulate a pattern in which the first factor shall be positive, leaving the subsequent factors bipolar. It is probably better to factor a correlation matrix and then examine the configuration before choosing an appropriate factor pattern. The examples of this chapter serve to illustrate the relations between the configuration, the choice of reference frame, and the resulting factor pattern. The principles illustrated in these examples can be generalized to configurations in any number of dimensions.

Some of the controversy about the general factor is caused by the insistence of some writers that there must be a general factor, even if it is only an average of the test vectors in a battery whose correlations are positive or zero. In order to illustrate this situation in three dimensions, we have drawn *Figure 9*, which shows a set of test vectors in a complete triangular configuration. When these are plotted on a sphere, the location of the reference frame, as in *Figure 9a*, is compelling and convincing. Instead of placing the reference frame in relation to the configuration, some writers place the first axis at *I*, as shown in *Figure 9b*, because this location is central for the whole battery and maximizes the test vector projections. The other axes

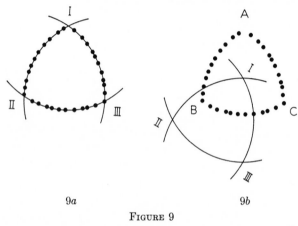

9a　　　　　　　　　　　　　　　　　　　9b

FIGURE 9

*Alternative locations of first reference axis*

are placed orthogonal to the first central or average axis, and they take positions like *II* and *III* outside the configuration so that they necessarily become bipolar. It is still possible to identify the more fundamental factors, *A*, *B*, and *C*, after a central axis has been placed in the configuration because, as is to be expected, the first-factor residuals will be largest for the tests near the corners of the triangle, and these are the tests that primarily identify the factors. One type of factorial interpretation that is rather common can be illustrated in *Figure 9b*. The third factor would have positive saturations on the tests near *B* and *C*, while it would have negative saturations on tests near *A*. Such a result is sometimes interpreted to mean that a factor such as *III* in *Figure 9b* is a "complex relationship" of some kind. If these writers could only be induced to plot their configurations and look at them, there would be less insistence on placing the first axis centrally in the configuration, and the factors would often yield to rather simple psychological interpretation instead of appearing as incongruous bipolarities. The factors would more often appear as understandable psychological entities or functions. When a bipolar factor appears in which the positive saturations form one or more meaningful groups and the negative saturations form other meaningful groups, of entirely different character, it is quite likely that these groups will resolve themselves in a simple manner by locating the reference frame in direct relation to the configuration in the manner that has been illustrated in these configurations and factor patterns. It must not be expected, however, that a factorial routine can be devised which is guaranteed to produce significant results by merely turning a crank according to rules.

# CHAPTER X

## ROTATION OF AXES

### Oblique axes

In previous chapters we have considered the rotation of axes in configurations that could be completely visualized on a diagram in two dimensions or on the surface of a sphere in three dimensions. In actual data the dimensionality nearly always exceeds three, so that the configuration cannot be completely visualized in a single diagram or model. The rotation of axes is then determined by two-dimensional sections, one section for each pair

*Table 1*

*A Centroid Factor Matrix* $F_0$

|  | I | II | III |
|---|---|---|---|
|  | $A$ | $B$ | $C$ |
| 1 | .659 | −.736 | .138 |
| 2 | .725 | .180 | −.656 |
| 3 | .665 | .537 | .500 |
| 4 | .869 | −.209 | −.443 |
| 5 | .834 | .182 | .508 |
| 6 | .836 | .519 | .152 |
| 7 | .856 | −.452 | −.269 |
| 8 | .848 | −.426 | .320 |
| 9 | .861 | .416 | −.299 |
| 10 | .880 | −.341 | −.354 |
| 11 | .889 | −.147 | .436 |
| 12 | .875 | .485 | −.093 |
| 13 | .667 | −.725 | .109 |
| 14 | .717 | .246 | −.619 |
| 15 | .634 | .501 | .522 |
| 16 | .936 | .257 | .165 |
| 17 | .966 | −.239 | −.083 |
| 18 | .625 | −.720 | .166 |
| 19 | .702 | .112 | −.650 |
| 20 | .664 | .536 | .488 |

of co-ordinate axes, or by three-dimensional sections of the multidimensional configuration. A four-dimensional configuration is represented by six diagrams when two-dimensional sections are used. A configuration of ten dimensions has forty-five such sections, since this is the number of pairs of co-ordinate axes.

In this chapter we shall use as an example a three-dimensional configuration with twenty test vectors. This example is used for illustrating several methods of rotating the axes, namely, (1) by plotting the normalized vec-

194

tors on a sphere, as shown in a previous chapter; (2) by two-dimensional sections, as will be shown in this chapter; and (3) by three-dimensional sections in the method of extended vectors, which will be described in *chapter xi.*

We start this problem with a factor matrix $F_0$ in which $n = 20$ and $r = 3$, as shown in *Table 1.* The columns of this matrix represent three arbitrary orthogonal axes as determined by the factoring method. These three axes are denoted $I, II, III$, and they will be referred to by the subscript $m$, as in previous chapters. These arbitrary orthogonal axes, as well as the test con-

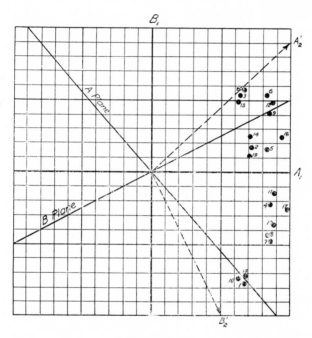

FIGURE 1

figuration, will be regarded as fixed in position, and our problem is to select by successive approximations another set of axes for which we hope to find scientific interpretation. The new set of axes will be called *reference axes,* and they will be denoted by the letters $A, B, C,$ etc., to distinguish them from the fixed orthogonal frame $I, II, III.$

In starting the rotational problem we locate the unit reference vector $A$ in the orthogonal axis $I$, the reference vector $B$ in the orthogonal axis $II$, and the reference vector $C$ in the orthogonal axis $III$. This is shown in *Table 1* and in *Figure 1.* The initial location of the reference vectors will be denoted $A_1, B_1, C_1,$ and they will be identified by the subscript $u$. Their direction cosines are shown in the matrix $\Lambda_{01}$ with elements $\lambda_{mu}$, as shown in the rectangular notation:

|   | $A_1$ | $B_1$ | $C_1$ |
|---|---|---|---|
| I | 1 |  |  |
| II |  | 1 |  |
| III |  |  | 1 |

$\Lambda_{01}$ with elements $\lambda_{mu}$

The subscripts of $\Lambda_{01}$ show that the columns of this matrix give the direction cosines of the initial locations (1) of the unit reference vectors with regard to the fixed orthogonal frame (0). The subscripts of $\lambda_{mu}$ refer to the axes of the fixed orthogonal frame $(m)$ and the given positions of the reference vectors $(u)$.

For each rotation we denote the given positions of the reference vectors $A_1$, $B_1$, and $C_1$. By inspection of the configurations in *Figures 1, 2*, and *3*, we determine the adjustments to be made in these vectors. Their new positions are denoted $A_2$, $B_2$, and $C_2$. After the first rotation the plots represent oblique axes, so that the true lengths of the vectors are not immediately evident. The adjusted vectors are therefore first determined as to their direction. They are then called *long reference vectors* and denoted $A_2'$, $B_2'$, and $C_2'$. When they have been reduced to unit length, they constitute the new *unit reference vectors*, $A_2$, $B_2$, and $C_2$. For each adjustment of the reference vectors we have, then, two steps in computation. Starting with the given unit reference vectors $A_1$, $B_1$, $C_1$, we determine, first, the long reference vectors $A_2'$, $B_2'$, $C_2'$, which give the desired directions. Second, we determine the lengths of these vectors, so that they can be reduced to the new unit reference vectors $A_2$, $B_2$, $C_2$.

The projections of the test vectors on these axes are then computed, and a new set of plots is made. By inspection of these plots the next adjustments are determined by inspection. In the computations for the second rotation the given unit reference vectors are denoted $A_1$, $B_1$, $C_1$, and their newly adjusted positions are denoted $A_2$, $B_2$, $C_2$. In this manner we avoid the use of numerically large subscripts, say 10 or 15, for as many rotations. For each rotation of the reference axes, the given positions are indicated by the subscript 1 and the new positions by the subscript 2.

The given reference vectors will be indicated by the subscript $u$. The new long reference vectors for each rotation will be indicated by the subscript $r$, and the new unit reference vectors by the subscripts $p$ and $q$.

In *Figure 1* we have plotted the first two columns, and each point is labeled with the number of the corresponding test vector. The points in this figure show the configuration of test vector termini as they would appear when seen along a line of regard orthogonal to the plane of $A_1B_1$. The two axes $A_1$ and $B_1$ are in the plane of the diagram. If the axis $A_1$ is moved in the plane $A_1B_1$ to the direction of $A_2'$, it will determine a plane (or a hyperplane if $r > 3$) which will intersect the plane $A_1B_1$ in the line which is marked $A$-plane. This line is a trace of the plane, or the hyperplane. The vectors $1$, $13$, and $18$ will then have vanishing projections on the vector $A_2'$. In the same manner the given position of the axis $B$, which is denoted $B_1$, can be moved in the plane $A_1B_1$ to the direction of $B_2'$. Orthogonal to this vector is the $B$-plane, as shown. When the axis $B_1$ is so moved, there will be a group of test vectors with small or vanishing projections on $B_2'$.

In *Table 2* we have summarized the computations for rotating the reference axes. Each step in the computations will be described in detail for the first rotation, but the computations will be summarized only for the subsequent rotations. The purpose of the rotations is to maximize the number of test vectors with zero projections on the reference axes. The given vectors, $A_1$, $B_1$, and $C_1$, are represented by the rows of the $3 \times 3$ matrix, $S_{12}$, with elements $s_{ur}$. The three columns represent the new long reference axes, here denoted $A_2'$, $B_2'$, $C_2'$. The vector $A_1$ is to be changed to the vector $A_2'$, which is orthogonal to the $A$-plane. The vector $A_2'$ is a linear combination of $A_1$ and $B_1$. It can be expressed in the form

$$(1) \qquad A_2' = 1.00A_1 + .90B_1 \,,$$

as read directly from the diagram of *Figure 1*.

In the same figure we determine $B_2'$, which is normal to the trace, $B$-plane, as a linear combination of $A_1$ and $B_1$. It is read graphically as

$$(2) \qquad B_2' = .50A_1 - 1.00B_1 \,.$$

The directions of $A_2'$ and of $B_2'$ are so chosen that the majority of the twenty points have positive projections.

The coefficients of these two equations are entered in the columns of matrix $S_{12}$ of *Table 2*. The columns of that matrix show the direction numbers of the new vectors as linear combinations of the given vectors. Two of the columns of that matrix are determined graphically from *Figure 1*.

In *Figure 2* we have plotted the given columns $A_1$ and $C_1$ from *Table 1*. In this figure we see the opportunity to move the vector $C_1$ to $C_2'$, orthogonal to the $C$-plane, whose trace passes through a group of points. The new vector can be expressed as a linear combination of $A_1$ and $C_1$, namely,

$$(3) \qquad C_2' = .40A_1 - 1.00C_1 \,,$$

as determined graphically, and the coefficients of this equation are entered in the third column of the matrix $S_{12}$ of *Table 2*. Here, again, the new vector $C_2'$ is drawn in such a direction that the majority of the points have

## Table 2

### Rotation 1

| Matrix $S_{12}$ | | $A_2'$ | $B_2'$ | $C_2'$ |
|---|---|---|---|---|
| $s_{ur}$ | $A_1$ | 1.00 | .50 | .40 |
| | $B_1$ | .90 | −1.00 | — |
| | $C_1$ | — | — | −1.00 |
| | | 1.90 | − .50 | − .60 |

| $\Lambda_{01}S_{12}=L_{02}$ | | $A_2'$ | $B_2'$ | $C_2'$ |
|---|---|---|---|---|
| $l_{mr}$ | I | 1.00 | .50 | .40 |
| | II | .90 | −1.00 | — |
| | III | — | — | −1.00 |
| | $\Sigma l^2$ | 1.81 | 1.25 | 1.16 |
| | $\sqrt{\Sigma l^2}$ | 1.3454 | 1.1180 | 1.0770 |
| $D_2$ | $d_{rp}$ | .7433 | .8944 | .9285 |

| $S_{12}D_2=H_{12}$ | | $A_2$ | $B_2$ | $C_2$ |
|---|---|---|---|---|
| $h_{up}$ | $A_1$ | .743 | .447 | .371 |
| | $B_1$ | .669 | − .894 | — |
| | $C_1$ | — | — | − .928 |
| | | 1.412 | − .447 | − .557 |

| $L_{02}D_2=\Lambda_{02}$ | | $A_2$ | $B_2$ | $C_2$ |
|---|---|---|---|---|
| $\lambda_{mp}$ | I | .743 | .447 | .371 |
| | II | .669 | − .894 | — |
| | III | — | — | − .928 |
| | $\Sigma$ | 1.412 | − .447 | − .557 |

| $\Lambda_{02}'\Lambda_{02}=C_2$ | | $A_2$ | $B_2$ | $C_2$ |
|---|---|---|---|---|
| $c_{pq}$ | $A_2$ | 1.000 | | |
| | $B_2$ | − .266 | .999 | |
| | $C_2$ | .276 | .166 | .999 |

## Table 3

### Factor Matrix $F_0\Lambda_{02}=V_2$

| | $A_2$ | $B_2$ | $C_2$ |
|---|---|---|---|
| 1 | − .003 | .953 | .116 |
| 2 | .659 | .163 | .878 |
| 3 | .853 | − .183 | − .217 |
| 4 | .506 | .575 | .734 |
| 5 | .741 | .210 | − .162 |
| 6 | .968 | − .090 | .169 |
| 7 | .334 | .787 | .567 |
| 8 | .345 | .760 | .018 |
| 9 | .918 | .013 | .597 |
| 10 | .426 | .698 | .655 |
| 11 | .562 | .529 | − .075 |
| 12 | .975 | − .042 | .411 |
| 13 | .011 | .946 | .146 |
| 14 | .697 | .101 | .840 |
| 15 | .806 | − .164 | − .249 |
| 16 | .867 | .189 | .194 |
| 17 | .558 | .645 | .435 |
| 18 | − .017 | .923 | .078 |
| 19 | .597 | .214 | .864 |
| 20 | .852 | − .182 | − .207 |
| $Ch$ | 11.655 | 7.043 | 5.792 |
| $\Sigma$ | 11.655 | 7.045 | 5.792 |

positive projections on $C_2'$. *Figure 3* was plotted from columns $B$ and $C$ of *Table 1*, but this figure was not used in this rotation of the reference frame.

The first step in the rotation of the reference axes is to determine graphically the numerical entries in the matrix $S_{12}$ with elements $s_{ur}$. The subscripts of $S_{12}$ indicate that this matrix shows the adjustments in the reference vectors from position 1 to position 2. The elements $s_{ur}$ represent the relation between the given unit reference vectors, $u$, and the new long reference vectors, $r$.

In order to determine the true lengths of the long reference vectors $A_2'$, $B_2'$, $C_2'$, they should be referred to the given orthogonal reference frame.

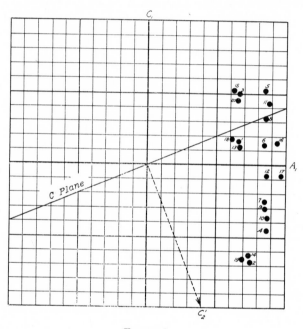

Figure 2

This frame is actually represented in $A_1$, $B_1$, and $C_1$ of the first three figures, but it is not so directly represented in the diagrams for subsequent rotations. Let a matrix $L_{02}$, with elements $l_{mr}$, represent the long reference vectors $r$ in terms of the fixed orthogonal frame $m$. The subscripts of $L_{02}$ indicate that the long reference vectors in the second position are expressed in terms of the fixed orthogonal frame (subscript 0).

The columns of the matrix $\Lambda_{01}$ with elements $\lambda_{mu}$ show the direction cosines of the reference vectors in their positions 1. Since the initial positions of the reference vectors are in the fixed orthogonal frame, we have $A_1$ in the axis $I$, $B$, in the axis $II$, and $C$, in the axis $III$, so that $\Lambda_{01}$ is an identity matrix. The elements of the matrix $\Lambda$ are denoted $\lambda_{mu}$ when it represents a

MULTIPLE-FACTOR ANALYSIS

set of reference vectors before adjustment. The elements of $\Lambda$ are denoted $\lambda_{mp}$ when it represents the reference vectors after an adjustment has been made.

Let $\Lambda_{02}$ be a matrix with elements $\lambda_{mp}$ whose columns show the direction cosines of the reference vectors in their second positions. The columns of this matrix show the direction cosines of the unit reference vectors $p$ in the second position, expressed in terms of the fixed orthogonal frame $m$.

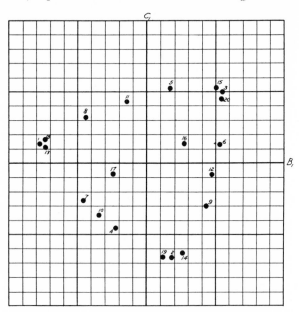

FIGURE 3

In order to determine the true lengths of the long reference vectors $A'_2$, $B'_2$, and $C'_2$, we describe them in terms of the fixed orthogonal frame. We then have

$$(4) \qquad \sum_u \lambda_{mu} s_{ur} = l_{mr} ,$$

which can be written in the rectangular form

(5)

|     | $A_1$ | $B_1$ | $C_1$ |     | $A'_2$ | $B'_2$ | $C'_2$ | $=$ |     | $A'_2$ | $B'_2$ | $C'_2$ |
|-----|-------|-------|-------|-----|--------|--------|--------|-----|-----|--------|--------|--------|
| I   | 1     |       |       | $A_1$ | 1.00 | .50   | .40   |     | I   | 1.00  | .50   | .40   |
| II  |       | 1     |       | $B_1$ | .90  | −1.00 | —     |     | II  | .90   | −1.00 | —     |
| III |       |       | 1     | $C_1$ | —    | —     | −1.00 |     | III | —     | —     | −1.00 |

|  $\lambda_{mu}$  |  $s_{ur}$  |  $l_{mr}$  |

In the matrix $\lambda_{mu}$ we have the vectors $A_1$, $B_1$, and $C_1$ expressed in terms of the orthogonal unit reference vectors $I, II, III$. In the matrix $s_{ur}$ we have the new vectors $A_2'$, $B_2'$, and $C_2'$ expressed in terms of the given vectors $A_1$, $B_1$, and $C_1$. The matrix multiplication gives the product matrix with elements $l_{mr}$, in which the long reference vectors $A_2'$, $B_2'$, and $C_2'$ are also expressed in terms of the fixed orthogonal unit reference vectors. The matrix $\lambda_{mu}$ is a unit matrix for the first rotation. Consequently, $s_{ur}$ and $l_{mr}$ are here identical, but they will differ for subsequent rotations.

The matrix equation can also be written in the form

$$(6) \qquad\qquad \Lambda_{01} S_{12} = L_{02} \,,$$

where the columns of $L_{02}$ show the direction numbers of the long reference vectors in position 2 in terms of the fixed orthogonal frame.

Since the columns of $L_{02}$ in *Table 2* show the projections of the long vectors on the fixed orthogonal reference frame, we can determine the true lengths of the vectors $A_2'$, $B_2'$, and $C_2'$. The sum of the squares in each column is written

$$\sum_m l_{mr}^2 \,,$$

or, more briefly, as $\Sigma l^2$ on the data sheets. The square root of each sum is $\sqrt{\Sigma l^2}$, and it is the length of the vector $r$. The reciprocal is

$$(7) \qquad\qquad d_{rp} = \frac{1}{\sqrt{\displaystyle\sum_m l_{mr}^2}} \,.$$

The values of $d_{rp}$ may be regarded as the elements of a diagonal matrix $D_2$.

The next step in the computations is to reduce the long reference vectors to unit length. This is done by the relation

$$(8) \qquad\qquad \sum_r l_{mr} d_{rp} = \lambda_{mp} \,,$$

or, in matrix form,

$$(9) \qquad\qquad L_{02} D_2 = \Lambda_{02} \,,$$

which can be written in rectangular form:

(10)

|   | $L_{02}$ | | | | $D_2$ | | | | $\Lambda_{02}$ | | |
|---|---|---|---|---|---|---|---|---|---|---|---|
|   | $A_2'$ | $B_2'$ | $C_2'$ |   | $A_2$ | $B_2$ | $C_2$ | $=$ | $A_2$ | $B_2$ | $C_2$ |
| I | 1.00 | .50 | .40 | $A_2'$ | .743 | | | I | .743 | .447 | .371 |
| II | .90 | −1.00 | — | $B_2'$ | | .894 | | II | .669 | −.894 | — |
| III | — | — | −1.00 | $C_2'$ | | | .929 | III | — | — | −.928 |
|   | $l_{mr}$ | | | | $d_{rp}$ | | | | $\lambda_{mp}$ | | |

The oblique factor matrix which is the result of this rotation can now be computed by the equation

(11)
$$\sum_m a_{jm}\lambda_{mp} = v_{jp}$$

or, in matrix form,

(12)
$$F_0\Lambda_{02} = V_2 ,$$

where $F_0$ is the given factor matrix and $V_2$ is the oblique factor matrix. This is the factor matrix in its second position. If the rotation of reference axes were limited to orthogonal transformations, we should have

(13)
$$F_0\Lambda_{02} = F_2 ,$$

where $F_2$ would show the projections of the test vectors on a new set of orthogonal axes.

If it is desired to compute each factor matrix $V$ from the just preceding factor matrix, instead of making the computations at each rotation from the original orthogonal factor matrix $F_0$, then we use the transformation matrix $h_{up}$ instead of $\lambda_{mp}$. The columns of the matrix $H$ with elements $h_{up}$ show the new unit reference vectors $A_2$, $B_2$, and $C_2$ in terms of the preceding reference vectors $A_1$, $B_1$, and $C_1$. We then have

(14)
$$\sum_r s_{ur}d_{rp} = h_{up}$$

or, in matrix form,

(15)
$$S_{12}D_2 = H_{12}$$

or, in rectangular form,

(16)

| | $S_{12}$ | | | | $D_2$ | | | | $H_{12}$ | |
| | $A'_2$ | $B'_2$ | $C'_2$ | | $A_2$ | $B_2$ | $C_2$ | $=$ | $A_2$ | $B_2$ | $C_2$ |
|---|---|---|---|---|---|---|---|---|---|---|---|
| $A_1$ | 1.00 | .50 | .40 | $A'_2$ | .743 | | | $A_1$ | .743 | .447 | .371 |
| $B_1$ | .90 | −1.00 | — | $B'_2$ | | .894 | | $B_1$ | .669 | −.894 | — |
| $C_1$ | — | — | −1.00 | $C'_2$ | | | .929 | $C_1$ | — | — | −.928 |
| | $s_{ur}$ | | | | $d_{rp}$ | | | | $h_{up}$ | | |

The oblique factor matrix $V_2$ can be determined from the preceding factor matrix $V_1$ by the transformation $H_{12}$. We then have

(17) $$V_1 H_{12} = V_2 .$$

The rotational problem starts with the factor matrix $F_0$ with elements $a_{jm}$, which give projections of the test vectors $j$ on the fixed orthogonal frame $m$. The first step is merely to assign the initial locations of the trial reference vectors in the orthogonal axes of the fixed frame. This is represented by the transformation

$$F_0 \Lambda_{01} = V_1 ,$$

in which $\Lambda_{01}$ is an identity matrix. The first rotation represents the independent adjustments of the reference vectors from their initial positions in the fixed axes. This adjustment is represented by the equation

$$F_0 \Lambda_{02} = V_2 ,$$

in which the columns of $\Lambda_{02}$ give the direction cosines of the new reference vectors in terms of the fixed orthogonal vectors $m$. The axes of $V_2$ are then, in general, oblique.

The second rotation is represented by the equation

$$F_0 \Lambda_{03} = V_3 ,$$

where the columns of $\Lambda_{03}$ show the direction cosines of the adjusted reference vectors. The oblique factor matrix $V_3$ can be obtained from the next preceding factor matrix, $V_2$, if desired. The relation then is

$$V_2 H_{23} = V_3 .$$

The cosines of the angles between the new reference axes should be determined, to make sure that no pair of them is approaching another pair so closely as to represent practically the same factor. If that should happen, the dimensionality of the oblique factor matrix would be reduced so that the columns would be linearly dependent. It would then be necessary to alter the location of one or more of the reference axes. With a little practice this error can be avoided. The cosines of the angles between the reference vectors are determined by the cross products

$$(18) \qquad \sum_m \lambda_{mp}\lambda_{mq} = c_{pq}$$

or, in matrix form,

$$(19) \qquad \Lambda'\Lambda = C \, .$$

After the first rotation we have

$$(20) \qquad \Lambda'_{02}\Lambda_{02} = C_2 \, .$$

It is useful to record these cosines on the corresponding diagrams for the next rotation, so as to avoid moving any pair of reference vectors so close together that a dimension is lost. The diagonal values of $\Lambda'\Lambda$ must be unity, since unit vectors are involved.

The successive steps in the computations for the first rotation are shown in *Table 2*, and they can be summarized as follows:

1) Write the elements of the matrix $S_{12}$ by inspection of the plots for $V_1$.

2) Perform the matrix multiplication

$$(6) \qquad \Lambda_{01}S_{12} = L_{02} \, ,$$

where $\Lambda_{01}$ is a unit matrix for the first rotation.

3) Determine the stretching factors $d_{rp}$ from the sums of squares in columns of $L_{02}$.

4) Compute elements $\lambda_{mp}$ of $\Lambda_{02}$ by the equation

$$(9) \qquad L_{02}D_2 = \Lambda_{02} \, .$$

5) If it is desired to compute the oblique factor matrix, $V_2$, from the next preceding factor matrix, $V_1$, then compute the elements $h_{up}$ in the matrix $H_{12}$ by the equation

$$(15) \qquad S_{12}D_2 = H_{12} \, .$$

6) Determine the cosines of the angular separations of the new unit reference vectors by the equation

$$(20) \qquad \Lambda_{02}'\Lambda_{02} = C_2 .$$

7) If these cosines are acceptable, compute the new oblique factor matrix, $V_2$, by either of the two following equations:

  a) In terms of the original factor matrix, we have

$$(12) \qquad F_0\Lambda_{02} = V_2 .$$

  b) In terms of the preceding factor matrix, we have

$$(17) \qquad V_1H_{12} = V_2 .$$

In the first rotation the initial factor matrix, $V_1$, is identical with $F_0$, which is the initial factor matrix obtained from the experimentally determined correlation matrix. The matrix $V_2$ is shown in *Table 3*.

8) Plot a new set of diagrams for all pairs of columns of $V_2$ and examine them to determine the adjustments, which will be the next rotation of axes.

It may be helpful to visualize in a single table the computations that are summarized in *Tables 2–7*, inclusive, for the several rotations of the reference axes in the present illustrative problem. The formulae have been arranged in order of computation and in a separate column for each rotation. The subscripts indicate the rotations to which the formulae belong. The same schema can be extended, of course, to any number of rotations.

## Computational formulae for three rotations

Given the factor matrix $F_0 = V_1$ as obtained from the correlations and the identity matrix $\Lambda_{01}$.

| *Rotation 1* | *Rotation 2* | *Rotation 3* |
|---|---|---|
| Determine $S_{12}$ graphically | Determine $S_{23}$ graphically | Determine $S_{34}$ graphically |
| $\Lambda_{01}S_{12} = L_{02}$ | $\Lambda_{02}S_{23} = L_{03}$ | $\Lambda_{03}S_{34} = L_{04}$ |
| $D_2$ from $L_{02}$ | $D_3$ from $L_{03}$ | $D_4$ from $L_{04}$ |
| $[S_{12}D_2 = H_{12}]$ | $[S_{23}D_3 = H_{23}]$ | $[S_{34}D_4 = H_{34}]$ |
| $L_{02}D_2 = \Lambda_{02}$ | $L_{03}D_3 = \Lambda_{03}$ | $L_{04}D_4 = \Lambda_{04}$ |
| $\Lambda_{02}'\Lambda_{02} = C_2$ | $\Lambda_{03}'\Lambda_{03} = C_3$ | $\Lambda_{04}'\Lambda_{04} = C_4$ |
| $\begin{cases} V_1H_{12} = V_2 \\ \quad or \\ F_0\Lambda_{02} = V_2 \end{cases}$ | $\begin{cases} V_2H_{23} = V_3 \\ \quad or \\ F_0\Lambda_{03} = V_3 \end{cases}$ | $\begin{cases} V_3H_{34} = V_4 \\ \quad or \\ F_0\Lambda_{04} = V_4 \end{cases}$ |
| (In first rotation these two formulae are identical) | (These are two alternative formulae) | (These are two alternative formulae) |
| Plot pairs of columns of $V_2$ | Plot pairs of columns of $V_3$ | Plot pairs of columns of $V_4$ |

It should be noted that the matrix product of the several transformations $H$ is equal to the transformation $\Lambda$ for the same rotations. We then have

(21) $$H_{01}H_{12}H_{23}H_{34} = \Lambda_{04},$$

where the transformation $H_{01} = \Lambda_{01} = I$. The transformation $h_{up}$ carries a factor matrix $V_{n-1}$ to the next factor matrix $V_n$, while the transformation $\Lambda_{0n}$ carries the original factor matrix $F_0$ to the oblique factor matrix $V_n$. In general, the computational labor is least when the oblique factor matrix is computed by the transformation $H$; but if a matrix-multiplying machine is available, the computations are performed best by the transformation $\Lambda$.

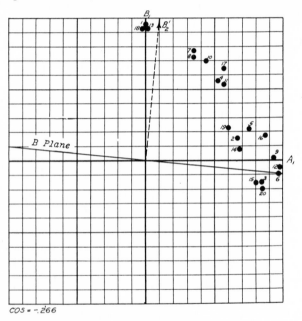

$COS = -.266$

FIGURE 4

The result of the first rotation of axes is shown in the next three figures ($4$–$6$), where pairs of columns of $V_2$ are plotted as before. It should be noted that, *while the reference axes are now oblique, they are nevertheless plotted on orthogonal co-ordinate cross-section paper, as indicated in the figures.* The procedures here described do not require that the plots be actually made with oblique axes on the graphs.

In stating each new rotation we denote the previous axes with the subscript 1 and the new axes with the subscript 2. In *Figure 4* we have plotted the columns $A$ and $B$ of *Table 3*. The vector $B_1$ is moved to the position $B_2'$, so that the trace of the $B$-plane goes through a group of points *3, 15, 20, 6, 9, 12*. The new vector $B_2'$ is described from the graph by the vector equation

(22) $$B_2' = 1.00B_1 + .10A_1.$$

In *Figure 5* we have plotted the columns $A$ and $C$ of *Table 3*. A radial trace for a new $A$-plane can be drawn, as shown, with the normal $A_2'$. Such a move of the $A$-axis will not only retain the zero, or near-zero, projections of *1*, *13*, and *18*, which are at the origin, but will add six more tests to the list of negligible or zero projections on the $A$-axis. The new reference axis $A_2'$ can be expressed as a linear combination of the axes $A_1$ and $C_1$ of *Figure 5*. This relation is

$$(23) \qquad A_2' = 1.00A_1 - .72C_1.$$

In the same diagram we see the opportunity to move the $C$-plane so as to obtain zero projections not only for those tests which are shown at the

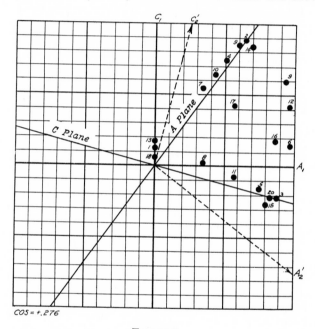

FIGURE 5

origin but also for the group *3, 5, 15, 20*. The normal to the $C$-trace is $C_2'$, which can be written in the form

$$(24) \qquad C_2' = 1.00C_1 + .25A_1.$$

In *Figure 6* the trace of the $C$-plane is drawn radially so as to include the group of tests *1, 13, 18*, and its normal is $C_2'$, which is written

$$(25) \qquad C_2' = 1.00C_1 - .12B_1.$$

In the same diagram the trace of the $B$-plane is drawn radially so as to pass through the group *2, 14, 19*, and the normal is written

$$(26) \qquad B_2' = 1.00B_1 - .20C_1.$$

The numerical values in equations (13)–(15) are entered in the $S_{23}$-matrix of *Table 4*. Here it will be noted that a new process has been introduced, namely, the combination of movements of a plane from more than one diagram. The new vector $B_2'$ is determined here as a sum of three vectors, namely, the previous $B$ vector plus two corrections, namely, $+.10A_1$, and $-.20C_1$. In a similar manner, the new vector $C_2'$ is determined by two corrections added to the previous vector $C$, namely, $+.25A_1$ and $-.12B_1$, as shown in the columns of $S_{23}$ in *Table 4*.

In combining several corrections in the same rotation it is useful to remember that the corrections should not be large—say, not over .30. If a

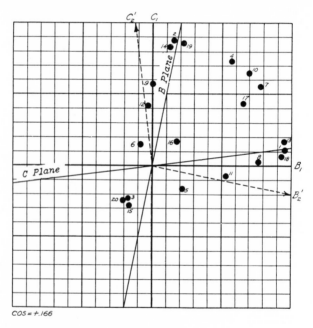

FIGURE 6

rotation whose sine is greater than about .30 is indicated on a diagram, it should be taken singly for that rotation. If several small rotations are indicated on the diagrams, they may be combined if they are independent. The independence of two small rotations can be seen in the present examples. The new vector $C_2'$ is determined by two corrections from *Figures 5* and *6*. In *Figure 5* the trace of $C$ is moved toward the group *3, 5, 15, 20*, and these are near the origin in *Figure 6*. In *Figure 6* the trace of $C$ is moved toward the group *1, 13, 18*, and these are near the origin in *Figure 5*. Hence the two movements can be combined. If a trace can be moved toward a certain group of tests in several diagrams, the move is made on only one diagram, for otherwise there would be an overcorrection. Another useful principle is

<table>
<tr><td colspan="4" align="center">*Table 4*</td></tr>
<tr><td colspan="4" align="center">Rotation 2</td></tr>
</table>

| Matrix $S_{23}$ | $A'_2$ | $B'_2$ | $C'_2$ |
|---|---|---|---|
| $A_1$ | 1.00 | .10 | .25 |
| $B_1$ | | 1.00 | $-$ .12 |
| $S_{ur}$ $\quad C_1$ | $-$ .72 | $-$ .20 | 1.00 |
| | .28 | .90 | 1.13 |

| $\Lambda_{02}S_{23}=L_{03}$ | $A'_2$ | $B'_2$ | $C'_2$ |
|---|---|---|---|
| I | .476 | .447 | .503 |
| II | .669 | $-$ .829 | .275 |
| $m\,r$ $\quad$ III | .668 | .186 | $-$ .928 |
| $\Sigma$ | 1.813 | $-$ .195 | $-$ .151 |
| $\Sigma l^2$ | 1.1204 | .9216 | 1.1898 |
| $\sqrt{\Sigma l^2}$ | 1.0585 | .9600 | 1.0908 |
| $D_3$ $\quad d_{rp}$ | .9447 | 1.0417 | .9168 |

| $S_{23}D_3=H_{23}$ | $A_2$ | $B_2$ | $C_2$ |
|---|---|---|---|
| $A_1$ | .945 | .104 | .229 |
| $B_1$ | | 1.042 | $-$ .110 |
| $h_{up}$ $\quad C_1$ | $-$ .680 | $-$ .208 | .917 |
| $\Sigma$ | .264 | .938 | 1.036 |

| $L_{03}D_3=\Lambda_{03}$ | $A_2$ | $B_2$ | $C_2$ |
|---|---|---|---|
| I | .450 | .466 | .461 |
| II | .632 | $-$ .864 | .252 |
| $\lambda_{mp}$ $\quad$ III | .631 | .194 | $-$ .851 |
| $\Sigma$ | 1.713 | $-$ .203 | $-$ .138 |

| $\Lambda'_{03}\Lambda_{03}=C_3$ | $A_2$ | $B_2$ | $C_2$ |
|---|---|---|---|
| $A_2$ | 1.000 | | |
| $B_2$ | $-$ .214 | 1.001 | |
| $c_{pq}$ $\quad C_2$ | $-$ .171 | $-$ .169 | 1.000 |

*Table 5*

Factor Matrix $F_0\Lambda_{03} = V_3$

| | $A_2$ | $B_2$ | $C_2$ |
|---|---|---|---|
| 1 | $-$ .082 | .970 | .001 |
| 2 | .026 | .055 | .938 |
| 3 | .954 | $-$ .058 | .016 |
| 4 | $-$ .021 | .500 | .723 |
| 5 | .811 | .330 | $-$ .002 |
| 6 | .800 | $-$ .031 | .387 |
| 7 | $-$ .071 | .737 | .510 |
| 8 | .314 | .825 | .011 |
| 9 | .462 | $-$ .017 | .756 |
| 10 | $-$ .043 | .636 | .621 |
| 11 | .582 | .626 | .002 |
| 12 | .642 | $-$ .030 | .605 |
| 13 | $-$ .090 | .958 | .032 |
| 14 | .088 | .001 | .919 |
| 15 | .931 | $-$ .037 | $-$ .026 |
| 16 | .688 | .246 | .356 |
| 17 | .231 | .641 | .456 |
| 18 | $-$ .070 | .946 | $-$ .035 |
| 19 | $-$ .024 | .104 | .905 |
| 20 | .945 | $-$ .060 | .026 |
| $Ch$ | 7.077 | 7.348 | 7.203 |
| $\Sigma$ | 7.073 | 7.342 | 7.201 |

that if a trace moves toward the configuration in one diagram (as $C$ in *Figure 6*) and away from the configuration in another diagram (as $C$ in *Figure 5*), then the two corrections can be added in the same rotation without checking the numbers of the variables.

Another example of the combination of two corrections is the $B$-trace in *Figures 4* and *6*. Here, again, one of the movements is toward the configuration (*Figure 6*) and the other is away from the configuration (*Figure 4*). The two movements are written as follows:

(27) $$B_2' = 1.00B_1 - .20C_1,$$

and

(28) $$B_2' = 1.00B_1 + .10A_1.$$

The two corrections are shown in the $S_{23}$-matrix of *Table 4*.

The steps in the computations of *Table 4* are as follows:

1) Compute the elements of $L_{03}$ by the relation

$$\Lambda_{02}S_{23} = L_{03}.$$

2) Compute the diagonal elements $d_{rp}$ of the diagonal matrix $D_3$.

3) Compute the elements of the matrix $\Lambda_{03}$ by the relation

$$L_{03}D_3 = \Lambda_{03}.$$

4) Compute the cosines $c_{pq}$ of $C_3$ by the relation

$$\Lambda_{03}'\Lambda_{03} = C_3.$$

5) Compute the elements of the next factor matrix by the relation

$$F_0\Lambda_{03} = V_3.$$

6) Plot pairs of columns of $V_3$ on orthogonal cross-section paper and record values of $c_{pq}$ on each diagram.

The computation of $H_{23}$ is optional as an alternative method of arriving at $V_3$. If it is desired to compute $V_3$ from $V_2$, then the computation is made by the formula

$$V_2H_{23} = V_3.$$

If it is desired to compute $V_3$ from the original factor matrix $F_0$, then we use the formula

$$F_0\Lambda_{03} = V_3.$$

In any event, the latter formula should be used for check on computations after five or six rotations have been made by the transformation $H$.

The three plots for $V_3$ of *Table 5* are shown in *Figures 7, 8,* and *9*. These plots show that the reference axes are nearly in their final positions in the

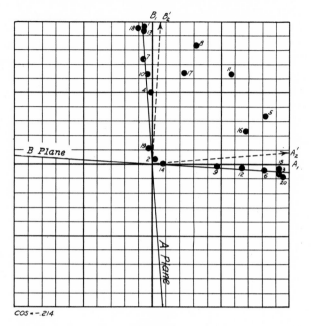

COS = –.214

FIGURE 7

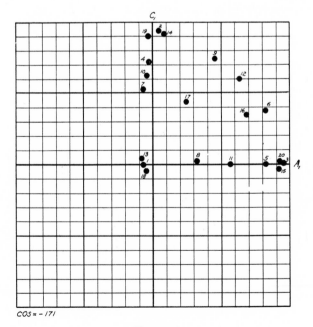

COS = – 171

FIGURE 8

configuration. The $A$-plane is adjusted slightly in *Figure 7*. The $B$-plane is given two corrections, as shown in *Figures 7* and *9*. The $C$-plane needs no further adjustment. These adjustments are shown in the matrix $S_{34}$ of *Table 6*. The computations of *Table 6* proceed in the same way as for the previous rotations. The oblique factor matrix $V_4$ is computed as shown in *Table 7*.

When the factor matrix $V_4$ of *Table 7* has been computed, the three pairs of columns are plotted as shown in *Figures 10, 11,* and *12*. Inspection of

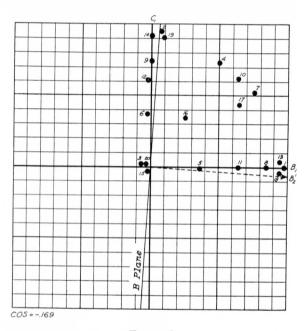

FIGURE 9

these three plots reveals the simple structure which became evident even after the first rotation. Since no further rotations are indicated in *Figures 10–12*, they are accepted as the configuration for interpretation. This phase of factor analysis cannot be illustrated in the present problem, which is fictitious. The reference vectors are denoted $\Lambda_p$, as shown in the columns of the oblique factor matrix $V_4$. The cosines between these reference vectors are shown in the matrix $C_4$ of *Table 6*. It is seen that these cosines are negative, from which we infer that the angles separating the reference vectors are obtuse. Hence the angular separations of the corresponding primary factors $T_p$ can be expected to be acute. The interpretation is that the primary factors are positively correlated.

**Table 6**

**Rotation 3**

| Matrix $S_{34}$ | | $A'_2$ | $B'_2$ | $C'_2$ |
|---|---|---|---|---|
| $s_{ur}$ | $A_1$ | 1.00 | .05 | |
| | $B_1$ | .09 | 1.00 | |
| | $C_1$ | | − .05 | 1.00 |
| | | 1.09 | 1.00 | 1.00 |

| $\Lambda_{03}S_{34}=L_{04}$ | | $A'_2$ | $B'_2$ | $C'_2$ |
|---|---|---|---|---|
| $mr$ | I | .492 | .465 | .461 |
| | II | .554 | − .845 | .252 |
| | III | .648 | .268 | − .851 |
| | | 1.694 | − .112 | − .138 |
| $D_4$ | $\Sigma l^2$ | .9689 | 1.0021 | 1.0002 |
| | $\sqrt{\Sigma l^2}$ | .9843 | 1.0010 | 1.0001 |
| | $d_{rp}$ | 1.0160 | .9990 | .9999 |

| $S_{34}D_4=H_{34}$ | | $A_2$ | $B_2$ | $C_2$ |
|---|---|---|---|---|
| $up$ | $A_1$ | 1.016 | .050 | |
| | $B_1$ | .091 | .999 | |
| | $C_1$ | | − .050 | 1.000 |
| | | 1.107 | .999 | 1.000 |

| $L_{04}D_4=\Lambda_{04}$ | | $A_2$ | $B_2$ | $C_2$ |
|---|---|---|---|---|
| $\lambda_{mp}$ | I | .500 | .465 | .461 |
| | II | .563 | − .844 | .252 |
| | III | .658 | .268 | − .851 |
| | | 1.721 | − .111 | − .138 |

| $\Lambda'_{04}\Lambda_{04}=C_4$ | | $A_2$ | $B_2$ | $C_2$ |
|---|---|---|---|---|
| $c_{pq}$ | $A_2$ | 1.000 | | |
| | $B_2$ | − .066 | 1.000 | |
| | $C_2$ | − .188 | − .226 | 1.000 |

**Table 7**

**Factor Matrix $F_0\Lambda_{04} = V_4$**

| | $\Lambda_A$ | $\Lambda_B$ | $\Lambda_C$ |
|---|---|---|---|
| 1 | .006 | .965 | .001 |
| 2 | .032 | .009 | .938 |
| 3 | .964 | − .010 | .016 |
| 4 | .025 | .462 | .723 |
| 5 | .854 | .370 | − .002 |
| 6 | .810 | − .009 | .387 |
| 7 | − .003 | .707 | .510 |
| 8 | .395 | .840 | .011 |
| 9 | .468 | − .031 | .756 |
| 10 | .015 | .602 | .621 |
| 11 | .649 | .654 | .002 |
| 12 | .649 | − .027 | .605 |
| 13 | − .003 | .951 | .032 |
| 14 | .090 | − .040 | .919 |
| 15 | .943 | .012 | − .026 |
| 16 | .721 | .263 | .356 |
| 17 | .294 | .629 | .456 |
| 18 | .016 | .943 | − .035 |
| 19 | − .014 | .058 | .905 |
| 20 | .955 | − .013 | .026 |
| $Ch$ | 7.865 | 7.335 | 7.203 |
| $\Sigma$ | 7.866 | 7.335 | 7.201 |

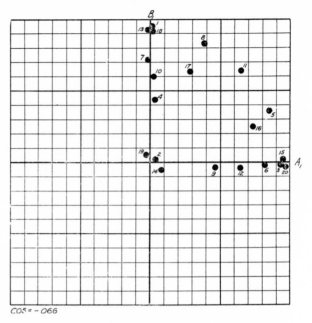

COS = -.066

FIGURE 10

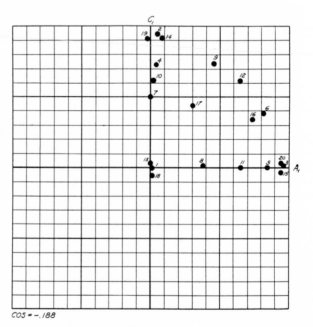

COS = -.188

FIGURE 11

The correlations between the primary factors $T_p$ can be determined by the relation

$$(29) \qquad R_{pq} = D(\Lambda'\Lambda)^{-1}D ,$$

where the diagonal matrix $D$ is so chosen that the diagonal elements of $R_{pq}$ are unity. The result is shown in *Table 8*. The procedures here described

*Table 8*

*Correlations between Primaries* $T_p$

|   | $R_{pq}$ | | | | |
|---|---|---|---|---|---|
|   | $A$ | $B$ | $C$ | $C_h$ | $\Sigma$ |
| $A$ | 1.000 | .112 | .208 | 1.320 | 1.320 |
| $B$ | .112 | 1.000 | .242 | 1.354 | 1.354 |
| $C$ | .208 | .242 | 1.000 | 1.450 | 1.450 |
| $\Sigma$ | 1.320 | 1.354 | 1.450 | ..... | 4.124 |

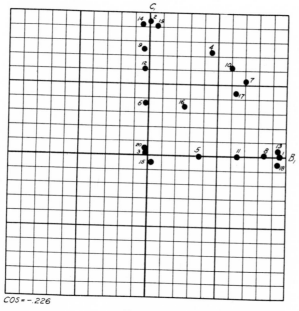

FIGURE 12

are applicable for rotation of axes in any number of dimensions. The investigator must make his own decision as to whether the axes are to be restricted by being orthogonal or are to be allowed to follow the configuration, as in the present example. He must also make his own decision as to whether to restrict the factors to the positive manifold. It is probably best to impose none of these restrictions and to allow the reference vectors to be oblique if the configuration demands it or to allow each factor to be either positive or bipolar.

There are several ways in which the results of a rotation can be anticipated. These become apparent with practice. Several have been described here. It is useful to be able to predict whether a rotation will increase or decrease the cosine of the angle between two reference axes. This can be illustrated by *Figure 4*. The cosine of the angle between the given vectors $\Lambda_A$ and $\Lambda_B$, denoted $A_1$ and $B_1$, is $-.266$. The negative sign means that they are separated by an obtuse angle. If the vectors should be orthogonal, then it is clear that $A_1$ must move toward $B_1$, or else $B_1$ must move toward $A_1$. In this diagram, $B_1$ is moved toward $A_1$ to the position $B_2'$. Hence we can expect that the cosine will be increased toward zero unless the vector $A_1$ is also moved either by this diagram or by some other diagram. If the cosine of the angle between two reference vectors were positive, then they would have to separate in order to make them more nearly orthogonal. When we are dealing with cosines of large absolute value, these rules are useful in avoiding a rotation by which two reference vectors might be made nearly collinear, in which case one of the dimensions would be lost. Special cases sometimes appear in large studies in which these principles are adapted in different ways, but these become evident with practice. It is unfortunate that the rotational problem cannot be resolved in some routine which can be applied without judgment. The reason is that in dealing with actual fallible data we frequently meet with an incomplete simple structure which is over-determined for some hyperplanes and not for others. Furthermore, we deal with some positive or bipolar factors that are clear and overdetermined, some factors that are only suggested by an almost indeterminate configuration in some dimensions, and with the unique variance and error variance, which obscure the less clearly defined hyperplanes. These conditions are determined by the test batteries that are assembled for investigation and which call for new factorial experiments. Factorial method as such does not give a determinate solution for an ill-conceived factorial experiment. This is, in one sense, fortunate because it becomes a question of experimental fact whether a hypothesis represented in the test battery is sustained in the factorial analysis. A principal-axis solution is always available, and it is unique for any arbitrary test battery; but it does not, except in special cases, enable us to ascertain whether a psychological hypothesis about factorial composition is sustained or refuted.

### A single-plane method of rotation

The rotation problem is, for most computers, one of the most difficult in factor analysis. The reason is in the circumstance that most of the rotational methods require some experience before the graphical representations can be handled effectively. It is our purpose in devising the present method to provide a procedure which can be handled by a clerk for most of the work. The method will be referred to as a *single-plane method of rotation*. The method seems to require little more experience than is necessary to estimate the slope of a line through the origin for a set of points. Questions of independence of rotation are minimized in importance, and the method seems to be convergent, so that a hyperplane can be located without a discouraging amount of labor. The computer need not think about the summation of vectors or about the distinction between a reference vector and its trace in the diagram. The method does not postulate a positive manifold, so that it can be used as well for locating positive and bipolar factors. The method proceeds by locating one hyperplane at a time, so that the investigator can begin the more interesting job of interpretation of each factor while the remaining ones are being computed. This method has only recently been devised, and it has been tried on several sets of experimental data with promising results.

While it is not necessary for a clerk-computer to understand the theory of the method, it will be given first and then the routine which can be explained to a novice in computing.

In *Figure 13* let $Q$ represent a trial unit reference vector whose direction cosines are denoted $\lambda_{mq}$. The fixed orthogonal reference axes are denoted by the subscript $m$, as in previous factorial work. We shall denote the given trial reference vector $Q$ and the adjusted trial reference vector $P$. This will be done for each trial, so that the reference vector $P$ that is obtained in one trial becomes the given trial vector $Q$ for the next adjustment. This process continues for, perhaps, five or six adjustments, until the reference vector seems to be located. If there is no simple structure or if the particular hyperplane is not defined by the configuration, that fact becomes evident.

It is first assumed in *Figure 13* that the trial vector $Q$ is orthogonal to one of the orthogonal reference axes $M$ as shown, but we shall see later that this restriction can be overcome. The projections of the test vectors $J$ on the trial vector $Q$ are computed and denoted $v_{jq}$ (not shown on diagrams). We then have

$$(30) \qquad v_{jq} = \sum_m a_{jm}\lambda_{mq} \, ,$$

where $a_{jm}$ are the direction numbers of the test vector $J$ with respect to the fixed orthogonal frame $M$.

Since $M$ is one of the unit vectors of the fixed orthogonal frame, we already have the projections of the tests on this vector. They are the values $a_{jm}$ in a column of the given factor matrix $F$. If $M$ in the figure represents the first centroid axis, then the projections $(JM_1)$ are given in the first

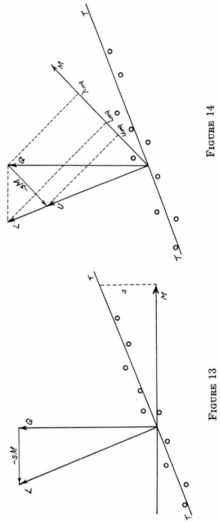

FIGURE 13

FIGURE 14

column of $F$. In the figure we have represented, by a set of points, the paired values from a column of $F$ and the column of $v_{jq}$. The object is to draw a line through the origin with a slope so chosen that a large number of the points will lie close to the line. This has been illustrated in *Figure 13*, and the slope $s_1$ is noted. It is simply the ordinate on the line $TT$ for $a = +1$.

Let $L$ be a vector so defined that (1) it has unit projection on $Q$ and (2) it is orthogonal to the line $TT$. The vector $L$ can be expressed

$$(31) \qquad\qquad L = Q - sM\,.$$

Let $l_{mq}$ be the direction numbers of $L$. Then we have

$$(32) \qquad\qquad l_{mq} = \lambda_{mq} - s\,,$$

since the vector $M$ is a unit vector on the co-ordinate axis $M$. The new vector $\Lambda_p$ will be collinear with $L$ and of unit length.

Let us now consider the oblique case, which is illustrated in *Figure 14*. The trial vector $Q$ has the projection $\lambda_{mq}$ on the vector $M$, as shown in the figure. The projection $\lambda_{mq}$ then is one of the direction cosines of $Q$, and $M$ is in one of the fixed orthogonal axes. When the values of $v_{jq}$ and $a_{jm}$ are plotted on orthogonal cross-section paper, the diagram will look like *Figure 13*. The vector $(-sM)$ is shown in *Figure 14*, where it is, of course, parallel to $M$. Here we write

$$(33) \qquad\qquad U = Q - sM\,,$$

where $U$ satisfies only one of the requirements for $L$. The vector $L$ is orthogonal to $TT$, and so is the vector $U$. But the vector $L$ is also defined as having unit projection on $Q$. The vector $U$ can be extended by a stretching factor $k$, so that it has unit projection on $Q$. Then we have

$$(34) \qquad\qquad L = kU\,,$$

as shown in *Figure 14*. In order to determine the stretching factor for $U$ to give it unit projection on $Q$, we write

$$(35) \qquad\qquad k(UQ) = 1\,,$$

so that

$$(36) \qquad\qquad k = \frac{1}{(UQ)}\,,$$

where $UQ$ is a scalar product. From (33) and (36) we have

$$(37) \qquad\qquad k = \frac{1}{(Q - sM)Q}$$

or

$$(38) \qquad k = \frac{1}{Q^2 - sMQ} ;$$

and, since $Q$ is a unit vector, we have

$$(39) \qquad k = \frac{1}{1 - sMQ} .$$

But the scalar product $MQ$ is merely the direction cosine $\lambda_{mq}$ for the axis $M$. Hence we write

$$(40) \qquad k = \frac{1}{1 - s\lambda_{mq}} .$$

The direction number of $Q$ for the axis $M$ is $\lambda_{mq}$, as shown in the figure. Since the vector $(-sM)$ is parallel to $M$, the direction number of the vector $U$ for the axis $M$ is

$$(41) \qquad u_{mq} = \lambda_{mq} - s .$$

The direction number of the vector $L$ for the same axis is $l_{mq}$, and it is

$$(42) \qquad l_{mq} = ku_{mq} ,$$

so that the desired direction number can be written in the form

$$(43) \qquad l_{mq} = \frac{\lambda_{mq} - s}{1 - s\lambda_{mq}} ,$$

which is a simple computing formula. Here the $\lambda_{mq}$'s are the direction cosines of the given unit trial vector $Q$. The slope $s$ is read directly from a graph. If there are $r$ columns of the factor matrix $F$, then there are as many graphs to be plotted. Each one gives a slope value $s_m$, which is set equal to zero if no rotation is indicated.

When formula (43) has been evaluated for each of the orthogonal axes $M$, the new vector $L$ is determined. It is then normalized and becomes the new trial vector $P$.

### A numerical example

A three-dimensional example will be used to illustrate numerically this method of rotation. *Table 9* shows a factor matrix $F$ for twenty variables and three orthogonal factors. This table is the same as part of *Table 3* of *chapter vii*, except that it is here recorded to only two decimals. The problem is to locate the reference axes $\Lambda_p$, which define a simple structure.

The procedure starts with the selection of a test vector. In the present example, test 15 was arbitrarily chosen as a starting vector. Its direction numbers are shown in row 15 of $F$ in *Table 9*. These three direction numbers, $a_{jm}$, are recorded in the first column of *Table 10*, trial 1. This vector is normalized, and it then becomes the first unit vector $\Lambda_q$ with direction cosines $\lambda_{mq}$, as shown in the second column. The computations for normalizing the given test vector are shown, in part, in *Table 10*. We then have

*Table 9*

| | Factor Matrix F | | | Plane A | | |
|---|---|---|---|---|---|---|
| | I | II | III | Trials | | |
| | | | | 1 | 2 | 3 |
| 1 | .66 | −.74 | .14 | .13 | −.04 | .01 |
| 2 | .72 | .18 | −.66 | .21 | −.03 | .02 |
| 3 | .66 | .54 | .50 | .99 | .94 | .96 |
| 4 | .87 | −.21 | −.44 | .23 | −.04 | .03 |
| 5 | .83 | .18 | .51 | .92 | .82 | .85 |
| 6 | .84 | .52 | .15 | .91 | .77 | .81 |
| 7 | .86 | −.45 | −.27 | .19 | −.07 | .00 |
| 8 | .85 | −.43 | .32 | .51 | .34 | .40 |
| 9 | .86 | .42 | −.30 | .62 | .42 | .47 |
| 10 | .88 | −.34 | −.35 | .22 | −.05 | .02 |
| 11 | .89 | −.15 | .44 | .75 | .60 | .65 |
| 12 | .88 | .48 | −.09 | .78 | .60 | .65 |
| 13 | .67 | −.72 | .11 | .13 | −.05 | .00 |
| 14 | .72 | .25 | −.62 | .27 | .04 | .09 |
| 15 | .63 | .50 | .52 | .96 | .92 | .94 |
| 16 | .94 | .26 | .16 | .84 | .67 | .72 |
| 17 | .97 | −.24 | −.08 | .47 | .23 | .30 |
| 18 | .62 | −.72 | .17 | .13 | −.03 | .02 |
| 19 | .70 | .11 | −.65 | .17 | −.07 | −.02 |
| 20 | .66 | .54 | .49 | .98 | .94 | .96 |
| $\Sigma$ | 15.71 | −.02 | .05 | 10.41 | 6.93 | 7.88 |

*Table 10*

| | | Test 15 Q | | | | | | | | |
|---|---|---|---|---|---|---|---|---|---|---|
| | | $a_{jm}$ | $\lambda_{mq}$ | $s$ | $\lambda - s$ | $s\lambda$ | $1 - s\lambda$ | $l$ | $\lambda_{mp}$ | $\Sigma a^2 = .9173 \quad c = 1.0441$ |
| Trial 1 | I | .63 | .66 | .25 | .41 | .16 | .84 | .49 | .44 | $\Sigma l^2 = 1.2122 \quad c = .90827$ |
| | II | .50 | .52 | −.18 | .70 | −.09 | 1.09 | .64 | .58 | $PQ = \cos \phi = .9592$ |
| | III | .52 | .54 | −.35 | .89 | −.19 | 1.19 | .75 | .68 | $\sin \phi = .28$ |
| Trial 2 | I | ... | .44 | −.07 | .51 | −.03 | 1.03 | .49 | .50 | $\Sigma l^2 = .9651 \quad c = 1.0179$ |
| | II | ... | .58 | .05 | .53 | .03 | .97 | .55 | .56 | $PQ = \cos \phi = .9936$ |
| | III | ... | .68 | .05 | .63 | .03 | .97 | .65 | .66 | $\sin \phi = .11$ |

$\Sigma a^2 = .9173$, as shown, and $1/\sqrt{\Sigma a^2} = c$, which is the multiplying factor by which

$$ca_{jm} = \lambda_{mq} ,$$

where $c = 1.0441$.

The projections $v_{jq}$ are then computed and recorded as shown under trial 1 in *Table 9*. The column $v_{jq}$ for the first trial is plotted against each of the three columns of the factor matrix $F$, and the three resulting diagrams are shown in the top row of *Figure 15*. On each diagram a line is drawn through the origin so that it goes through groups of points wherever possible. Large angular deviations of 30°–45° from the horizontal are not made unless the configuration of points clearly demands so large an angular deviation from the $X$-axis. The slope $s_m$ of each line is noted, and it is recorded in the next column of *Table 10*. The slope of each line is read graphically. It is read directly from a vertical line through the point $+1$ on the base line. The rest of the calculations for trial 1 are self-explanatory, as shown in *Table 10*. The column $l_{mq}$ is normalized and then becomes the column $\lambda_{mp}$. The calculations show $\Sigma l^2 = 1.2122$, which gives the multiplying factor $c = .90827$. The column $\lambda_{mp}$ shows the direction cosines of $\Lambda_p$, which is the trial vector $\Lambda_q$ for the next trial.

When the direction cosines $\lambda_{mp}$ of the next trial vector have been determined, it is useful to compute the scalar product of the given vector $Q$ and the new unit vector $P$. This is the cosine of the angular displacement $\phi$, represented by the trial in question. The corresponding value of sine $\phi$ is recorded as shown. For the first trial, sin $\phi = .28$. It will be found that trials should be continued until sin $\phi$ is about .10 or less. In the present example it is found that the second trial gives sin $\phi = .11$, which is small enough that two adjustments are considered sufficient in this case.

In the second section of *Table 10* these direction cosines are copied in the column $\lambda_{mq}$, as shown. The projections $v_{jq}$ are computed and recorded in *Table 9* in the column for trial 2. This column is plotted against the columns of the factor matrix $F$, and we then have the three diagrams in the bottom row of *Figure 15*. Here the groups of points are closer to the horizontal line in all diagrams, a fact which shows that the desired solution is being approached. A line through the origin is drawn on each of these three diagrams which goes through the concentrations of points. The slopes $s_m$ are recorded in *Table 10*, and the rest of the computations proceed as before.

The value of sin $\phi = .11$, which is small enough so that further rotation is not indicated. The projections $v_{jp}$ of the test vectors on the reference vector determined in two trials are computed and recorded in the last column of *Table 9*. This last column is, in fact, one column of the oblique factor matrix $V$.

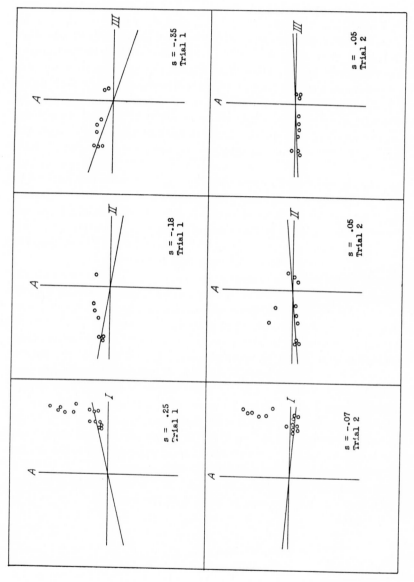

FIGURE 15

In locating the next reference vector we start with one of the test vectors which lie in or near the plane already determined. We choose, therefore, one of the vectors that have small values in the last column of *Table 9*. We might start with any one of the vectors 1, 2, 4, 7, 10, 13, 14, 18, 19. These would not all lead to the same plane, but it does not matter in which order the planes are determined. The starting vector for determining the third plane is chosen from those test vectors which have small projections on both the first and the second reference vectors $\Lambda_p$. In this manner one avoids starting with a vector that leads to a plane that has already been determined. If the configuration is indeterminate, this fact becomes evident when there is no clear indication of where to draw the lines on the graphs, or when the adjustments indicate large deviations that would carry the new trial vector into one of the reference vectors that have already been determined.

It has been found that inexperienced student assistance can be used on these computations, most of which can be arranged with check columns. The check sums have not been shown here for *Table 10*. It is a fortunate circumstance that an error in these calculations is self-correcting, in that the adjustment is made by the computations in the next trial. It is best to provide rather complete check columns so that each step is self-checking.

The work of plotting the diagrams can be considerably reduced by not plotting the points for which $a$ is smaller than $v$. These points have rarely any effect in determining the slope of the desired line through the origin, and they might as well be omitted in plotting the diagrams.

When all the planes have been located by this method, either as planes of considerable variance or as residual planes, the columns of the oblique factor matrix $V$ should be plotted in pairs. Small final adjustments can then be made, if necessary, by the methods described earlier in this chapter.

The present method has been tried on several large factor studies, on small test batteries, and on fictitious examples, and it has so far been found to be rapidly convergent to the solution. One of its advantages seems to be that the computer need not worry about the independence of the several angular adjustments in each trial, because each of them affects only one of the direction cosines of the new trial vector. The difficulty caused by over-correction does not seem to be a problem with this method.

# CHAPTER XI

## THE METHOD OF EXTENDED VECTORS

This method has proved to be effective in analyzing a factorial matrix of more than three dimensions, but it is applicable only in those cases in which a central reference vector can be found on which all the test vectors have positive projections. The method of extended vectors will be described, first, for a simple case of three dimensions, in which the new method gives the solution in one diagram if a simple-structure solution exists. The method will then be described with a five-dimensional fictitious example, which illustrates, perhaps better than the simpler example, just how the method is used in practice.

### The method of extended vectors for three dimensions

In the previous chapter we described the method of rotation of axes by two-dimensional sections, which are represented on diagrams. Each diagram represented the plane determined by two of the reference vectors, and it was plotted from pairs of columns of the factor matrix $V$. In the method of extended vectors these sections represent three dimensions. The principle of the method will be explained briefly before the numerical example is given.

Let *Figure 1* represent a configuration of test vectors with origin at $O$. Let the axis $I$ represent the first centroid axis, the major principal axis, or any other axis that is central in the configuration and on which all the test vectors have positive projections. Let the arc $CC$ represent a unit sphere with center at $O$, and let the reference vector $I$ be of unit length. Consider, next, the plane $PP$, which is tangent to the unit sphere and orthogonal to the central axis $I$. In a configuration of $r$ dimensions this plane becomes an $(r-1)$-dimensional hyperplane. Let each test vector be extended so that its terminus is in the plane $PP$. All the test vectors will then have unit projection on the axis $I$. Each test vector is extended by the multiplier

$$(1) \qquad\qquad D_e = \frac{1}{a_{j1}},$$

so that its projection on the $I$-axis is unity. This has been done in *Table 1*. The extended factor loadings were obtained from *Table 1* of the previous chapter. The multiplier $D_e$ for test $j$ is applied to all the factor loadings $a_{jm}$ of that test to determine the corresponding extended factor loadings $A_{jm}$ of *Table 1*.

225

In *Figure 1* let $OAB$ represent one of the co-ordinate planes containing a number of the test vectors. When these have been extended, their termini also lie in the tangent plane $PP$. Since the intersection of two planes is a straight line, it is clear that the termini of the test vectors in the co-ordinate plane $OAB$ will lie in a straight line in the plane $PP$ and that this linear arrangement of test vector termini should be evident if a plot is made of columns II and III in the extended factor matrix.

The normal $\Lambda$ defines the co-ordinate plane $OAB$ of a simple structure.

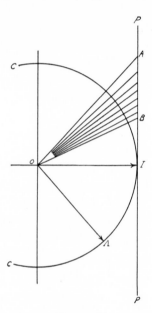

FIGURE 1

The direction cosines of $\Lambda$ may be denoted $\lambda_1, \lambda_2, \lambda_3$, and, hence, the equation of the plane $OAB$ may be written in normal form as

(2) $$\lambda_1 x_1 + \lambda_2 x_2 + \lambda_3 x_3 = 0 ,$$

where $x_1$ is the projection of any point $(x_1, x_2, x_3)$ of the plane on the $I$-axis. Since the plane $PP$ is tangent to the unit sphere and orthogonal to the $I$-axis, all points in that plane have unit projection on that axis, so that $x_1 = 1$. The equation of the line of intersection $AB$ of the two planes is, therefore,

(3) $$\lambda_1 + \lambda_2 x_2 + \lambda_3 x_3 = 0 ,$$

when referred to orthogonal axes in the plane $PP$ which are parallel to *II* and *III*.

When a plot is made of columns II and III of *Table 1*, we have *Figure 2*, where the points are clearly arranged in three intersecting lines. The equations of these lines were determined graphically, and they are as follows:

Trace of $X$-plane $\quad .58 - x_2 + .32x_3 = 0$,

Trace of $Y$-plane $\quad .55 + .30x_2 - x_3 = 0$,

Trace of $Z$-plane $\quad .71 + .83x_2 + x_3 = 0$.

These equations correspond to equation (3), and it will be seen that the constant term of this equation is the coefficient of $x_1$ in equation (2).

*Table 1*

*Extended Factor Matrix* $E_0$

| Test | $D_e$ | I | II | III |
|------|-------|-----|------|------|
| 1 | 1.5175 | 1.000 | −1.117 | .209 |
| 2 | 1.3793 | 1.000 | .248 | −.905 |
| 3 | 1.5038 | 1.000 | .808 | .752 |
| 4 | 1.1507 | 1.000 | − .241 | −.510 |
| 5 | 1.1990 | 1.000 | .218 | .609 |
| 6 | 1.1962 | 1.000 | .621 | .182 |
| 7 | 1.1682 | 1.000 | − .528 | −.314 |
| 8 | 1.1792 | 1.000 | − .502 | .377 |
| 9 | 1.1614 | 1.000 | .483 | −.347 |
| 10 | 1.1364 | 1.000 | − .388 | −.402 |
| 11 | 1.1249 | 1.000 | − .165 | .490 |
| 12 | 1.1429 | 1.000 | .554 | −.106 |
| 13 | 1.4992 | 1.000 | −1.087 | .163 |
| 14 | 1.3947 | 1.000 | .343 | −.863 |
| 15 | 1.5773 | 1.000 | .792 | .823 |
| 16 | 1.0684 | 1.000 | .275 | .176 |
| 17 | 1.0352 | 1.000 | − .247 | −.086 |
| 18 | 1.6000 | 1.000 | −1.152 | .266 |
| 19 | 1.4245 | 1.000 | .160 | −.926 |
| 20 | 1.5060 | 1.000 | .807 | .735 |

The plot shown in *Figure 2* enables us to determine the direction numbers of a normal to each co-ordinate plane. When these are normalized, we have the direction cosines of each reference axis $\Lambda_p$.

The successive steps in the numerical work will now be described. On *Figure 2* the three traces are denoted the $X$-, $Y$-, and $Z$-planes, as shown. The coefficients are recorded in the $S$-matrix of *Table 2*. In this case the matrices $S$ and $L$ are identical. The columns of $L$ are normalized as in the previous work, and the multipliers $d_{rp}$ are determined. Applying these multipliers to the columns of $L$, we get the matrix $\Lambda$, the columns of which show the direction cosines of the three reference vectors $\Lambda_p$. It will be seen that this matrix $\Lambda$ is the same as $\Lambda_{04}$ of *Table 6* of *chapter x*, which was obtained after three rotations. The slight discrepancies are due to the fact that the two solutions were obtained graphically. The columns $X$, $Y$, and $Z$ of $\Lambda$ in *Table 2* correspond to the columns $B$, $C$, and $A$, respectively, in the matrix $\Lambda_{04}$ of *Table 6* of *chapter x*. The order in which the reference vectors are listed in the columns of $\Lambda$, or of the factor matrix, is, of course, immaterial.

The oblique factor matrix $V$ of *Table 2* was obtained directly from the given factor matrix $F_0$ of *Table 1* in *chapter x* by the transformation $\Lambda$ in *Table 2*. The matrix $\Lambda'\Lambda = C$ shows the cosines of the angles between the reference vectors, and the matrix $T$ shows the direction cosines of the primary vectors $T_p$. Their angular separations are shown in the matrix $TT'$.

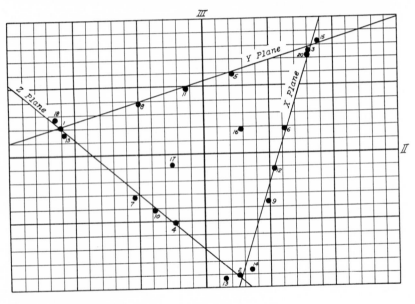

FIGURE 2

This is the matrix $R_{pq}$, which gives the correlations between the primary factors $T_p$. These correlations are the same as the correlations shown in *Table 8* of *chapter x*. The slight discrepancies are due to graphical methods. For example, the correlation $+.105$ in one table corresponds to the correlation $+.112$ in the other table.

We have shown here an application of the method of extended vectors to a problem in three dimensions. Since this method consists in taking three-dimensional sections of an $r$-dimensional configuration and since $r=3$ in this case, the whole configuration as to its co-ordinate planes is defined here in one diagram, *Figure 2*. When $r$ exceeds 3, it is necessary to make more plots, but not so many as in the method of plotting two-dimensional sections described in the previous chapter.

The advantage of the method of extended vectors is that traces can be drawn anywhere on the plot, since they need not be radial, as in the two-dimensional method. A streak of points anywhere on the diagram can be brought into a co-ordinate plane. The number of rotations is usually much smaller than with the two-dimensional method, but the extended form of the factor matrix must first be computed. The method of extended vectors is not applicable when the configuration is of such a character that no central vector exists on which all the test vectors have appreciable positive projections. It is sometimes possible to use the method when all but a few of the test vectors have positive projections on some central axis, but special

*Table 2*

*Factor Matrix V*

| Matrix $S = L$ | | $X'$ | $Y'$ | $Z'$ | | X | Y | Z |
|---|---|---|---|---|---|---|---|---|
| | I | .58 | .55 | .71 | 1 | .969 | .003 | −.003 |
| | II | −1.00 | .30 | .83 | 2 | .025 | .939 | .005 |
| $l_{mr}$ | III | .32 | −1.00 | 1.00 | 3 | .007 | .023 | .957 |
| | | | | | 4 | .476 | .727 | .000 |
| | $\Sigma l^2$ | 1.4388 | 1.3925 | 2.1930 | 5 | .387 | .005 | .844 |
| | $\sqrt{\Sigma l^2}$ | 1.1195 | 1.1800 | 1.4809 | 6 | .012 | .393 | .794 |
| | $d_{rp}$ | .8337 | .8475 | .6753 | 7 | .719 | .512 | −.025 |
| | | | | | 8 | .850 | .016 | .384 |
| | | | | | 9 | −.011 | .760 | .444 |
| Matrix $\Lambda$ | | X | Y | Z | 10 | .615 | .623 | −.008 |
| | | | | | 11 | .668 | .008 | .638 |
| | | | | | 12 | −.007 | .610 | .628 |
| | I | .483 | .466 | .479 | 13 | .956 | .034 | −.013 |
| | II | −.834 | .254 | .560 | 14 | −.024 | .921 | .063 |
| $\lambda_{mp}$ | III | .267 | −.847 | .675 | 15 | .028 | −.019 | .937 |
| | | | | | 16 | .282 | .362 | .704 |
| | | | | | 17 | .644 | .460 | .273 |
| Matrix $C = \Lambda'\Lambda$ | | X | Y | Z | 18 | .947 | −.032 | .008 |
| | | | | | 19 | .072 | .906 | −.040 |
| | X | 1.000 | | | 20 | .004 | .032 | .948 |
| | Y | −.213 | .999 | | | | | |
| $c_{pq}$ | Z | −.055 | −.206 | .999 | | | | |

| Matrix $T'$ | | X | Y | Z |
|---|---|---|---|---|
| | I | .661 | .713 | .654 |
| | II | −.736 | .199 | .545 |
| $t_{mp}$ | III | .144 | −.671 | .524 |

| Matrix $TT'$ | | X | Y | Z |
|---|---|---|---|---|
| | X | 1.000 | | |
| $R_{pq}$ | Y | .229 | 1.000 | |
| | Z | .105 | .224 | 1.000 |

adjustments are then necessary to write the final rotated factor matrix for the whole battery.

### The method of extended vectors for $n$ dimensions

The principle that has been described for a three-dimensional example will now be applied to a fictitious five-dimensional example. We start this problem with a simple structure, shown in *Table 3*. Here we have twenty-five variables, and arbitrary factor loadings have been recorded in this factor matrix for the five columns shown. This matrix may be denoted $F_x$.

*Table 3*

*A Fictitious Simple Configuration* $F_x$

|    | $P_1$ | $P_2$ | $P_3$ | $P_4$ | $P_5$ | $h^2$ |
|----|-------|-------|-------|-------|-------|-------|
| 1  | .0    | .3    | .0    | .0    | .8    | .73   |
| 2  | .0    | .9    | .0    | .0    | .0    | .81   |
| 3  | .5    | .5    | .0    | .5    | .0    | .75   |
| 4  | .5    | .7    | .0    | .0    | .0    | .74   |
| 5  | .0    | .3    | .3    | .0    | .7    | .67   |
| 6  | .0    | .4    | .6    | .4    | .0    | .68   |
| 7  | .0    | .0    | .8    | .0    | .0    | .64   |
| 8  | .0    | .5    | .7    | .0    | .0    | .74   |
| 9  | .0    | .0    | .6    | .6    | .0    | .72   |
| 10 | .0    | .0    | .4    | .6    | .5    | .77   |
| 11 | .6    | .0    | .5    | .4    | .0    | .77   |
| 12 | .7    | .3    | .3    | .0    | .0    | .67   |
| 13 | .0    | .0    | .0    | .0    | .9    | .81   |
| 14 | .0    | .8    | .0    | .4    | .0    | .80   |
| 15 | .6    | .0    | .5    | .0    | .3    | .70   |
| 16 | .6    | .0    | .6    | .0    | .0    | .72   |
| 17 | .0    | .0    | .7    | .0    | .5    | .74   |
| 18 | .4    | .0    | .0    | .0    | .7    | .65   |
| 19 | .8    | .0    | .0    | .0    | .0    | .64   |
| 20 | .0    | .0    | .0    | .6    | .6    | .72   |
| 21 | .0    | .0    | .0    | .8    | .0    | .64   |
| 22 | .3    | .0    | .0    | .4    | .7    | .74   |
| 23 | .0    | .5    | .0    | .5    | .5    | .75   |
| 24 | .7    | .3    | .0    | .0    | .3    | .67   |
| 25 | .3    | .0    | .0    | .8    | .0    | .73   |

The communalities are also recorded. In *Table 4* we have an arbitrary orthogonal matrix $\Lambda_{x0}$, which transforms $F_x$ into the factor matrix $F_0$ of *Table 5*. We then have the relation

$$(4) \qquad\qquad F_x \Lambda_{x0} = F_0 .$$

We start the problem with this matrix as given, and our problem is to analyze it in such a way as to rediscover the simple structure of *Table 3*, which will be regarded as unknown during the computations.

The first step is to extend the test vectors of *Table 5*. The last column of that table shows the reciprocal of the first-factor loading by equation (1). Multiplying each row of $F_0$ by the corresponding value $D_e$, we have

(5)                                    $D_e F_0 = E_0$ ;

and we then have the extended factor matrix $E_0$ of *Table 6*, in which each entry in the first column is unity.

There are four columns that can be plotted to show the configuration, and these give six diagrams. Only three of these diagrams are shown in

*Table 4*

*An Arbitrary Orthogonal Transformation $\Lambda_{x0}$*

|  | I | II | III | IV | V |
|---|---|---|---|---|---|
| $P_1$ | .447 | −.148 | −.092 | −.832 | −.282 |
| $P_2$ | .409 | .543 | .595 | −.084 | .420 |
| $P_3$ | .447 | −.431 | −.375 | .128 | .678 |
| $P_4$ | .447 | .554 | −.554 | .307 | −.307 |
| $P_5$ | .484 | −.438 | .438 | .438 | −.438 |

*Table 5*

*A Centroid Matrix $F_0$ of the Fictitious Test Battery*

|  | I | II | III | IV | V | $D_e$ |
|---|---|---|---|---|---|---|
| 1 | .510 | −.188 | .529 | .325 | −.224 | 1.9608 |
| 2 | .368 | .489 | .536 | −.076 | .378 | 2.7174 |
| 3 | .652 | .474 | −.026 | −.304 | −.084 | 1.5337 |
| 4 | .510 | .306 | .370 | −.475 | .153 | 1.9608 |
| 5 | .596 | −.273 | .373 | .320 | .023 | 1.6779 |
| 6 | .611 | .180 | −.209 | .166 | .452 | 1.6367 |
| 7 | .358 | −.345 | −.300 | .102 | .542 | 2.7933 |
| 8 | .517 | −.030 | .035 | .048 | .685 | 1.9342 |
| 9 | .536 | .074 | −.557 | .261 | .223 | 1.8657 |
| 10 | .689 | −.059 | −.263 | .454 | −.132 | 1.4514 |
| 11 | .670 | −.083 | −.464 | −.312 | .047 | 1.4925 |
| 12 | .570 | −.070 | .002 | −.569 | .132 | 1.7544 |
| 13 | .436 | −.394 | .394 | .394 | −.394 | 2.2936 |
| 14 | .506 | .656 | .254 | .056 | .213 | 1.9763 |
| 15 | .637 | −.436 | −.111 | −.304 | .038 | 1.5699 |
| 16 | .536 | −.347 | −.280 | −.422 | .238 | 1.8657 |
| 17 | .555 | −.521 | −.044 | .309 | .256 | 1.8018 |
| 18 | .518 | −.366 | .270 | −.026 | −.419 | 1.9305 |
| 19 | .358 | −.118 | −.074 | −.666 | −.226 | 2.7933 |
| 20 | .559 | .070 | −.070 | .447 | −.447 | 1.7889 |
| 21 | .358 | .443 | −.443 | .246 | −.246 | 2.7933 |
| 22 | .652 | −.129 | .057 | .180 | −.514 | 1.5337 |
| 23 | .670 | .330 | .240 | .330 | −.162 | 1.4925 |
| 24 | .581 | −.072 | .246 | −.476 | −.203 | 1.7212 |
| 25 | .492 | .399 | −.471 | −.004 | −.330 | 2.0325 |

*Figures 3, 4, 5,* and *6,* since these are the only ones that were used for determining the initial locations of the reference vectors.

The successive computations are shown in the formulae for each part of *Table 8* and subsequent tables. It will be seen that some of the matrices have an added column for the first centroid factor, which was used in writing the extended factor matrix. The new notation is for the matrix $M$, which is identical with $\Lambda$ except for the added column for the central axis $(I)$.[1] At any stage in the rotations, the matrix $\Lambda$ can be written by merely omitting

Table 6

*Extended Factorial Matrix* $E_0$

|  | I | II | III | IV | V |
|---|---|---|---|---|---|
| 1 | 1.000 | − .369 | 1.037 | .637 | − .438 |
| 2 | 1.000 | 1.329 | 1.457 | − .207 | 1.027 |
| 3 | 1.000 | .727 | − .040 | − .466 | − .129 |
| 4 | 1.000 | .600 | .725 | − .931 | .300 |
| 5 | 1.000 | − .458 | .626 | .537 | .039 |
| 6 | 1.000 | .295 | − .342 | .272 | .740 |
| 7 | 1.000 | − .964 | − .838 | .285 | 1.514 |
| 8 | 1.000 | − .058 | .068 | .093 | 1.325 |
| 9 | 1.000 | .138 | −1.039 | .487 | .416 |
| 10 | 1.000 | − .086 | − .382 | .659 | − .192 |
| 11 | 1.000 | − .124 | − .693 | − .466 | .070 |
| 12 | 1.000 | − .123 | .004 | − .998 | .232 |
| 13 | 1.000 | − .904 | .904 | .904 | − .904 |
| 14 | 1.000 | 1.296 | .502 | .111 | .421 |
| 15 | 1.000 | − .684 | − .174 | − .477 | .060 |
| 16 | 1.000 | − .647 | .522 | − .787 | .444 |
| 17 | 1.000 | − .939 | − .079 | .557 | .461 |
| 18 | 1.000 | − .707 | .521 | − .050 | − .809 |
| 19 | 1.000 | − .330 | − .207 | −1.860 | − .631 |
| 20 | 1.000 | .125 | − .125 | .800 | − .800 |
| 21 | 1.000 | 1.237 | −1.237 | .687 | − .687 |
| 22 | 1.000 | − .198 | .087 | .276 | − .788 |
| 23 | 1.000 | .493 | .358 | .493 | − .242 |
| 24 | 1.000 | − .124 | .423 | − .819 | − .349 |
| 25 | 1.000 | .811 | − .957 | − .008 | − .671 |

the first column from the matrix $M$. In the method of extended vectors the matrices $S$, $L$, $H$, and $C$ have the additional column for $(I)$.

*The new* B-*plane*

*Figure 3* shows the plot for columns II and IV of *Table 6.* A unit vector is indicated by an arrowhead on the *II*-axis, and another unit vector is shown similarly on the *IV*-axis. These are the given unit reference vectors $(II)$ and $(IV)$. A line has been drawn through a streak of points to represent the trace of one of the planes. It is not necessary that the traces should

---

[1] The notation "$(I)$" will be used to denote a unit vector in the axis $I$, and similarly for the other orthogonal reference axes.

bound the configuration as in the present case. A normal is drawn through the origin, as shown by the dotted line. The direction of the normal is shown by the arrowhead. The direction of the normal is so chosen that the projections of most of the points, which represent test vector termini, will be positive. Since this normal is closer to the $II$-axis than to the other axis, we denote the trace the $B$-plane, and the normal is denoted $B_2'$. The sub-

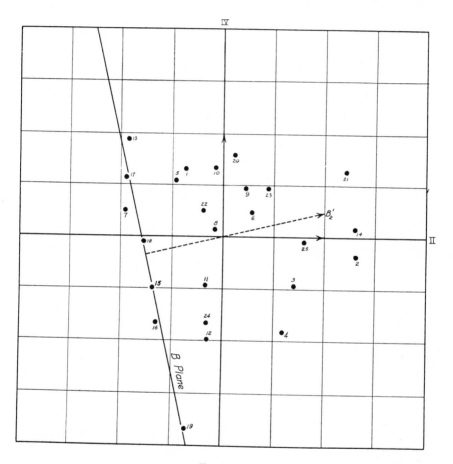

FIGURE 3

script of $B_2'$ represents a new location, and the prime indicates that the new vector is a long vector that has not yet been normalized.

Since the new vector is closer to $(II)$ than to $(IV)$, we shall describe it as equal to the unit vector $(II)$ plus corrections in the directions of $(IV)$ and $(I)$. The vector $(II)$ is then a base vector for $B_2'$. In *Figure 3* we draw the normal $B_2'$ so that its terminus is directly above the terminus of the unit vector $(II)$. The new long reference vector $B_2'$ can be described by the vector equation

(6)                    $B_2' = (II) + d(IV) + i(I)$ ,

which requires only two numerical values to be found from the graph, namely, $d$ and $i$. When found, these values are recorded in the $B_2'$ column of the matrix $S_{01}$ in *Table 8*.

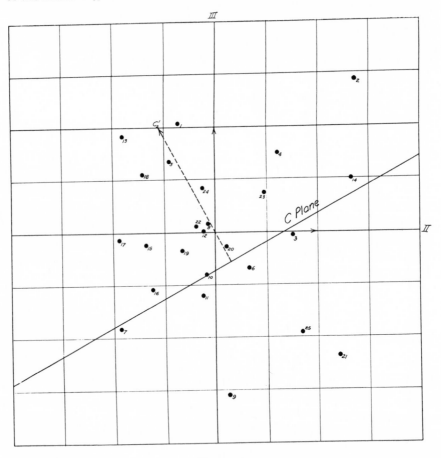

FIGURE 4

The value of the coefficient $d$ is read directly from the graph. It is merely the vertical distance from the terminus of $(II)$ to the terminus of $B_2'$ on *Figure 3*, namely, 0.23. These diagrams are ordinarily drawn on cross-section paper, where finer gradations are available than on the figures of this chapter.

The absolute value of the coefficient $i$ is read directly as the intercept of the trace on the same axis as the base vector $(II)$. This intercept is 0.79. The coefficient $i$ is taken as positive if the origin and the new vector are on the same side of the trace, as in this case. The coefficient $i$ is taken negative if the origin and the new vector are on opposite sides of the trace.

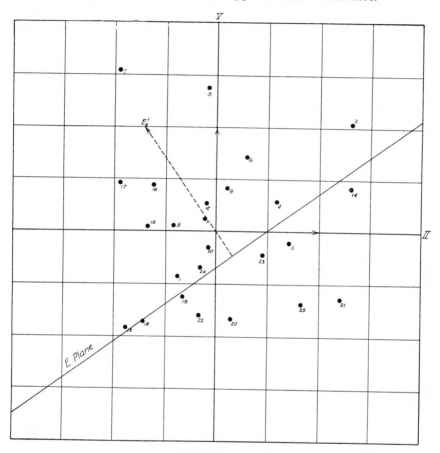

FIGURE 5

Having read the two numerical values $d$ and $i$ on the graph, we can write the vector equation (6) in numerical form, namely,

(7) $$B_2' = 1.00(II) + .23(IV) + .79(I) ,$$

and these coefficients are written in the column $B_2'$ of the matrix $S_{01}$ in *Table 8*.

*The new* C-*plane*

In *Figure 4* we have the plot for columns II and III of the extended factor matrix $E_0$ of *Table 6*. The two unit vectors $(II)$ and $(III)$ are shown by arrowheads in the *II*- and *III*-axes, respectively. A trace has been drawn through or near eight points. The normal is nearer *III* than *II*, and hence the trace is labeled the *C*-plane.

Since the unit vector (*III*) is the base vector for this diagram, we draw

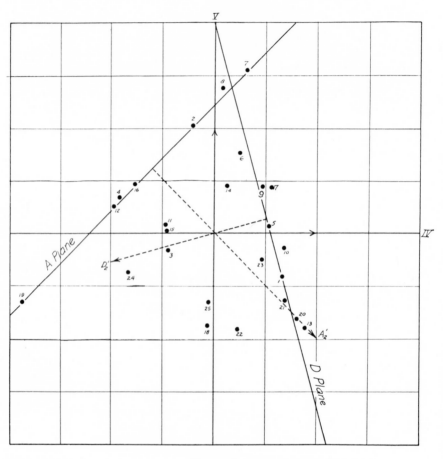

FIGURE 6

the normal $C_2'$ so that its terminus has unit projection on (*III*), as in the previous figure. The new vector $C_2'$ is described by the vector equation

$$(8) \qquad C_2' = (III) + b(II) + i(I) .$$

The coefficient $b$ is read directly from *Figure 4* as the distance between the termini of (*III*) and $C_2'$, namely, $-.52$. The intercept of the trace on the *III*-axis has the absolute value .35. It is taken positive, since the origin and the vector $C_2'$ are on the same side of the trace. Hence we have the vector in numerical form,

$$(9) \qquad C_2' = 1.00(III) - .52(II) + .35(I) ,$$

and the coefficients are recorded in the column $C_2'$ of $S_{01}$ in *Table 8*.

*The new* E-*plane*

In *Figure 5* we have the plot for columns II and V of *Table 6*. Here a trace has been drawn through, or near, twelve points. The normal is drawn through the origin to $E_2'$ so that it has unit projection on $(V)$, which is taken as a unit base vector. The vector equation of $E_2'$ then is

$$(10) \qquad E_2' = (V) + b(II) + i(I) ,$$

where $b$ and $i$ are to be determined from the graph. The value of $b$ is read as $-.70$. The absolute value of the intercept of the trace on the $V$-axis is .35. It is taken as positive because the vector $E_2'$ and the origin are on the same side of the trace. Hence we have the vector equation in numerical form,

$$(11) \qquad E_2' = 1.00(V) - .70(II) + .35 ,$$

the coefficients of which are recorded in column $E_2'$ of $S_{01}$ in *Table 8*.

*The new* A- *and* D-*planes*

*Figure 6* shows an example of a graph in which two new planes are determined. In locating two planes on the same diagram, one avoids drawing traces that are parallel, for reasons to be discussed. One trace is drawn through seven points. Such a configuration is useful in locating the simple structure not only because a number of points lie in a straight line but also because they extend over some length on the diagram. In the case of two alternative traces with the same number of points, one prefers the one that has more length on the diagram.

Another trace is drawn through about thirteen points, and a normal is drawn through the origin. Both normals are drawn in the direction of the configuration, so that most of the test vectors will have positive projections. Since the normal to this trace is nearly parallel to $(IV)$, this trace is denoted the $D$-plane. The first trace might have been denoted the $E$-plane, but such a plane has already been chosen, so this one is denoted the $A$-plane, thus locating five new planes, $A$ to $E$, inclusive.

The normal to the $D$-trace is drawn through the origin and extended so that it has unit projection on the base vector $(IV)$. The vector equation for the normal then is

$$(12) \qquad D_2' = -(IV) + e(V) + i(I) ,$$

where $e$ and $i$ are to be read graphically. The value of $e$ is $-.26$, and the absolute value of $i$ is .54. This is taken positive because the normal $D_2'$ and the origin are on the same side of the trace. We then have the vector equation in numerical form,

$$(13) \qquad D_2' = -1.00(IV) - .26(V) + .54 ,$$

the coefficients of which are recorded in columns $D_2'$ of $S_{01}$ in *Table 8*.

The normal to the $A$-trace is drawn through the origin to the point $A_2'$ with unit projection on $(IV)$, which is arbitrarily chosen as a base vector. The vector equation for $A_2'$ can be written

$$(14) \qquad A_2' = (IV) + e(V) + i(I) .$$

The numerical value of $e$ is $-.97$, and the absolute value of $i$ is 1.20, which is taken positive because $A_2'$ and the origin are on the same side of the trace. We then have the vector equation in numerical form,

$$(15) \qquad A_2' = 1.00(IV) - .97(V) + 1.20(I) ,$$

the coefficients of which are recorded in the $A_2'$ column in $S_{01}$ of *Table 8*.

It so happened that all the increments $i$ for the vector $(I)$ were positive in this set of four diagrams. In each of the subsequent rotations there will be cases of negative increments for $(I)$, as may be seen from the diagrams and from the first row of the matrix $S$ in *Tables 9, 10,* and *11*.

### Independence of planes

When the traces have been drawn for the planes, it is desirable to ascertain, before proceeding with the computations, whether the planes are linearly independent. It sometimes happens that the same plane is represented by streaks of points on several diagrams. If these traces were identified as different planes, one would discover in the subsequent computation that the two corresponding normals had an angular separation with a cosine of, say, .80 or .90. The result might be that one of the common-factor dimensions had been lost. In order to avoid the annoyance of the computational adjustments that would then be necessary, it is well to inspect the planes for linear independence. This is not necessary in the later rotations where the planes are easily identified from one rotation to the next, but it is advisable to make an inspectional check on linear independence at the start of a factorial analysis. The check will be described here only for the initial location of the reference vectors.

In *Table 7* we have five columns, one for each of the five normals that have been chosen. In column $A$ there is recorded a plus sign for each test variable that has a large positive projection on the normal $A_2'$, a zero for each test that has nearly vanishing projection on that normal, and a blank space for those tests whose projections are neither conspicuously high nor vanishingly small. In some of the columns there are recorded minus signs for those tests which have conspicuously strong negative projections.

For every pair of columns, there must be differentiation as to the plus signs, the minus signs, and the zeros. In the present case we have chosen the five normals so that they are linearly independent. If we had chosen two normals with small angular separation, they would have had the same

Table 7

Projections on New Planes

|   | A | B | C | D | E |
|---|---|---|---|---|---|
| 1  | + |   | + | 0 | 0 |
| 2  | 0 | + | + |   | 0 |
| 3  |   | + | 0 | + | 0 |
| 4  | 0 | + | + | + | 0 |
| 5  | + |   | + | 0 |   |
| 6  |   | + | 0 | 0 |   |
| 7  | 0 | 0 | 0 | 0 | + |
| 8  | 0 |   |   | 0 | + |
| 9  |   | + | + | 0 |   |
| 10 | + |   | 0 | 0 | 0 |
| 11 |   |   | 0 | + |   |
| 12 | 0 |   |   | + |   |
| 13 | + | 0 | + | 0 | 0 |
| 14 |   | + | 0 | 0 | 0 |
| 15 |   | 0 |   | + |   |
| 16 | 0 | 0 | 0 | + | + |
| 17 |   | 0 | + | 0 | + |
| 18 | + | 0 | + |   | 0 |
| 19 | 0 | 0 |   | + | 0 |
| 20 | + | + | 0 | 0 | − |
| 21 | + | + | − | 0 | − |
| 22 | + |   |   |   | 0 |
| 23 | + | + |   | 0 | 0 |
| 24 |   |   | + | + | 0 |
| 25 | + | + | − |   | − |

tests with high positive projections, the same tests with strong negative saturation, and the same tests with small projections. That would indicate the fact of linear dependence, and one of the normals could then be discarded in favor of a new one which should be linearly independent of the other four normals. If such a situation arises, it is a useful procedure to select the tests which have no plus signs or minus signs and to find a trace on whose normal the missing tests would have significant projection, either positive or negative. That would, in general, insure the recovery of all the dimensions of the common-factor space. One way to avoid the loss of a dimension is to designate a new reference vector by the fixed orthogonal axis to which it is the closest, but this procedure is not always feasible.

## Table 8

### Computations from Figures 3, 4, 5, 6

#### $E_1 = E_0 H_{01}$

| | I | A | B | C | D | E |
|---|---|---|---|---|---|---|
| 1 | 1.000 | 1.231 | .439 | 1.338 | .014 | .134 |
| 2 | 1.000 | -.002 | 1.599 | .945 | .412 | .352 |
| 3 | 1.000 | -.468 | 1.088 | -.057 | .892 | .226 |
| 4 | 1.000 | .012 | .907 | .646 | 1.195 | .182 |
| 5 | 1.000 | .925 | .352 | 1.029 | -.006 | .559 |
| 6 | 1.000 | .410 | .886 | -.123 | .065 | .696 |
| 7 | 1.000 | .009 | .083 | .012 | .119 | .999 |
| 8 | 1.000 | -.004 | .582 | .380 | .088 | 1.999 |
| 9 | 1.000 | .698 | .803 | .644 | .048 | 1.351 |
| 10 | 1.000 | 1.113 | .661 | .011 | -.060 | .527 |
| 11 | 1.000 | .363 | .431 | .235 | .847 | .172 |
| 12 | 1.000 | -.012 | .337 | .355 | 1.268 | .399 |
| 13 | 1.000 | 1.622 | .073 | 1.461 | .111 | .526 |
| 14 | 1.000 | .491 | 1.630 | .151 | .274 | .063 |
| 15 | 1.000 | .362 | -.003 | .451 | .859 | .107 |
| 16 | 1.000 | .010 | -.030 | .140 | 1.039 | .700 |
| 17 | 1.000 | .713 | -.016 | .644 | .118 | .982 |
| 18 | 1.000 | .053 | .055 | 1.050 | .686 | 1.156 |
| 19 | 1.000 | -.026 | .024 | .267 | 2.200 | .029 |
| 20 | 1.000 | 1.511 | .849 | .136 | -.045 | .039 |
| 21 | 1.000 | 1.389 | 1.687 | -1.296 | .027 | .422 |
| 22 | 1.000 | 1.219 | .506 | .458 | .402 | .946 |
| 23 | 1.000 | 1.049 | 1.078 | .383 | .094 | .235 |
| 24 | 1.000 | .392 | .368 | .710 | 1.244 | .186 |
| 25 | 1.000 | 1.003 | 1.235 | .871 | .619 | .070 |

#### $C_1 = M_{01}M_{01}$

| | I | $A_3$ | $B_3$ | $C_3$ | $D_3$ | $E_3$ |
|---|---|---|---|---|---|---|
| I | 1.000 | | | | | |
| A | .653 | 1.000 | | | | |
| B | .610 | .495 | 1.000 | | | |
| C | .297 | .194 | .159 | 1.000 | | |
| D | .463 | -.047 | -.130 | .138 | 1.000 | |
| E | .276 | -.235 | -.257 | .325 | -.048 | 1.000 |

#### Matrix $S_{0a}$

| | I | $A'_2$ | $B'_2$ | $C'_2$ | $D'_2$ | $E'_2$ |
|---|---|---|---|---|---|---|
| I | 1.00 | | | | | |
| II | | 1.20 | .79 | .35 | .54 | .35 |
| III | | | 1.00 | -.52 | | -.70 |
| IV | | 1.00 | | 1.00 | -1.00 | |
| V | | -.97 | .23 | | -.26 | 1.00 |

#### $S_{01} = L_{01}$

| | I | $A'_2$ | $B'_2$ | $C'_2$ | $D'_2$ | $E'_2$ |
|---|---|---|---|---|---|---|
| I | 1.00 | | | | | |
| II | | 1.20 | .79 | .35 | .54 | .35 |
| III | | | 1.00 | -.52 | | -.70 |
| IV | | 1.00 | | 1.00 | -1.00 | |
| V | | -.97 | .23 | | -.26 | 1.00 |
| $\Sigma r^2$ | | 3.3809 | 1.6770 | 1.3929 | 1.3592 | 1.6125 |
| $\sqrt{\Sigma r^2}$ | | 1.8387 | 1.2950 | 1.1802 | 1.1658 | 1.2698 |
| $D_1$ | | .5439 | .7722 | .8473 | .8577 | .7875 |

#### $H_{01} = S_{01}D_1$

| | I | $A_3$ | $B_3$ | $C_3$ | $D_3$ | $E_3$ |
|---|---|---|---|---|---|---|
| I | 1.000 | | | | | |
| II | | .653 | .610 | .297 | .463 | .276 |
| III | | | .772 | -.441 | | -.551 |
| IV | | .544 | | .847 | -.858 | |
| V | | -.528 | .178 | | -.223 | .787 |

#### $M_{01} = L_{01}D_1$

| | I | $A_3$ | $B_3$ | $C_3$ | $D_3$ | $E_3$ |
|---|---|---|---|---|---|---|
| I | 1.000 | | | | | |
| II | | .653 | .610 | .297 | .463 | .276 |
| III | | | .772 | -.441 | | -.551 |
| IV | | .544 | | .847 | -.858 | |
| V | | -.528 | .178 | | -.223 | .787 |

## Alternative method of writing the S-matrix

A variant of the method that has been described for *Figures 3, 4, 5*, and *6* may be preferred by some students. One writes the equation of the trace in the form

$$(16) \qquad a_2\,x_2 + a_3 x_3 + d = 0\,,$$

which might represent the $A$-plane determined from a diagram of two columns II and III. If most of the points of the configuration are on the same side of the trace as the origin, then the constant term in (16) should be positive. If the constant term in (16) is negative, the signs of all the terms are reversed. If most of the points in the configuration are on the opposite side of the trace from the origin, then the constant term must be negative. The three coefficients are then recorded in the appropriate column of the $S$-matrix. Other variations of these procedures can be easily devised to suit individual preferences.

## Computations for *Table 8*

When the matrix $S_{01}$ has been written by inspection of the graphs, the remaining computations of *Table 8* follow the formulae given and in the order given in the table. In the initial location of the reference vectors the matrices $S_{01}$ and $L_{01}$ are identical because the matrix $S$ describes the new reference vectors in terms of the fixed orthogonal frame. From the matrix $L_{01}$ we obtain the diagonal entries of $D_1$ as shown. Then we determine $H_{01}$, which is in this case identical with $M_{01}$. For subsequent rotations they will be different. The matrix $C_1$ shows the cosines of the angular separations between the reference vectors. These cosines are recorded on the diagrams for the next rotation, as shown in all subsequent figures. The new oblique factorial matrix $E_1$ is computed either from $H_{01}$ or from $M_{01}$. In practice it is not necessary to write the column $I$ in the extended factor matrices. The column is here given explicitly to show the complete result of the indicated matrix multiplications. The factor matrix $E_1$ is used for plotting the next set of diagrams.

## The first rotation

The ten pairs of columns of the factor matrix $E_1$ are plotted on as many diagrams, and these are inspected to select the first rotation of the reference axes. Only three of the ten diagrams were used, and they are represented in *Figures 7, 8*, and *9*. *Figure 7* shows a type of plot that occurs rather frequently in factor analysis, which indicates an almost rigid rotation of two axes, $A_1$ and $C_1$, through a large angle. In all these diagrams we record in the corner of the diagram the cosine of the angle separating the two reference axes that are represented by the plot. When these cosines deviate markedly from zero, they are used in making a choice of rotation. From this diagram we obtain the entries in columns $A_2'$ and $C_2'$ of the matrix $S_{12}$ in *Table 9*. We have here an example of a negative correction for the vector $(I)$ in the column $C_2'$. The negative sign of this correction is determined by the fact that the vector $C_2'$ and the origin are on opposite sides of the trace for the new $C$-plane. The procedure is the same as that bescribed for the previous diagrams and for *Table 8*.

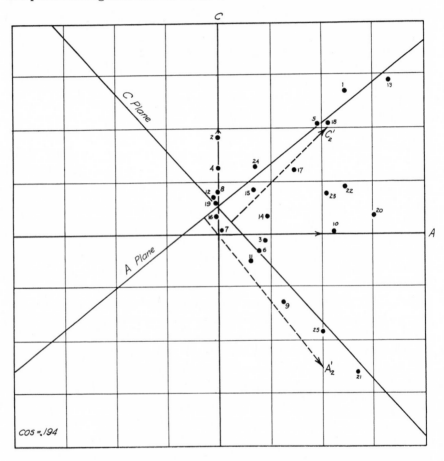

Figure 7

In *Figure 8* we have the plot for $B$ and $D$, on which has been drawn the trace for the new $D$-plane, with a slight adjustment. In *Figure 9* we have the plot for columns $C$ and $E$, which indicates a rather compelling adjustment in the $E$-plane. The cosine of the angular separation between $E_1'$ and $C_1'$ is $+.325$. The positive sign of this cosine indicates that the two reference vectors should separate if they are to be orthogonal or nearly orthogonal. In the present case the vector $E_1$ moves away from the vector $C_1$ to the new position $E_2'$. The positive sign of the cosine and the appearance of the diagram show that the two vectors $E$ and $C$ will be orthogonal, or nearly so. In this rotation no adjustment is made in the $B$-plane. This is represented by the entry of unity in the $B$ column of $S_{12}$ in *Table 9*. Hence $B_2' = B_1$.

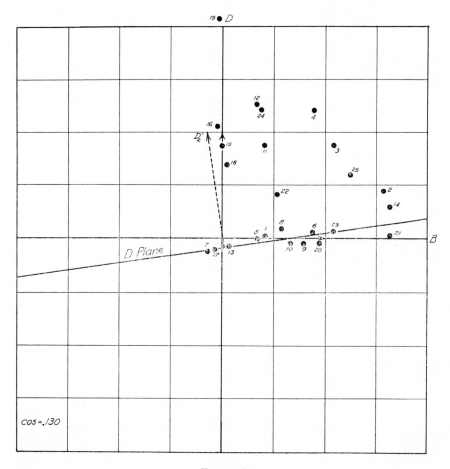

FIGURE 8

## The second rotation

Pairs of columns of the oblique extended factor matrix $E_2$ are plotted on ten diagrams, three of which were used to select the adjustments for the second rotation of the reference axes. These three plots are shown in *Figures 10, 11,* and *12*.

*Figure 10* gives two clear traces of the planes. On the vertical axis we see a large collection of points near the origin and no points elsewhere on

Table 9

Computations from Figures 7, 8, 9

**Matrix $S_{12}$**

| | $I$ | $A'_2$ | $B'_2$ | $C'_2$ | $D'_2$ | $E'_2$ |
|---|---|---|---|---|---|---|
| $I$ | 1.00 | .33 | | -.23 | .12 | .33 |
| $A_1$ | | 1.00 | | 1.06 | | |
| $B_1$ | | | 1.00 | | | |
| $C_1$ | | -1.26 | | 1.00 | -.15 | .45 |
| $D_1$ | | | | | 1.00 | |
| $E_1$ | | | | | | 1.00 |

**$L_{02} = M_{01}S_{12}$**

| | $I$ | $A'_2$ | $B'_2$ | $C'_2$ | $D'_2$ | $E'_2$ |
|---|---|---|---|---|---|---|
| I | 1.000 | .609 | .610 | .759 | .492 | .472 |
| II | | .556 | .772 | .441 | -.116 | -.353 |
| III | | -1.067 | .178 | .847 | -.885 | -.381 |
| IV | | -.544 | | .577 | -.223 | .787 |
| V | | -.528 | | .560 | | |
| $\Sigma I^2$ | | 2.3932 | .9998 | 2.1345 | 1.0885 | 1.1119 |
| $\sqrt{\Sigma I^2}$ | | 1.5470 | 1.0000 | 1.4610 | 1.0433 | 1.0545 |
| $D_2$ | | .6464 | 1.0000 | .6845 | .9585 | .9483 |

**$H_{12} = S_{12}D_2$**

| | $I$ | $A_3$ | $B_3$ | $C_3$ | $D_3$ | $E_3$ |
|---|---|---|---|---|---|---|
| $I$ | 1.000 | .213 | | -.156 | .115 | .313 |
| $A_1$ | | .646 | | .726 | | |
| $B_1$ | | | 1.000 | | | |
| $C_1$ | | -.814 | | .684 | -.144 | -.427 |
| $D_1$ | | | | | .958 | |
| $E_1$ | | | | | | .948 |

**$M_{02} = L_{02}D_2$**

| | $I$ | $A_3$ | $B_3$ | $C_3$ | $D_3$ | $E_3$ |
|---|---|---|---|---|---|---|
| I | 1.000 | .394 | .610 | .520 | .472 | .448 |
| II | | .359 | .772 | .302 | -.111 | -.335 |
| III | | -.690 | .178 | .580 | -.848 | -.361 |
| IV | | -.352 | | .395 | -.214 | .746 |
| V | | -.341 | | .383 | | |

$E_2 = E_1H_{12}$

| | $I$ | $A$ | $B$ | $C$ | $D$ | $E$ |
|---|---|---|---|---|---|---|
| 1 | 1.000 | -.081 | .439 | 1.653 | .065 | -.131 |
| 2 | 1.000 | -.558 | 1.599 | .489 | .279 | .243 |
| 3 | 1.000 | -.562 | 1.088 | .145 | .813 | .123 |
| 4 | 1.000 | -.321 | .907 | .277 | 1.129 | .210 |
| 5 | 1.000 | -.027 | .352 | 1.219 | .059 | .404 |
| 6 | 1.000 | .578 | .886 | .058 | .050 | 1.025 |
| 7 | 1.000 | .209 | -.083 | .141 | .013 | 2.203 |
| 8 | 1.000 | -.094 | .582 | .107 | .115 | 1.431 |
| 9 | 1.000 | 1.188 | .803 | -.090 | -.047 | 1.088 |
| 10 | 1.000 | .923 | .661 | .660 | -.038 | .471 |
| 11 | 1.000 | .639 | .431 | .053 | .864 | .792 |
| 12 | 1.000 | .084 | .337 | .078 | 1.281 | .660 |
| 13 | 1.000 | .072 | .073 | 2.021 | -.002 | -.251 |
| 14 | 1.000 | .407 | 1.630 | .304 | .143 | .147 |
| 15 | 1.000 | .080 | -.003 | .415 | .938 | .784 |
| 16 | 1.000 | .093 | -.030 | .068 | 1.115 | 1.184 |
| 17 | 1.000 | .149 | .016 | .802 | .004 | 1.134 |
| 18 | 1.000 | .039 | .055 | 1.327 | .764 | -.108 |
| 19 | 1.000 | -.021 | .024 | .008 | 2.219 | .162 |
| 20 | 1.000 | 1.078 | .849 | 1.034 | -.050 | .145 |
| 21 | 1.000 | 2.165 | 1.687 | .034 | -.102 | -.030 |
| 22 | 1.000 | .628 | .506 | 1.042 | .427 | -.105 |
| 23 | 1.000 | .579 | 1.078 | .868 | .050 | .027 |
| 24 | 1.000 | -.112 | .368 | .614 | 1.254 | -.076 |
| 25 | 1.000 | 1.570 | 1.235 | .024 | .530 | .022 |

$C_2 = M'_{02}M_{02}$

| | $I$ | $A$ | $B$ | $C$ | $D$ | $E$ |
|---|---|---|---|---|---|---|
| $I$ | 1.000 | | | | | |
| $A$ | .394 | 1.000 | | | | |
| $B$ | .610 | .580 | 1.000 | | | |
| $C$ | .520 | -.034 | .154 | 1.000 | | |
| $D$ | .472 | -.079 | .051 | .026 | 1.000 | |
| $E$ | .448 | -.051 | .015 | -.161 | .089 | 1.000 |

the vertical axis. Two points, namely, *2* and *4*, are in a radial line, and these are combined with the points near the origin for the trace of the new $A$-plane. The corresponding entries are made in the matrix $S_{23}$ of *Table 10*. The other trace on this diagram is also clearly indicated. There are no points on the horizontal axis of this diagram, except those which are at the origin, and consequently there is no configuration to hold the reference

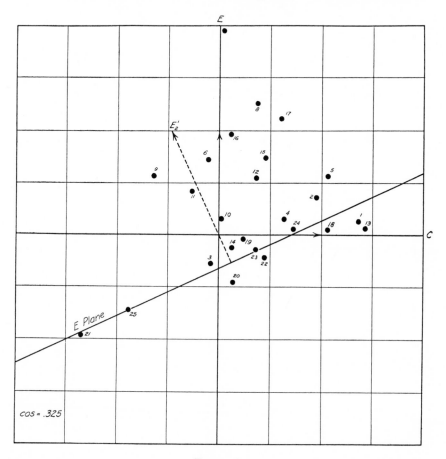

FIGURE 9

normal $B$ in its given position. On the other hand, there are seven points in the first quadrant which are radial, and these are used in selecting a newly adjusted position for the $B$-plane. In each case the plane is identified by adjustments that are less than 45°. The corresponding entries are made in the matrix $S_{23}$ of *Table 10*.

In *Figure 11* we have a small adjustment in the $D$-plane as shown, and in *Figure 12* there is indicated a small adjustment in the $E$-plane. These

# Table 10

## Computations from Figures 10, 11, 12

### Matrix $S_{23}$

| | $I$ | $A'_2$ | $B'_2$ | $C'_2$ | $D'_2$ | $E'_2$ |
|---|---|---|---|---|---|---|
| $I$ | 1.00 | −.07 | .07 | | | |
| $A_1$ | | 1.00 | −.80 | | | |
| $B_1$ | | .40 | 1.00 | | | |
| $C_1$ | | | | 1.00 | −.08 | −.22 |
| $D_1$ | | | | | 1.00 | .24 |
| $E_1$ | | | | | .08 | 1.00 |

### $L_{03} = M_{02}S_{23}$

| | $I$ | $A'_2$ | $B'_2$ | $C'_2$ | $D'_2$ | $E'_2$ |
|---|---|---|---|---|---|---|
| $I$ | 1.000 | .568 | .365 | .520 | .424 | .353 |
| $II$ | | .668 | .485 | .302 | .082 | .407 |
| $III$ | | −.690 | .552 | .580 | −.055 | −.222 |
| $IV$ | | −.423 | −.104 | .395 | −.820 | −.095 |
| $V$ | | −.341 | .273 | .383 | −.241 | .654 |
| $\Sigma I^2$ | | 1.5402 | .7585 | 1.0000 | .9200 | .7763 |
| $\sqrt{\Sigma I^2}$ | | 1.2410 | .8709 | 1.0000 | .9592 | .8811 |
| $D_3$ | | .8058 | 1.1482 | 1.0000 | 1.0426 | 1.1350 |

### $H_{23} = S_{23}D_3$

| | $I$ | $A_3$ | $B_3$ | $C_3$ | $D_3$ | $E_3$ |
|---|---|---|---|---|---|---|
| $I$ | 1.000 | −.056 | .080 | | | |
| $A_1$ | | .806 | −.919 | | | |
| $B_1$ | | .322 | 1.148 | | | |
| $C_1$ | | | | 1.000 | −.083 | −.250 |
| $D_1$ | | | | | 1.043 | .272 |
| $E_1$ | | | | | .083 | 1.135 |

### $M_{03} = L_{03}D_3$

| | $I$ | $A_3$ | $B_3$ | $C_3$ | $D_3$ | $E_3$ |
|---|---|---|---|---|---|---|
| $I$ | 1.000 | .458 | .419 | .520 | .442 | .401 |
| $II$ | | .538 | .557 | .302 | .085 | .462 |
| $III$ | | −.556 | .634 | .580 | −.057 | −.252 |
| $IV$ | | −.341 | −.119 | .395 | −.855 | −.108 |
| $V$ | | −.275 | .313 | .383 | −.251 | .742 |

### $E_3 = E_2H_{23}$

| | $I$ | $A$ | $B$ | $C$ | $D$ | $E$ |
|---|---|---|---|---|---|---|
| 1 | 1.000 | .020 | .658 | 1.653 | .022 | .051 |
| 2 | 1.000 | .009 | 2.428 | .489 | .162 | .159 |
| 3 | 1.000 | −.747 | .813 | .145 | .812 | −.071 |
| 4 | 1.000 | .023 | 1.416 | .277 | 1.068 | .064 |
| 5 | 1.000 | .036 | .509 | 1.219 | .024 | .540 |
| 6 | 1.000 | .695 | .566 | .058 | .017 | .929 |
| 7 | 1.000 | .086 | .207 | −.141 | −.052 | 2.212 |
| 8 | 1.000 | .056 | .835 | .090 | .029 | 1.403 |
| 9 | 1.000 | 1.160 | −.090 | .660 | .033 | .960 |
| 10 | 1.000 | .901 | −.009 | −.053 | .046 | .464 |
| 11 | 1.000 | .598 | −.012 | .078 | .871 | .635 |
| 12 | 1.000 | −.015 | .544 | 2.021 | 1.246 | .520 |
| 13 | 1.000 | .026 | .098 | .304 | .079 | .015 |
| 14 | 1.000 | .797 | 1.577 | .415 | .100 | .000 |
| 15 | 1.000 | .008 | .003 | .068 | .902 | .753 |
| 16 | 1.000 | .009 | .040 | .802 | 1.088 | 1.075 |
| 17 | 1.000 | .059 | −.075 | — | .066 | 1.255 |
| 18 | 1.000 | .007 | .107 | 1.327 | .717 | .012 |
| 19 | 1.000 | −.065 | .127 | .008 | 2.230 | .064 |
| 20 | 1.000 | 1.086 | .064 | 1.034 | −.046 | .133 |
| 21 | 1.000 | 2.232 | .027 | −.034 | −.010 | −.293 |
| 22 | 1.000 | .613 | .084 | 1.042 | .414 | .086 |
| 23 | 1.000 | .758 | .785 | .868 | −.017 | .045 |
| 24 | 1.000 | .028 | .605 | .614 | 1.216 | .003 |
| 25 | 1.000 | 1.607 | .055 | .024 | .600 | .232 |

### $C_3 = M'_{63}M_{03}$

| | $I$ | $A$ | $B$ | $C$ | $D$ | $E$ |
|---|---|---|---|---|---|---|
| $I$ | 1.000 | | | | | |
| $A$ | .458 | 1.000 | | | | |
| $B$ | .419 | .012 | 1.000 | | | |
| $C$ | .520 | −.007 | .251 | 1.000 | | |
| $D$ | .442 | −.034 | .125 | −.019 | 1.000 | |
| $E$ | .401 | −.092 | −.030 | −.040 | −.048 | 1.000 |

diagrams indicate very clearly that the configuration is closing in toward a simple structure. No compelling adjustment was found for the $C$-plane in this set of diagrams, and consequently there is only one entry of unity in the $C$-column of matrix $S_{23}$, according to which the new reference vector $C_2'$ is collinear with the given reference vector $C_1$.

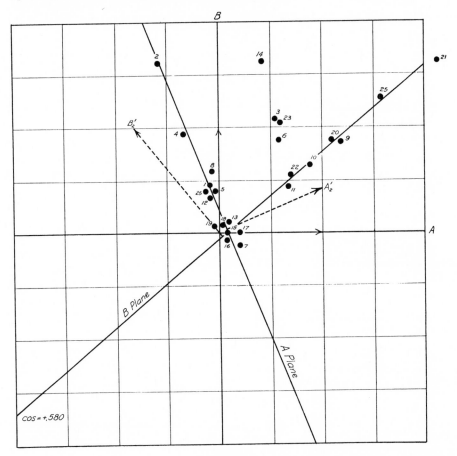

FIGURE 10

Inspection of the angles in this set of diagrams shows one large cosine, namely, $AB$, which is $+.580$. If the simple structure is orthogonal, or nearly so, we should expect the two reference axes, $A$ and $B$, to separate. Inspection of *Figure 10* shows that, when we follow the configuration, the two new reference axes, $A_2'$ and $B_2'$, do separate, as shown by their new locations in the dotted lines. Their given positions are plotted as orthogonal in the figure, but their new separation is an obtuse angle. Further rotations should give only small angular adjustments. The computations for this rotation are indicated in *Table 10*, and the result is the extended factor matrix $E_3$, which is used for plotting the next set of diagrams.

### The third rotation

The third rotation is determined by the traces that are drawn on *Figures 13–17*, inclusive. The procedure is the same as for the rotations selected on

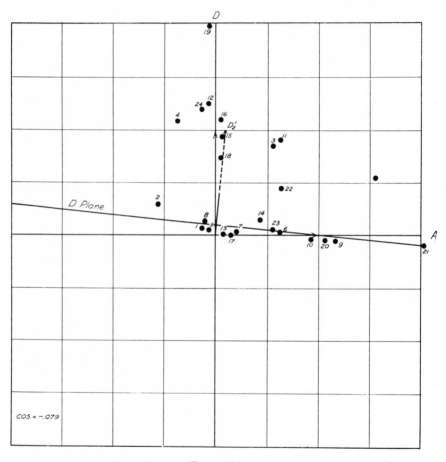

FIGURE 11

the previous diagrams, except for the combination of two rotations for the *E*-plane. *Figure 17* indicates a small adjustment in the *E*-plane as shown, and *Figure 14* indicates a smaller adjustment of the same plane. *If the corrections are limited to small angular adjustments of a plane with traces through the origin, then two or more adjustments can be combined in the same rotation.*

*Figures 14* and *17* show the combination of two adjustments of the *E*-plane in the same rotation. In *Figure 17* the long vectors that are brought into the plane are *20*, *21*, and *25*, and these are near the origin of *Figure 14*. Hence a small adjustment in the *E*-plane on *Figure 14* does not affect the factor loadings on *E* of these three tests. On the other hand, a small adjust-

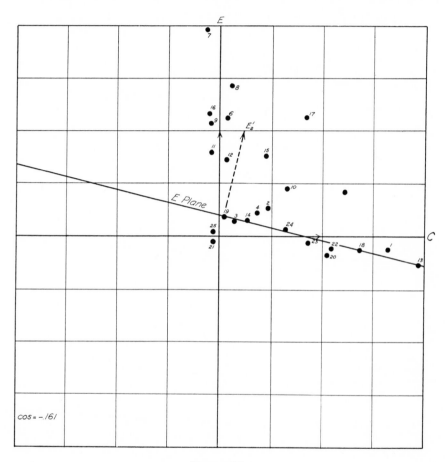

FIGURE 12

ment of the *E*-plane in *Figure 14* involves test *2*, which is near the origin in *Figure 17*. The two adjustments are therefore said to be independent. If tests *20*, *21*, and *25* had high projections on both *A* and *B*, then the two adjustments from these diagrams could not be combined because they would result in an overcorrection. In making the adjustments from *Figures 14* and *17*, it would not even be necessary to identify the numbers of the test vectors in both figures because of a principle that is often useful: *When one adjustment moves a configuration slightly out of a plane while the other adjustment moves it slightly into the plane, then the two adjustments can be combined with assurance that they are independent without identifying the test vectors in both diagrams.* In the present example the adjustment shown

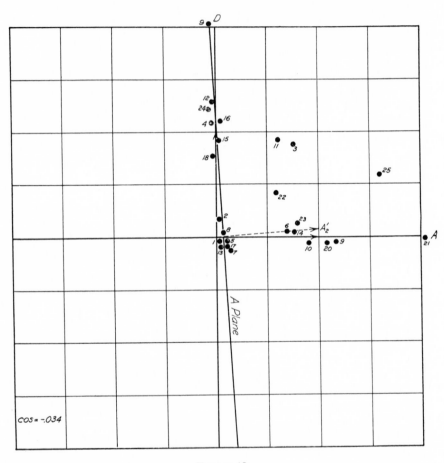

FIGURE 13

in *Figure 17* tends to move the plane down from the configuration, whereas the adjustment shown in *Figure 14* tends to move the plane up into the configuration. Hence the two adjustments can be combined with assurance that they are independent. The adjustment in *Figure 14* will produce a small negative factor loading for test *14*, whereas the adjustment in *Figure 17* will produce a small positive factor loading for test *14*. The result should be a negligible factor loading for this test when the two adjustments are combined.

The adjustments selected in *Figures 13–17*, inclusive, are recorded in the matrix $S_{34}$ of *Table 11*. The remaining computations for this table proceed according to the formulae shown and as described for previous rotations.

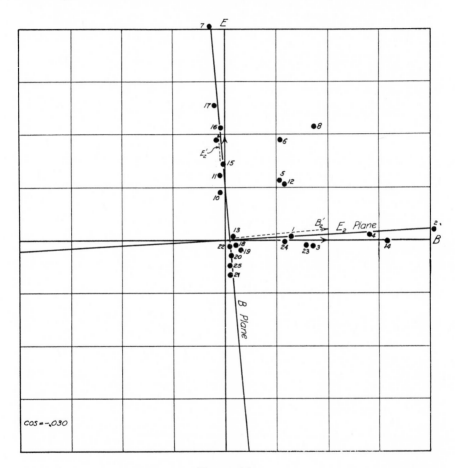

FIGURE 14

The result is shown in the oblique extended factor matrix $E_4$ of *Table 11*. The matrix $C_4$ gives the cosines of the angles between the reference vectors, as well as the projections of these vectors on the unit centroid vector ($I$). It is seen from this table that the reference vectors are nearly orthogonal. In dealing with an oblique factor problem it should be recalled that the matrix $C$ gives the cosines of the angles between the reference vectors. The

Table 11

Computations from Figures 13, 14, 15, 16, 17

## Matrix $S_{34}$

| | $I$ | $A'_2$ | $B'_2$ | $C'_2$ | $D'_2$ | $E'_2$ |
|---|---|---|---|---|---|---|
| $I$ | 1.00 | −.05 | −.05 | .05 | .04 | .13 |
| $A_1$ | | 1.00 | | −.21 | −.08 | −.06 |
| $B_1$ | | | 1.00 | 1.00 | 1.00 | 1.00 |
| $C_1$ | | .05 | .11 | | | |

## $L_{04} = M_{03}S_{34}$

| | $I$ | $A'_2$ | $B'_2$ | $C'_2$ | $D'_2$ | $E'_2$ |
|---|---|---|---|---|---|---|
| $I$ | 1.000 | .430 | .413 | .482 | .448 | .435 |
| $II$ | | .534 | .506 | −.419 | .130 | −.425 |
| $III$ | | −.559 | .606 | −.447 | −.108 | −.362 |
| $IV$ | | −.298 | −.107 | .420 | .845 | .159 |
| $V$ | | −.288 | .395 | .449 | .276 | .687 |
| $\Sigma l^2$ | | .9543 | .9613 | .9857 | 1.0195 | .9981 |
| $\sqrt{\Sigma l^2}$ | | .9769 | .9805 | .9928 | 1.0097 | .9991 |
| $D_4$ | | 1.0238 | 1.0199 | 1.0072 | .9904 | 1.0009 |

## $H_{34} = S_{34}D_4$

| | $I$ | $A_3$ | $B_3$ | $C_3$ | $D_3$ | $E_3$ |
|---|---|---|---|---|---|---|
| $I$ | 1.000 | −.051 | −.051 | .050 | .040 | .130 |
| $A_1$ | | 1.024 | | −.212 | −.079 | −.060 |
| $B_1$ | | | 1.020 | 1.007 | .990 | 1.001 |
| $C_1$ | | .051 | .112 | | | |

## $M_{04} = L_{04}D_4$

| | $I$ | $A_3$ | $B_3$ | $C_3$ | $D_3$ | $E_3$ |
|---|---|---|---|---|---|---|
| $I$ | 1.000 | .440 | .421 | .485 | .444 | .435 |
| $II$ | | .547 | .516 | −.422 | .129 | −.425 |
| $III$ | | −.572 | .618 | −.450 | −.107 | −.362 |
| $IV$ | | −.305 | −.109 | .423 | .837 | .159 |
| $V$ | | −.295 | .403 | .452 | .273 | .688 |

## $E_4 = E_3H_{34}$

| | $I$ | $A$ | $B$ | $C$ | $D$ | $E$ |
|---|---|---|---|---|---|---|
| 1 | 1.000 | −.032 | .626 | 1.575 | .034 | .014 |
| 2 | 1.000 | −.034 | 2.443 | .028 | .009 | .015 |
| 3 | 1.000 | .755 | .770 | .024 | .780 | .023 |
| 4 | 1.000 | −.020 | 1.400 | .029 | .985 | .024 |
| 5 | 1.000 | −.015 | .529 | 1.170 | .024 | .515 |
| 6 | 1.000 | .662 | .630 | −.012 | .012 | .986 |
| 7 | 1.000 | −.034 | .014 | −.048 | .005 | −2.238 |
| 8 | 1.000 | .008 | .958 | −.019 | .003 | −1.362 |
| 9 | 1.000 | 1.135 | .035 | .022 | .014 | −1.117 |
| 10 | 1.000 | .869 | .008 | .717 | .005 | .582 |
| 11 | 1.000 | .606 | .008 | .001 | .903 | .714 |
| 12 | 1.000 | .003 | .562 | .013 | 1.231 | .486 |
| 13 | 1.000 | −.028 | 1.558 | 2.064 | .046 | .013 |
| 14 | 1.000 | −.770 | .036 | .022 | .014 | .009 |
| 15 | 1.000 | .003 | .029 | .467 | .933 | .755 |
| 16 | 1.000 | .014 | .013 | .010 | 1.120 | 1.080 |
| 17 | 1.000 | −.006 | .057 | .874 | .019 | 1.268 |
| 18 | 1.000 | −.022 | .001 | 1.364 | .741 | .019 |
| 19 | 1.000 | −.004 | .071 | .031 | 2.238 | −.080 |
| 20 | 1.000 | 1.059 | −.001 | 1.078 | .011 | −.004 |
| 21 | 1.000 | 2.234 | −.056 | .010 | .028 | −.005 |
| 22 | 1.000 | .598 | .025 | 1.081 | .443 | −.011 |
| 23 | 1.000 | .726 | .745 | .758 | .005 | .006 |
| 24 | 1.000 | −.018 | .566 | .540 | 1.196 | .037 |
| 25 | 1.000 | −1.625 | .021 | .014 | .630 | .027 |

## $C_4 = M'_{04}M_{04}$

| | $I$ | $A$ | $B$ | $C$ | $D$ | $E$ |
|---|---|---|---|---|---|---|
| $I$ | 1.000 | | | | | |
| $A$ | .440 | 1.000 | | | | |
| $B$ | .421 | −.038 | 1.000 | | | |
| $C$ | .485 | −.012 | .036 | .999 | | |
| $D$ | .444 | .011 | .035 | −.009 | 1.000 | |
| $E$ | .435 | .012 | .000 | −.016 | −.034 | 1.000 |

correlations between the corresponding primary factors are then determined by the formulae that have been described in *chapter x*.

In *Figures 18* and *19* we have the complete set of ten diagrams which show the configuration in relation to a set of reference vectors, and there is no further indication of adjustments in the reference vectors. This set of diagrams is therefore accepted as final for this problem. The matrix $M_{04}$ of

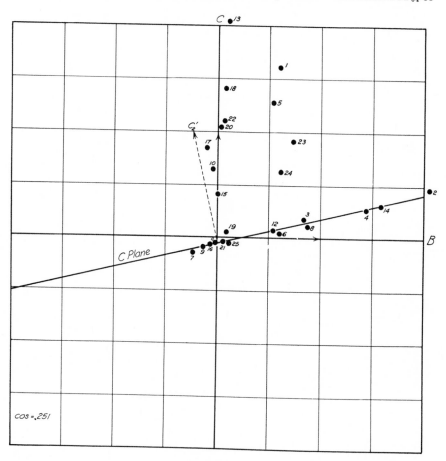

FIGURE 15

*Table 11* gives the transformation which carries the given extended factor matrix $E_0$ to the final extended factor matrix $E_4$. The same transformation carries the given factor matrix $F_0$, that was obtained by factoring, into a factor matrix $V_4$, which happens to represent a set of orthogonal axes in the present problem. We then have

(17)                         $E_0 M_{04} = E_4 ,$

which is an alternative for

(18) $$E_3 H_{34} = E_4 .$$

We also have

(19) $$F_0 \Lambda_{04} = V_4 .$$

Table 12

$$V_4 = F_0 \Lambda_{04}$$

|  | A | B | C | D | E |
|---|---|---|---|---|---|
| 1 | −.016 | .319 | .803 | −.017 | .008 |
| 2 | −.012 | .899 | .010 | .003 | .006 |
| 3 | .493 | .502 | .014 | .509 | −.015 |
| 4 | −.010 | .715 | .015 | .503 | −.012 |
| 5 | −.010 | .315 | .697 | −.014 | .307 |
| 6 | .404 | .385 | −.008 | .008 | .602 |
| 7 | .012 | −.005 | −.018 | .002 | .800 |
| 8 | .004 | .495 | −.010 | .002 | .704 |
| 9 | .609 | −.019 | −.012 | .009 | .598 |
| 10 | .599 | −.006 | .492 | −.002 | .401 |
| 11 | .406 | .005 | −.002 | .606 | .477 |
| 12 | −.001 | .320 | .007 | .702 | .277 |
| 13 | −.013 | .022 | .900 | −.020 | .006 |
| 14 | .390 | .788 | .010 | .008 | .005 |
| 15 | .001 | .023 | .297 | .595 | .480 |
| 16 | .007 | .015 | −.006 | .601 | .579 |
| 17 | .003 | .007 | .484 | −.010 | .704 |
| 18 | −.011 | .030 | .706 | .384 | −.009 |
| 19 | −.001 | .026 | .011 | .801 | −.029 |
| 20 | .592 | −.001 | .601 | −.005 | .002 |
| 21 | .801 | −.020 | .003 | .010 | −.002 |
| 22 | .390 | .016 | .705 | .290 | −.007 |
| 23 | .486 | .499 | .507 | −.003 | .005 |
| 24 | −.010 | .330 | .313 | .695 | −.021 |
| 25 | .800 | −.011 | .006 | .311 | −.013 |

This is the formula shown at the top of *Table 12*, which gives the factor matrix $V_4$ for the twenty-five test vectors with normal length. This factor matrix is used for purposes of interpretation.

In the present fictitious example we are interested to find that we have rediscovered the factorial composition of the matrix with which we started. That factorial composition is shown in *Table 3*, and it will be seen that the two tables are nearly identical. In making the comparison, we must identify the five columns. The columns $P_1$ to $P_5$ of *Table 3* correspond to columns $D$, $B$, $E$, $A$, and $C$ in *Table 12*. The reason for the arbitrary rearrangement of the columns is that in locating the traces of the planes in the diagrams and in giving letter identifications to the planes during the rotations we have no way of knowing which planes are emerging during the successive rota-

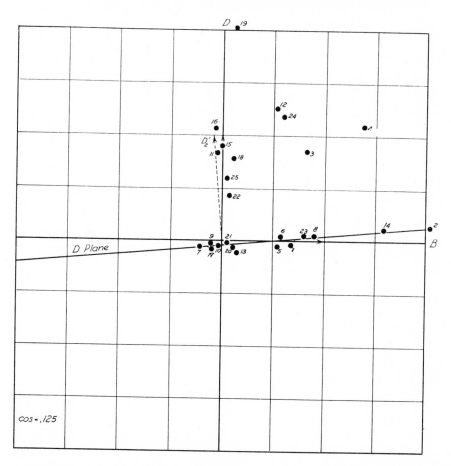

FIGURE 16

tions. Therefore, in making several factorial analyses of comparable test batteries, the order in which the primary factors appear in the successive columns of the factor matrix is entirely arbitrary.

When the test vectors are identified by their test names, as well as by their code numbers, one learns to identify early in the rotations the well-established primary factors. In some problems that are concerned mainly with methodology, the planes are given code numbers, which are relied upon exclusively for the location of the traces on the diagrams. In exploratory factorial studies it is often found that the primary factors are not completely determined in some of the diagrams because the test batteries in exploratory work seldom reveal a complete simple structure. It is then

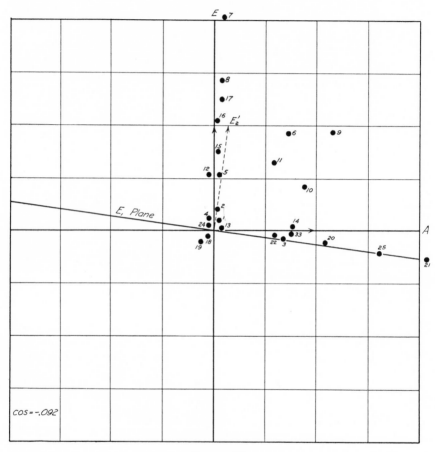

FIGURE 17

advisable to use all the information available, including the configuration as well as the psychological nature of the tests, to determine the co-ordinate planes, which are then interpreted as in the nature of hypotheses concerning the underlying parameters or primary factors. These must then be investigated with further factorial studies to determine whether one or more hypotheses concerning the postulated functional unities can be sustained. The purpose of this chapter is to show that when a clear and complete

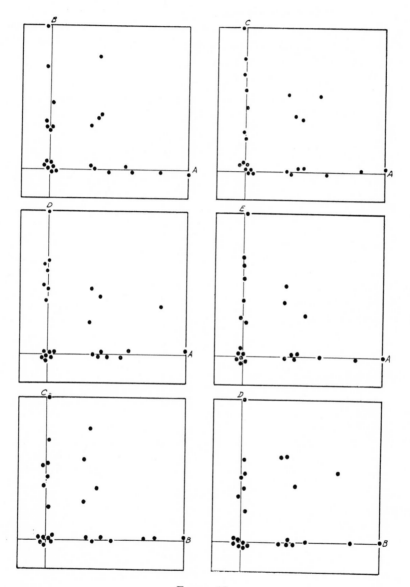

FIGURE 18

simple structure exists, as in the present fictitious example, the rotational methods that have been described enable us to identify the underlying order. The example here used was a five-dimensional orthogonal test battery. The methods of this chapter enable us to handle, in the same manner, factorial problems of any number of dimensions in which the underlying order is either orthogonal or oblique.

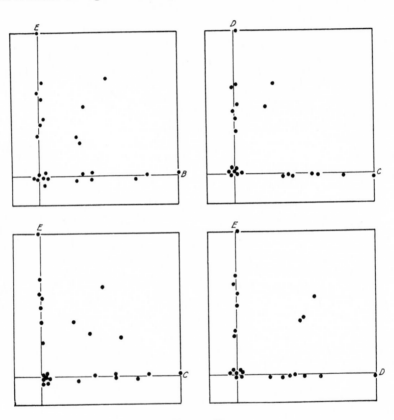

FIGURE 19

# CHAPTER XII

## THE SPECIAL CASE OF UNIT RANK

### The one-column factor matrix

If a correlation matrix can be accounted for by a single common factor, then we have a factor matrix of one column, as shown in *Table 1*. The factor loadings can then be denoted with a single subscript, $a_j$ for test $j$. By the fundamental factor theorem we have $FF' = R$, so that the diagonal elements become $a_j^2 = h_j^2$. Each communality $h_j^2$ is then simply the square of the single-factor loading, namely, $a_j^2$. In dealing with actual data it is not often that one can account for the correlations by a single common factor,

*Table 1*

| | Correlation Matrix | | | | | | Factor Matrix |
|---|---|---|---|---|---|---|---|
| | 1 | 2 | 3 | 4 | 5 | | I |
| 1 | $a_1^2$ | $r_{12}$ | $r_{13}$ | $r_{14}$ | $r_{15}$ | 1 | $a_1$ |
| 2 | $r_{12}$ | $a_2^2$ | $r_{23}$ | $r_{24}$ | $r_{25}$ | 2 | $a_2$ |
| 3 | $r_{13}$ | $r_{23}$ | $a_3^2$ | $r_{34}$ | $r_{35}$ | 3 | $a_3$ |
| 4 | $r_{14}$ | $r_{24}$ | $r_{34}$ | $a_4^2$ | $r_{45}$ | 4 | $a_4$ |
| 5 | $r_{15}$ | $r_{25}$ | $r_{35}$ | $r_{45}$ | $a_5^2$ | 5 | $a_5$ |

but this case is of historical interest because it was the case to which students of factorial theory devoted almost their entire attention for a quarter of a century after Spearman's first provocative paper on this subject in 1904.* We shall consider the single-common-factor problem as a special case of the multiple-factor problem instead of by the statistical methods formerly used. We shall refer to some of the controversial issues about the single-common-factor problem that were debated formerly, and they will be discussed here in the light of multiple-factor theory.

For the case of a single common factor we have

$$(1) \qquad\qquad r_{jk} = a_j a_k ,$$

where $a_j$ and $a_k$ are the single-common-factor loadings of tests $j$ and $k$. Inspection of this equation shows that pairs of columns, $k$ and $l$, must be proportional. We then have the theorem that *if a correlational matrix is of unit*

---

* "Correspondence between General Discrimination and General Intelligence," Part III of "General Intelligence Objectively Determined and Measured," *American Journal of Psychology*, XV (1904), 268–72.

*rank, then all pairs of columns, or rows, are proportional.* The converse of this theorem is also true, for if all pairs of columns are proportional, then all minors of second order or higher vanish, and hence the rank must be less than 2. The trivial case of rank 0 is here of no significance. The case in which the rank is 0 is, of course, identified by the fact that all the inter-correlations are 0. That is a case of no scientific interest. We have, therefore, the theorem that *if all pairs of columns, or rows, of a correlational matrix are proportional, then the rank of the matrix is 1 or 0.*

One of the earlier criteria used by Spearman for showing that the inter-correlations of a set of tests could be accounted for by a single common factor was the proportionality of the columns of coefficients. Because of sampling errors the proportionality was not exact when experimental data were used. A later criterion of the degree of correspondence between pairs of columns was the correlation between them. In general, if two columns are proportional, their correlation is $+1$ or $-1$. The degree of proportionality was expressed in terms of the coefficient of correlation. We then have the theorem that *if the correlational matrix is of rank 1, then the correlation between pairs of columns, or rows, is $+1$ or $-1$.* The converse of this theorem is not necessarily true. If the correlation between pairs of columns is $+1$ or $-1$, the columns are not necessarily proportional. A specific case which disproves the converse is that in which a constant is added to each element of a column. A linear plot is then obtained which does not pass through the origin. The correlation is $+1$, but the columns are not proportional.

Spearman's former use of the intercolumnar criterion depended on the converse, in that the high correlation between columns was the basis for the inference that a single factor was sufficient to describe the intercorrelations. While the intercolumnar correlation criterion is demonstrably fallible, it would be a rare situation in which a set of mental tests would satisfy the criterion of unit correlation, or very high correlation between columns when the rank is higher than 1. Hence Spearman's use of the correlation criterion could be defended.

But another type of difficulty appeared with the intercolumnar correlation criterion. If all the coefficients in $R$ are of the same order of magnitude and if these are overlaid with sampling errors, then the dispersion of a column may be comparable with the sampling errors, and the correlation between columns may be low because of the restricted range of the entries in the correlation matrix. The proportionality would still be maintained within sampling errors, but the points in each correlation table would be so restricted in range that the correlation coefficient would not reveal the proportionality. The intercolumnar proportionality criterion is therefore superior to the intercolumnar correlation criterion.

The limiting case of this effect is of some interest. If all the coefficients in a correlation matrix are equal, then the proportionality criterion is satisfied, but the correlation coefficient is indeterminate. The proportionality criterion would give the correct inference, namely, that the correlation matrix is of rank 1. We then have

(2)
$$\begin{cases} r_{jk} = a_j a_k \,, \\ r_{kl} = a_k a_l \,, \\ r_{jl} = a_j a_l \,. \end{cases}$$

But

(3)
$$r_{jk} = r_{jl} = r_{kl} \,,$$

and hence

(4)
$$a_j a_k = a_j a_l = a_k a_l \,,$$

and

(5)
$$a_j = a_k = a_l \,.$$

It follows from (1) and (4) that

(6)
$$a_j = a_k = a_l = \sqrt{r_{jk}} \,.$$

This limiting case is represented in the theorem that *if all the coefficients* $r_{jk}$ *in a correlation matrix are equal, then the matrix is of unit rank, and each test has a single-factor loading of* $\sqrt{r_{jk}}$.

If sampling errors are superimposed on this limiting case, the correlation between columns shows only the correlation between random errors. This correlation should be zero or near zero. The intercolumnar proportionality criterion is still valid, and it would be only slightly affected by the sampling errors in a finite test battery.

Spearman's use of the correlational, rather than the proportionality, form of the intercolumnar criterion was determined, probably, by the fact that the standard error of a correlation coefficient could be determined, whereas the proportionality form of the criterion would require the development of an appropriate standard error formula. There does not seem to be any fundamental difficulty in developing such a formula.

Since the diagonal values of the correlation matrix are frequently discussed in factor analysis, it is useful to know the theorem that *if a correlation matrix is of unit rank and if the diagonal elements are unity, then all elements in the matrix are +1 or −1.*

It is sometimes useful to note a restriction on the numerical values in a single-common-factor correlation matrix. It can be stated in the theorem that *when the rows and corresponding columns have been reversed in sign so that all the coefficients in a single-common-factor correlation matrix are positive, then the three side correlations of any third-order principal minor are such that any one of them is greater than the product of the other two.* This property follows directly from the proportionality of the columns and the further restriction that the diagonals are positive numbers that do not exceed unity. We then have

$$\frac{r_{12}}{r_{13}} = \frac{r_{22}}{r_{23}} .$$

But $r_{22} = h_2^2 < 1$, so that

$$\frac{r_{12}r_{23}}{r_{13}} < 1 ,$$

and hence

$$r_{12}r_{23} < r_{13} .$$

If a set of three tests have intercorrelations that do not satisfy this restriction, then a diagonal value is greater than unity. Such a set of three tests can be a part of a correlation matrix of rank that is higher than 1.

## The number of tests for unit rank

It is useful to inquire how many factors can be determined from the intercorrelations of any given number of tests or measures. Here we are concerned about the number of tests which are necessary to determine a single common factor. In a correlation matrix of $n$ tests we have

$$\tfrac{1}{2}n(n - 1)$$

independently determined correlation coefficients, because these include only the side correlations and not the diagonal or self-correlations, which are unknown. In *Table 1* we see that for rank 1 the diagonal elements are simply the squares of the factor loadings, which are the unknown communalities. The corresponding factor matrix has a single column with $n$ factor loadings. We cannot expect to determine $n$ factor loadings unless we are given at least as many independent correlation coefficients. We then have

$$(7) \qquad \frac{n(n - 1)}{2} \geq n ,$$

or

$$(8) \qquad n \geq 3 ,$$

by which we infer that *at least three tests are necessary to determine a single common factor.* In that case we have three unknown saturations $a_j$ to be determined whose squares are the unknown communalities $h_j^2 = a_j^2$. We have also three intercorrelations, namely, $r_{jk}$, $r_{jl}$, $r_{kl}$. The solution of this case can be found from the three intercorrelations,

$$(9) \qquad\qquad r_{jk} = a_j a_k \,,$$

$$(10) \qquad\qquad r_{jl} = a_j a_l \,,$$

and

$$(11) \qquad\qquad r_{kl} = a_k a_l \,.$$

Divide (10) by (11). Then

$$(12) \qquad\qquad \frac{r_{jl}}{r_{kl}} = \frac{a_j}{a_k} \,,$$

so that

$$(13) \qquad\qquad a_k = \frac{a_j r_{kl}}{r_{jl}} \,.$$

Substituting (13) in (9), we have

$$(14) \qquad\qquad r_{jk} = \frac{a_j^2 r_{kl}}{r_{jl}} \,,$$

from which we have Spearman's formula* for the correlation of test $j$ with the single common factor, namely,

$$(15) \qquad\qquad a_j = \sqrt{\frac{r_{jk} r_{jl}}{r_{kl}}} \,,$$

in which $a_j$ is the factor loading of test $j$. The correlation $r_{j1}$ between test $j$ and the single common factor is the factor loading $a_j$, so that $r_{j1} = a_{j1}$.

The intercorrelations of three tests can usually be accounted for by one common factor, but such is not always the case. Consider the two correla-

*Table 2*

| — | .14 | .25 | | — | .14 | .35 |
|---|-----|-----|---|---|-----|-----|
| .14 | — | .50 | | .14 | — | .50 |
| .25 | .50 | — | | .35 | .50 | — |
| | (a) | | | | (b) | |

tion matrices (a) and (b) in *Table 2*, which have been used by Wilson and Worcester to show that the correlations between three tests cannot always be accounted for by one common factor.† The correlation matrix (a) is of

* C. Spearman, *The Abilities of Man* (New York: Macmillan Co., 1927), Appendix, p. xvi, eq. (19).

† E. B. Wilson and Jane Worcester, "The Resolution of Tests into Two General Factors," *Proceedings of the National Academy of Sciences*, XXV (January, 1939), 24, n. 3.

rank 1 if we insert the communalities .07, .28, .89, which determine the single-common-factor loadings. The matrix (*b*) is of rank 1 if we insert the diagonals .098, .20, 1.25; but, since one of these is greater than unity, the solution is incorrect. Matrix (*b*) can be considered as a correlation matrix of rank 2, and there will be two general common factors. In this case the resolution into factors is, of course, not unique.

The value of $a_j$ as determined by equation (15) is subject to fluctuation with the sampling errors of the three correlation coefficients in terms of which it is expressed. It is desirable to minimize this effect by taking an average value for $a_j$ based on different pairs of tests $k$ and $l$, with which test $j$ is combined. With $n$ tests, the number of ways in which (15) can be written for test $j$ is the number of pairs of tests that may be taken from the remaining $(n-1)$ tests, excluding test $j$. Hence the number of ways in which

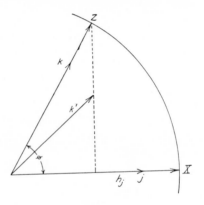

FIGURE 1

(15) may be written is $\frac{1}{2}(n-1)(n-2)$. The total number of formulae (15) for ascertaining all the single-factor loadings for $n$ tests is $\frac{1}{2}n(n-1)(n-2)$. If we have twenty tests, then formula (15) can be evaluated in 3,420 different ways in determining the correlation of each of the twenty tests with the single common factor.

We have seen that three tests are required in order to determine a single common factor. It is of some interest to see the nature of the indeterminacy when only two tests are available. Consider *Figure 1*, in which are shown the two test vectors, $j$ and $k$. The correlation between tests $j$ and $k$ can be expressed as the scalar product of the two test vectors, so that

$$(16) \qquad r_{jk} = h_j h_k \cos \phi_{jk} ;$$

but the figure cannot be drawn uniquely unless we know three things, namely, the two vector lengths and their angular separation. The same correlation is represented in *Figure 1* by the pair of vectors $j$ and $k'$, where the angle and the communality of $k'$ are both altered so as to retain the same given scalar product or correlation. The case of one test determines an axis that may be defined as collinear with the test itself, but the problem of common factors does not appear except for two or more tests. If equation (16) is interpreted for one dimension or common factor, then the cosine of the angle is, of course, unity, and we have two communalities which cannot be determined by a single correlation coefficient. We see, therefore, that two tests do not define a single common factor.

Students of factor analysis who confined their attention primarily to the single common factor have used sets of four tests to determine the common factor. The reason for this is that, in general, three tests determine a single common factor uniquely, since there are three intercorrelations to determine three factor loadings. Hence nothing is proved scientifically by doing it. A scientific demonstration of any kind must always be overdetermined

*Table 3*

| | 1 | 2 | 3 | 4 | | 1 | 2 | 3 | 4 |
|---|---|---|---|---|---|---|---|---|---|
| 1 | $+.64$ | $-.56$ | $+.48$ | $-.40$ | 1 | .64 | .56 | .48 | .40 |
| 2 | $-.56$ | $+.49$ | $-.42$ | $+.35$ | 2 | .56 | .49 | .42 | .35 |
| 3 | $+.48$ | $-.42$ | $+.36$ | $-.30$ | 3 | .48 | .42 | .36 | .30 |
| 4 | $-.40$ | $+.35$ | $-.30$ | $+.25$ | 4 | .40 | .35 | .30 | .25 |

by the data in order to be convincing. Hence the smallest number of tests by which a single common factor can be demonstrated is four. Of course, the larger the number of tests in the correlation matrix, the more convincing will be the demonstration of a single common factor, assuming that the variables are otherwise properly chosen.

The case of rank 1 requires that all the correlation coefficients be positive or that they can be made positive by reversal of one or more of the measures. Consider, for example, the correlation matrices in Table 3, which are both of rank 1. The absolute values are the same. The first matrix can be transformed into the second by reversing the signs of the second and then the fourth variables. Each reversal represents a reversal of a column and then the corresponding row. The reason for this arrangement for rank 1 is that the test vectors are collinear and they may be reversed in direction.

### The tetrad difference

Spearman's later method was to evaluate what are called "tetrad differences." The tetrad difference is of the form

$$(17) \qquad r_{km}r_{ln} - r_{lm}r_{kn} = \rho \, ,$$

where $k$ and $l$ refer to two rows, while $m$ and $n$ refer to two columns of $R$. The four subscripts refer to as many tests, and it is implied that four separate tests are involved in the tetrad difference equation. Hence the tetrad difference is not written so as to include any diagonal terms of $R$. This is consistent with the fact that the communalities are unknown. Spearman has shown that if only one factor is involved, then all the tetrad differences in $R$ vanish.

The tetrad differences have a very simple matrix interpretation. They are simply the expansions of second-order minors in the correlation matrix. If the rank of $R$ is 1, then all second-order minors vanish. The converse is also true; for, if the second-order minors vanish, then the rank must be 1, except for the trivial case when all entries are 0. The matrix interpretation of Spearman's tetrad difference procedure is that unit rank  (i.e., a single common factor) is established by evaluating separately the second-order minors in the correlational matrix.

To establish that a matrix is of any particular rank $r$, it is, of course, necessary to prove that $r$ is the highest order of the non-vanishing minors. Taken literally, this requires that all minors of order higher than $r$ must be shown to be 0; but for computational purposes this is probably the most awkward way possible, especially for the single-common-factor case.

The tetrad difference method of examining a correlation matrix cannot be recommended even for the restricted single-common-factor case to which it is theoretically applicable. The reason is that more effective methods are available for ascertaining whether one common factor is sufficient to account for the intercorrelations. If more than one factor is required, then the tetrad difference criterion is not applicable. Because of historical interest, some of the properties of the tetrad differences will be described here.*

Because of the great amount of labor that is involved in the computation of the tetrads for a large correlation matrix, it is convenient to know how many tetrads must be evaluated for $n$ tests in order to cover the whole table. Since a tetrad difference is the value of a second-order minor which does not contain diagonal terms, there are as many tetrads as there are second-order minors which do not involve the diagonals. Each of these minors is defined by two rows and two columns. The number of pairs of rows that can be taken is the number of combinations of $n$ things taken two at a time, or

$$(18) \qquad\qquad C_2^n = \frac{n(n-1)}{2} .$$

---

* Tetrad differences are no longer in general use. The single-factor methods have been replaced by multiple-factor methods of analysis by most students of factorial theory. This was not the case when the matrix interpretation was introduced in 1932 or when the first edition of this text was published in 1935.

The number of possible pairs that can be taken from the remaining columns, since diagonal elements are excluded, then is

$$(19) \qquad C_2^{n-2} = \frac{(n-2)(n-3)}{2}.$$

Hence the total number of second-order minors in the correlation matrix, excluding diagonals, is

$$(20) \qquad C_2^n C_2^{n-2} = \frac{n(n-1)(n-2)(n-3)}{4}.$$

But, since the correlational matrix is symmetric, it follows that every one of these minors is duplicated by a symmetric minor of the same value. Hence *the total number of different tetrads is*

$$(21) \qquad \tfrac{1}{2}C_2^n C_2^{n-2} = \frac{n(n-1)(n-2)(n-3)}{8}.$$

Since every set of four variables gives three tetrads, it is possible to obtain the same result by considering the number of combinations of $n$ things taken four at a time. Then the number of tetrads is

$$(22) \qquad 3C_4^n = \frac{n(n-1)(n-2)(n-3)}{8}.$$

EXAMPLE: If the number of tests is 20, then the correlation matrix contains 14,535 tetrads.

When the computation of all these tetrads has been made, the result is usually that the tetrads do not vanish. The inference must then be made that one common factor is insufficient to account for the intercorrelations of the tests. If it is found that the tetrads do vanish within the sampling errors, then the next problem is to ascertain how much of the variance of each test is attributable to the single common factor. This can be done in terms of the correlation coefficients by Spearman's formula (15).

Spearman's procedure takes into consideration that the tetrad difference in (17) does not quite vanish because of sampling errors in the four correlation coefficients. If a single common factor is fundamentally present and if the four coefficients have known standard errors, an expression for the standard error of $\rho$ can be derived. This has been done by Wishart and by Holzinger.[*] The experimentally observed deviations of $\rho$ from zero should not exceed those which might be expected from the standard errors of $\rho$.

[*] John Wishart, "Sampling Errors in the Theory of Two Factors," *British Journal of Psychology*, XIX (1928), 180–87; Karl J. Holzinger, *Statistical Résumé of the Spearman Two-Factor Theory* (Chicago: University of Chicago Press, 1930), pp. 6–16.

This is the central idea in Spearman's single-common-factor method. The tetrads in a correlation matrix are first evaluated. A frequency distribution of these tetrad differences is then made and its standard deviation determined. If this dispersion is of an order of magnitude comparable with that which would be expected from the known standard errors of the tetrad differences, then Spearman draws the legitimate conclusion that a single common factor is sufficient to account for the observed intercorrelations. Applications of formulae of type (15) give the loading of each test with the single common factor whose sufficiency has been established by the fact that the tetrads vanish within sampling errors. In order to reduce the labor of computing probable errors of the tetrads, Spearman and his students have developed several abbreviated procedures. These are limited, however, to the single-common-factor case.

### Factorial reduction to unit rank

There are several types of situations which are of both theoretical and practical interest, in which a factor matrix or a correlation matrix is reduced to rank 1. Consider, first, the two-column factor matrix in *Table 4*. If the

*Table 4*

| | Factor Matrix F | | | Single-Factor Matrix | |
|---|---|---|---|---|---|
| | I | II | | | I |
| 1 | .60 | .30 | | 1 | .6708 |
| 2 | .40 | .20 | | 2 | .4472 |
| 3 | .80 | .40 | | 3 | .8944 |
| 4 | .20 | .10 | | 4 | .2236 |
| 5 | .30 | .15 | | 5 | .3354 |

matrix $F$ is multiplied by its transpose $F'$, it will be seen that the columns in $R$ are proportional and that it is of rank 1. The tetrads vanish, and the intercorrelations of the tests can be described as well by one factor, as shown in the single-factor matrix.

The reason why this result is obtained is that Matrix $F$ is of unit rank. It corresponds to the conceivable psychological situation in which each test of a battery calls for two primary mental abilities in the same ratio, although they differ in specificity and reliability. In practice, it is possible to select from a large table of tests several groups whose intercorrelations are high when corrected for uniqueness. Each one of these groups of tests can be described in terms of one factor, but that factor is not necessarily psychologically significant. The tests may be composites, as illustrated in the two matrices. One way of avoiding this ambiguity is to work with several abilities or factors simultaneously, as is done in the multiple-factor methods.

The simple illustrative case that has been described here can be generalized into a useful theorem, namely, that *if two columns of any factor matrix are proportional, then the two columns are of unit rank, and the rank of the factor matrix is correspondingly reduced.* It can be easily seen that this situation is more likely to occur in analyzing a small test battery. Two factors that are actually distinct may then collapse so that they appear in the analysis as a single factor, with consequent confusion or error of interpretation. Only by further investigation of the same domain would the error be discovered. It is quite likely that this does happen in exploratory factorial investigation where the domain covered by several factors is not adequately covered by tests. With these limitations of method the solution seems to be to explore rather intensively each domain with a large number of specially constructed measurements until the factorial composition of each new test can be anticipated with confidence.

Godfrey Thomson has discussed a very interesting case of reduction in rank in his sampling theory. Consider a factor matrix of order $n \times n_t$, in which each test of unit variance is defined only in terms of the number of its elements, namely, $n_j$. Let there be a total of $n_t$ elements involved in the domain defined by the factor matrix. Then, in the row $j$, we have $n_j$ factor loadings $a_j$ distributed at random, and the remaining factor loadings are zeros. If each test is of unit variance, we have

$$(23) \qquad \sum a_j^2 = 1 \; ;$$

but, since there are $n_j$ non-vanishing elements in row $j$, we have

$$(24) \qquad n_j a_j^2 = 1 \; ,$$

so that

$$(25) \qquad a_j = \frac{1}{\sqrt{n_j}} \; .$$

Let similar notation designate test $k$. Then the correlation $r_{jk}$ will be the cross product of the two rows $j$ and $k$. The probability that there will be non-vanishing cell entries in the same column for both rows $j$ and $k$ is $p_j p_k$, where

$$(26) \qquad p_j = \frac{n_j}{n_t} \quad \text{and} \quad p_k = \frac{n_k}{n_t} \; ,$$

so that

$$(27) \qquad p_j p_k = \frac{n_j n_k}{n_t^2} \; .$$

The correlation $r_{jk}$ then is

(28)                      $r_{jk} = p_j p_k a_j a_k n_t$ ,

which reduces to

(29)                      $r_{jk} = \dfrac{\sqrt{n_j n_k}}{n_t}$ ;

but this is the well-known case of the correlation expressed in terms of common elements. It can be expressed as the product of the single factors $A_j$ and $A_k$, where

(30)          $A_j = \sqrt{\dfrac{n_j}{n_t}}$    and    $A_k = \sqrt{\dfrac{n_k}{n_t}}$ ,

so that the correlation matrix is of unit rank. This result is approached as $n_t$ becomes large. Here we have the case in which a factor matrix with a large number of columns $n_t$, constructed in the manner described, approaches unit rank. It is quite another matter to decide whether this type of factor matrix is psychologically plausible for the description of mental traits and test performances.

*Table 5*

|   | 1 | 2 | 3 | 4 | 5 |
|---|---|---|---|---|---|
| 1 |     | .56 | .48 | .40 | .32 |
| 2 | .56 |     | .42 | .35 | .28 |
| 3 | .48 | .42 |     | .30 | .24 |
| 4 | .40 | .35 | .30 |     | .20 |
| 5 | .32 | .28 | .24 | .20 |     |
| Σ | 1.76 | 1.61 | 1.44 | 1.25 | 1.04 |

### Graphical analysis of tetrads

If one is interested in the task of tabulating separately the values of all the second-order minors in a correlation matrix which Spearman has called the tetrads, then some simple graphical methods might be useful. Because of the proportionality of the columns and rows in this case we see that, if the correlational matrix is of rank 1 and if any column $k$ is plotted against any other column $l$, then the plot is linear through the origin with a slope which is the ratio of the single-factor loading of test $k$ to that of test $l$. An example can be seen by plotting any pair of columns of the correlation matrix of *Table 5*.

Let two points on the diagram represent tests $m$ and $n$. If the two points are radial, then

(31)                      $\dfrac{r_{ln}}{r_{kn}} = \dfrac{r_{lm}}{r_{km}}$ ,

so that

(32) $$r_{km}r_{ln} - r_{lm}r_{kn} = 0 .$$

If the points $m$ and $n$ are not radial, the proportionality of (31) does not obtain, and the tetrad (32) does not vanish. By this simple graphical method one can identify the tetrads that do not vanish.

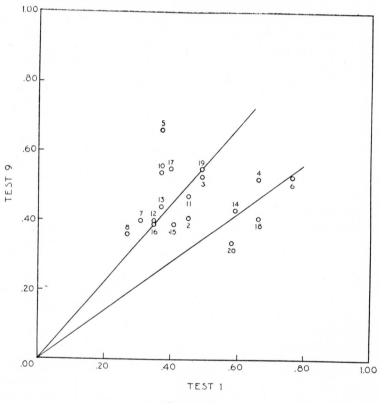

FIGURE 2

If the test battery as a whole cannot be described by a single common factor, the plot will not be linear but will scatter, as shown in *Figure 2*. This figure shows the plot of column 9 against column 1 from a correlation matrix in a factorial investigation by William Brown and William Stephenson.* Column 9 represents a test of pattern perception, and column 1 represents a test of inventive synonyms. Although it is evident in *Figure 2* that

* "A Test of the Theory of Two Factors," *British Journal of Psychology* (Gen. Sec.), XXIII (1935), 352-70.

a single factor is not sufficient to account for the intercorrelations and that, therefore, all the tetrads do not vanish, it is still possible for smaller groups of tests to be of such a character that their intercorrelations can be described by a single common factor. Their tetrads should then vanish. The smallest group for which a tetrad can be written is four tests. Two tests are represented by the two columns that are plotted. Any pair of points on the diagram determines a tetrad. If they lie in a radial line through the origin, the corresponding tetrad vanishes. If they do not lie in a radial line through the origin, the corresponding tetrad does not vanish.

*Figure 2* gives further information about the possibility of a single-factor hypothesis for the tests concerned. Radial lines can be drawn through *8* and *17*, through *12* and *19*, through *6* and *14*, with small residuals. Any one of these three pairs can be combined with tests 1 and 9 to form vanishing tetrads, but it does not follow that all eight of the tests can be included in a single-factor correlation matrix. The fact that the points spread on different radial lines means that other tetrads which include tests from different radial lines will not vanish. It should be carefully noted that, if the tetrads fail to vanish, we can say that one factor is not sufficient to account for the correlations, but it still remains a possibility that a Spearman general factor is present in addition to other factors, so that more than one factor is required for the battery of tests as a whole. We see, therefore, that *the tetrad criterion is inadequate for disproving a Spearman general factor.* See, for example, *Figure 5b* and *Figure 6* of *chapter ix*, which illustrate three-dimensional configurations that include an orthogonal general factor, which we are here calling a "Spearman general factor." The tetrads do not vanish for such a test battery, but it contains a Spearman general factor. Neither do the tetrads give any information about the existence of a second-order general factor, to be discussed in *chapter xviii*.

### Spearman's terminology

Spearman's hypothesis that the correlations between psychological tests can be accounted for by a single general intellective factor has been known as *the theory of two factors.* The general factor was denoted *g*. In giving this name to his theory, Spearman had in mind two factors, namely, a general intellective factor and a specific or unique factor in each test. As long as factorial investigation was dominated by the central theme of the general intellective factor, Spearman's formulation could be called a theory of two factors, one common and one unique. With the extension of factor analysis to *n* dimensions and with the principal scientific interest directed to the multiple common factors, it is confusing to speak of Spearman's theory of two factors, one common and one unique. In order to avoid confusion we shall speak of *Spearman's theory of a single common factor*, a terminology that is consistent with that of multiple-factor analysis.

When Spearman found a set of tests for which the intercorrelations were proportional, he called the table a *hierarchy*. Such a table had the characteristic that the highest correlations could be placed near the upper left corner and the lowest correlations in the lower right corner. Much of the early debate about the question of whether Spearman's single general intellective factor was adequate to account for the observed correlations between tests turned about the statistical question as to whether the tables of intercorrelations exhibited so-called *hierarchical order*. The table of correlations was not treated as a matrix, and the question of its rank was not discussed in relation to this problem.*

Before multiple-factor analysis was introduced as an explicit psychological method without any assumption that there should be a single dominant general intellective factor, there was frequent discussion of other factors besides the general intellective factor $g$. These other factors were regarded as secondary to the general factor $g$. They were described as the "disturbers" of the tetrad equation, and they were avoided by eliminating similar tests from the battery. For example, if two number tests were in a battery, their correlation would add a number factor to the common-factor variance, and the tetrad equations were consequently not satisfied. Instead of adding more number tests to the battery in order to investigate number ability, the preferred procedure was to keep only *one* of the number tests in the battery, eliminating the others. The number factor was thereby relegated to the unique variance, and the tetrads were undisturbed. Whenever these additional and disturbing factors were investigated, the accepted procedure was, first, to extract a general factor which dominated factorial studies. Then the residuals were investigated in groups for additional factors. These were always treated as secondary and residual to the dominant general factor $g$. This type of factorial analysis is still current among British psychologists. Most of them have not yet adopted the multiple-factor methods, which include extraction of multiple factors and rotation of the reference frame to a simple structure. The newer methods leave it as a question of fact whether a general factor is in the battery and whether it is an orthogonal general factor or a second-order general factor.

## Special factoring methods for unit rank

*Spearman's single-factor formula*

We shall consider, first, *Spearman's formula* for factoring a correlation matrix of unit rank. The single-common-factor loading of each test may be determined by a summation procedure. This method is simpler than the

* L. L. Thurstone, *Theory of Multiple Factors* (Ann Arbor, Mich., 1933), pp. v, vi, 20. This publication is out of print, but it can be obtained at the University of Chicago Library as microfilm document No. 1648.

tetrad method for a single common factor, and it gives more information about the variables than the tetrad differences give.

If the correlation $r$ can be described by a single common factor, we have

(1) $$r_{jk} = a_j a_k .$$

The sum of column $k$ in the correlation matrix is

(33) $$\sum_{j=1}^{n} r_{jk} = a_k \sum_{j=1}^{n} a_j .$$

Since the diagonal terms are unknown, the summation in the left member of (33) is unknown and hence not suitable for computing purposes. Let $(r)_k$ be the sum of column $k$, omitting the unknown diagonal entry. Then

(34) $$(r)_k = \sum_{j=1}^{n} r_{jk} - a_k^2 ,$$

and hence

(35) $$(r)_k = a_k \sum_{j=1}^{n} a_j - a_k^2 .$$

Summing for all given coefficients in $R_0$ and omitting the unknown diagonals, we have

(36) $$(r)_t = \sum_{k=1}^{n} a_k \sum_{j=1}^{n} a_j - \sum_{k=1}^{n} a_k^2 ,$$

or

(37) $$(r)_t = \left[ \sum_{k=1}^{n} a_k \right]^2 - \sum_{k=1}^{n} a_k^2 ,$$

where $(r)_t \equiv \sum_k (r)_k$ denotes the sum of all the coefficients in $R_0$ except the diagonal ones.

Each of the two terms in the right member of (37) may be expressed in terms of summations of known coefficients, as follows:

(1) $$r_{jk} = a_j a_k ,$$

and hence

(38) $$\frac{r_{jk}}{a_k} = a_j .$$

Summing for column $k$, we obtain

$$(39) \qquad \frac{1}{a_k} \sum_{j=1}^{n} r_{jk} = \sum_{j=1}^{n} a_j ,$$

and, from (34), it follows that

$$(40) \qquad \frac{1}{a_k}[(r)_k + a_k^2] = \sum_{j=1}^{n} a_j$$

or

$$(41) \qquad \frac{(r)_k}{a_k} + a_k = \sum_{j=1}^{n} a_j = \sum_{k=1}^{n} a_k .$$

Hence the first term of the right member of (37) is

$$(42) \qquad \left[ \sum_{k=1}^{n} a_k \right]^2 = \frac{(r)_k^2}{a_k^2} + 2(r)_k + a_k^2 .$$

The last term of (37) may be expressed in terms of summations of coefficients, as follows:

$$(1) \qquad r_{jk} = a_j a_k ,$$

so that

$$(43) \qquad r_{jk}^2 = a_j^2 a_k^2 ,$$

and hence

$$(44) \qquad \frac{r_{jk}^2}{a_k^2} = a_j^2 .$$

Summing for column $k$, we have

$$(45) \qquad \frac{1}{a_k^2} \sum_{j=1}^{n} r_{jk}^2 = \sum_{j=1}^{n} a_j^2 = \sum_{k=1}^{n} a_k^2 .$$

Summing for column $k$, except for the entry in row $k$, we have

$$(46) \qquad \frac{1}{a_k^2} \left[ \sum_{j=1}^{n} r_{jk}^2 - r_{kk}^2 \right] = \sum_{j=1}^{n} a_j^2 - a_k^2 .$$

Let the sum of the squares of the known coefficients in column $k$ be denoted by $(r^2)_k$, so that

$$(47) \qquad (r^2)_k = \sum_{j=1}^{n} r_{jk}^2 - r_{kk}^2 \,.$$

Then (46) can be written in the form

$$(48) \qquad \frac{(r^2)_k}{a_k^2} + a_k^2 = \sum_{k=1}^{n} a_k^2 \,.$$

Substituting (42) and (48) in (37), we obtain

$$(49) \qquad (r)_t = \frac{(r)_k^2}{a_k^2} + 2(r)_k + a_k^2 - \frac{(r^2)_k}{a_k^2} - a_k^2 \,,$$

or

$$(50) \qquad (r)_t - 2(r)_k = \frac{(r)_k^2}{a_k^2} - \frac{(r^2)_k}{a_k^2} \,,$$

from which it follows that

$$(51) \qquad a_k^2 = \frac{(r)_k^2 - (r^2)_k}{(r)_t - 2(r)_k} \,,$$

where

$(r)_k$ = the sum of the coefficients in column $k$, omitting unknown diagonal entry ,

$(r)_k^2$ = the square of $(r)_k$ ,

$(r^2)_k$ = the sum of the squares of the known coefficients in column $k$ ,

$(r)_t$ = the sum of all known coefficients in the correlation matrix .

Formula (51) gives the single-common-factor loading of each test in a correlation matrix of rank one. This formula has been given, in different notation, by Spearman.*

In *Table 5* we have a small correlation matrix of unit rank. To find the factor loadings for the first test by Spearman's formula (51) we have

$$(r)_1 = 1.7600\,, \qquad (r^2)_1 = .8064\,,$$

$$(r)_1^2 = 3.0976\,, \qquad (r)_t = 7.1000\,,$$

which when substituted in Spearman's formula (51) give $a_1 = .80$. By the same method we get $a_2 = .70$, $a_3 = .60$, $a_4 = .50$, and $a_5 = .40$.

* *The Abilities of Man*, Appendix, p. xvi, eq. (21).

*A logarithmic solution*

Another direct method of solving the single-factor problem is the logarithmic solution.* The logarithmic formula is

$$(52) \qquad \log a_k = \frac{2(n-1)\sum_j \log r_{jk} - \sum_j \sum_k \log r_{jk}}{2(n-1)(n-2)},$$

where $j \neq k$. For Spearman's formula (51) the square of each correlation coefficient must be listed, and for the logarithmic formula (52) the logarithm of each coefficient must be listed. The logarithmic formula is not applicable when some coefficients are near zero, in which case the large negative logarithms unduly weight the determination.

*A direct summation method*

A third direct method of determining the factor loadings for rank 1 can be derived from the graphical representation of proportional columns. If one

*Table 6*

| | 1 | 2 | 3 | 4 | 5 | | Σ | |
|---|---|---|---|---|---|---|---|---|
| 1 | | .56 | .48 | .40 | .32 | | | |
| 2 | .56 | | .42 | .35 | .28 | | | |
| 3 | .48 | .42 | | .30 | .24 | | | |
| 4 | .40 | .35 | .30 | | .20 | | | |
| 5 | .32 | .28 | .24 | .20 | | | | |
| $s_k$ | 1.76 | 1.61 | 1.44 | 1.25 | 1.04 | | 7.10 | $s_t$ |
| $s_k - r_{k1}$ | 1.76 | 1.05 | .96 | .85 | .72 | | 5.34 | $(s_t - s_1)$ |
| $s_1 - r_{k1}$ | 1.76 | 1.20 | 1.28 | 1.36 | 1.44 | | 7.04 | $(n-1)s_1$ |
| $a_k/a_1$ | 1.000 | .875 | .750 | .625 | .500 | | 3.750 | $c/a_1$ |
| $a_k^2/a_1^2$ | 1.000 | .7656 | .5625 | .3906 | .2500 | | 2.9687 | $v/a_1^2$ |
| $a_k$ | .80 | .70 | .60 | .50 | .40 | | | $c$ |

column $k$ is plotted against another column $l$, the slope is the ratio of $a_k$ to $a_l$. For a correlation matrix of order $n \times n$, there will be $(n-2)$ points in such a plot because the diagonal entries are unknown, being the squares of the quantities sought. The slope can be determined by the method of averages, as

$$(53) \qquad \frac{a_k}{a_l} = \frac{s_k - r_{kl}}{s_l - r_{kl}},$$

where $s_k$ and $s_l$ denote the sums of the known coefficients in columns $k$ and $l$. A numerical example is shown in *Table 6*. In the first summation row we have the sums $s_k$, and the total is $s_t$, which here denotes the sum of all the known coefficients in the matrix. In the next row record values of $(s_k - r_{k1})$. The sum of this row is $(s_t - s_1)$, by which the summations can

---

* For proof see Thurstone, *op. cit.*, p. 62.

be checked. In the next row record values of $(s_1 - r_{k1})$. The sum of this row is $(n - 1)s_1$, by which that summation is checked. In the next row record the ratios $a_k/a_1$ by equation (53). In the next row record the squares of these ratios.

The square of the sum of the factor loadings is equal to the sum of all the coefficients in the correlation matrix, including the diagonal correlations (*chapter viii*, equation [9]). We then have

$$(54) \qquad r_t = \left[ \sum_j a_j \right]^2 .$$

Let the sum of the factor loadings be denoted $c$ and the sum of their squares $v$, which is also the sum of the unknown diagonal coefficients or communalities. We then have

$$(55) \qquad r_t = s_t + v$$

and

$$(56) \qquad c = \sum_j a_j ,$$

so that

$$(57) \qquad s_t + v = c^2 .$$

Divide (57) by $a_1^2$, then

$$(58) \qquad \frac{s_t}{a_1^2} + \frac{v}{a_1^2} = \frac{c^2}{a_1^2} .$$

Hence

$$(59) \qquad a_1 = \sqrt{\frac{s_t}{\left(\dfrac{c}{a_1}\right)^2 - \left(\dfrac{v}{a_1^2}\right)}} ,$$

in which all numerical values are known except $a_1$. Applying this multiplier ($a_1 = .8$ by equation [51]) to the row $a_k/a_1$, we get the factor loadings $a_k$, as shown in the last row of *Table 6*.

*Successive approximations*

In addition to direct methods, there are several methods of successive approximation. One of these is to insert trial values in the diagonal cells and then determine the factor loadings by the centroid method. The squares of the factor loadings so determined are used in the diagonal cells for a new trial, and the process is repeated until the factor loadings are found to any required degree of consistency. For small correlation matrices the approximation methods require more trials than for larger correlation matrices.

For large tables of twenty or more variables, the first trial is usually close enough for practical purposes.

When the centroid method is applied to the case of rank 1, there is no problem concerning the reflection of test vectors or the changing of signs, and the method is then reduced to its first step, namely, the summation for each column of the correlation matrix. It is assumed here that if there are any negative coefficients in the table, the corresponding columns and rows have been reversed in sign so as to make all the coefficients positive. If this cannot be done, then the correlation matrix is certainly not exactly of rank 1. The first-factor loadings are then determined by the summation formula

$$(60) \qquad a_k = \frac{r_k}{\sqrt{r_t}},$$

which is equation (16) of *chapter viii*. Here the first-factor loading for test $k$ is determined by $r_k$, which is the sum of column $k$, including the estimated diagonal, and $r_t$, which is the sum of all the coefficients in the correlation matrix, including the estimated diagonal values. This first step of the centroid method is identical with a formula described by Cyril Burt for a correlation hierarchy. The principal feature of the centroid method, which was devised for multiple-factor analysis, is the treatment of residuals by reflection of test vectors and corresponding sign changes in order to avoid the circumstance that the column sums of the residuals vanish identically.

In using the centroid method for the case of rank 1, we must estimate the diagonal values, and consequently the solution depends on taking trial values, which require successive adjustment until the solution is found to any required degree of accuracy. The adjustments are small when large correlation matrices are used. This procedure is theoretically incorrect, if it is the intention to extract further factors from the residuals. In that case the first-factor determinations again become subject to adjustment with new communalities in the diagonal cells.

Hotelling's iterative method of factoring can be applied to the case of unit rank, but it requires several trials for the successive adjustment of the diagonals which become communalities when the correct solution has been obtained. This solution has the characteristic, when applied successively to a case of unit rank, that the resulting factor loadings minimize the squares of the residuals of the side correlations. The residuals for the diagonal entries are zero when the correct values have been found.

## Limitations of single-factor formulae for multiple-factor analysis

In dealing with actual data it is always a question of fact whether any given table of intercorrelations is of rank 1. When a correlation matrix is to be analyzed with the assumption that it is of unit rank, it is, of course, implied that only one factor needs to be extracted. The values inserted in the diagonal cells are then the squares of the factor loadings. If the diagonal values are known, then the factor loadings are also known. In the special case of rank 1, it is possible to solve directly for the diagonal values, which are the squares of the desired factor loadings. Several such methods have been described here, and others could be devised. In practice such methods are not of great importance because it is rare that a correlation matrix has a rank as low as 1.

The student should be cautioned that if he solves for the first-factor loadings by any of the single-factor formulae, and then attempts to extract

Table 7

Correlation Matrix

|  | 1 | 2 | 3 | 4 | 5 |  |
|---|---|---|---|---|---|---|
| 1 |  | .50 | .41 | .30 | .21 |  |
| 2 | .50 |  | .58 | .44 | .34 |  |
| 3 | .41 | .58 |  | .54 | .57 |  |
| 4 | .30 | .44 | .54 |  | .62 |  |
| 5 | .21 | .34 | .57 | .62 |  |  |
| $(r)_k$ | 1.42 | 1.86 | 2.10 | 1.90 | 1.74 | $9.02 = (r)_t$ |
| $(r^2)_k$ | .5522 | .8956 | 1.1210 | .9596 | .8690 |  |
| $(r)_k^2$ | 2.0164 | 3.4596 | 4.4100 | 3.6100 | 3.0276 |  |
| $a_k^2$ | .2369 | .4838 | .6824 | .5077 | .3896 |  |
| $a_k$ | .49 | .70 | .83 | .71 | .62 | By equation (51) |

Factor Matrix

|  | I | II | $h^2$ |
|---|---|---|---|
| 1 | .1 | .6 | .37 |
| 2 | .2 | .8 | .68 |
| 3 | .5 | .6 | .61 |
| 4 | .6 | .4 | .52 |
| 5 | .9 | .2 | .85 |

First-Factor Residuals

|  | 1 | 2 | 3 | 4 | 5 |
|---|---|---|---|---|---|
| 1 |  | .16 | .00 | −.05 | −.09 |
| 2 | .16 |  | .00 | −.06 | −.09 |
| 3 | .00 | .00 |  | −.05 | .06 |
| 4 | −.05 | −.06 | −.05 |  | .18 |
| 5 | −.09 | −.09 | .06 | .18 |  |

additional factors in the same manner from the residuals, the solution will be theoretically incorrect. This fact is of considerable theoretical significance, and it may be worth while to give a numerical example to show the nature of this error.

In Table 7 we have a factor matrix for five variables and two factors. The communalities are listed in the last column of the factor matrix. Figure 3 shows a plot of the two-dimensional configuration. The corresponding correlation matrix is also shown in Table 7. Now suppose that this correlation matrix is analyzed by one of the single-factor formulae. We have taken Spearman's formula (51) for this example. The first-factor loadings are shown in the row $a_k$, and the squares of these loadings are also listed.

By using these factor loadings we can compute a table of first-factor residuals, as shown at the bottom of *Table 7*.

The correlation matrix was constructed so that it is of rank 2. After extracting one factor, the first-factor residuals should be of rank 1, but inspection of the residuals shows that such is not the case. Furthermore, the square of the first-factor loading of the third variable is higher than the communality of that variable for two factors, as shown in the given factor matrix. The square of the factor loading is .68, as determined by the single-factor formula, whereas the communality is only .61. Therefore, there exists no axis in the configuration of *Figure 3* on which the five tests have the

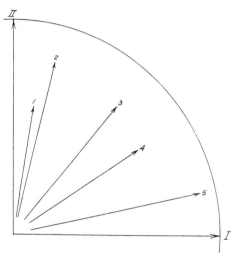

FIGURE 3

projections given by the single-factor formula. These factor loadings are therefore impossible if the rank is assumed to be higher than one. The only way in which the single-factor formulae can be justified is to regard them as single-factor descriptions of the correlation matrix, in which case the first-factor residuals are regarded as variable errors. If the attempt is made to analyze the correlations as due to more than one factor, then the communalities must be adjusted to fit the higher rank. Any valid factoring formula should give a set of factor loadings which are the projections of the test vectors on an axis in the configuration. The same idea can also be expressed by saying that the factor loadings should be linear combinations of the columns of correlation coefficients. The single-factor formulae give correct factor loadings, or approximations to them, when the correlation matrix is regarded as of unit rank or as an approximation to that rank.

# CHAPTER XIII

## THE UNKNOWN COMMUNALITIES

### Nature of the problem

The communality of a test is its common-factor variance. The complement of this variance is the uniqueness of the test, as previously defined. The term "communality"* was adopted to distinguish the common-factor variance from the reliability coefficients, which are conventionally recorded in the diagonal cells of a correlation matrix. The notation $h_j^2$ was adopted for the communality so that $h_j$ was the length of the test vector $j$ in the geometrical representation of the common-factor space. The communality is, then, the square of the length of the test vector, and it is the scalar product of test $j$ with itself. This interpretation of the diagonal makes it consistent with the side correlations, so that the whole correlation matrix represents scalar products in the common-factor space. To estimate the communalities is, in fact, to make a cleavage between the common-factor variance and the unique variance of the test battery. If this is done badly, then the identification of the common factors and their relations is obscured in the resulting factor matrix.

No matter what values are recorded in the diagonal cells, we have the theorem that *the number of linearly independent factors represented by the intercorrelations of* n *tests is equal to the rank of their correlational matrix* $R_1$.† If unity is written in the diagonal cells of a correlation matrix, we call it the "complete correlation matrix $R_1$," and its rank is usually equal to its order, namely, $n$. If the communalities are written in the diagonal cells, we call it the "reduced correlation matrix $R$," and the theorem then states that *the number of linearly independent common factors in a battery of* n *tests is the rank of their reduced correlation matrix* R. In making a factor analysis one usually gambles that the number of common factors is smaller than the number of tests, so that $r < n$.

Since the diagonals are unknown, we have the problem of determining the communalities so that they are consistent with the rank of the side correlations, subject to the restriction that the communalities must be positive numbers between 0 and $+1$. If we take the estimated communalities too high, then we shall increase the rank of the correlation matrix which is due to the diagonals. Factoring such a matrix would force some of the unique variance into the factor matrix, which would give an incorrect re-

---

* L. L. Thurstone, *Theory of Multiple Factors* (Chicago, 1933), p. 8.

† *Ibid.*, p. 20.

sult. If we take the estimated communalities too low, then we destroy the Gramian properties of the matrix, so that it is no longer a correlation matrix. If we take the communalities at their correct values, then the rank of the side correlations is maintained by the communalities, subject to the restriction that they be positive numbers between 0 and $+1$.

The relations between the experimentally given side correlations and the unknown communalities can also be stated in the theorem that *the smallest number of independent factors that will account for the intercorrelations of* n *tests is the minimum rank of the correlational matrix with the diagonal entries treated as unknown positive values between 0 and $+1$.*\* This theorem has been misinterpreted to mean that the rank is itself a variable, which can be given different values, and that the minimum rank should be chosen for which the communalities take possible values. The theorem is operationally true as far as computational procedures are concerned, but the essential fact about the communalities is that they are really determined by the side correlations, which are given. The problem is to determine the communalities which are implied by the given side correlations. When found, they do give the minimum rank for which the communalities have possible values.†

In dealing with experimentally determined correlation coefficients, it must be remembered that the sampling errors of the coefficients are fortuitous and that, consequently, the rank of the correlation matrix with experimental values is, in general, equal to its order, namely, $n$. The scientific problem of analyzing a set of experimentally given correlation coefficients is, then, to find another correlation matrix of minimum rank whose discrepancies from the experimentally given coefficients are small enough to be ignored. We may summarize the multiple-factor problem as follows: From the experimental data we obtain the side correlations, and the diagonal cells are left blank. A matrix of minimum rank is to be obtained which deviates only slightly from the given side correlations. The diagonals are then filled in so as to be consistent with the side correlations. We then have the reduced correlation matrix which is to be factored. In practice the computational procedure does not follow this route, which is merely a statement of the theoretical problem.

\* 1st ed., p. 73.

† Professor Godfrey Thomson has discussed this aspect of the factor problem as if the object were to minimize the number of common factors (*The Factorial Analysis of Human Ability* [Boston: Houghton Mifflin Co., 1939], chap. viii). Operationally, and as regards computational methods, it is correct to say that when the communalities have been written in the diagonal cells, the rank is a minimum. If the communalities were taken smaller, the rank would rise. If the communalities were taken larger, then the rank of the matrix would also rise. This problem is resolved if we realize that the communalities are actually determined by the given side correlations, and it is merely a statistical problem to find their numerical values or approximations to them. The theorem is correct in that the communalities maintain the rank of the side correlations, and this is the minimum possible rank.

## High and low diagonal values

Among students of factor analysis it is universal practice to leave the diagonal elements as unknown when dealing with the case of unit rank. This is Spearman's case of the central intellective factor. The tetrad difference equation is so written as to avoid the unknown diagonal elements, and Spearman's single-factor formula is also written so as to avoid the unknown diagonals. When the single-factor saturations or loadings have been determined, the communalities become the squares of these loadings. The correlation matrix is, then, of unit rank, with all cell entries determined. Some students of the factor problem deviate from this logic as soon as they deal with higher ranks. Then they insert unity in each diagonal cell, regardless of the rank of the side correlations. This leads to an erroneous factorial solution if the purpose is to analyze the factorial composition of the tests as given by the correlation coefficients.

The question as to whether unity or the communalities are to be recorded in the diagonal cells is determined by the purpose of the factor analysis. If the purpose is to reproduce the original *test scores* as closely as possible by means of any specified number of factors, then unity should be written in the diagonal cells. This is true even for Spearman's hierarchy if the purpose is to reproduce the actual test scores. If the purpose of the factor analysis is to analyze the common factors that produced the intercorrelations, then the communalities should be written in the diagonals. The objective is then to reproduce the *intercorrelations* as closely as possible. When unity is written in the diagonals, the original test scores can be reproduced with small residuals. When communalities are written in the diagonals, the intercorrelations can be reproduced with small residuals, but the original test scores will leave larger residuals because the unique factor in each test is unaccounted for. The problem of analyzing the common factors that are represented by the intercorrelations is likely to be the more significant for scientific work, but there are legitimate problems that call for unity in the diagonals. The two objectives—to account for the test scores and to account for the intercorrelations—merge in the same correlation matrix when the communalities are unity. They differ even in this case, however, in the reference frame that is chosen for final description of the variables. If the test scores are to be reproduced as accurately as possible with a small number of factors, the principal axes of the test configuration is the indicated reference frame. If the intercorrelations are to be reproduced as accurately as possible with a small number of factors, then the reference frame is chosen by the principles of simple structure if it can be found in the configuration. If it is not found, then the reference axes may be placed according to clusters or in regions of the configuration which can be identified with any convenient descriptive names, even though the axes so located do not represent well-defined functional unities that are indicated when a simple structure can be discovered in the configuration.* The principal axes can also be used in this case if there is no intention to interpret the factors.

In *Table 1* we have a small numerical example that has been prepared to show the effect of taking communalities that are too high or too low. In the first section we have a correlation matrix for three tests. Unity has been

*Table 1*

1) $d = 1$     Correlation Matrix

| | 1 | 2 | 3 |
|---|---|---|---|
| 1 | 1.00 | − .48 | .56 |
| 2 | − .48 | 1.00 | − .42 |
| 3 | .56 | − .42 | 1.00 |

Factor Matrix

| | I | II | III |
|---|---|---|---|
| 1 | .8384 | .2797 | − .4677 |
| 2 | − .7809 | .6247 | .0000 |
| 3 | .8138 | .3449 | .4677 |

2) $d = h^2$

| | 1 | 2 | 3 |
|---|---|---|---|
| 1 | .64 | − .48 | .56 |
| 2 | − .48 | .36 | − .42 |
| 3 | .56 | − .42 | .49 |

| | I |
|---|---|
| 1 | .80 |
| 2 | − .60 |
| 3 | .70 |

3) $1 > d > h^2$

| | 1 | 2 | 3 |
|---|---|---|---|
| 1 | .70 | − .48 | .56 |
| 2 | − .48 | .50 | − .42 |
| 3 | .56 | − .42 | .60 |

| | I | II | III |
|---|---|---|---|
| 1 | .8009 | .1240 | − .2078 |
| 2 | − .6444 | .2911 | .0000 |
| 3 | .7273 | .1671 | .2078 |

4) $d < h^2$

| | 1 | 2 | 3 |
|---|---|---|---|
| 1 | .60 | − .48 | .56 |
| 2 | − .48 | .25 | − .42 |
| 3 | .56 | − .42 | .40 |

| | I | II | III |
|---|---|---|---|
| 1 | .8031 | .1070$i$ | − .1831$i$ |
| 2 | − .5632 | .2591$i$ | .0000 |
| 3 | .6758 | .1521$i$ | .1831$i$ |

written in the diagonal, and the corresponding centroid factor matrix is also shown. Since we have here as many factors as there are tests, the test scores should be reproduced exactly, as well as the intercorrelations. In this case we have gained nothing by way of condensation or simplification, since the number of factors is equal to the number of tests. We might, then,

---

* An example of a factorial analysis with a set of descriptive reference axes that are not primary factors is given in a paper by the writer, "A Multiple Factor Study of Vocational Interests," *Personnel Journal*, X (1931), 198–205. The configuration was not analyzed for simple structure.

just as well use the original test scores as they stand, without any factor analysis. However, if it is desired to represent the test scores with fewer factors than tests, the factor matrix here shown could be rotated to the principal axes, and the major principal axis could be used as the best single-factor representation of the scores. In that case the intercorrelations would not be well reproduced.

In the second correlation matrix we have the same intercorrelations, but we have here the communalities that reduce the matrix to unit rank. The corresponding factor matrix shows one factor which reproduces the inter-correlations exactly. The test scores would not be well reproduced by this factor matrix. In fact, no single-column factor matrix can be written that would reproduce the test scores, since each test has a unique factor.

In the third correlation matrix we have the same intercorrelations, but here we have written diagonal values that are less than unity but greater than the communalities. The corresponding factor matrix is also shown, and it will be seen that here again it shows three factors.

Finally, in the fourth correlation matrix we have the same intercorrelations, but we have written diagonal values that are less than the communalities. Here the Gramian properties of the matrix have been destroyed. The principal minors are no longer positive or zero, and consequently this cannot be a correlation matrix. It can be factored by the centroid method, however, and the resulting factor matrix is shown. It is seen that the factor loadings contain imaginaries.

The examples of *Table 1* serve to illustrate the principle that the communalities should be so chosen that they are consistent with the rank that is determined by the intercorrelations. When the diagonal elements exceed the communalities, the rank of the whole matrix is, in general, equal to its order. The same result happens when the diagonal elements are lower than the communalities, in which case we have imaginaries in the factor matrix. The rank of the matrix does not seem to be in any sense a continuous function of the communalities. On the contrary, the communalities are, in general, a singular set of diagonal values that are determined by the side correlations. In general, the rank of a correlation matrix is either $n$ or $r$, but special cases could be constructed in which diagonal values could be chosen to make the rank take intermediate values between $r$ and $n$. This could be done in fictitious examples by using the communalities in some of the diagonal cells and higher values in the rest of the diagonal cells. It is evident that the diagonal values cannot be chosen so as to reduce the rank below that of the given side correlations.

It should be recalled that the unique variance of each test is determined entirely by the other tests with which it is associated in the test battery that is being analyzed. Except for the variable errors in the unreliability of a test, it can be associated with other tests that involve the same factors so as to bring its communality up to the reliability of the test. This is, in fact, the challenge of factor analysis, namely, to formulate hypotheses about the nature of the factors that produce the intercorrelations and then to combine a test of unknown unique variance with other tests in such a manner that the common-factor variance becomes completely known. In that case the communality is equal to the reliability of the test.*

### Minimum rank and minimum trace

The trace of a correlation matrix is defined as the sum of the communalities, and it may be denoted $t$. Then

$$(1) \qquad\qquad t = \sum_j h_j^2 .$$

The problem has been raised by Godfrey Thomson as to whether the trace of a correlation matrix is a minimum when the diagonal elements have been so chosen as to minimize the rank. The question then is whether or not minimum rank and minimum trace coincide in the same set of diagonal values. The problem was investigated by Walter Ledermann,† who finds that, while the attainment of minimum rank by the choice of the proper set of diagonal elements gives a small value for the trace, this is not necessarily the minimum possible value for the trace for which the matrix remains Gramian.

For the case of unit rank, the trace of the communalities is a minimum

* In stating his objections to the use of communalities, Professor Kelley considers a hypothetical battery of ten tests, two of which involve a certain musical capacity not present in the other eight tests. The communalities of the music tests include their variance in the music factor, since it is common to two tests in the battery. Now, if one of the musical tests is dropped from the battery, the other musical test will have a reduced communality. The decrement is due to the music factor, which then becomes a specific factor and is no longer a common factor. "Capacity in music reflected in part in the one test retained is now specificity, and according to Thurstone not worthy of retention in the analytical picture" (Truman L. Kelley, *Essential Traits of Mental Life* [Cambridge: Harvard University Press, 1935], p. 56). It is, of course, not a question of whether the specific musical ability is "worthy" of retention. The question is how to disentangle the music factor from other specific factors in the same test and from the error variance in that test. The separation of the specific music factor from the other specific factors in the remaining musical test is not solved by writing unity in the diagonal cells. But the problem can be solved by using an augmented test battery, writing the communalities in the diagonal, and rotating the axes in the common-factor space. Professor Kelley does not approve of this procedure, but he has not offered any other solution for the problem.

† "On a Problem concerning Matrices with Variable Diagonal Elements," *Proceeding of the Royal Society of Edinburgh*, LX, Part I (1939–40), 1–17.

except when one of the loadings is larger than the sum of the others. If we let $h_1$ be the largest saturation, we have, for the exceptional case,

$$(2) \qquad h_1 > \sum_{j=2}^{n} h_j .$$

The exceptional case is obtained by taking another set of values $u_j$ so that the new diagonal values become

$$(3) \qquad d_j = h_j^2 + u_j .$$

A unique set of values of $u_j$ is obtained from the relations

$$(4) \qquad u_1 = -h_1(h_1 - h_2 - h_3 - \cdots - h_n) ,$$

$$(5) \qquad u_j = h_j(h_1 - h_2 - h_3 - \cdots - h_n) , \quad (j = 2, 3, \ldots, n) .$$

The trace for the new diagonal values $d_j$ is then smaller than the trace for the unit rank diagonals $h_j^2$ by an increment $e$, which is

$$(6) \qquad e = \sum_{j} u_j = -(h_1 - h_2 - h_3 - \cdots - h_n)^2,$$

but the rank of the matrix with diagonals $d_j$ is $(n-1)$. The matrix is still Gramian.

*Table 2*

| | Correlation Matrix | | | | | | Factor Matrix | |
|---|---|---|---|---|---|---|---|---|
| | 1 | 2 | 3 | 4 | 5 | | | I |
| 1 | | .2250 | .1800 | .1350 | .0900 | | 1 | .90 |
| 2 | .225⟩ | | .0500 | .0375 | .0250 | | 2 | .25 |
| 3 | .1800 | .0500 | | .0300 | .0200 | | 3 | .20 |
| 4 | .1350 | .0375 | .0300 | | .0150 | | 4 | .15 |
| 5 | .0900 | .0250 | .0200 | .0150 | | | 5 | .10 |
| $h_j^2$ | .8100 | .0625 | .0400 | .0225 | .0100 | | | |
| | trace = .9450 | | rank = 1 | | | | | |
| $u_j$ | −.1800 | .0500 | .0400 | .0300 | .0200 | | | |
| $d_j$ | .6300 | .1125 | .0800 | .0525 | .0300 | | | |
| | trace = .9050 | | rank = $(n-1) = 4$ | | | | | |

In *Table 2* we have a numerical example. The correlation matrix of order $5 \times 5$ is of unit rank when the communalities $h_j^2$ are used. The corresponding single-column factor matrix is also shown in the table. The trace for

$h_j^2$ is .9450, and the rank is 1. The corrections $u_j$ were computed by (4) and (5), producing the new diagonals $d_j$ as shown. The new trace is lower, namely, .9050, and the decrement is $(.20)^2 = .04$ by equation (6) with rank $(n-1)$. The same author investigated the minimum trace for higher ranks with the same conclusion, namely, that the minimum trace for which the matrix remains positive-definite is not necessarily that which gives minimum rank.

On the basis of these findings we can write the useful theorems that *the communalities are a set of diagonal values which retain the rank determined by the side correlations. The communalities give the matrix its minimum rank, namely, the rank of the side correlations. The minimum trace does not necessarily give the minimum rank even when the diagonals are so chosen that the matrix remains Gramian.* In practice, it may be expected that the matrix will no longer be positive-definite when the diagonals are chosen lower than the communalities.

### The Heywood case

A special correlation matrix that has attracted the attention of some students of factor analysis is that in which the rank is 1 (Spearman's hierarchy) but in which one of the diagonal elements must be greater than unity in order to preserve the low rank. A correlation matrix of rank 1 in which a diagonal entry exceeds unity is called a "Heywood case."[*] This curious type of matrix will be discussed here with the example used by Godfrey Thomson in his analysis of this interesting case.[†]

The correlation matrix of *Table 3* is of order 5×5, and it is of rank 1, as far as this can be determined by the proportionality of the columns of side correlations. If we determine the single-factor loadings that will produce the correlations, we have the single-column factor matrix as shown in the table. Since one of these loadings is greater than unity, we have here a Heywood case. Instead of worrying about this circumstance as if it were some insuperable obstacle in factor analysis, it would seem better to regard this finding as showing merely that the first test does not conform to unit rank, which has been imposed on this correlation matrix. If we confine our attention to the other four tests, we have a clear case of unit rank, but not when all five of the tests are considered together.

In the same table we have exhibited one of an infinite number of consistent factor matrices that could be written to cover this case. We have here a common factor, as shown, with a unique variance for each test. These are arbitrarily written so that the total variance is unity for each of the four tests 2–5, but consistent factor matrices could be written for this

---

[*] H. B. Heywood, "On Finite Sequences of Real Numbers," *Proceedings of the Royal Society*, A, CXXXIV (1931), 486–501.

[†] *Op. cit.*, p. 231.

case in many other ways. Test 1 is shown here as a complex test. If this consistent five-column factor matrix is multiplied by its transpose, then by the fundamental factor theorem, $FF' = R$, the given correlation matrix is reproduced. The communality of test 1 is now .9802, which is less than unity, and the mystery of the Heywood case has been resolved. It could have been done in many other ways that imply more than one factor in the complexity of the offending test 1. It is advisable to restate here the condition under which a correlation matrix can be accounted for by a single common factor. *A correlation matrix can be described by a single common factor if it is of unit rank (proportional columns) and if the diagonals are positive numbers between 0 and +1.* If these conditions are not satisfied, then more than one

### Table 3

| Correlation Matrix | | | | | | Factor Matrix | |
|---|---|---|---|---|---|---|---|

| | 1 | 2 | 3 | 4 | 5 | | I |
|---|---|---|---|---|---|---|---|
| 1 | | .945 | .840 | .735 | .630 | 1 | 1.05 |
| 2 | .945 | | .720 | .630 | .540 | 2 | .90 |
| 3 | .840 | .720 | | .560 | .480 | 3 | .80 |
| 4 | .735 | .630 | .560 | | .420 | 4 | .70 |
| 5 | .630 | .540 | .480 | .420 | | 5 | .60 |

*Consistent Factor Matrix*

| | I | II | III | IV | V | $h^2$ |
|---|---|---|---|---|---|---|
| 1 | .90 | .3097 | .2000 | .1470 | .1125 | .9802 |
| 2 | .90 | .4359 | | | | 1.0000 |
| 3 | .80 | | .6000 | | | 1.0000 |
| 4 | .70 | | | .7141 | | 1.0000 |
| 5 | .60 | | | | .8000 | 1.0000 |

common factor is required to describe the correlations. Mathematically, a symmetric square matrix with proportional columns and positive diagonals can be described as the product of a single-column matrix and its transpose, but the product cannot be a correlation matrix if any of the diagonals are negative or if they exceed unity.

The treatment of analogous Heywood cases in multiple-factor analysis is similar to that for unit rank. In the case of multiple factors the appearance of a diagonal value greater than unity means merely that the rank of the factor matrix is higher than that which produced the Heywood case.*

* Godfrey Thomson (*ibid.*, p. 234) discusses the analysis of Spearman's hierarchy for a large number of tests, with the conclusion that a Heywood case would necessarily arise. When the number of tests is the same as the number of persons, the determinant of the correlation matrix vanishes. Thomson concludes that the determinant of a hierarchy cannot vanish with unity in the diagonals except by introducing a Heywood case, i.e., a

## The number of independent factors

In the analysis of experimental data in relation to some hypothesis, one always considers, either explicitly or implicitly, whether or not the experimental observations are adequate to sustain the hypothesis. Attention usually centers on the discrepancies between the fallible experimental observations and the proposed theoretical relations. This is the principal domain of statistical method. But even before such analysis can be undertaken, one must satisfy an even more fundamental requirement. The number of experimentally independent observations or readings must exceed the number of independent parameters in the hypothesis in order for the demonstration to be determinate and convincing. This principle is universal, and it is so fundamental that every scientist takes it for granted intuitively even when he does not formulate it explicitly.

We shall consider a simple example of the principle. Suppose that the hypothesis states that two variables are proportional. Writing this hypothesis explicitly, we have $y = kx$ for all observations. There is only one parameter in this hypothesis of proportionality. The hypothesis would be represented by a straight line through the origin, and all observations should lie on that line. Suppose that we take only one observation, which consists of an observed numerical value for $x$ and the associated numerical value for $y$. Plotting the observation on cross-section paper, we have only one point. No one would accept such a demonstration, because one point on the graph does not demonstrate that the two variables are proportional for all possible values of $x$ and corresponding values of $y$. The hypothesis involves only one parameter, and we have only one observation. We must have more observations than there are independent parameters to be determined. Two observations which fall on a line through the origin would look promising, but they would not be convincing. Five or six observations or twenty or thirty would be convincing. We demand intuitively in any scientific demonstration that the number of experimental observations exceed the number of independent parameters in the hypothesis that is to be sustained. This is, in one sense, the opposite of the mathematical requirement in solving simultaneous equations. If we have more simultaneous equations than unknowns, we are afraid of inconsistencies. In scientific work the parameters must be many times overdetermined, with small experimental inconsistencies, before we accept a hypothesis as plausible.

---

diagonal element greater than unity. We have the theorem that if a correlation matrix with unity in the diagonals is of unit rank, then all side correlations are either $+1$ or $-1$. The determinant then vanishes exactly as is to be expected. Then all the tests are perfect measures of the single common factor, and there is no Heywood case. If the side correlations are less than unity and if unity is recorded in the diagonal cells, then the determinant still vanishes when $n = N$, but the rank is then higher than 1 and there is no Heywood case.

In a large and more complex problem one might forget this principle in the attempt to determine more parameters than there are experimentally independent observations. In factor analysis it is useful to know how many independent factors can be determined from any experimentally given correlation matrix. In order to find this relation we consider the number of experimentally independent correlation coefficients for a battery of $n$ tests and the number of linearly independent factor loadings in a factor matrix for $n$ tests and $r$ factors.

The number of intercorrelations in the correlation matrix of *Table 4* is

$$\frac{n(n-1)}{2},$$

since we regard the diagonal elements as unknown. In considering the number of linearly independent cell entries in the factor matrix, we must take

*Table 4\**

| Correlation Matrix | | | | | | | | | | Factor Matrix | | | | | |
|---|---|---|---|---|---|---|---|---|---|---|---|---|---|---|---|

| | | | | *n* tests | | | | | | | | | *r* factors | | |
|---|---|---|---|---|---|---|---|---|---|---|---|---|---|---|---|
| *n* tests | 1 | 2 | 3 | 4 | 5 | 6 | 7 | 8 | | *n* tests | I | II | III | IV | V |
| 1 | | | | | | | | | | 1 | $a_{11}$ | 0 | 0 | 0 | 0 |
| 2 | $r_{12}$ | | | | | | | | | 2 | $a_{21}$ | $a_{22}$ | 0 | 0 | 0 |
| 3 | $r_{13}$ | $r_{23}$ | | | | | | | | 3 | $a_{31}$ | $a_{32}$ | $a_{33}$ | 0 | 0 |
| 4 | $r_{14}$ | $r_{24}$ | $r_{34}$ | | | | | | | 4 | $a_{41}$ | $a_{42}$ | $a_{43}$ | $a_{44}$ | 0 |
| 5 | $r_{15}$ | $r_{25}$ | $r_{35}$ | $r_{45}$ | | | | | | 5 | $a_{51}$ | $a_{52}$ | $a_{53}$ | $a_{54}$ | $a_{55}$ |
| 6 | $r_{16}$ | $r_{26}$ | $r_{36}$ | $r_{46}$ | $r_{56}$ | | | | | 6 | $a_{61}$ | $a_{62}$ | $a_{63}$ | $a_{64}$ | $a_{65}$ |
| 7 | $r_{17}$ | $r_{27}$ | $r_{37}$ | $r_{47}$ | $r_{57}$ | $r_{67}$ | | | | 7 | $a_{71}$ | $a_{72}$ | $a_{73}$ | $a_{74}$ | $a_{75}$ |
| 8 | $r_{18}$ | $r_{28}$ | $r_{38}$ | $r_{48}$ | $r_{58}$ | $r_{68}$ | $r_{78}$ | | | 8 | $a_{81}$ | $a_{82}$ | $a_{83}$ | $a_{84}$ | $a_{85}$ |

$\dfrac{n(n-1)}{2}$ *coefficients*     $\left[nr - \dfrac{r(r-1)}{2}\right]$ *parameters*

\* This example shows that five common factors cannot be determined from the intercorrelations of eight tests.

into consideration that the configuration of test vectors can be so rotated that a certain number of zero entries can always be introduced. These are indicated in the factor matrix of *Table 4*. The first axis can be placed so as to be collinear with the first test vector. The second orthogonal axis can be placed in the plane of the first two test vectors. The third axis can be placed orthogonal to the first two test vectors in the space spanned by the first three test vectors. The fourth axis can be placed orthogonal to the first three test vectors in the four-dimensional space that is spanned by the first four test vectors, and so on. This will introduce a number of cell entries that are identically zero. The number of such entries is $\frac{1}{2}r(r-1)$, and hence the number of linearly independent factor loadings in $F$ is

$$nr - \frac{r(r-1)}{2}.$$

In order that there may be a unique configuration of test vectors for the correlation matrix, the number of experimentally independent correlation coefficients in $R$ must equal or exceed the number of linearly independent parameters in $F$. Hence

$$(7) \qquad nr - \frac{r(r-1)}{2} \leqq \frac{n(n-1)}{2} .$$

The condition for a maximum value of $r$ for a given value of $n$ is represented by substituting an equality sign for the inequality. The condition then becomes

$$(8) \qquad nr - \frac{r(r-1)}{2} = \frac{n(n-1)}{2}$$

or

$$(9) \qquad 2nr - r(r-1) - n(n-1) = 0 .$$

Solving the quadratic in $r$, we have the following theorem: *In order that the correlational matrix* R *with unknown diagonals for* n *tests and* r *common factors shall represent a unique configuration, it is necessary that*[*]

$$(10) \qquad r \leqq \frac{(2n+1) - \sqrt{8n+1}}{2} .$$

The suppression of the positive sign before the radical in (10) is justified by the postulate that $r < n$. When the equality sign is used in (10), the value of $r$ becomes integral for certain values of $n$. Then the number of independent parameters of $F$ is exactly equal to the number of experimentally independent coefficients in $R$. Such is the case when $n=6$ and $r=3$. We see also, for example, that at least three tests are required to determine one common factor and that at least four tests are required in order that one common factor shall be overdetermined. This is the situation in Spearman's tetrad difference equation, which involves four tests for the determination of a single common factor. At least five tests are required to determine two common factors.

Since equation (9) is symmetric in $n$ and $r$, $n$ can be expressed explicitly in terms of $r$ by analogy from (10), so that

$$(11) \qquad n \geqq \frac{(2r+1) + \sqrt{8r+1}}{2} .$$

This relation shows the minimum number of tests required for the determination of $r$ factors. Equation (11) shows, for example, that there must be at least eight tests in order to determine four common factors.

[*] 1st ed., p. 76; see also E. B. Wilson, "Review of *Crossroads in the Mind of Man* [by T. L. Kelley]," *Journal of General Psychology*, II (1929), 158.

An actual count of the correlation coefficients in *Table 4* shows 28, whereas the count of independent parameters in the factor matrix is 30. Hence the five indicated factors cannot be determined from the correlations of eight tests. Four factors can be determined, since 28 > 26; but this calculation assumes that the correlation coefficients are infallible. With actual data one would not ordinarily attempt to find more than two or, at most, three factors for eight tests.

It is useful to have a table to show the smallest number of tests that will just determine a given number of factors or the largest number of factors that can be determined by a given number of tests. This information is summarized for ten factors in *Table 5*. This table must not be used to de-

*Table 5*

| No. of Factors $r$ | No. of Tests $n$ | No. of Factors $r$ | No. of Tests $n$ |
|:---:|:---:|:---:|:---:|
| 1 | 3* | 6 | 10* |
| 2 | 5 | 7 | 12 |
| 3 | 6* | 8 | 13 |
| 4 | 8 | 9 | 14 |
| 5 | 9 | 10 | 15* |

* The asterisks refer to integral values of both $r$ and $n$ in (11).

termine the number of factors to extract from experimentally given data. A battery of fifteen tests cannot be expected to determine ten factors with any degree of stability. In order for a factor analysis to be stable and scientifically significant and convincing, the number of tests must be two or three times greater than those which are shown in the table. The table shows only the number of factors that can be determined from the intercorrelations of a given number of tests, as far as the count of independent parameters is concerned. It does not consider the degree of overdetermination which is necessary for the scientific acceptance of a factorial interpretation of fallible data.

### Methods of estimating the communalities

Before the numerical work of factoring is begun, it is necessary to estimate the communalities. The estimation of communalities will be considered under three general heads, namely, (1) when exact, or nearly exact, communalities are desired; (2) when factoring is to be done with adjustment in the diagonal cells after each factor has been extracted; and (3) when factoring is to be done without adjustment in the diagonal cells after each factor has been extracted. The third case implies any factoring method that avoids the computation of residuals after each factor has been computed.

The first case is that in which it is desired to estimate the communalities very closely. For large correlation matrices it is seldom necessary to insist on close estimates of the communalities. The reason is that in this case the factorial results are not seriously affected by coarse initial estimates for the diagonal cells. It is another matter when the correlation matrix is small, say, of order 8 or 10 or less. For small correlation matrices the factorial results can be markedly affected by wrong estimates for the communalities.

The best procedure for small correlation matrices is probably to do the factoring with such estimates as can be made. The resulting factor matrix will then give a new set of communalities, which can be reinserted in the original correlation matrix. The factoring can then be repeated with the new communality estimates. But in the subsequent trials one does not make any adjustment in the diagonal cells after each factor. After a few trials it will be found that the communalities determined by the factor matrix are practically the same as those with which the factoring was started. These values may then be accepted as close estimates of the communalities. It is a fortunate circumstance that the necessity for repeating the factoring in order to get stable factorial results and stable communalities occurs with only small correlation matrices for which the computational labor is not prohibitive. For large correlation matrices this repetition of the factoring is seldom if ever necessary.

In dealing with experimental data it must be recalled that the rank of the correlation matrix is, in general, equal to its order. It is then a question of statistical judgment when the residuals are small enough so that they can be ignored. If the factoring is continued without adjustment in the diagonal cells after each factor has been determined, the residuals will be identically zero after $n$ factors have been extracted. This is true for the various centroid methods and for other methods of factoring. In practice the computer stops the process before such a result has been obtained. He stops extracting further factors when he judges the residuals to be sufficiently small. At this stage it is evident that each additional factor contributes very little to the total variance of each test in the common factors. Since each factor contributes a small increment to the communality, it is evident that the estimated communality must be judged in relation to the number of factors that are extracted. It follows also that the true communalities can be determined only by extracting $(n-1)$ factors with $n$ tests in the battery. It would usually be a waste of time to carry the work to this extreme, and consequently the true communalities are not ordinarily determined for experimental data. In determining the best-fitting communalities by repeating the factoring several times, we must remember that each trial should be taken to the same number of factors. The revised estimate of the communalities should then be stated for the number of factors that were determined. When it is desirable to obtain a very close estimate of the communalities for a specified number of factors, the ideal procedure is to obtain the principal-axes solution to the specified number of factors and to repeat this process with adjusted communalities, as determined in each trial.

Our second case is that in which a factoring method is used which gives a set of residuals after each factor. There is then an opportunity after each factor to adjust the diagonal cells. The simplest method is that of recording in the diagonals the highest coefficient in the column. This method has been used in a large number of studies with satisfactory results.

Our third case is that in which the diagonals are not adjusted after each factor. This is necessarily also the case when the factoring is done without computing residuals after each factor. In this case it is necessary to make a fairly good estimate of the communalities before the factoring is begun. If in this method of factoring it should be discovered that a large error has been made in estimating the diagonals, it might be necessary to repeat the factoring in order to correct the error. This will be true especially for small correlation matrices.

A number of principles and computing formulae will be considered by which the communalities may be estimated. Most of these formulae are approximate.

## 1. Expansion of a minor of order $(r+1)$

If the correlation coefficients are infallible and if the rank of the correlation matrix is assumed to be $r$, then the communalities can be computed on

*Table 6*

| *Factor Matrix* | | | *Correlation Matrix of Rank 2* | | | | | | | | |
|---|---|---|---|---|---|---|---|---|---|---|---|
| | I | II | | 1 | 2 | 3 | 4 | 5 | 6 | 7 | 8 |
| 1 | .8 | .0 | 1 | | .56 | .16 | .24 | .72 | .64 | .40 | .24 |
| 2 | .7 | .4 | 2 | .56 | | .38 | .49 | .67 | .72 | .63 | .53 |
| 3 | .2 | .6 | 3 | .16 | .38 | | .48 | .24 | .40 | .52 | .54 |
| 4 | .3 | .7 | 4 | .24 | .49 | .48 | | .34 | .52 | .64 | .65 |
| 5 | .9 | .1 | 5 | .72 | .67 | .24 | .34 | | .76 | .52 | .35 |
| 6 | .8 | .4 | 6 | .64 | .72 | .40 | .52 | .76 | | .68 | .56 |
| 7 | .5 | .7 | 7 | .40 | .63 | .52 | .64 | .52 | .68 | | .71 |
| 8 | .3 | .8 | 8 | .24 | .53 | .54 | .65 | .35 | .56 | .71 | |
| | | | True communalities | .64 | .65 | .40 | .58 | .82 | .80 | .74 | .73 |

the basis of this assumption and tested for consistency. In order to compute the communality of a test $j$, select any minor in the correlation matrix which contains the diagonal entry for test $j$ but not other diagonal entries and which is of order greater than the assumed rank. By the definition of rank this minor must vanish. Its expansion is a linear equation in one unknown, by which the communality may be computed.

In *Table 6* are reproduced the intercorrelations of eight hypothetical variables. The rank of the matrix is 2. *Table 7* shows a minor of order 3 with one unknown entry, namely, the communality for variable number 1. In order that the expansion of the minor may vanish, the unknown diagonal entry must be .64. If the rank is assumed too high, say 3, it will be found that the coefficients of $h_1^2$, as well as the numerical terms, all vanish. This indeterminacy can be removed by assuming a lower rank. The fact that the minor of *Table 7* vanishes does not demonstrate, of course, that the correlation matrix is of rank 2. Instead of evaluating all the minors of order 3, one might proceed to factor the matrix after all the communalities have been determined by this method, and it would then be found in the factoring routine whether

*Table 7*

|   | 1 | 2 | 3 |
|---|---|---|---|
| 1 | $h_1^2$ | .56 | .16 |
| 4 | .24 | .49 | .48 |
| 5 | .72 | .67 | .24 |

the assumed rank was correct. It is evident that this simple method is not stable when used on fallible data.

## 2. Grouping of similar tests

If a test battery is large and if it contains constellations or clusters of similar tests, then the tests in each constellation will be represented by vectors in the common-factor space with relatively small angular separations. The communality of a test is the square of the length of its vector. If the angular separations between several test vectors are relatively small, then the projection of a test vector on the centroid vector of the constellation will be nearly the same as the length of the vector. The square of the projection may be used as an estimate of the communality of the test. The estimate will usually be slightly too low. The projection of each test vector on the best-fitting single vector for the constellation can be regarded as an approximation to the loading of the test with the single common factor which best describes the intercorrelations of the tests in the constellation.

Let the communality to be estimated be denoted $h_1^2$ and let the tests which correlate highest with number 1 be denoted 2, 3, . . . , s, so that there are $s$ tests in the group. The intercorrelations of the tests in this group may be assembled in the accompanying tabular arrangement, which is particular-

|   | 1 | 2 | 3 | 4 |
|---|---|---|---|---|
| 1 | $h_1^2$ | $r_{12}$ | $r_{13}$ | $r_{14}$ |
| 2 | $r_{12}$ |   | $r_{23}$ | $r_{24}$ |
| 3 | $r_{13}$ | $(r_{23})$ |   | $r_{34}$ |
| 4 | $r_{14}$ | $(r_{24})$ | $(r_{34})$ |   |
|   | $\Sigma r_1$ | $(\Sigma r_0)$ |   |   |

ized for $s = 4$. It is desired to estimate the communality $h_1^2$ from the projection of test 1 on the centroid axis for this subgroup of test vectors. A slight underestimation may be expected, because the length of the first test vector will be slightly longer than its projection on the centroid axis for the group, unless they should happen to coincide. To compensate for this underestimation we may underestimate the communalities of the adjacent tests 2, 3, 4, by writing in the three adjacent diagonals the average of each column. The sum of the adjacent columns 2, 3, . . . , $s$, may then be written

$$\frac{s(\Sigma r - \Sigma r_1)}{(s - 1)} ,$$

where $\Sigma r$ denotes the sum of all known coefficients in the table and $\Sigma r_1$ denotes the sum of all known coefficients in the first column.

The sum of all the coefficients in the table can then be estimated as

$$(\Sigma r_1 + h_1^2) + \frac{s(\Sigma r - \Sigma r_1)}{(s - 1)} ,$$

and the complete sum for the first column is

$$\Sigma r_1 + h_1^2 .$$

The projection of the first test vector on the centroid axis is the ratio of the first-column sum to the square root of the sum of all coefficients in the table. This projection should be an estimate of $h_1$. Hence we should have, as an estimate for $h_1^2$,

$$h_1^2 \doteq \frac{(\Sigma r_1 + h_1^2)^2}{\Sigma r_1 + h_1^2 + \dfrac{s(\Sigma r - \Sigma r_1)}{(s - 1)}} ,$$

which simplifies to

$$(12) \qquad\qquad h_1^2 \doteq \frac{(s - 1)(\Sigma r_1)^2}{s\Sigma r - (2s - 1)\Sigma r_1} .$$

Equation (12) may be written in several equivalent forms. In computation it may be simpler to determine only two sums, namely, the sum of the known coefficients in the first column, $\Sigma r_1$, and the sum of the known adjacent coefficients in the half-table which are not in the first column or row. These are marked in parentheses in the present tabular arrangement. Let their sum be denoted $\Sigma r_0$. Then the sum $\Sigma r$ must be equal to $2(\Sigma r_1 + \Sigma r_0)$. Substituting this expression for $\Sigma r$ in (12), we have the equivalent formula

$$(12a) \qquad\qquad h_1^2 \doteq \frac{(s - 1)(\Sigma r_1)^2}{\Sigma r_1 + 2s\Sigma r_0} ,$$

where $\Sigma r_1$ is the sum of the known coefficients in the first column and $\Sigma r_0$ is the sum of the adjacent coefficients in the half-table which are marked in parentheses in the tabular arrangement. These formulae will be referred to as "centroid formulae."

For convenience we may list the equivalent formula for small subgroups of related tests. When the group contains 3 tests, we have for $s = 3$,

$$(12b) \qquad h_1^2 \doteq \frac{2(\Sigma r_1)^2}{\Sigma r_1 + 6 r_{23}} \qquad \text{(3-test formula)} .$$

When $s = 4$, we have

$$(12c) \qquad h_1^2 \doteq \frac{3(\Sigma r_1)^2}{\Sigma r_1 + 8 \Sigma r_0} \qquad \text{(4-test formula)} .$$

It is interesting to note that for a doublet when $s = 2$ this formula reduces to $h_1^2 = h_2^2 = r_{12}$. A doublet is factorially indeterminate, but it will be seen that, when the coefficients for a doublet in a large battery do not entirely vanish, a graphical method may be applicable.

## 3. Grouping of three tests

A special case of the grouping of similar tests is that of using only three tests that are highly correlated in a constellation or cluster. One procedure for estimating the communality of a test $j$ is to select the two tests, $k$ and $l$, which have the highest correlations with $j$. If a test battery is so constructed that each postulated ability is represented by several tests, it can be expected that the three tests, $j$, $k$, and $l$, will be represented by test vectors with relatively small angular separations. The communality of test $j$ can be estimated by one of Spearman's formulae, namely,

$$(13) \qquad h_j^2 \doteq \frac{r_{jk} r_{jl}}{r_{kl}} ,$$

which is equation (15) of *chapter xii*. It is here written as an approximation formula because the communality of test $j$ in a test battery is not necessarily determined by only three tests. This would be a simple method of estimating the communalities in practical work except for the fact that it is unstable because of sampling errors. It can be used as one estimate of the communality if it is combined with other more stable estimates. It will be referred to as a "3-test formula."

## 4. Highest coefficient in each column

Inspection of equation (13) for estimating the communality of a test suggests a further simplification in the estimate. The numerator contains the product of the two highest correlations in the column for test $j$. The denominator is the intercorrelation of the two tests so selected, namely, $k$ and $l$. If these coefficients are of the same order of magnitude, then the estimated communality of test $j$ will be nearly equal to the highest intercorrelation in column $j$. This is the method that has been used in a large number of studies in which the factoring was done by one of the centroid methods, adjusting the diagonal values of the residuals after each factor had been computed. This simple method of estimating communalities is useful only for large correlation matrices. It is not applicable to small tables.

The principles of No. 3 and No. 4 can be combined in another computing formula. Let test 1 be the test whose communality is to be estimated, and let tests 2, 3, and 4 be several other tests which have high correlations with test 1. The coefficients may be shown in the accompanying tabular arrange-

|   | 1 | 2 | 3 | 4 |
|---|---|---|---|---|
| 1 | $h_1^2$ | $r_{12}$ | $r_{13}$ | $r_{14}$ |
| 2 | $r_{12}$ | $h_2^2$ | $r_{23}$ | $r_{24}$ |
| 3 | $r_{13}$ | $r_{23}$ | $h_3^2$ | $r_{34}$ |
| 4 | $r_{14}$ | $r_{24}$ | $r_{34}$ | $h_4^2$ |

|   | 1 | 2 | 5 | 6 |
|---|---|---|---|---|
| 1 | .72 | .56 | .72 | .64 |
| 2 | .56 | .72 | .67 | .72 |
| 5 | .72 | .67 | .76 | .76 |
| 6 | .64 | .72 | .76 | .76 |
| $\Sigma$ | 2.64 | 2.67 | 2.91 | 2.88    11.10 |

ment for four tests. If, as a first estimate for each test, we record the highest coefficient in the column for this subgroup of four tests, we have the numerical entries which were obtained from *Table 6*. The tests 2, 5, and 6 are those which correlate highest with test 1. The first-column sum is, then, $(\Sigma r_1 + t_1)$, where $\Sigma r_1$ denotes the sum of the known coefficients in the first column and $t_1$ is the highest coefficient in that column as recorded in the diagonal cell. The sum of all the coefficients in the table is $(\Sigma r + \Sigma t)$, where $\Sigma r$ is the sum of all known coefficients. By the centroid formula we then have

$$(14) \qquad h_1 \doteq \frac{\Sigma r_1 + t_1}{\sqrt{\Sigma r + \Sigma t}},$$

so that

$$(15) \qquad h_1^2 \doteq \frac{(\Sigma r_1 + t_1)^2}{\Sigma r + \Sigma t}.$$

For test 1 we then have the numerical estimate $(2.64)^2/11.10$, which gives .58 as an estimated communality. The true value in this case is .64. Equation (14) is a centroid formula.

## 5. Linear dependence of rows and columns

If the rank of a correlation matrix is $r$, then any row may be expressed linearly in terms of any $r$ independent rows. It may be possible to generalize this principle into a method of computing the communalities for fallible data. In using this method one assumes a rank for the correlation matrix, and it is also essential that the rows chosen for the computation be linearly independent.

The idea of using linear dependence of rows and columns of the correlation matrix could perhaps be used for estimating the communalities if the matrix were divided into four or into nine sections. The method can be outlined with the adjoining table showing a correlation matrix divided into nine

$$\left\| \begin{array}{ccc} R_{11} & R_{12} & R_{13} \\ R_{21} & R_{22} & R_{23} \\ R_{31} & R_{32} & R_{33} \end{array} \right\|$$

square sections. Let us assume that the tests have been divided into clusters by inspection of the correlations. Each cluster should be represented by at least one test in each of the three groups into which the tests have been divided. The notation in the table means that $R_{23}$, for example, is the square section showing the correlations of the tests in the second group with the tests in the third section. With this prearrangement of the tests in three groups and with the assumption that the rank does not exceed one-third of the number of tests, it should follow that the third group of columns can be represented by a linear transformation of the second group of columns, and similarly for the rows. If $T$ denotes a linear transformation, we should write $R_{31}T = R_{21}$, $R_{32}T = R_{22}$, $R_{33}T = R_{23}$. Since the sections $R_{31}$ and $R_{21}$ are known, the transformation $T$ could be determined and hence the other sections. The side correlations of the symmetric sections so computed should not deviate far from the experimentally given values in the three diagonal sections, and the communalities would then be estimated. This idea has not been developed into a practical computing method for the communalities, but it might be done.*

## 6. Sectioning of the matrix

The unknown communalities can be solved for by sectioning the correlation matrix. This method has not been used because it requires more computation than the simpler methods that have been found adequate in practice, and it is not a stable method for fallible data. The sectioning theorem will be given here because of its interest in relation to the correlation matrix. *If any matrix of rank* r *is sectioned into a composite square matrix of order* s, *where* s > r, *then the determinant of the composite matrix vanishes.*

The matrix will be said to be sectioned when the columns have been divided into s groups, and when the rows have also been divided into the same

* Since this chapter was written the idea has been developed into a computing formula, as described in a later section of this chapter on "Further Studies of Linear Dependence."

number of groups. Let $r=2$ as an example. Since $s>r$, we may let $s=3$. Then the $n$ columns of $R$ will be divided into three groups of $p$, $(q-p)$, and $(n-q)$ columns, respectively; while the $n$ rows of $R$ will be divided into three groups of $t$, $(u-t)$, and $(n-u)$ rows, respectively. The matrix $R$ will then be sectioned.

The composite matrix will be defined as the square matrix of order $s$ in which the entries are the sums of the elements in the corresponding parts of the sectioned matrix. The example of *Table 8* illustrates the formation of a

*Table 8*

| 14 | 12 | 6 | 8 | 2 |
|----|----|----|----|----|
| 6 | 104 | 21 | 9 | 17 |
| 7 | 6 | 3 | 4 | 1 |
| 35 | 30 | 15 | 20 | 5 |

composite matrix. This $4 \times 5$ matrix is of rank 2. It has been sectioned into a $3 \times 3$ square matrix by arbitrarily dividing the columns into three groups of 2, 2, and 1 columns, respectively, and by arbitrarily dividing the rows into three groups of 1, 1, and 2 rows, respectively. The composite matrix is shown in *Table 9*. Its determinant vanishes.

*Table 9*

$$\begin{Vmatrix} 26 & 14 & 2 \\ 110 & 30 & 17 \\ 78 & 42 & 6 \end{Vmatrix}$$

The proof of the theorem will be written for rank 2, but it can readily be generalized for any rank. If $R$ is of rank 2, it is possible to find two rows that are linearly independent. Let these be the first and second rows. Then the elements of the $j$th row can be expressed as a linear function of the first two rows so that

$$(16) \quad \begin{cases} r_{j1} = m_1 r_{11} + m_2 r_{21} , \\ r_{j2} = m_1 r_{12} + m_2 r_{22} , \\ \cdot \quad \cdot \quad \cdot \quad \cdot \quad \cdot \quad \cdot \\ r_{jk} = m_1 r_{1k} + m_2 r_{2k} . \end{cases}$$

It is evident that the sum of the first $p$ entries of row $j$ can also be expressed as the same linear function of the corresponding sums in the first two rows. We then have

$$(17) \qquad \sum_{k=1}^{p} r_{jk} = m_1 \sum_{k=1}^{p} r_{1k} + m_2 \sum_{k=1}^{p} r_{2k} \,.$$

Similar summations may be written for the other two groups of columns so that

$$(18) \qquad \left\{ \begin{array}{l} \displaystyle\sum_{k=(p+1)}^{q} r_{jk} = m_1 \sum_{k=(p+1)}^{q} r_{1k} + m_2 \sum_{k=(p+1)}^{q} r_{2k} \,, \\[3ex] \displaystyle\sum_{k=(q+1)}^{n} r_{jk} = m_1 \sum_{k=(q+1)}^{n} r_{1k} + m_2 \sum_{k=(q+1)}^{n} r_{2k} \,. \end{array} \right.$$

These summations may be represented in an $n \times 3$ matrix as shown in *Table 10*. Since each of the rows can be expressed as a linear function of the

*Table 10*

| | | |
|---|---|---|
| $\displaystyle\sum_{1}^{p} r_{1k} = b_{11}$ | $\displaystyle\sum_{p+1}^{q} r_{1k} = b_{12}$ | $\displaystyle\sum_{q+1}^{n} r_{1k} = b_{13}$ |
| $\displaystyle\sum_{1}^{p} r_{2k} = b_{21}$ | $\displaystyle\sum_{p+1}^{q} r_{2k} = b_{22}$ | $\displaystyle\sum_{q+1}^{n} r_{2k} = b_{23}$ |
| $\displaystyle\sum_{1}^{p} r_{3k} = b_{31}$ | $\displaystyle\sum_{p+1}^{q} r_{3k} = b_{32}$ | $\displaystyle\sum_{q+1}^{n} r_{3k} = b_{33}$ |
| | | |
| $\displaystyle\sum_{1}^{p} r_{nk} = b_{n1}$ | $\displaystyle\sum_{p+1}^{q} r_{nk} = b_{n2}$ | $\displaystyle\sum_{q+1}^{n} r_{nk} = b_{n3}$ |

first two rows, it follows that the rank of this $n \times 3$ matrix is also 2. The columns may be so arranged that the third column of this matrix may be expressed in terms of the first two columns. This reduction by columns is similar to the reduction by rows that has been described. This reduction by columns gives a $3 \times 3$ composite matrix whose rank is 2, and hence its determinant vanishes. If the rank of $R$ is equal to or greater than the order $s$

of the square composite matrix, then the determinant of the composite does not necessarily vanish.

The communalities can be solved for by sectioning, if this is done in such a manner that one row and the corresponding column are taken as sections. Their intersection will be a section with a single entry, namely, the communality to be determined.

## 7. Expansion of principal minors of order $(n-1)$

It is possible to write $n$ principal minors of order $(n-1)$ in a square matrix of order $n$. If the expansion of each of these $n$ principal minors of order $(n-1)$ is set equal to zero, the rank of the matrix is assumed to be not greater than $(n-2)$. This follows from the property of a Gramian matrix that if all of its principal minors of order $m$ vanish, then the rank of the matrix does not exceed $(m-1)$. Since there are $n$ principal minors of order $(n-1)$, their expansions give as many equations as there are unknown diagonal entries. A unique solution is obtained if the inequality (10) is satisfied. If this inequality is not satisfied, there should be no unique solution. In this method it is not necessary to know the rank. These considerations are of some analytical interest, but they do not seem to lend themselves to computing purposes.

## 8. Expansion of principal minors of order $(r+a)$

This should be a special case of the preceding method but less laborious. It is not necessary that the rank be known, but it is assumed that $(r+a)$ is taken larger than the rank. The simplest case is that in which $a=1$. This method requires that the number of tests covered by the expanded principal minors be such as to satisfy inequality (10), even though all the tests in the correlational matrix are not utilized. The development of this type of analysis would be of interest, but so far it has not led to practical computing methods.

## 9. A summation formula

Let the test whose communality is to be determined be denoted number 1, and let number 2 be the test which correlates highest with test 1. These two tests will usually have a small angular separation, and hence their intercorrelations should be nearly proportional. Hence

$$(19) \qquad \frac{\Sigma r_1 - r_{12}}{\Sigma r_2 - r_{12}} \doteq \frac{h_1^2}{r_{12}},$$

where $\Sigma r_1$ and $\Sigma r_2$ are the sums of the known coefficients in the two columns. This gives the approximate computing formula

$$(20) \qquad h_1^2 \doteq \frac{r_{12}(\Sigma r_1 - r_{12})}{(\Sigma r_2 - r_{12})},$$

which may be referred to as a "summation formula." Its source of instability is the single coefficient $r_{12}$, whose variable error influences directly the estimate of $h_1^2$. This formula makes the assumption that the two columns 1 and 2 are of unit rank and hence that they are proportional.

## 10. Spearman's formula

The summation formula of equation (20) can be generalized for a group of four correlated tests, including test 1, which may be assumed to be nearly collinear. From (20) we may write for each of the three tests 2, 3, 4,

$$(21) \qquad h_1^2 = \frac{r_{12}(\Sigma r_1 - r_{12})}{(\Sigma r_2 - r_{12})} = \frac{r_{13}(\Sigma r_1 - r_{13})}{(\Sigma r_3 - r_{13})} = \frac{r_{14}(\Sigma r_1 - r_{14})}{(\Sigma r_4 - r_{14})},$$

where $\Sigma r_x$ is the sum of the known coefficients in column $x$. From these three expressions we write

$$(22) \qquad h_1^2 = \frac{r_{12}(\Sigma r_1 - r_{12}) + r_{13}(\Sigma r_1 - r_{13}) + r_{14}(\Sigma r_1 - r_{14})}{(\Sigma r_2 - r_{12}) + (\Sigma r_3 - r_{13}) + (\Sigma r_4 - r_{14})},$$

which simplifies to one of Spearman's formulae for the single common factor, namely,

$$(23) \qquad h_1^2 \doteq \frac{(\Sigma r_1)^2 - (\Sigma r_1^2)}{\Sigma r - 2\Sigma r_1},$$

which is the same as equation (51) in *chapter xii* in different notation. Here $\Sigma r$ is the sum of all known coefficients for the subgroup and $\Sigma r_1^2$ is the sum of the squares of the coefficients in the first column. This formula of Spearman should give a good estimate of the communality, although it was not originally written in the present context. The formula assumes approximation to unit rank for the subgroups.

## 11. Grouping of four tests

Spearman's 3-test formula, equation (13), can be adapted to the case of four correlated tests where test 1 is the one whose communality is to be estimated. In the 3-test form we have

$$(24) \qquad h_1^2 \doteq \frac{r_{12}r_{13}}{r_{23}},$$

and this can be extended to four tests in the relations

$$(25) \qquad h_1^2 \doteq \frac{r_{12}r_{13}}{r_{23}} \doteq \frac{r_{13}r_{14}}{r_{34}} \doteq \frac{r_{12}r_{14}}{r_{24}}.$$

These three formulae can be combined into a single 4-test formula by taking the geometric mean of the three expressions, and we then have

$$(26) \qquad h_1^2 \doteqdot \sqrt[3]{\frac{r_{12}^2 r_{13}^2 r_{14}^2}{r_{23} r_{24} r_{34}}} .$$

## 12. Graphical methods of estimation

If two test vectors (1 and 2) are nearly collinear, the correlations of their respective columns should be proportional to the ratio of $h_1/h_2$. We should then have

$$(27) \qquad \frac{r_{2j}}{r_{1j}} = \frac{h_2 h_j \cos \phi_{2j}}{h_1 h_j \cos \phi_{1j}} ;$$

and, since the two cosines should be nearly the same, we have

$$(28) \qquad \frac{r_{2j}}{r_{1j}} = \frac{h_2}{h_1}$$

or

$$(29) \qquad r_{2j} = \frac{h_2}{h_1} r_{1j} = s_{21} r_{1j} .$$

Hence there should be a linear plot of $r_{2j}$ against $r_{1j}$ through the origin. Since the correlation $r_{12}$ should be nearly equal to $h_1 h_2$, we should have, approximately,

$$(30) \qquad h_1^2 \doteqdot \frac{r_{12}}{s_{21}} \quad \text{and} \quad h_2^2 \doteqdot r_{12} s_{21} ,$$

by which the communalities can be estimated. When the plot is clearly linear through the origin, this method of estimation is good except for the variable error in $r_{12}$. A clear linear plot indicates that the two test vectors are nearly collinear. This method of estimation is probably the best one in dealing with a doublet, in which case there is only one appreciable coefficient in the column.

If two tests, 2 and 3, are coplanar with test 1, a computing formula can be written for estimating the communalities by plotting $r_{2j}/r_{3j}$ against $r_{1j}$. The plot should then be linear but not ordinarily through the origin. From the slope and one of the intercepts one could then determine the linear combination of columns 2 and 3, which reproduces column 1. This coplanar method is of some interest, but it is not, in this form, readily applicable. The collinear form of graphic estimation is often quite useful.

## Summary of methods

When a column of the correlation matrix contains a number of coefficients that are quite high, the estimate can be made with one of the formulae which include the correlations of several tests. In general, we should expect instability with fallible data when the error in the estimate is directly affected by the error in a single coefficient as in equations (13), (20), and (30).

When a column contains only one high coefficient, none of the computing formulae apply because we then have essentially a doublet. The estimate might then be made by the graphical method. A pure doublet in which there is only one non-vanishing coefficient in the column, while all the rest are zeros, is factorially indeterminate. Theoretically, this case is the same as that of a correlation matrix for only two variables. There is only one correlation which is insufficient to determine two communalities. In practical work one seldom finds a pure doublet, but one does find approximations to them. If a doublet is to be retained in a battery, one can sometimes make a good estimate graphically if the remaining coefficients do not entirely vanish. Another procedure is to set both communalities equal, in which case they are both equal to their correlation, the highest in the column.

If the factoring is to be done by a method with adjustment in the diagonals after each factor and if the battery is large, say, more than twenty or thirty variables, then one may record the highest coefficient of the residual column in each diagonal cell. This procedure is not adequate for small correlation matrices. For very small tables of, say, less than ten variables, one may need to repeat the factoring several times to obtain good estimates of the communalities and an acceptable factor matrix.

## Uniqueness of communalities

We have considered the problem of ascertaining whether there are enough independent correlation coefficients in $R$ to determine the factor matrix for $r$ factors. This problem is solved by the relations of the inequality (10), which gives the maximum number of common factors that can be determined from the intercorrelations of $n$ tests. In the theorem for the inequality we stated that for any given number of common factors $(r)$ to be determined by a given number of tests $(n)$ it is *necessary* that the inequality be satisfied. The theorem does not state that the satisfying of the inequality (10) is *sufficient* to insure that $r$ factors can be determined from the intercorrelations of $n$ tests. In deriving the inequality we merely counted the number of independent parameters in the correlation matrix and the number of independent parameters in the desired factor matrix. The relation between these two counts does not insure that the diagonal values will be positive numbers between 0 and $+1$, and it does not take into consideration the possibility of multiple solutions with real or imaginary diagonal entries in the correlation matrix.

If a correlation matrix is factored by the diagonal method with unit communalities (*chapter ii*), a factor matrix can be obtained which accounts for the intercorrelations exactly with not more than $n$ factors. If $n$ factors are required to account for the intercorrelations, then the last column of the factor matrix contains only one entry. Hence it may be regarded as a specific factor for the last test. We therefore have the theorem that *there exists at least one set of communalities between 0 and +1 for which the rank of the reduced correlation matrix is less than the number of tests. Every correlation matrix can be accounted for by not more than* $(n-1)$ *common factors.*

In making an exact solution for the communalities, one would take a trial rank $r$ and then expand minors of order $(r+1)$ which should vanish.

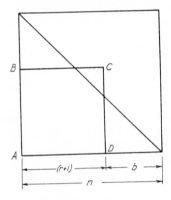

Figure 1

These minors should be so selected that they contain a minimum number of diagonal cells. In *Figure 1* we have represented the correlation matrix and the principal diagonal. Let $ABCD$ be a minor which is so placed that it contains a minimum number of diagonal cells. Let the number of columns which do not contain any part of the minor be denoted $b$. The number of columns $b$ then is

$$n - r - 1 ,$$

and hence the number of diagonal cells outside the indicated minor is

$$2(n - r - 1) ;$$

so that the minimum number of communalities $M$ that can be placed in the minor is

(31)    $$M = n - 2(n - r - 1)$$

or

$$(32) \qquad M = 2r - n + 2 .$$

When $M < 0$, a number of minors of order $(r+1)$ can be taken which contain a particular communality and no others. If $M \le 1$, then a minor can be so placed that it will contain only one communality. By expanding such a minor and setting it equal to zero, we have a linear equation with one unknown, namely, the desired communality, which can then be numerically determined. We then have

$$(33) \qquad r \le \frac{n - 1}{2} \quad \text{for} \quad M \le 1 .$$

*The number of factors is then less than half of the number of tests.* When this condition obtains, there is a single analytic solution from the selected minor. If the communality so determined should exceed unity, then the rank of the correlation matrix must be assumed to be higher than $r$ and a higher trial value for the rank must be taken. When $r$ is taken so that $M \le 0$, the consistency of the several possible determinations of the communalities must be examined.

Multiple solutions for the communalities are of special interest, and they may arise when $r$ is taken so large that the minor $ABCD$ in *Figure 1* contains two or more communalities. If we set $M = 2$, we have $r = n/2$, so that the minor $ABCD$ of order $(r+1)$ contains two communalities. When this minor is expanded and equated to zero, we have a quadratic which may in some circumstances give two real solutions for the diagonal value between 0 and $+1$.

This problem has been investigated by E. B. Wilson and Jane Worcester* in several papers. They exhibit as an example a correlation matrix with $n = 6$ and $r = 3$. Their example is reproduced in *Table 11*, which shows the correlation matrix and two factorial resolutions, both for three factors and with different sets of communalities. In *Table 12* we have another example from the same authors, which reduces to only one set of communalities. A second solution gives diagonal values that do not lie between 0 and $+1$. A third example from the paper, "The Resolution of Six Tests into Three General Factors," is shown in *Table 13*, for which the authors find no set of communalities between 0 and $+1$ that reduce the rank to 3. A higher rank must then be assumed for this example. It is pointed out by the authors

* E. B. Wilson and Jane Worcester, "The Resolution of Six Tests into Three General Factors," *Proceedings of the National Academy of Sciences,* XXV, No. 2 (February, 1939), 73–77; and "Team Tests for Generals and Specifics," *ibid.,* No. 7, July, 1939, pp. 358–64; also, E. B. Wilson, "Review of *Crossroads in the Mind of Man* [by T. L. Kelley]," *Journal of General Psychology,* II (1929), 153–74, esp. 156.

## Table 11

### Correlation Matrix

|   | 1 | 2 | 3 | 4 | 5 | 6 |
|---|---|---|---|---|---|---|
| 1 | $h_1^2$ | .56 | .16 | .48 | .24 | .64 |
| 2 | .56 | $h_2^2$ | .20 | .66 | .51 | .86 |
| 3 | .16 | .20 | $h_3^2$ | .18 | .07 | .23 |
| 4 | .48 | .66 | .18 | $h_4^2$ | .30 | .72 |
| 5 | .24 | .51 | .07 | .30 | $h_5^2$ | .41 |
| 6 | .64 | .86 | .23 | .72 | .41 | $h_6^2$ |

### Factor Matrix

| I | II | III | $h^2$ |
|---|----|-----|-------|
| .8 | 0 | 0 | .64 |
| .7 | .6 | 0 | .85 |
| .2 | .1 | −.1 | .06 |
| .6 | .4 | −.2 | .56 |
| .3 | .5 | .4 | .50 |
| .8 | .5 | −.2 | .93 |

### Alternative Factor Matrix

| I′ | II′ | III′ | $h^2$ |
|----|-----|------|-------|
| .6524 | 0 | 0 | .425616 |
| .8584 | .4068 | 0 | .902308 |
| .2453 | −.0259 | .0515 | .063569 |
| .7358 | .0699 | .0265 | .546923 |
| .3679 | .4774 | −.1530 | .386667 |
| .9810 | .0441 | .1835 | .998000 |

## Table 12

### Correlation Matrix

|   | 1 | 2 | 3 | 4 | 5 | 6 |
|---|---|---|---|---|---|---|
| 1 | $h_1^2$ | .56 | .16 | .48 | .24 | .64 |
| 2 | .56 | $h_2^2$ | .20 | .66 | .51 | .86 |
| 3 | .16 | .20 | $h_3^2$ | .08 | .27 | .13 |
| 4 | .48 | .66 | .08 | $h_4^2$ | .30 | .72 |
| 5 | .24 | .51 | .27 | .30 | $h_5^2$ | .41 |
| 6 | .64 | .86 | .13 | .72 | .41 | $h_6^2$ |

### Factor Matrix

| I | II | III | $h^2$ |
|---|----|-----|-------|
| .8 | 0 | 0 | .64 |
| .7 | .6 | 0 | .85 |
| .2 | .1 | .4 | .21 |
| .6 | .4 | −.2 | .56 |
| .3 | .5 | .4 | .50 |
| .8 | .5 | −.2 | .93 |

*Factor matrix unique*

## Table 13

### Correlation Matrix

|   | 1 | 2 | 3 | 4 | 5 | 6 |
|---|---|---|---|---|---|---|
| 1 | $h_1^2$ | .56 | .16 | .48 | .24 | .64 |
| 2 | .56 | $h_2^2$ | .20 | .66 | .51 | .86 |
| 3 | .16 | .20 | $h_3^2$ | .18 | .07 | .25 |
| 4 | .48 | .66 | .18 | $h_4^2$ | .30 | .76 |
| 5 | .24 | .51 | .07 | .30 | $h_5^2$ | .33 |
| 6 | .64 | .86 | .25 | .76 | .33 | $h_6^2$ |

*No solution in three factors*

("Team Tests for Generals and Specifics," p. 362) that, when the number of tests is much larger than the number of factors, then $M$ is negative, and the question of multiple solutions does not arise.

It is of interest to note the number of independent conditions in the correlation coefficients for the resolution of $n$ tests into $r$ common factors. This is the difference between the number of independent correlation coefficients and the number of independent parameters in the factor matrix. It can be obtained from the inequality (7). Denoting the number of independent conditions in the correlation coefficients $T$, we have

$$(34) \qquad T = \frac{n(n-1)}{2} - nr + \frac{r(r-1)}{2} ,$$

which has been written by Wilson and Worcester (in "The Resolution of Six Tests . . . ." and "Team Tests for Generals and Specifics") in the form

$$(35) \qquad T = \tfrac{1}{2}(n-r)^2 - \tfrac{1}{2}(n+r) .$$

When the number of independent conditions in the correlation coefficients is zero, the resolution is unique in the sense that no arbitrary parameter is involved in the solution but not necessarily in the sense that there is only one solution. In the numerical examples of *Tables 11, 12,* and *13, $T = 0$,* since $n = 6$ and $r = 3$; but $M = 2$, and hence multiple solutions may arise. In one example the solution is unacceptable because of diagonal values that exceed unity.

These relations are of importance in dealing with factor problems in which the rank is as high as half of the number of tests. If the test battery can be so constructed that the rank is not more than one-fourth or one-third of the number of tests, then the question of multiple solutions for the communalities does not arise.

The uniqueness of communalities is discussed further in a later section of this chapter.

### Adjustment of communalities for each factor

In factoring a correlation matrix, one may adjust the communalities after each factor if residuals are computed. The simplest method of making this adjustment is to record in the diagonal entry the highest correlation or residual of the column. If the highest coefficient of the column is negative, one records this value in the diagonal with positive sign. This procedure is useful for large correlation matrices, and it can be used as a first approximation for the factoring of a small table. The procedure will be illustrated by a numerical example.

In *Table 14* we have a small correlation matrix of order $5 \times 5$ and rank 2. Although method No. 4 would be used only as a first approximation in factoring a correlation matrix as small as this, it will be used here as a numerical example of the effects. The true communalities are shown in the diagonal cells of $R$. The first factor matrix was obtained with the group centroid method, using the known communalities. The second-factor residuals were then identically zero, and the obtained communalities were the true ones, as shown in the table.

The second factor matrix was obtained by using the highest coefficient in each column as the estimated communality. The discrepancies for a small correlation matrix are then often marked. In the fifth column, for example, the highest coefficient in the column is .72, whereas the true communality

*Table 14*

*Correlation Matrix of Rank 2*

|   | 1 | 2 | 3 | 4 | 5 |
|---|---|---|---|---|---|
| 1 | (.64) | .56 | .16 | .24 | .72 |
| 2 | .56 | (.65) | .38 | .49 | .67 |
| 3 | .16 | .38 | (.40) | .48 | .24 |
| 4 | .24 | .49 | .48 | (.58) | .34 |
| 5 | .72 | .67 | .24 | .34 | (.82) |

*Factor Matrix Computed with Known Communalities*

|   | I | II | $h^2$ |
|---|---|---|---|
| 1 | .680 | − .421 | .640 |
| 2 | .806 | − .029 | .650 |
| 3 | .486 | .404 | .399 |
| 4 | .624 | .437 | .580 |
| 5 | .817 | − .390 | .820 |

*Factor Matrix Computed with Unknown Communalities*

|   | I | II | $h^2$ | Discrepancy |
|---|---|---|---|---|
| 1 | .703 | − .447 | .694 | .054 |
| 2 | .812 | − .029 | .660 | .010 |
| 3 | .510 | .442 | .455 | .056 |
| 4 | .598 | .400 | .518 | − .062 |
| 5 | .788 | − .375 | .762 | − .058 |

is .82. Using these estimates, we obtained column I of the second factor matrix by the group centroid method. The correlational residuals were computed, and the diagonal entries were adjusted by recording the highest residual in each column. The second factor column II was then obtained. In the last column are shown the resulting discrepancies between the obtained communalities and the true values. It will be seen that the discrepancies are smaller, the largest discrepancy being .06. For large correlation matrices the discrepancies between obtained and true communalities are still smaller.

In *Figure 2* we have the true configuration of the five test vectors obtained from the first factor matrix of *Table 14*. These test vectors are represented by solid lines in the figure. In the same figure we have superimposed the configuration obtained with the estimated communalities. These vectors are shown in dotted lines. It will be seen that the configurations are essentially the same in spite of the coarse method of estimation of the diagonal entries for each factor. The second factor residuals do not vanish identically in this case, but they are so small as to discourage the attempt to write a third factor.

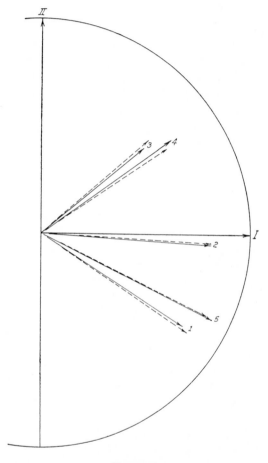

In planning a factorial analysis it is desirable to cover the domain to be investigated as completely as possible with a large number of related variables, which should be experimentally independent but correlated and representative of different aspects of the domain. When a study has been planned in this way, it will nearly always happen that every test vector lies near some other vector in the system. This arrangement is desirable for several reasons, principally in order to make it possible to discover a simple structure if it exists in the domain. The same plan will also make it almost certain that the computing formulae, including the collinear graphic method, will be applicable in the estimation of communalities at the start so that the investigator is free to use any factoring method, including those which avoid the computation of residuals. The most troublesome correlation matrices are those which were not planned for factor analysis. In such cases the rank is often a considerable fraction of the order, and the computational problems then become more difficult.

### Further study of linear dependence

Since this chapter was written, the method of estimating communalities by linear dependence of rows and columns (method No. 5) has been investigated further, and two papers have been written on this problem by A. A. Albert, of the Department of Mathematics at the University of Chicago.* The method of estimation of communalities by linear dependence of rows of $R$ will be described here with computing formulae and a numerical example.

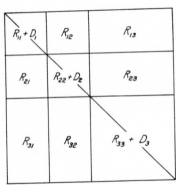

FIGURE 3

In *Figure 3* we have represented the correlation matrix, partitioned as described earlier in this chapter. The symmetric submatrices, $R_{11}$, $R_{22}$, and $R_{33}$, are here defined with zero diagonal elements. The corresponding diagonal elements are given in the diagonal matrices $D_1$, $D_2$, and $D_3$. It will be assumed that the correlation matrix has been inspected for clusters and that the number of distinguishable clusters represents a good estimate of the rank. In assigning tests to the three groups into which the correlation matrix is sectioned, it will be assumed that one test from each cluster has been assigned to the first group and that one test from each cluster has been as-

* "The Matrices of Factor Analysis," *Proceedings of the National Academy of Sciences*, XXX, No. 4 (April, 1944), 90–95; and "The Minimum Rank of a Correlation Matrix," *ibid.*, No. 6, June, 1944, pp. 144–48.

signed to the second group. The result will be that the submatrices, $R_{11}$, $R_{21}$, $R_{12}$, and $R_{22}$, are square and of order $r$ where $r$ is the number of clusters. The matrix $R_{33}$ is square and of order $(n-2r)$. The remaining submatrices may or may not be square. The underlying assumption is that if all the factors are represented in each of the first two groups, then the correlations of the third group can be accounted for as linear combinations of rows of either the first or the second group. This is the central idea of this method of estimating communalities. If a doublet cluster is found consisting of two tests which show unusually large correlation, then one test from the doublet is assigned to group 1 and the other test of the doublet is assigned to group 2. A doublet is fundamentally indeterminate as to factorial analysis, and it appears as an ambiguity in the rotational problem.

When the correlation matrix has been arranged in this manner and as shown in *Figure 3*, we can express the rows of $R_{31}$ as linear combinations of the rows of $R_{21}$. The transformation can be written

$$(36) \qquad AR_{21} = R_{31} ,$$

from which we can determine the transformation matrix $A$, since all the elements of the two submatrices are known and contain no communalities. We then have

$$(37) \qquad A = R_{31} R_{21}^{-1} .$$

It will be found that $R_{21}$ is the only inverse that needs to be computed. If it is found that $R_{21}$ does not have an inverse, then either the assumed rank is too high, so that its determinant vanishes, or the clusters have been chosen inappropriately.

When the transformation matrix $A$ has been determined, we express the rows of $R_{33}$ as linear combinations of the rows of $R_{23}$ by the same transformation, and we then have

$$(38) \qquad AR_{23} = R_{33} + D_3 .$$

The side correlations of this matrix must agree with those of the submatrix $R_{33}$. If this is not the case, then the rank has probably been assumed too low. If this agreement is obtained, then the diagonals are those of $R_{33}$. The communalities of $R_{33}$ are then known.

Applying the same transformation to $R_{22}$, we have

$$(39) \qquad A(R_{22} + D_2) = R_{32} ,$$

or

$$(40) \qquad R_{32} - AR_{22} = AD_2 .$$

We compute the left member of this equation. The ratio of each column sum to the corresponding column sum of $A$ is then the desired communality for the corresponding column of $R_{22}$.*

The same process is carried out for the remaining set of three submatrices. The rows of $R_{32}$ can be expressed as linear combinations of the rows of $R_{12}$, and we then have

$$(41) \qquad\qquad BR_{12} = R_{32},$$

so that

$$(42) \qquad\qquad B = R_{32}\, R_{12}^{-1}.$$

We can write this equation in terms of the inverse already computed, and we then have

$$(43) \qquad\qquad B' = R_{21}^{-1}\, R_{23},$$

so that

$$(44) \qquad\qquad B = (R_{21}^{-1}\, R_{23})'.$$

Applying this transformation to $R_{11}$, we have

$$(45) \qquad\qquad B(R_{11} + D_1) = R_{31}$$

or

$$(46) \qquad\qquad BR_{11} + BD_1 = R_{31},$$

so that

$$(47) \qquad\qquad BD_1 = (R_{31} - BR_{11}).$$

The ratio of the columns of the right member to the columns of $B$ give the corresponding estimates of the communalities of $R_{11}$.

*Table 15* shows the computations for this method of estimating communalities which is illustrated on a correlation matrix of order 6 and rank 2. The summarized computations follow the outline as shown.

A limitation of this method for experimental data is that the rank is never exactly $r$ where $r < n$ and that the determinations will therefore be ap-

---

* In practice one can save computational work by finding only the column sums because these enter into the determination of elements of $D_2$.

proximate. Even when the approximate rank $r$ is adequate, as far as correlational residuals are concerned, the present method may, nevertheless, show discrepancies in the estimated communalities for experimental data. The method has not yet been tried extensively enough on experimental data to show whether it is preferable to the simpler methods of estimation. The method is certainly amply justified for correlation matrices in which the low rank is exact or very closely approximated.

In the two papers on the communality problem Albert defines the *ideal rank* of $R$ as the largest order of a non-vanishing minor of $R$ which does

*Table 15*

|  |  | 1 | 2 | 3 | 4 | 5 | 6 |
|---|---|---|---|---|---|---|---|
|  | 1 | .00 | .72 | .61 | .92 | −.26 | .59 |
|  | 2 | .72 | .00 | .80 | .68 | .20 | .68 |
| $R =$ | 3 | .61 | .80 | .00 | .54 | .40 | .69 |
|  | 4 | .92 | .68 | .54 | .00 | −.39 | .55 |
|  | 5 | −.26 | .20 | .40 | −.39 | .00 | .21 |
|  | 6 | .59 | .68 | .69 | .55 | .21 | .00 |

$R_{21} =$
| .61 | .80 |
|---|---|
| .92 | .68 |

$R_{23}^{-1}R_{23} = $ (43)
| −1.8181 | −.0909 |  |
|---|---|---|
| 1.8863 | .9318 | $= B'$ |

$R_{21}^{-1} =$
| −2.1170 | 2.4906 |
|---|---|
| 2.8642 | −1.8991 |

$B =$
| −1.8181 | 1.8863 |
|---|---|
| −.0909 | .9318 |

$s_3 =$
| −1.9090 | 2.8181 |
|---|---|

$A = R_3 . R_{21}^{-1} =$ (37)
| 1.1233 | −1.0274 |
|---|---|
| .6986 | .1781 |

$s_1 =$
| 1.8219 | −.8493 |
|---|---|

$R_{31} - BR_{11} =$ (47)
| −1.6181 | 1.5090 |  |
|---|---|---|
| −.0809 | .7454 | $= BD_1$ |

$s_4 =$
| −1.6990 | 2.2544 |
|---|---|

$A R_{23} =$
| .850 | .210 |  |
|---|---|---|
| .210 | .580 | $= R_{33}+D_3$ |

|  | $h_1^2$ | $h_2^2$ |
|---|---|---|
| $s_4/s_3 =$ | .8900 | .8000 |

$R_{32} - AR_{22} =$ (40)
| .9548 | −.9966 |  |
|---|---|---|
| .5938 | .1728 | $= AD_2$ |

$s_2 =$
| 1.5486 | −.8238 |
|---|---|

|  | $h_3^2$ | $h_4^2$ |
|---|---|---|
| $s_2/s_1 =$ | .8500 | .9700 |

| $h_1^2$ | $h_2^2$ | $h_3^2$ | $h_4^2$ | $h^2$ | $h_6$ |
|---|---|---|---|---|---|
| .890 | .800 | .850 | .970 | .850 | .580 |

not contain diagonal elements. He proves the interesting theorem that *if the ideal rank* r *of* R *is also the rank of the submatrices* $R_{31}$ *and* $R_{32}$, *then there exist unique communalities such that the resulting correlation matrix* R *has rank* r. This is an encouraging finding because it has been assumed in the development of multiple-factor analysis that there exists a unique set of communalities which are consistent with the experimentally given off-diagonal correlations. The existence of such a set of communalities merely maintains the rank of the off-diagonal entries, which Albert has called the ideal rank of *R*. It had previously been pointed out by E. B. Wilson that if the number of tests is much larger than the number of factors $(n > r)$, then the question of multiple solutions for the communalities does not arise.

### Experimental comparison of communality estimates

Since this chapter was set in type Mr. Frank Medland has completed a Master's dissertation, entitled "An Empirical Comparison of Methods of Communality Estimation." Nine methods of estimating communalities were tried on a 63-variable correlation matrix from *Psychometric Monograph No. 2*. These communality estimates were compared with communalities that were computed by the centroid method, with diagonal adjustment after each factor. Medland found that the centroid formula of equation (15) gave the most consistent communality estimates. Practically the same results were obtained by the graphical method that is represented by equation (30). Since the centroid formula of equation (15) is computationally the more convenient of these two methods, it may be considered the preferred method.

# CHAPTER XIV

## THE SIMPLE-STRUCTURE CONCEPT

### The score function

Simple structure has been briefly mentioned in previous chapters, but it will be considered here in more detail as to its significance and implications. The principles of simple structure are fundamental in making factor analysis a scientific method rather than merely a method of statistical condensation, and it is therefore one of the central themes in factorial theory. Some writers on factorial theory have not yet accepted this concept as a powerful aid in exploratory factorial investigation. It is surely not the only way to resolve the problem of finding a significant reference frame, but it has so far yielded some very illuminating results.

Consider a set of measurements $S_{ji}$ of individuals $i$ in traits $j$. The measurements selected for factorial study are correlated, and hence they can be assumed to have some parameters in common. Let the measurements be expressed in terms of these parameters by the equations

$$(1) \quad \begin{cases} s_{1i} = \phi_1(x_{1i}, x_{2i}, \dots, x_{pi}, \dots, x_{ri}) , \\ s_{2i} = \phi_2(x_{1i}, x_{2i}, \dots, x_{pi}, \dots, x_{ri}) , \\ \dots \quad \quad \dots \quad \quad \dots \quad \dots \dots \quad \dots \\ s_{ji} = \phi_j(x_{1i}, x_{2i}, \dots, x_{pi}, \dots, x_{ri}) , \\ \dots \quad \quad \dots \quad \quad \dots \quad \dots \dots \quad \dots \\ s_{ni} = \phi_n(x_{1i}, x_{2i}, \dots, x_{pi}, \dots, x_{ri}) . \end{cases}$$

Here we have each measurement $s_{ji}$ for individual $i$ expressed in terms of $r$ parameters $x_{pi}$, which are descriptive of individual $i$. The functions $\phi_j$ are in general non-linear, and they are unknown. They may be assumed to be unique for each measurement $j$. If a measurement $S_j$ does not depend on a parameter $X_p$, then that parameter is absent in the function $\phi_j$. Every pair of measures, $j$ and $k$, will be assumed to have one or more parameters in common if $r_{jk} \neq 0$. If $r_{jk} = 0$, they may or may not have parameters in common.

For any given list of $n$ measurements $S_j$, let there be $q$ parameters involved. Some of these parameters will be unique in that they are not involved in two or more of the score functions $S_j$. We limit the analysis to the $r$ parameters which are involved in two or more of these score functions and which determine correlation between the scores. It is this set of $r$ parameters that determines the side correlations and the intercorrelations $r_{jk}$, where

$j \neq k$. The $(q-r)$ unique parameters influence only the diagonal correlations $r_{jj}$, which are eliminated from the analysis in order to make the problem soluble. If we knew all the parameters and all the functions $\phi_j$, we should probably be able to design a set of measurements for any set of parameters so as to make a determinate solution, irrespective of whether the parameters were common or unique. But when the parameters become known, there will be no provocation for factor analysis. It is our ignorance about the parameters and the score functions that prompts us to use the exploratory factorial methods. In our present state of knowledge we are likely to add unique parameters with every new measurement, so that we are likely to have $q > n$, a situation that involves more parameters than there are measurements for each individual.

Any particular list of $r$ parameters defines a *domain*, which includes all possible measurements that are determined in whole or in part by these parameters. In practice, a domain is defined by a field of related measurements, since the underlying parameters are unknown. A domain is described in practical work in terms of the content and nature of the measurements, such as auditory perception or visual illusions or speed performances. The *complexity* of a measurement $S_j$ is the number of parameters $X_p$ that it involves and which it shares with one or more other measurements in the battery. Hence the complexity of a test or measurement is dependent on the test battery in which it is being analyzed. The complexity of a test $j$ is, in part, dependent on the test battery. When we speak of the complexity of a single test apart from a test battery, we refer to the total number of parameters in the score function $S_j$.

Consider a table of order $n \times r$, in which each cell represents a parameter for a particular test. Each row represents a function $\phi_j$, and each column represents a parameter. The complexity of a battery of $n$ tests is $r$, and it should be the aim of the investigator to choose a set of $n$ tests or measurements for the domain which he is studying so that $n > r$. His scientific intuitions and hypotheses are his chief guides here. If the score functions were known, we could mark an $x$ in each cell $(jp)$ to show that a parameter $X_q$ is involved in the score function $\phi_j$, and we could leave blank each cell $(jp)$ in which the parameter $X_p$ is absent in the score function $\phi_j$. We call such a table a *factor pattern* (see *chapter ix* for different types of factor patterns).

If an analysis is to be made by the principles of simple structure, then the investigator gambles that the complexity of each test or measurement is less than the complexity $r$ of the battery as a whole. He hopes that the test complexities are considerably less than that of the battery. If the test complexities are less than $r$, then there will be one or more blank cells in each row of the factor pattern. Such a pattern will be considered as evidence of an underlying *simple order* in which each parameter or process in the domain is not involved in every test measurement. If the parameters are uncorrelated in the experimental population, then the pattern will be indicative of an *orthogonal simple order* for that population. If the parameters are correlated in the experimental population, then the pattern indicates an *oblique simple order*. The question of whether the parameters are correlated or uncorrelated among the subjects who happen to be used for studying the domain is, in general, a secondary matter when compared with the scientific problem of discovering an underlying order in the domain.

The score functions $S_j$ may be represented by a surface, as in *Figure 1*. In this figure we have considered only two of the parameters, $X_1$ and $X_2$, as well as the score $S_j$. If the score $S_j$ is independent of $X_2$, then the surface $S_j$ will be a cylinder parallel to $X_2$. (A cylinder is, of course, not necessarily circular in section. I is a surface parallel to an axis.) An individual with parameters $x_{1i}$ and $x_{2i}$ will have a score $s_{ji}$ as shown, and this score will be

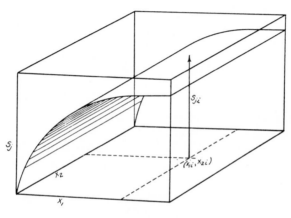

FIGURE 1

independent of the parameter $X_2$. This reasoning can be extended to $n$ dimensions. If the surfaces could be constructed or otherwise represented, the cylindrical forms of the surfaces could be taken as clues for locating the reference frame, especially if a number of such surfaces were found which defined the same axes in this manner. If a reference frame could be determined by the cylindrical surfaces, it could be expected that the axes, so determined, would represent parameters for which some physical or operational interpretation could be made. It would not necessarily follow that such a reference frame would be the only feasible one, but the simple order indicated by these axes should be illuminating in the exploratory study of a domain for which no hypotheses are available. Each axis should represent some underlying process, parameter, or category which may or may not have been suspected in setting up the test battery. Unfortunately, these surfaces are not immediately available in the measurements and their relations, so that approximations must be used.

There are certain characteristics of the surfaces $S_j$ which may be surmised by psychological considerations. Most of the factorial studies have been made with those mental traits which can be called "abilities." An ability may be considered to be any trait which describes how well a person can do something. It has been observed that all such traits have correlations that are positive or zero, and this seems to be the rule for the most diverse abilities. The parameters that underlie individual differences in the mental abilities may be tentatively assumed to be of such a nature that they are covariant with the overtly manifested abilities. If that should be found to be acceptable, then we should be able to infer that the surface $S_j$ rises with an increment in any of the underlying parameters $X_p$. By these psychological considerations we should infer that

$$(2) \qquad\qquad\qquad \frac{\partial S_j}{\partial X_p} \geq 0$$

for those traits that are classified as abilities. In other words, the surfaces $S_j$ for mental abilities may be assumed to be monotonic increasing functions of the parameters $X_p$*. If this inference is acceptable, then it should be possible to represent all the surfaces $S_j$ reasonably well with second-degree equations for the mental abilities, barring what might seem now to be strange irregularities or discontinuities in the second derivatives.

While these characteristics of the surfaces $S_j$ may seem plausible for the mental abilities, there do not seem to be any similar obvious restrictions for the surfaces that represent temperamental traits. If some of these surfaces are characterized by conspicuous maxima and minima, then the observation equations for them might have to be of the third or higher degree. Gross discrepancies and large residuals may then be found in the crude linear assumptions on which present-day factorial methods are based. Most of the statistical methods in current use involve the same assumption.

The various rating schedules for personality traits are frequently arranged with special reference to social acceptability and success rather than with reference to the degree of some underlying trait. Such ratings may give trouble in factorial studies if the relation between the amount of some underlying trait and the rating on some kind of social acceptability has a maximum for an optimal amount of the underlying trait. The assumption of linearity between the underlying parameters and the overtly observed social acceptability is then violated more seriously than if we were dealing with personality descriptions that are monotonic increasing or decreasing

---

* If time per unit task is used as a score, then the score function is decreasing monotonic, in which case it can be reversed so that all correlations become positive. This applies to abilities and not to all psychological measurements.

functions of the underlying parameters. An example may clarify these restrictions. Let us suppose that one of the important underlying parameters in describing a man is the rate at which he moves generally. A person with a very low value of this parameter would be described as slow, inert, and unresponsive. The upper extreme of this parameter would be described as a personality that is jerky, scatterbrained, nervous, irritable, and perhaps unstable. An optimum value between the extremes is likely to be associated with more favorable descriptive categories as regards social acceptability and success. The sketches of *Figure 2* are drawn to show that a monotonic increasing or decreasing surface can usually be fitted better by a linear approximation than can a surface with conspicuous maxima or minima.

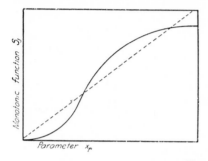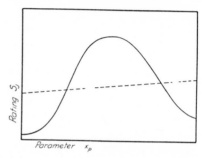

FIGURE 2

In *Figure 3* we have represented two plane surfaces which may be thought of as best-fitting planes for the score surfaces $S_j$ and $S_k$. The score surface $S_j$ of *Figure 1* represents raw scores. Such a surface also could represent standard scores by merely moving the origin to the level of the mean and adopting a vertical scale with the standard deviation as a unit of measurement. With this translation of the origin and with the stretching factor, we have the planes passing through the origin as shown in *Figure 3*. It is of some interest to note, in passing, that *the rank of a matrix of raw scores is reduced by 1 when the scores are modified to deviation scores about the mean.*

The two vectors $J$ and $K$ in *Figure 3* are unit normals to the planes $S_j$ and $S_k$, respectively. The direction cosines of each normal are also the coefficients of the equation of the corresponding test score plane. If a surface $S_j$ is cylindrical and parallel to some axis $X_p$, then the best-fitting plane for that surface is also parallel to that axis except for the accidents of sampling. The direction cosines of the normal to the plane will have a zero-direction cosine for the axis $X_p$. The vectors $J$ and $K$ are unit test vectors in the total test space. If $X_1$ and $X_2$ are correlated and if a number of test vectors are orthogonal to them so that these axes are chosen for the oblique factorial matrix $V_{jp}$, then the test vectors will have zero projections on these axes and the corresponding entries in the factor matrix will be zeros. In this manner we see that if a number of test score surfaces $S_j$ are cylindrical and parallel to each other, then the corresponding axis $X_p$ is chosen as a reference vector and is represented by a large number of zero entries in a column of the oblique factor matrix.

The relations of *Figure 1* may be used to illustrate another fundamental principle in factor analysis as regards the scientific interpretation of a simple structure when it is found. Suppose that there are individual differences in the ability to visualize space. A test battery could be assembled, including visual tests that do not involve this factor and other visual tests that do involve it. The factorial separation would sustain the hypothesis that such a

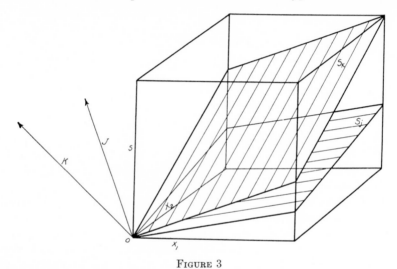

FIGURE 3

factor is distinguishable among visual functions. If a parameter or factor or function exists which becomes operative in some way in the visualizing of space and not in other visual tasks, then we should expect those score surfaces to be parallel to an axis which does not involve the particular parameter. If the separation of the score surfaces actually agrees with the classification of the tests as including or excluding the particular function, then the factorial results sustain the hypothesis.

The principle of interest here is that the identification of a factor or parameter does not presuppose the experimental population to be in any sense representative of any sort of hypothetical general population. In factorial studies that are made for the discovery of an underlying order in a domain, the best procedure is not to select a random group of subjects, but rather to select the subjects so that their attributes are as diverse as possible in the domain to be studied. Two or three freaks in the characteristics of interest are worth more than fifty average subjects. This principle is not new. If you wanted to inquire informally about the existence of the ability to visualize space, you would gain most by selecting some draftsmen or engineers and some people who evidently avoid visualizing tasks and methods of thinking. Later, when the factor had been identified clearly on exceptionally gifted or deficient individuals, you could proceed to the task of establishing norms to determine the actual range of ability in random samples of the general population. Here, again, we see how the purpose of a factorial study determines the kind of subjects to be selected for the experimental group. If we have no hypotheses about the kind of people who differ fundamentally in the domain to be studied, then we proceed by inviting any conveniently available group of subjects in the hope that they will differ markedly among themselves in the several parameters or factors of the domain to be investigated. If a few subjects can be found who are known to differ widely in the domain, they should be included. No assumption of normality of the distribution is involved in factorial analysis. If we could find bimodal distributions for some tests and factors, they would be especially interesting, provided, of course, that the bimodalities were not artifacts. The question of whether the correlations between the tests in an experimental population are in any sense representative of a general population is irrelevant. Nor does it matter whether the correlations for one experimental group differed markedly from the correlations of the same tests in another experimental group. If the factorial analyses are made independently, the same factors should be identified, but the numerical values would, of course, be different if the groups differ widely. The correlations for each group are determined by the factors involved in the tests and by the correlations of the factors in each experimental group.

We have defined the domain as the field of all possible measurements that are determined, at least in part, by a set of parameters. In exploratory studies the domain is defined tentatively in terms of the content or nature of the tests of a battery. The principal purpose is to discover the parameters or factors and something about the nature of the individual differences that they produce. The individual subjects are examined, not for the purpose of learning something about them individually, but rather for the purpose of discovering the underlying factors. Ultimately, we want to be able to appraise each individual as to each of the factors, but this problem raises certain other questions about the domain.

In setting up the fundamental linear observation equation for factor analysis, the individual score $s_{ji}$ is expressed in terms of the test coefficients $c_{jm}$ and the individual scores in a set of arbitrary orthogonal factors $x_{mi}$. By rotation of axes the scores can be expressed as linear combinations of individual scores $x_{pi}$ in the primary factors $p$ instead of the arbitrary factors $m$. Some writers have attributed to factor analysis the assumption that all the subjects in an experimental group use the same factors in doing a test, but such an assumption is not made in factor analysis. Suppose that a task can be done in one of two ways that involve either of two factors, 1 and 2. Suppose, further, that some subjects use factor 1 and that other subjects prefer factor 2 in doing this task. If this test is included in a battery for factor analysis and if the battery contains other tests by which factors 1 and 2 can be clearly differentiated, then the test in question will have a complexity of at least 2. We should then infer that the test has these two factors, in that $v_{j1}$ and $v_{j2}$ are non-vanishing in the factor matrix $V$; but it would not follow that *each individual subject* used both of these factors in doing the test. To decide whether this is true, one turns, first, to introspection in doing the task to ascertain whether it seems psychologically necessary that both factors should be simultaneously used, or whether it is a question for each subject to decide which method to adopt in doing the test. Here one must be careful not to be biased by one's own preferred ways of doing things. In case of doubt, we ask a number of subjects how they did the task, including the instructions and fore-exercise, and to describe any useful tricks or dodges that they may have discovered in doing the test. These informal reports are sometimes very illuminating. A little experience of this kind soon emphasizes the importance of introspection as compared with casual judgments about the factorial composition of a test merely by a superficial inspection of its content. For example, a syllogism test about the relative statures of three men was found to have a significant saturation on the space factor, although the test was entirely verbal in appearance. It was found that some subjects, but not all, used simple diagrammatic representation of the premises such as "S−J" to represent the premise that Smith is taller than Jones, so that the inference was also spatially represented. In order to make the analysis more complete, one might separate the subjects into two groups according to preferred methods of doing a test and reanalyze the results. In such a situation we should expect to find a different factorial composition of a test for the two groups of subjects.

Another situation in which the factorial composition of a test can be altered is that in which the subjects are given instruction in doing a task. The factorial composition can be markedly changed, since the test is itself modified by the instruction, even though the test form remains identical after instruction. After all, *the psychological nature of a test is determined by what goes on in the mind of the subject and not only by what is printed on the test paper.* In the same manner the factorial composition of a test is changed with the age of the subjects. Sometimes we have arranged the order of the tests in a battery with reference to the suggestive effects of one test on a following test, especially if one test requires a mental set similar, or opposite, to that of a previous test. Fortunately, these overlapping effects are not often serious.

When it comes to the problem of using the tests, not for the purpose of identifying mental factors, but for the purpose of appraising the factors in each individual, we resort to the same methods that are in current use with psychological tests. The best that we can do is to determine the correlation of each test with each primary factor, $r_{jp}$. These are the *validity coefficients* of the tests with respect to the primary factors. We select several tests whose validities are the highest available for a particular primary factor $p$. These several tests are pooled in a composite. The composite score is then used as the best available estimate of the individual's score $x_{pi}$ in the primary factor $p$. If each test has saturations in several factors, such as $(1, 2)$, $(1, 3, 5)$, $(1, 4, 7)$, then we try to distribute the distracting saturations for other factors so as to emphasize the validity for one of the factors. The same result can be obtained by multiple correlation analysis in the usual ways where $r_{jp}$ are validity coefficients which should be studied with the intercorrelations of the separate tests.

### Simple structure in $r$ dimensions

The simple-structure principle will be restated here for $r$ dimensions. Some of the previously given definitions will be repeated in this context.*

The $r$ orthogonal reference vectors that are implied in the orthogonal factor matrix $F$ are called *orthogonal reference vectors*. These vectors are regarded as a fixed orthogonal frame in terms of which the various factorial relations are expressed. It is this fixed frame in terms of which we describe the test vectors $j$ in the rows of $F$, the $r$ hyperplanes of an orthogonal or oblique simple structure, and the primary trait vectors. These fixed orthogonal axes are referred to by the subscript $m$, or $M$ and $m$ if two subscripts are desired. Thus the test vector $j$ has the projections $a_{jm}$ on these orthogonal axes, as shown in the rows of $F$. When this reference frame is determined by some form of the centroid method, the frame will be called *centroid reference vectors*.

The unique configuration of trait vectors defined by the correlation matrix is called the *correlational configuration* or the *trait configuration*. This is the configuration described in terms of the fixed orthogonal frame by the factor matrix $F$. The combination of the correlational configuration and any set of reference vectors is called a *structure*, and it can be seen that a structure is itself a configuration of $(n+r)$ vectors. The problem is to substitute for the arbitrary reference frame another frame, orthogonal or oblique, which will have scientific interpretation. Each reference vector of

* First ed., chap. vi.

the new frame should represent a scientific category, a parameter, or a function in terms of which the trait configuration can be interpreted.

The $r$ linearly independent reference vectors define the same number of co-ordinate hyperplanes. Each hyperplane is a subspace of dimensionality $(r-1)$, and it is defined by a reference vector. The subspace of $(r-1)$ dimensions which is orthogonal to the reference vector $\Lambda_p$ will be called the *co-ordinate hyperplane* $L_p$. If a reference frame can be found such that each test vector is contained in one or more of the $r$ co-ordinate hyperplanes, then the combined frame and configuration is called a *simple structure*. If the new reference vectors are orthogonal, the total configuration is called an *orthogonal simple structure*. If a set of $r$ hyperplanes of dimensionality $(r-1)$ exists such that each test vector is in one or more of the hyperplanes and if the normals $\Lambda_p$ are oblique, then the total configuration of test vectors and reference vectors is called an *oblique simple structure*. It follows from these definitions that each test vector that contributes to the identification of a simple structure must be of complexity less than $r$. A configuration of test vectors which defines a simple structure will be called a *simple configuration*.

If an $n \times r$ factorial matrix is set up with arbitrary entries in all cells, there is, in general, no transformation by which each of the $n$ variables can be described in terms of fewer than $r$ factors. It is assumed that $n$ is large in comparison with $r$. Therefore, the appearance of simple structure in a factorial matrix derived from observation commands attention. It is not a chance matter. When found in experimental data, it reveals order within the $n$ variables, in that $r < n$ categories are required for describing them collectively and *fewer* than $r$ categories are required for each one of them separately.

If an underlying physical order of the $n$ traits is such that each of the traits can be described in terms of a smaller number of factors than are required for describing the traits collectively, then the underlying physical order will be called a *simple order*.

If a simple order exists for a set of $n$ traits and if the $r$ factors are statistically independent in the experimental population, then the corresponding physical order will be called an *orthogonal simple order*. Hence the configuration which represents an orthogonal simple order among the $n$ traits is an orthogonal simple structure. An order among the traits involves, of course, not only the traits themselves but also the categories in terms of which they are described. These categories are themselves traits which may or may not be experimentally isolable.

It is useful to summarize the several fundamental concepts in this analysis. The concept *order* refers to the relation between the traits and the categories in terms of which the traits are to be described and comprehended. The *correlational matrix* describes merely the relations among the traits, independent of the descriptive categories. The *factorial matrix* describes the traits or variables in terms of a set of descriptive categories. The *trait configuration* is a geometrical representation of the correlational matrix, and hence it is also independent of the descriptive categories. The *structure* is a configuration which represents not only the traits but also the descriptive categories. The scientific problem is essentially a search for a set of descriptive categories in terms of which our conception of the traits or variables is the simplest possible. If an overdetermined simplicity in our conception can be achieved, then the traits or variables will be said to reveal a *simple order*. The search for these categories has its direct analytical counterpart in the search for a set of *reference vectors* which will reveal a *simple structure*. A simple structure is a configurational representation of a simple order. If the simplifying descriptive categories happen to be statistically independent in the experimental population, then the trait configuration can be so rotated in its arbitrary orthogonal frame that each trait vector is contained in one or more of the $r$ orthogonal co-ordinate hyperplanes. The result is an *orthogonal simple structure*, and the reference vectors represent a set of statistically independent traits that serve the simplest possible comprehension of the given traits or variables.

## Alternative simple structures for the same domain

We should distinguish between uniqueness of the simple structure for a given correlation matrix and uniqueness of the descriptive parameters or concepts which the primary axes represent. In earlier chapters we have considered examples, such as the cylinder problem and the box problem, in which the simple structure does not give the only meaningful set of parameters or descriptive concepts for a configuration. It is unlikely that uniqueness in that sense could be found in any domain. Furthermore, it is conceivable that a domain could be represented by two sets of measures which would show two different simple structures, if the two sets of measures were taken in quite different ways. Both sets of primary axes would then represent underlying parameters for which meaningful interpretation could be expected. The two sets of parameters could be regarded as alternative sets, and they should be revealing as to the nature of the underlying order.

The box problem, which can be easily visualized, has served to illustrate these principles. Consider one set of measurements of the boxes which are simple functions of the three independent edges, as in the previous examples. Consider also another set of conceivable measures of the same population of boxes in which each measure is some simple function of the basic parameters for volume, $v$, and the ratios $t = x/z$ and $u = x/y$. The three measures $v$, $t$, and $u$ are superimposed on the simple structure $x$, $y$, and $z$ in *Figure 4*. The basic measures $x$, $y$, and $z$ might represent width, height, and depth, respectively. It is instructive to see what would happen with different sets of measurements of the boxes. First, consider the case in which we merely add the three measures $v$, $t$, and $u$ to the measures previously listed and which contribute to the simple structure of the box problem. The result would be merely the same triangular arrangement of the measures forming the triangle $x$, $y$, and $z$, and there would be the three additional measures $v$, $u$, and $t$, which would not contribute to the identification of the simple structure. In the first example of the box problem we had two such measures, namely, 16 and 17, which represented the volume and the principal diagonal of each box. These did not participate in the simple structure.

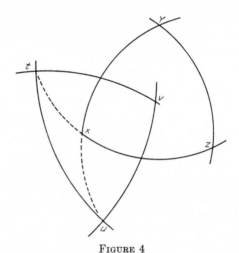

FIGURE 4

If we should construct an entirely new set of measurements which were so composed that they were linear combinations of the three measures $v$, $t$, and $u$, then they would define a new simple structure with primary vectors $v$, $t$, and $u$. The previous configuration $x$, $y$, and $z$ would not be seen. If we proceeded to construct this new simple structure, we should have measures such as "one-half of the volume in cubic inches plus three-fourths of the ratio $x/z$" and perhaps twenty others similarly constructed. We should then be able to show that the previous structure $x$, $y$, $z$ was not unique for the domain. The response of a scientist to such a finding would depend entirely on the manner in which the new structure $v$, $t$, $u$ was obtained. If the new structure had been obtained merely by picking three linearly independent measures in the first configuration and then arbitrarily assembling linear combinations of them for a new battery, then, of course, the new structure would be regarded as an artifact, and it would demonstrate nothing regarding the underlying order for the domain. If an author were caught doing such a thing, his scientific honesty would be questioned unless he presented it merely as some sort of stunt. The arbitrary character of his battery of measurements would be questioned.

But there could be situations in which the new structure $v$, $t$, $u$ would be valid and significant. Suppose that these new parameters were significantly related to the manner in which the box shapes were generated or in which they were used or interpreted. Then an investigator who assembled a battery of measurements to represent the domain might find the structure $v$, $t$, $u$, and it would serve him in studying the underlying order. The assembled battery would reveal its organization in the new structure.

Let us suppose that two investigators found these two simple structures, using two different batteries of box measurements. Each of them might find a set of primary factors, and each might succeed in discovering some appropriate interpretation for his own set of three basic parameters. Such a finding would not necessarily show that one of them was wrong They might have found two sets of alternative parameters for describing different aspects of the domain in question. The challenge is then to study closely the two sets of measures to see what different aspects of the domain they cover. A new factorial experiment could be set up with both sets of measures in the same battery, and the configuration would then be like *Figure 4*. Additional factors might appear because the previous specifics might appear as common factors in the new analysis; but our present concern is about the principle involved in the possibility of alternative structures. This would be a case in which there would be more hyperplanes defined by the test vectors than there are dimensions in the common-factor space. Such a situation should not be regarded as a failure in factorial analysis. It might reveal alternative sets of parameters in the domain, which should all eventually be interpreted. So far we have found only an occasional suggestion of secondary hyperplanes, but none of them have seemed to us to be sufficiently overdetermined to justify special investigation.

In judging the difference between alternative structures that should be separately interpreted and the artifact which could be arbitrarily constructed from any test battery, it is well to look at the nature of the measurements involved. Both sets of measurements should be natural and apparently relevant measures descriptive of the domain in question. If one set of measurements consists merely of a set of linear combinations of a few previous measures, or the equivalent as to arbitrary character, then its relevance to the problem of analyzing the domain may be questioned. In any event, subsequent factorial study of the same domain should reveal whether a previously found structure is to be sustained.

### Uniqueness of primary factors

One of the most fundamental problems in factor analysis concerns the uniqueness of the primary factors and their interpretation. When a factor analysis has been completed with a clear simple structure, the first question is naturally: "What *are* the parameters or factors?" It seems to be in the nature of science that such a question has no unique answer. *In scientific work a parameter is one of the measurable attributes of an object in terms of which it is described.* In general, one tries to choose a small number of parameters which define all the relevant attributes of the object. The author is successful if he finds a small number of easily comprehended parameters that cover his problem. Parameters in scientific work and the concepts which they represent become the conventionalized chapter headings in textbooks. Even notation becomes a matter of convention. A circle on a graph is defined by the two co-ordinates $(x, y)$ of its center and by the radius $r$. These parameters are easily understood and easily used in most problems, but, of course, they are not unique. For some problems they would be awkward, and another set of parameters would be chosen. The same is true in scientific work. The familiarity of mass, momentum, and acceleration should not lead us to suppose that they are necessary absolutes for the description of objects in motion. If these reservations about the uniqueness of parameters apply to physical science, it would seem wise to acknowledge them also in the search for descriptive parameters or functional unities of mind.

The choice of a set of fundamental concepts in terms of which any domain of nature is to be comprehended is probably meaningless to nature. The choice is for us to make in terms that will attain intellectual control and consistency, as empirically determined, and by which this control can be attained, as far as possible, with ideas that are already familiar to us. Fundamental scientific concepts that are successful in this sense are as social as other inventions. To hunt for a unique solution in the comprehension of a set of related phenomena is an illusory hunt for absolutes. It is probably safe to say that an apparently unique set of concepts in any domain is merely the symbol of our immaturity in the exploration of that domain. The recognition of the lack of uniqueness in scientific concepts does not imply that some sets are not more useful and fruitful than others. Those parameters are preferred which reveal the phenomena as of a simple underlying order.

Recognition of the fact that descriptive parameters are not unique has led some writers on factor analysis to give up the problem in defeat. They remain content with a set of statistically determined parameters or factors which are wholly determined by the circumstances of the experiment at the moment. The simple-structure concept was invented, if anything so simple can be called an "invention," as a compromise with this problem. It was the simple idea of finding *the smallest number of parameters for describing each test*. In numerical terms this is a demand for the smallest number of non-vanishing entries in each row of the oblique factor matrix. It seems strange indeed, and it was entirely unexpected, that so simple and plausible an idea should meet with a storm of protest from the statisticians. This simple idea has turned out to be a much more powerful analytical device than was at first anticipated.

The primary factors that are identified by the simple-structure principle seem to be unique in the sense that they reappear in successive studies with different test batteries in the same domain. It is to be expected, however, that a primary factor may be found to be itself a complex when a part of a domain is investigated with large test batteries. It will then give place to several new primary factors, which should retain their identity in successive test batteries that are adequate to isolate them. As regards psychological interpretation, it may be expected that this will also be modified or extended with repeated studies. The number factor, for example, has been named so far only in terms of the numerical content of the tests, but this type of interpretation cannot be regarded as satisfactory. The psychological interpretation should be made eventually in terms of psychological processes that will generally transcend test content except in those cases in which the test content and the psychological processes are described by the same name. In order for the interpretation of primary factors to be satisfactory, their psychological interpretation should be sufficiently clear so that the factorial composition of new tests can be predicted with confidence. Progress has been made in that direction, but this goal can be attained only after many factorial studies of the same domain.

Analysis of a large number of factorial studies seems to indicate that those tests which are of low complexity and which, consequently, are the best indices of the nature of a primary factor are generally quite simple as judged by usual psychological considerations. However, a test which seems simple without a knowledge of the primary factors may seem to be rather complex after the primary factors are understood. Tests of high complexity, such as a mental age score, cannot be expected to contribute to the identification of primary factors. Job analysis in the future will be done in terms of known primary factors, so that counseling and employment procedures can be designed on rational grounds rather than, as at present, by a hit-or-miss hunt for acceptable validities for each particular task.

In the work of finding a set of fundamental psychological categories for the description of mental traits it should be possible to supplement the simple-structure principle by other principles. In psychological work the choice of a set of basic parameters for describing mental traits could be facilitated by examining their genetic basis and by noting the order and the rate of development of the different functions. Thus, for example, the ability to do the Street Gestalt Completion test seems to be a function that matures very early, perhaps as early as six or seven years, while the verbal factor seems to show continued growth through the high-school years. The growth of the verbal factor may be explained by the imperfection of present tests, which are markedly influenced by schooling and experience or by slow maturation of the ability itself. At any rate, the primary factors which are identified by the study of individual differences at point age should be related to other findings on the rate of growth of the mental functions. The primary factors should preferably be a set of parameters which can be identified at each age by appropriate tests. The acceptance of primary factors in psychological investigation will depend on the extent to which they are fruitful in non-factorial psychological research. If they represent truly significant parameters for the description of mental traits, then they should also be revealed as distinguishable in the study of mental inheritance. It is to be hoped that at least some of the primary factors that are now being identified in the study of individual differences at point age will also be found to be useful and simplifying parameters in the study of mental inheritance and in the study of mental growth.

## Uniqueness of simple structure in a given correlation matrix

When reference axes have been found which produce a simple structure, it is of considerable scientific interest to know whether the simple structure is unique for the given correlation matrix. The necessary and sufficient conditions for uniqueness of a simple structure need to be investigated. In the absence of a complete solution to this problem, five criteria will here be listed which probably constitute sufficient conditions for the uniqueness of a simple structure. The scientific interpretation of the cell entries in the oblique factor matrix $V$ should not be attempted except after reasonable assurance that the simple structure of $V$ is unique for the given configuration. If this assurance is not available, then the interpretation should be tentative.

When the factor matrix has been rotated to an oblique simple structure, one can eliminate from consideration, as regards the uniqueness, those tests which have complexity equal to $r$. Those tests are in the middle of the configuration, and they do not contribute to the location of the reference frame. At the start of the factorial analysis those tests are eliminated which have zero communality, as indicated by the fact that their correlations are all vanishingly small. Similarly, those tests can be eliminated from consideration of simple structure whose communalities are low if they have not been eliminated at the start because of their low correlations. In practice, one need only eliminate from consideration those tests in the oblique factor matrix which have complexity $r$, because the other eliminations are made routinely in factoring the correlation matrix to save the unnecessary labor of carrying some tests through the factoring when they cannot contribute to the analysis.

If we eliminate the tests of complexity $r$, the remaining tests should contribute to the location of the reference frame. We shall describe five useful criteria by which the $r$ reference vectors can be determined. These are as follows:

1) Each row of the oblique factor matrix $V$ should have at least one zero.

2) For each column $p$ of the factor matrix $V$ there should be a distinct set of $r$ linearly independent tests whose factor loadings $v_{jp}$ are zero.

3) For every pair of columns of $V$ there should be several tests whose entries $v_{jp}$ vanish in one column but not in the other.

4) For every pair of columns of $V$, a large proportion of the tests should have zero entries in both columns. This applies to factor problems with four or five or more common factors.

5) For every pair of columns there should preferably be only a small number of tests with non-vanishing entries in both columns.

When these conditions are satisfied, the plot of each pair of columns shows (1) a large concentration of points in two radial streaks, (2) a large number of points at or near the origin, and (3) only a small number of points off the two radial streaks. For a configuration of $r$ dimensions there are $\frac{1}{2}r(r-1)$ diagrams. When all of them satisfy the three characteristics, we say that the structure is "compelling," and we have good assurance that the simple structure is unique. In the last analysis it is the appearance of the diagrams that determines, more than any other criterion, which of the hyperplanes of the simple structure are convincing and whether the whole configuration is to be accepted as stable and ready for interpretation.*

The first criterion demands that each trait should be describable in terms of fewer categories than are required by the whole set of $n$ traits. It is conceivable that, in some experimental work, one or more of the traits will be so complex as to require description in terms of all the factors that enter into the traits collectively. For the purpose of isolating the fundamental categories, these traits are not useful, and they should therefore be ignored. The criterion demands that the list of traits be long enough so that, after elimination of several traits of complexity $r$, enough traits of complexity less than $r$ remain to determine uniquely both the trait configuration and the simple structure. This principle may be illustrated with psychological

---

* Ever since I found the simple-structure solution for the factor problem, I have never attempted interpretation of a factorial result without first inspecting the diagrams.

tests. If one of the abilities to be isolated should be number sense, then this primary ability should not be required in all the tests of a battery. The same restriction applies to each of the abilities that is to be isolated.

The second criterion seems to be essential for the following reason. Each column $p$ of $V$ is determined by a hyperplane $L_p$. A hyperplane through the origin is determined by $(r-1)$ trait vectors. These trait vectors are contained in $L_p$, and therefore they have vanishing entries $v_{jp}$ in column $p$. Therefore, there must be at least $(r-1)$ traits with vanishing entries in each column of $V$ in order that the hyperplanes may be determined. Since the hyperplanes should be overdetermined by the data, it follows that the number of vanishing entries in each column of $V$ should equal or exceed $r$.

The third criterion is suggested by the fact that the $r$ hyperplanes must be distinct. If two columns of $V$ contain the same vanishing entries and if these exceed $(r-2)$ in number, then, assuming the test vectors to be linearly independent, the two corresponding hyperplanes are identical. The third criterion was written so as to insure both overdetermination and distinctness of the hyperplanes that define the columns of $V$.

When the fourth criterion is not satisfied, i.e., when there are no points at or near the origin for a problem of more than four or five dimensions, we can be reasonably sure that the hyperplanes have not been correctly located. This has been our experience with large and small factor problems. The fourth criterion is of importance in factor problems of four or more dimensions. In a three-dimensional problem a point at the origin on the diagram for factors 1 and 2 would have to be a measure of only the third common factor, so that its complexity would be 1. In two dimensions there can be no points at the origin except for a null vector. Such a vector is not found in a factor problem because its correlations would all be zero or small so that it would be eliminated from the test battery before factoring was begun.

The problem of determining the uniqueness of a simple structure may not be so serious as it seems at first sight. We are accustomed to the demand of statistical methods that a solution shall be unique in order to be classified as a preferred method. Actually, we do not often attain uniqueness. The curve-fitting methods in general use are not unique even when the same methods are used, as, for example, when a least-squares solution gives several variant answers, depending on which of the variables the investigator chooses to be dependent on the rest of the variables. However, it would be very useful to have a solution to the simple-structure problem by which we could know by some explicit method whether or not a frame exists in the configuration that gives a better fit than the one we may have found.

In presenting a simple structure as a solution to a factor problem, several considerations determine the plausibility and acceptability of the solution.

The plausibility of a solution should be considered separately for each factor. Some of the relevant criteria will be mentioned briefly:

1) The degree of ambiguity or plausibility of each hyperplane as judged by the configuration. In *Figure 5* we have illustrated for a three-dimensional configuration how the several co-ordinate planes frequently differ widely in degree of plausibility and convincingness. The plane $L_1$ is overdetermined by more than enough points (test vectors) to define the plane, and hence the existence of a parameter $T_1$ seems clearly indicated. The plane $L_3$ is barely determined, since two points are the least that will define the plane in three dimensions. The existence of the parameter $T_3$ is suggested but not demonstrated. The plane $L_2$ is indeterminate, as shown by several possible locations in the dotted lines. The parameter $T_2$ is suggested but not demonstrated. In *Figure 6* we have a three-dimensional configuration of six test vectors, in which the structure is not at all convincing.

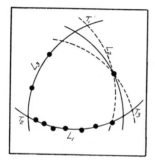

FIGURE 5

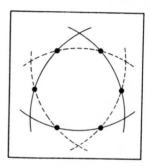

FIGURE 6

The sets of solid lines and dotted lines show two entirely different simple structures, neither of which is overdetermined. We see here how it is not likely that some single criterion will be found for the uniqueness of *a* simple structure, because the several planes and their corresponding parameters may differ widely in their degree of overdetermination and convincingness in any particular factor study.

2) The plausibility of the theoretical interpretation that the investigator may be able to find for each hyperplane. When an unexpected plane appears in a factorial study, it is a challenge to find an interpretation for it. If the interpretation seems plausible and if it clearly divides the tests into two categories, those with strong non-vanishing values of $V_{jp}$ and those with negligible factor loadings, the interpretation can be accepted at least as a hypothesis worthy of further study. This task of interpreting the factors found is clearly the most important part of a factorial study. If the interpretation is foggy, then so is the whole study, no matter how elegant

the statistical work may have been. Exploratory studies in a new domain are likely to give clues only as to the nature of the underlying functions or parameters.

3) The predictability of a postulated factor. In order to set up a crucial test of the word fluency factor $W$, two new tests of synonyms were constructed, one of which was predicted to have high saturation on $W$ and no saturation on the verbal factor $V$, while the other synonyms test was predicted to behave in just the opposite way, namely, zero on word fluency $W$ and high on the verbal factor $V$. They did behave in the way predicted in the next factorial study. This did not prove the interpretation of $W$ to be finally correct, but it did sustain the hypothesis concerning the differentiation of $V$ and $W$. Eventually, the factor $W$ may be redefined by other studies so that it might even transcend the verbal content altogether. Here, as in other experimentation, success depends very largely on how successful we may be in inventing tests and measurements that will be crucial in differentiating between rival hypotheses concerning the nature of the factors or in testing a tentative interpretation indicated by previous studies. It may happen that one experimenter will find a factor, that another will interpret it with some hypothesis, and that a third will invent the crucial tests by which the hypothesis can be examined factorially or otherwise. It is in this manner that factor analysis can find an important role as a scientific method not only in psychology but in other sciences in which exploratory studies may reveal an underlying order in a new domain.

In making interpretations for a new factor that has been identified factorially, we distinguish, in the spontaneity of our approval, between interpretations that seem vague or far-fetched and those occasional incisive interpretations that "click," as it were, and by which the factorial results snap into a meaningful whole. This is only to say that the scientific interpretation of experiments is as subjective now as it always has been. To demand that factorial interpretation shall be objective is as absurd as to demand that the interpretation of a physical experiment shall be objective. It never is.

4) The degree of convincingness of a simple structure. This has been described as due, in part, to the overdetermination of each hyperplane, but this judgment is made also with due regard to the relative number of test vectors that do not contribute to define the simple structure. In *Figure 7* we have drawn two plots that might be found for a pair of columns of a factor matrix. In the first we could fit the planes anywhere in a random configuration with perhaps enough points to determine a hyperplane, but it would not be convincing. In the second plot we should feel quite convinced that an underlying order is revealed because the distribution of the points makes the location of the two axes quite compelling. Here our judgment is influenced by the relative number of points that do not contribute

to the definition of the simple structure. In the second plot we have drawn several points in the middle of the first quadrant. If an interpretation can be found for the factors $A$ and $B$, then it is necessary to explain how it comes about that the several tests in the first quadrant have some saturation in both $A$ and $B$. If such an explanation seems plausible, it strengthens the interpretation of the factors. A configuration such as the first in *Figure 7* leaves one unconvinced, no matter where the axes are drawn, unless an interpetation can be found that seems right. Random configurations like this seldom yield clear interpretations, but they are not, of course, physically impossible.

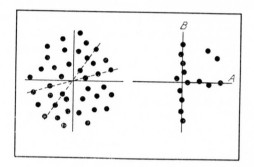

FIGURE 7

Some critics have pointed out that if the factorial composition is known for a large test battery, it would be possible to pick and choose a set of tests from the larger battery so that they would reveal a simple structure even for some more or less arbitrarily selected reference frame and that the simple structure so put together would not demonstrate any validity for the arbitrary reference frame. This is entirely correct. This is only one of many ways in which a dishonest author can fake scientific data. Another well-known case is that in which one can pick and choose points in a correlation table, erasing the points in the second and fourth quadrants, so as to change a zero correlation to a high positive value. If a test battery is assembled with tests that are crucial for one or several rival hypotheses, the configuration of the whole battery should be used in the interpretation. If the interpretation is valid, it should be possible to construct new and different tests with prediction as to how they should behave factorially. Again we should want to see the hypotheses, the tests, and the whole configuration.

Another criticism of simple structure which is in the same class is that one gets factorially only what one puts into a test battery and hence that the separate factors have no validity and represent only the arbitrary categories imposed by an author. It is a platitude to say that one gets out of a test battery only what one puts into it. Again, that is true for any scientific experiment. When a test battery is constructed with some hypothesis which is to be examined, it does not follow that the factorial analysis necessarily supports the categories that guided the construction of the battery. Most of our disappointments in factorial studies are, in fact, exactly of this kind. Hence we can say on the basis of considerable experience that a factor analysis does not necessarily reproduce the categories that constitute the preconceptions of the investigator. Any factors that are found are certainly represented by the tests that were put into the battery, but they do not necessarily fit the preconceptions of the experimenter.

The various criteria that have been discussed here seem obvious enough when we deal with graphical methods of inspecting the configuration, but they are likely to prove troublesome for anyone who attempts to reduce them all in some algebraic manner to a single criterion of uniqueness of simple structure. Any contributions in this direction are likely to be helpful in dealing with partial aspects of the problem of finding the most plausible reference frame for any given configuration. It must not be forgotten that it is an open question for each factorial study whether any simple structure exists at all or whether any one or several hyperplanes can be defined. It should also be noted that a factor study may be a major scientific contribution if it reveals only a single clear factor which can be given a fruitful and provocative interpretation, even if all the other factors in the same study prove to be entirely indeterminate. Furthermore, such a factorial result might be of fundamental significance, even if, say, only a fourth or a third of the variance of the crucial tests is accounted for by the factor in question. Other things being equal, a factor will be the more convincing, the higher the saturations involved in the tests that involve the factor. But the existence of large parts of the variance as unique or as uninterpreted common factors does not preclude significant findings.

Factorial studies may be roughly classified as of two kinds. When there are no hypotheses to guide the study of a new domain, the experimenter tries to cover the domain with tests or measures that are diversified within the domain. The factorial result is likely to give an incomplete simple structure at best, but the exploratory study is justified if one or more functions or parameters appear in the interpretation that can be used as starting-points for more crucial subsequent studies. The second kind is the experiment in which some hypotheses are available and in which tests are specially constructed to represent the presence and the absence of each postulated factor or parameter. Such studies are likely to be more productive of definitive results.

### Interpretation of zero factor loadings

There is occasional misunderstanding about the interpretation of zero factor loadings. A zero factor loading in a test is sometimes spoken of as if it meant the absence of the factor in the test, but that is not the correct interpretation. A zero factor loading means that the factor in question does not contribute to the *variance* of the test. The difference can be seen by an example. Consider two hypothetical factors, spelling and writing speed. If a simple spelling test were given by the time-limit method to a group of educated adults, the number of right answers might represent nothing but speed of writing, because the educated adults could be assumed to be able to spell all the simple words. Hence the variance of this test would be attributable entirely to writing speed and none to spelling ability. But it would be incorrect, strictly speaking, to say that the *test* does not involve any spelling ability. If the subjects were all equally good in a factor or if they all reach the ceiling of the test as regards power, the factor would not be responsible for any individual differences in the test, and the factor would not be identified.

If a spelling test of greater difficulty were given to the same population with ample writing time, then the factorial composition would be markedly changed. The greater part of the variance might then be attributable to the spelling factor, while the loading on writing speed would be zero. The zero loading on writing speed would be caused by the fact that this factor contributed nothing to the variance of the test, even though all the subjects actually wrote the test.

In the interpretation of zero factor loadings we sometimes say that the factor is not involved in the *test* when we really should say that the factor is not involved in the *test variance*. Since we deal mostly with common factors, we speak of the factors in a test when common factors are implied.

### The positive manifold

The principle of simple structure is frequently described as if it assumed all factor loadings to be positive or zero. That is perhaps the most common misunderstanding about the principle. The reason is probably that the factorial methods have been applied more in the field of mental abilities than in any other field, and it is here that test correlations have been found universally to be positive or zero. It is therefore natural to postulate that when a unique simple structure is found for a battery of tests of mental abilities, then the non-vanishing entries in the factorial matrix are positive. But it must be understood that this is a postulate of much psychological investigation in a particular field and that it does not constitute a restriction upon the principle of simple structure, which is applicable either with or without the special restriction that the factor loadings shall be positive or zero.

The scientific problems to which the factor methods are applied may require different restrictions on the elements of the factorial matrix. Some of these restrictions may be considered under four cases, as follows:

1) The simplest case is that in which the factorial matrix $F$ can be used as determined by the centroid method, or by any other equivalent method, without restrictions beyond those that are inherent in $F$. It is probably seldom that a scientific problem can be adequately solved without some restrictions on the elements of $F$.

2) One form of constraint that is of very general scientific interest as regards the factorial matrix is that of simple structure.

3) If the scientific problem is such that negative cell entries in $F$ are excluded, then we have the important case of a simple structure in which $a_{jm} \geqq 0$. This is the assumption that underlies the application of factorial methods to the problem of isolating primary mental abilities; but the assumption is not absolutely necessary, since ideal constructs can be devised for a science of psychology which do not require that the cell entries of $F$, or those of the oblique factorial matrix $V$, be positive or zero.

4) A special case of the positive entries of $F$ is the further restriction that each factor of $F$ or of $V$ be either completely present or completely absent in each test. This is a case of possible interest in genetics, but it is not likely that it will be directly applicable to scientific data without admitting a specific variance for each variable.

If all the elements of $V$ are positive or zero, then each column of $V$ is defined by a *positive hyperplane* so located that all the trait vectors which are not contained in it are on the same side of it. If it is assumed that all the factors have positive or zero contributions to each variable, then all the trait vectors are in the positive region. The bounding planes of this region are then of special interest.

It will be convenient to name the bounded space within which any radial vector has only positive direction cosines. The bounded space in which any radial vector has only positive direction cosines will be called the *positive region.*

If all the trait vectors that do not lie in a hyperplane are on the same side of it, the hyperplane will be called a *positive hyperplane* with reference to the trait configuration.

If, in addition, a set of $r$ positive hyperplanes exists such that each trait vector is contained in one or more of them, then the combined configuration of the trait vectors and the reference vectors will be called a *positive simple structure.*

The geometrical interpretation of the restriction upon the numerical value of $v_{jp}$ in $V$ in the case of mental ability tests is that all the test vectors lie in the positive region of the common-factor space. When this condition is satisfied for orthogonal vectors, all the intertest correlations are positive or zero. It is a universally accepted fact that intertest correlations for mental abilities are positive.

The converse is not necessarily valid. The well-known fact that all intertest correlations are positive implies that all the test vectors lie inside a cone with center at the origin and with a generating angle of $\pi/4$. Such a cone cannot be inscribed in the positive region except when the number of dimensions is as low as two.

The restriction that all the test vectors shall be in the positive region of the common-factor space is not sufficient to determine $F$ uniquely. In general, there exists an infinite number of orthogonal transformations by which all the entries in $F$ become positive or zero if the configuration of $F$ can be inscribed in the positive region. Special cases may be set up in which one, and only one, orthogonal transformation will make the entries $a_{jm}$ in $F$ positive or zero. Such a case in three dimensions is that in which three test vectors are mutually orthogonal. These cases are not likely to be found in practice. Hence a unique matrix $F$ is not to be expected with the single criterion that $a_{jm} \geqq 0$ in $F$.

The orthogonal hyperplanes which bound the positive region in $r$ dimensions will be called the *orthogonal positive manifold.*

A set of $r$ distinct and oblique positive hyperplanes for a trait configuration in $r$ dimensions will be called an *oblique positive manifold.*

If the factor matrix of the traits which are contained in a positive hyperplane is of rank $(r-1)$, then the hyperplane is a *bounding hyperplane* or a *positive co-ordinate hyperplane.*

The identification of a positive simple structure is done by noting the bounding hyperplanes if they are found in the rotations. If a positive manifold is not postulated or suspected in the test battery, the rotations are made toward linear concentrations of test points in the diagrams without reference to the question of whether the hyperplanes are bounding planes.

### Unitary factors

A special case of the positive manifold is that in which each factor is either completely present or entirely absent in each member of the experimental population. Each individual member of the population has, then, one of only two possible standard scores—one positive, which represents the presence of the trait, and the other negative, which represents the complete absence of the trait. The numerical values of these two possible standard scores are determined by the proportion of the population that has the trait. If it is assumed in first approximation that the unitary factors are equally weighted, then the correlations take only certain possible values which are determined by the number of the unitary factors or elements in each of the test variables. By inspecting the experimental correlations, one can make estimates of the number of elements in each test variable. This method of factor analysis seems to be limited in practical application because of the serious effects of unique variance and because the elements are not likely to be equally weighted in each test variable. However, the restriction of the correlation coefficients to certain values makes this principle of some theoretical interest, and it might be adapted to factorial studies of certain types. It can be regarded as a different type of restriction on the factorial composition by which the reference axes may be located. This method has not yet found practical application.*

### Constellations

In formulating hypotheses concerning the nature of the primary traits, it is sometimes a considerable aid to know of constellations that may exist in the trait configuration. By a *constellation* is meant a grouping of trait vectors. It happens not infrequently that the trait configuration consists essentially of groups of trait vectors. The angular separations between the trait vectors within a constellation are relatively small, while the separations between constellations are marked.

When the dimensionality of the factorial matrix is less than four, the constellations may be inspected readily by graphical methods. When the dimensionality exceeds three, the graphical methods are not available, and it is then useful to have a routine by which the constellations may be isolated in the trait configuration.† Since the constellations are to be used as an aid to intuition regarding the nature of the primary traits, it is not advisable to define a constellation rigorously as regards maximum angular separations or as regards the maximum generating angle of the cone which will include a constellation. Such restrictions may be arbitrarily imposed by the investigator for each study.

If an attempt is made to isolate constellations from a large battery of traits—say, fifty or more—without some systematic procedure, it is usually found that the groupings become entangled in annoying complexity. If the constellations do not exist, the procedure must make this fact evident; but, on the other hand, constellations can be drawn for the purposes of studying the battery, even though the traits arrange themselves more in the nature of chains than of constellations. In three dimensions this situation is illustrated by a battery of traits whose configuration reveals a spherical triangle, in which the sides of the triangle are well defined by the trait vectors. If all of them lie in the sides of a spherical triangle, then the isolation of constellations would be difficult, because there may be no sharp break between one constellation and the next. In three dimensions the graphical methods would, of course, be used because of their simplicity and directness; but in higher dimensions the groupings may be obtained by inspectional methods from the intercorrelations corrected for uniqueness.‡

* See first ed., pp. 205–12.        † See first ed., p. 174.

‡ Lately, Professor Tryon has proposed that we return to cluster analysis instead of the factorial methods that have been developed in the last decade. The inspection of a correlation matrix for groupings or clusters was naturally the first attempt in analyz-

One useful procedure is to ascertain, first, the average correlation in each column of the correlational matrix $R_u$, where the given coefficients have been corrected for uniqueness. (An alternative is to count in each column the number of coefficients whose absolute values exceed some specified values.) Select the trait $T_x$ with highest mean coefficient. List all the traits whose correlations with $T_x$ exceed the specified value and complete the correlation matrix for the traits so selected. Eliminate from the table the trait which has the largest number of small intercorrelations. Repeat the eliminating process until all the traits that remain in the table have appreciable intercorrelations. These traits constitute a constellation. Select the trait whose mean coefficient is next highest and which is not listed in the group just formed, and proceed with it in the same manner as with $T_x$ until the majority of the traits have been assigned. These groupings are flexible, and they may be arranged to overlap. The arrangement of the traits in constellations should be regarded merely as a rough method of inspectional analysis. The procedure here outlined can, of course, be modified in many ways.

### A note about static and dynamic factors

Investigators who are using the factorial methods as an aid in testing psychological hypotheses find themselves involved not only in legitimate controversies about techniques and about interpretation with rival hypotheses but also in some forms of criticism that are not much more than verbalisms. One of these that recurs too frequently is the charge that differentiable functions or parameters that can be identified factorially are invalid because they are supposed to be static, mechanical, atomistic, and isolated and that any such factors imply behavioral anarchism. In contrast, we are told that factors, instead of being static, must be functional and dynamic "relationships" and that these must somehow embrace the whole personality. It is doubtful whether any real issue exists to justify such talk. It is doubtful whether any psychologist who has good training in his subject ever really looks for a factor that is truly isolated from the rest of man's mind. Further, if a factor is a relation of some kind, then surely there must be some distinguishable things that are related; and if these things are not to be identified, then the relation will be obscure indeed.

In the box problem one of the factors was the height. That was a parameter that entered into the measurements of each box, but it does not follow that the height was in any sense isolated from the totality of the box. But to this example there would be the objection that the boxes and their measurements are static, whereas in psychology we must be dynamic. Instead of using boxes as an example, we could have used flywheels. This ex-

---

ing the correlations. The early inspectional methods for clusters are hardly to be preferred to the factorial methods, which identify not only the clusters but also groupings in hyperplanes.

ample would have shown dynamic factors, such as momentum, the radius of gyration, and revolutions per second of the flywheels. Such an example would work just as well in differentiating between factors which would then refer to kinetic aspects of the objects. Factor analysis would apply as well in one case as in the other. Pedagogically it is perhaps better to use the boxes because the reader can then devote himself to factorial ideas instead of trying also at the same time to learn some theoretical mechanics.

Another verbalism in the interpretation of factors is the insistence that they must be treated as "relationships." Let us not talk about relations without giving at least some hint about the entities that are being related. Relations do not float around by themselves. They are tied to the concepts or things that are related. In some current factorial writing, mental organization is similarly described as consisting of "relationships." If factors are the relations, then it would be interesting to have some hint about the things that are related.

# CHAPTER XV

## OBLIQUE STRUCTURE

### Primary trait vectors

The fundamental concepts of oblique structure will be here defined for $r$ dimensions. *Figure 1* has been drawn to show the relations of the reference vectors $\Lambda_p$, the hyperplanes $L_p$, and the primary vectors $T_p$. *Figure 2* has been drawn to show these relations in rectangular form.

In *Figure 2* we have the factor matrix $F$ with elements $a_{jm}$, which are determined by the factoring process from the correlation matrix. The transformation matrix $\Lambda$ with elements $\lambda_{mp}$ carries the factor matrix $F$ into the oblique factor matrix $V$ with elements $v_{jp}$. This is expressed in the equation

$$(1) \qquad\qquad F\Lambda = V .$$

The test vectors $j$ are defined in $F$ by their projections on a set of orthogonal reference axes. The same test vectors are defined in $V$ by their projections on a set of oblique reference axes $\Lambda_p$. In *Figure 1* the oblique reference axes $\Lambda_p$ are shown, but not the orthogonal reference frame. Each column of the transformation matrix $\Lambda$ gives the direction cosines of one of the reference vectors in terms of the orthogonal frame.

The $r$ hyperplanes, whose normals produce a simple structure with a test configuration, will be called the *co-ordinate hyperplanes* for the test configuration. The simple structure is defined by the test configuration and the normals $\Lambda_p$ to the co-ordinate hyperplanes $L_p$. In *Figure 1* each reference vector $\Lambda_p$ is orthogonal to the hyperplane $L_p$. In particular, the reference vector $\Lambda_1$ is orthogonal to the hyperplane $L_1$, and similarly for the other planes. The reference vector defines the hyperplane, which is a subspace of $(r-1)$ dimensions in the total common-factor space of $r$ dimensions.

The intersection of any set of $(r-1)$ co-ordinate hyperplanes defines a *co-ordinate axis* of the structure. In *Figure 1* the intersection of the hyperplanes $L_1$ and $L_2$ defines the co-ordinate axis $T_3$. The total number of sets of $(r-1)$ hyperplanes that can be taken is $r$, and consequently their intersections define $r$ co-ordinate axes. These are of scientific interest because they define the descriptive categories of the simple order in terms of the tests.

The test vectors that lie in the hyperplane $L_1$ are orthogonal to the reference vector $\Lambda_1$, and hence these tests have zero projection on that reference vector. In *Figure 2* these tests are identified by zero projections $v_{j1}$ in the column 1 of the oblique factor matrix $V$. Each of these projections is determined by the cross product of a row of $F$ and the first column of $\Lambda$.

The unit vector defined by a co-ordinate axis will be called a *primary trait vector* or a *primary vector*. The trait which corresponds to a primary vector will be called a *primary trait* or a *primary factor*. The object of a factorial analysis is to discover the primary traits and to describe them in terms

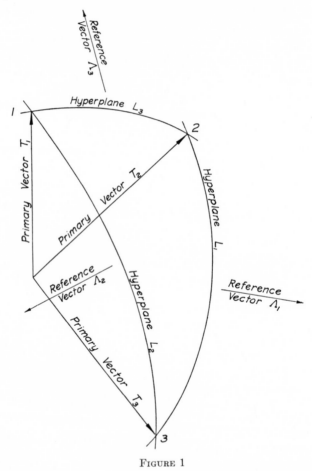

FIGURE 1

of the tests that are experimentally observed. In *Figure 1* it is seen that the trait vector $T_1$ is the unit vector in the intersection of hyperplanes $L_2$ and $L_3$. The subscript for each primary vector is identical with that of the hyperplane which does *not* contain the primary factor. Each primary vector $T_p$ is the unit vector in the intersection of the $(r-1)$ hyperplanes $L_q$, where $q \neq p$. In three dimensions there are three planes $L_p$ which contain the origin. Their intersections determine the primary vectors $T_p$.

The intersection of all the co-ordinate hyperplanes, excepting $L_p$, defines a primary trait vector, which is denoted $T_p$. Hence $T_p$ defines the linear subspace which is common to all the hyperplanes, excepting $L_p$. The trait vector $T_p$ is not contained in the hyperplane $L_p$, but it is contained in all the other hyperplanes. It follows that in *Figure 2* the primary trait $T_p$ is absent in all the tests which have vanishing entries $v_{jp}$ in column $p$ of $V$. The primary trait $T_p$ is present in all tests that have non-vanishing entries $v_{jp}$ in column $p$ of $V$.

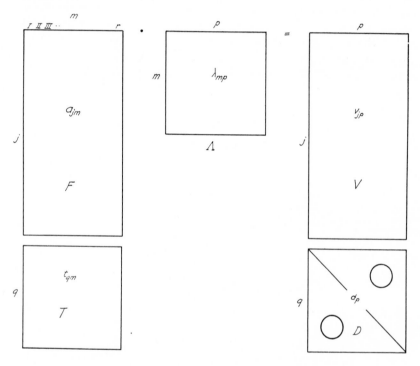

FIGURE 2

Since the primary trait vector $T_p$ is not contained in the hyperplane $L_p$, it might be inferred that it is identical with the normal to the hyperplane $L_p$. This is not necessarily the case. If the primary traits are uncorrelated in the experimental population, then the vectors $T_p$ are orthogonal, and so are also the co-ordinate hyperplanes $L_p$ and their normals $\Lambda_p$. In this case the reference vectors $\Lambda_p$ are identical with the primary vectors $T_p$. However, if the primary traits $T_p$ are correlated in the experimental population, then the hyperplanes $L_p$ are oblique, and their normals $\Lambda_p$ are oblique. The two sets of vectors $\Lambda_p$ and $T_p$ are then, in general, distinct.

The geometrical interpretation of primary traits may be illustrated in three dimensions. Let the entries $a_{jm}$ in each row of $F$ be augmented by the multiplier $1/h_j$. The geometric representation of the augmented co-ordinates is that each test vector is extended to unit length. The augmented co-ordinates are therefore the direction cosines of unit test vectors. The termini of the test vectors can be represented as points on the surface of a hypersphere. If $r=3$, the test configuration can be studied graphically on the surface of a ball.

Let *Figure 3* represent the test configuration, and let the points represent the termini of the test vectors on the surface of the sphere. Simple structure is shown by the fact that each point lies in one of the three arcs of great circles. All the tests on the arc *1–2* can be described by two primary factors, since all the corresponding test vectors are coplanar. The whole set of tests can be described by three factors. Hence the same primary factor is absent

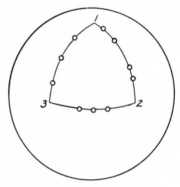

Figure 3

in all the tests along *1–2*. The subspace *1–2* is defined by the direction cosines of the normal to the plane *1–2*. Let this normal be denoted $\Lambda_3$. The subscript of $\Lambda_3$ refers to the primary trait $T_3$, that is absent in the subspace $L_3$. The vector $\Lambda_3$ is the normal which defines the subspace $L_3$.

By analogy, the vector $\Lambda_1$ is the normal to the plane *2–3*, and $\Lambda_2$ is the normal to the plane *1–3*. If all test vectors in the plane *1–2* represent two primary factors and if all test vectors in the plane *1–3* represent two primary factors, it is clear that the vector which is determined by the intersection of these two planes represents the primary factor which the two planes have in common, namely, the primary factor 1. In the same manner the other primary factors, 2 and 3, are determined by intersections of planes.

Equation (1) is shown in rectangular notation in *Figure 2*. The equation can be written in terms of its elements,

$$(2) \qquad \sum_m a_{jm} \lambda_{mp} = v_{jp}.$$

In *Figure 2* let the rows of a matrix $T$ with elements $t_{qm}$ represent a set of $r$ primary unit vectors $T_p$. The rows of the square matrix $T$ are normalized, since $T_p$ are unit vectors. These are the vectors $T_1$, $T_2$, and $T_3$ of *Figure 1*, and they are defined as intersections of the planes $L_p$. The direction cosines of the first primary vector, the first row of $T$, are $t_{11}$, $t_{12}$, $t_{13}$. The direction cosines of the normal to the plane $L_2$, the second column of $\Lambda$, are $\lambda_{12}$, $\lambda_{22}$, $\lambda_{32}$. Since the vector $T_1$ lies in the plane $L_2$, we should have

$$(3) \qquad t_{11}\lambda_{12} + t_{12}\lambda_{22} + t_{13}\lambda_{32} = 0 .$$

In a similar manner, since the vector $T_1$ also lies in the plane $L_3$, we have

$$(4) \qquad t_{11}\lambda_{13} + t_{12}\lambda_{23} + t_{13}\lambda_{33} = 0 .$$

A similar substitution of the direction cosines of $T_1$ in the equation of plane $L_1$ gives

$$(5) \qquad t_{11}\lambda_{11} + t_{12}\lambda_{21} + t_{13}\lambda_{31} = d_1 ,$$

which should not vanish, since the vector $T_1$ does not lie in the plane $L_1$. Let the constant term be denoted $d_1$. These three equations are, in fact, the multiplication of the first row of $T$ and the three columns of $\Lambda$, with products recorded in the first row of the diagonal matrix $D$, as shown in *Figure 2*. The other rows of $T$ can be regarded in a similar manner, so that we have the matrix equation

$$(6) \qquad T\Lambda = D ,$$

where $D$ is a diagonal matrix with diagonal elements $d_p$. Hence we get

$$(7) \qquad T = D\Lambda^{-1} ,$$

by which the numerical values of $T$ may be determined. The inverse of $\Lambda$ is normalized by rows to give $T$.

The matrix $T$ is placed in *Figure 2* as a continuation of the factor matrix $F$. Each row of $T$ can be regarded as if it represented a perfect test $j$ of one of the primary factors, each of these tests being of unit communality. After the transformation $\Lambda$, each of these tests will have unit complexity in the oblique factor matrix $V$, in that there is only one entry $d_p$ in each row of the corresponding section of $V$, namely, the diagonal matrix $D$.

The correlations between the primary factors, $R_{pq}$, can be found by the fundamental factor theorem, since $T$ is a factor matrix for the primary abilities. We then have

$$(8) \qquad R_{pq} = TT' ,$$

or, by (7),

$$(9) \qquad R_{pq} = D\Lambda^{-1}(D\Lambda^{-1})' ,$$

which can be written in the form

$$(10) \qquad R_{pq} = D\Lambda^{-1}(\Lambda^{-1})'D ;$$

and this can be expressed as

$$(11) \qquad R_{pq} = D(\Lambda'\Lambda)^{-1}D .$$

Equation (11) can be used to find the correlation between the primary factors directly from $\Lambda$ and without writing $T$ explicitly. The matrix multiplication $(\Lambda'\Lambda)$ is first performed, then the inverse is found, namely, $(\Lambda'\Lambda)^{-1}$. The columns and rows are adjusted by premultiplication and postmultiplication with the same diagonal matrix $D$ to make the diagonal entries of $R_{pq}$ unity. Let the diagonal entry of $(\Lambda^1\Lambda)^{-1}$ be $m_p$. Then the corresponding diagonal entry of $D$ is

$$(12) \qquad d_p = \frac{1}{\sqrt{m_p}} .$$

Since the derived pure tests $T$ of the primary factors have unit communality, the self-correlations must be unity.

Each diagonal element $d_p$ is the scalar product of the primary vector $T_p$ and the corresponding reference vector $\Lambda_p$. Since both of these vectors are unit vectors, the diagonal element $d_p$ is the cosine of the angular separation of the primary vector $T_p$ and the corresponding reference vector $\Lambda_p$. We then have

$$(12a) \qquad d_p = \sum_m t_{qm}\lambda_{mp} \text{ where } q = p ,$$

which becomes unity in the orthogonal case where $T_p$ and $\Lambda_p$ are identical.

In case we have an orthogonal simple structure, the reference frame of $V$ is also orthogonal. Then the transformation $\Lambda$ in (1) is an orthogonal transformation, so that $\Lambda^{-1}=\Lambda'$. Then in (11) $\Lambda'\Lambda=\Lambda^{-1}\Lambda=I$. Then, by (11), we have $R_{pq}=I$, as would be expected.

### Test vectors as linear combinations of primary vectors

So far we have considered the test vectors in terms of the fixed orthogonal frame ($a_{jm}$ in $F$) and the primary vectors in terms of the same frame, $t_{qm}$ in the primary factor matrix $T$, as shown in *Figure 2*. Consider again the test vectors which lie in the co-ordinate planes of *Figure 3*, and the primary factors *1*, *2*, and *3* at the corners of the configuration. The test vectors in the plane *1–2*, for example, can be expressed as linear combinations of the primary vectors $T_1$ and $T_2$. We should then have

$$(13) \qquad \sum_p A_{jp} t_{pm} = a_{jm} ,$$

in which $A_{jp}$ is the weight given to the primary vector $p$ in the description of test vector $j$. This equation can be written in the matrix form

$$(14) \qquad AT = F ,$$

and hence the desired weights in $A$ are

$$(15) \qquad A = FT^{-1} ;$$

but by (7) we have

$$(16) \qquad A = F(D\Lambda^{-1})^{-1} ,$$

which becomes

$$(17) \qquad A = F\Lambda D^{-1} .$$

By (1) we have

$$(18) \qquad A = VD^{-1} ,$$

from which we infer that the weights by which the test vectors $j$ can be expressed as linear combinations of the primary factors $T$ are proportional by columns to the entries in the oblique factor matrix $V$. When the transformation $\Lambda$ becomes known by rotational analysis, the proportionality constants of $D$ are the reciprocals of the diagonal entries in equation (12).

### The test correlations in terms of the primary vectors

Since the test vectors can be expressed as linear combinations of the primary vectors, the test correlations $r_{jk}$ can also be expressed in terms of the primaries. By the fundamental factor theorem for orthogonal factors we have

$$(19) \qquad R_{jk} = FF' ,$$

and by (14) we get

$$(20) \qquad R_{jk} = AT(AT)'$$

or

(21)
$$R_{jk} = ATT'A' ,$$

which, by (8), becomes

(22)
$$R_{jk} = AR_{pq}A' ,$$

where $R_{pq}$ is the matrix of correlations between the primary factors. Equa‑ tion (22) is Tucker's generalization of the fundamental factor theorem to the general oblique case.* The matrix $A$ is proportional by columns to the oblique factor matrix $V$, as in equation (18). If the primary factors are un‑ correlated, $R_{pq}$ becomes the identity matrix, so that

(23)
$$R_{jk} = AA' ;$$

or, by (15),

(24)
$$R_{jk} = FT^{-1}(FT^{-1})' .$$

But in this case $T$ is an orthogonal matrix, so that $T^{-1} = T'$. Hence the rela‑ tion reduces to

(25)
$$R_{jk} = FF' ,$$

which is the fundamental factor theorem for the case of orthogonal factors.

### The equation of an oblique simple structure

A simple structure is a set of $r$ oblique hyperplanes, all of which contain the origin. This set of $r$ hyperplanes may be regarded as a degenerate cone whose apex is at the origin and whose surface consists of the $r$ hyperplanes. The equation of the hyperplane $L_p$ is

(26)
$$\sum_{m=1}^{r} x_m \lambda_{mp} = 0 .$$

The equation of a simple structure in $r$ dimensions may be written by set‑ ting the product of $r$ polynomials, like (26) for $p = 1, 2, 3, \ldots , r$, equal to zero. Then we have

(27)
$$\left[ \sum_{m=1}^{r} x_m \lambda_{m1} \right] \left[ \sum_{m=1}^{r} x_m \lambda_{m2} \right] \cdots \left[ \sum_{m=1}^{r} x_m \lambda_{mr} \right] = 0 .$$

* Ledyard R. Tucker, "The Role of Correlated Factors in Factor Analysis," *Psychometrika*, V, No. 2 (June, 1940), 142, eq. (7).

This equation* may be written in the more condensed form

$$(28) \qquad \prod_{p=1}^{r} \left[ \sum_{m=1}^{r} x_m \lambda_{mp} \right] = 0 \, .$$

Fitting (28) to a given test configuration in which a simple structure is assumed, we have, for each test $j$,

$$(29) \qquad v_{j1} v_{j2} \dots v_{jr} = 0 \, ,$$

or

$$(30) \qquad \prod_{p=1}^{r} v_{jp} = 0 \, .$$

If the point $j$ is in at least one of the $r$ hyperplanes of (30), at least one of the $r$ factors $v_{jp}$ vanishes, and hence equation (30) is satisfied. Equation (28) or its equivalent, (30), is therefore satisfied by all points in the $r$ co-ordinate hyperplanes of a simple structure.

In order to determine the best-fitting degenerate cone for a given set of $n$ points in a space of $r$ dimensions, equation (28) may be written in the form of an observation equation, namely,

$$(31) \qquad \prod_{p=1}^{r} \left[ \sum_{m=1}^{r} a_{jm} \lambda_{mp} \right] = \rho_j \, ,$$

where $\rho_j$ is the discrepancy for the point $j$. The best-fitting simple structure may be defined as that in which

$$\sum_{j=1}^{n} \rho_j^2$$

is minimized. Hence the criterion for a best-fitting simple structure is the minimizing of

$$(32) \qquad \sum_{j=1}^{n} \prod_{p=1}^{r} \left[ \sum_{m=1}^{r} a_{jm} \lambda_{mp} \right]^2 = \sum_{j=1}^{n} \prod_{p=1}^{r} v_{jp}^2 = \phi \, .$$

The function $\phi$ is then a criterion for the isolation of a simple structure.

* This equation was suggested by Professor Raymond W. Barnard, of the Department of Mathematics at the University of Chicago.

Equation (32) is an example of analytical criteria for the isolation of simple structure. A number of attempts have been made to devise practical computing methods with analytical criteria by which the simple-structure solution would be obtained with fewer graphs than are required by the methods of *chapters x* and *xi*. Lately, several solutions have been found that seem to be computationally feasible and which may replace a part of the graphical work.

### The population matrix

The population matrix $P_{mi}$ for the common factors is of order $r \times N$ with elements $x_{mi}$. Each element is the standard score $x_{mi}$ of individual $i$ in the arbitrary orthogonal factor $m$. In matrix form we have, for the test score $s_{ji}$,

$$(33) \qquad s_{ji} = \sum_{m} a_{jm} x_{mi} ,$$

or

$$(34) \qquad S = FP .$$

By (14) we have

$$(35) \qquad S = ATP .$$

The test scores $s_{ji}$ can also be expressed as linear combinations of scores on the correlated primary factors. Then

$$(36) \qquad s_{ji} = \sum_{p} A_{jp} x_{pi} ,$$

where $A_{jp}$ are coefficients and $x_{pi}$ are standard scores of individuals $i$ on the correlated primary factors $p$. In matrix form*

$$(37) \qquad S = AP_c ,$$

where $x_{pi}$ are the elements of $P_c$. By (35) and (37) we have

$$(38) \qquad ATP = AP_c ,$$

so that

$$(39) \qquad TP = P_c ,$$

where $P_c$ is the population matrix for the correlated primary factors $p$.

---

* Tucker, *op. cit.*, p. 141. We are using notation $A$ and $P$ for the oblique case, corresponding to Tucker's generalized notation $F$ and $P$.

The correlations between the primary factors can be expressed in terms of oblique population matrix $P_c$. Since $x_{mi}$ are standard scores, we have

$$(40) \qquad r_{pq} = \frac{1}{N} \sum_i x_{pi} x_{qi}$$

or, in matrix form,

$$(41) \qquad R_{pq} = \frac{1}{N} P_c P_c' .$$

This equation can be related to the population matrix for the arbitrary orthogonal frame $m$. By (39) we have

$$(42) \qquad R_{pq} = \frac{1}{N} (TP)(TP)'$$

or

$$(43) \qquad R_{pq} = \frac{1}{N} TPP'T' ,$$

which can be written in the form

$$(44) \qquad R_{pq} = T\left( \frac{1}{N} PP' \right) T' .$$

But, since the factors in $P$ are orthogonal by definition, we have

$$(45) \qquad \frac{1}{N} PP' = R_{mM} = I ,$$

and hence

$$(46) \qquad R_{pq} = TT' ,$$

as previously demonstrated.

## The oblique observation equation

The relations of oblique structure have been described here with reference to the fixed and arbitrary orthogonal frame $m$. The fundamental observation equation on which multiple-factor theory has been developed is

$$(33) \qquad s_{ji} = \sum_m a_{jm} x_{mi} .$$

This is the familiar equation that we write in matrix form as

$$(34) \qquad S = FP .$$

Here the arbitrary factors of $P$ are those which appear in the factoring of a correlation matrix, and they are orthogonal.

An observation equation can also be written in which the scores $s_{ji}$ are expressed directly in terms of standard scores on the correlated primary factors. This has been done by Tucker in the form

$$(36) \qquad s_{ji} = \sum_{p} a_{jp} x_{pi} ,$$

where $x_{pi}$ is the standard score of individual $i$ in the primary factor $p$ and where $a_{jp}$ are the test coefficients. In matrix form we have

$$(37) \qquad S = AP_c .$$

The relations of oblique structure can be easily derived from (36) as an observation equation for oblique or correlated factors.

The correlation between tests $j$ and $k$ is

$$(47) \qquad r_{jk} = \frac{1}{N} \sum_{i} s_{ji} s_{ki} ,$$

which has been written in the term

$$(48) \qquad R_{jk} = \frac{1}{N} SS' .$$

In the same way, the correlation between the primary factors $p$ and $q$ can be written

$$(40) \qquad r_{pq} = \frac{1}{N} \sum_{i} x_{pi} x_{qi} ;$$

and in matrix form this becomes

$$(41) \qquad R_{pq} = \frac{1}{N} P_c P_c' .$$

Substituting (37) in (48), we have

$$(49) \qquad R_{jk} = \frac{1}{N} (AP_c)(AP_c)'$$

or

$$(50) \qquad R_{jk} = A\left(\frac{1}{N}P_c P'_c\right)A' .$$

By (41) we have

$$(22) \qquad R_{jk} = A R_{pq} A' ,$$

which is the generalized factor theorem. This becomes

$$(25) \qquad R_{jk} = AA' = FF'$$

when the factors of $A$ are orthogonal.

# CHAPTER XVI

## FACTORIAL INVARIANCE

**Nature of the problem**

The problem of factorial invariance should be analyzed with regard to the central purpose of factor analysis, the object of which is to discover a set of significant and meaningful parameters for describing a domain. In the box problem that we have found useful for illustrative purposes, the domain is the whole range of measurements which can be taken on rectangular boxes and which are functions merely of the shapes of the boxes. We have found that one simplifying set of parameters for this domain is the lengths of three adjacent edges, denoted $x$, $y$, and $z$, for the height, the length, and the width, respectively. Now let one of the measurements $s_j$ be determined in large part by the height, $x$, and let it be assumed that in a random collection of boxes, selected for analysis, there is marked variance in this parameter, the height. It would then be expected that the measurement $s_j$ would have a certain part of its variance, $a_{jx}^2$, attributable to the height factor in this collection of boxes. This is simply the square of the factor loading of the factor $x$ in test $j$. If the boxes were to be arranged in order from lowest to highest in accordance with the factor $x$, we should expect to see an array of boxes from low to tall. Inspection of such an array would aid in guessing the meaning of the factor $x$. Ordinarily, one proceeds more simply by examining all the measures which have high positive, small or negligible, and marked negative saturations, in order to guess from the nature of the measurements what is implied by each factor.

As regards the particular measurement $s_j$, which has an appreciable part of its variance attributable to the height factor, its factorial composition is evidently dependent on the population of boxes, so that the factor loadings would be affected by selection. Several collections, such as packing boxes, pencil boxes, jewelry boxes, would probably vary in relative dispersions of the three parameters. One could imagine a collection of boxes selected so that they were all of the same height. The variance in the height factor would then be zero. The factor loadings $a_{jx}$ would vanish, and, in fact, the rank would be 2 instead of 3, which is expected for most box populations. Hence *the factor loadings cannot be expected to be invariant from one population to a different population.* Any criterion of invariance in factor analysis assumes that it is applied to analyses on the same population or to equivalent populations.* In psychological analysis this principle means that fac-

* First ed., p. 55.

torial composition cannot be expected to be invariant for different age groups, for example, or different groups of subjects, selected by criteria that are related to the factors involved. (We shall see later that the configuration may remain invariant for different populations, but we are here concerned with the numerical invariance of the factor loadings.) Limiting ourselves here to analyses that are made on the same population, we should expect to find that if several samples are drawn from the same population and if independent factor analyses are made with the same battery of tests for the several samples, then the factor loadings should remain invariant for the different samples within sampling errors if the simple structure is complete and overdetermined.

Let the measurement $s_j$ be made on each one of a group of boxes, as well as twenty other measurements of the same domain, relating to the rectangular box shapes. Now if the measurement $s_j$ is heavily saturated with the height factor, we should certainly be disappointed with our factorial methods if the saturation of $s_j$ on the height factor should turn out to be dependent on the other measurements that are taken on the same boxes. In the psychological field there is a comparable situation in studying the saturation of an opposites test, for example, on the verbal factor. If that test calls for a verbal factor, then the saturation of the factor in the test should not change if additional tests are given to the same subjects and then incorporated into the test battery for analysis. When the multiple-factor methods were being developed, these considerations led to certain demands as to what should constitute an acceptable factorial method. *It is a fundamental criterion of a valid method of isolating primary abilities that the weights of the primary abilities for a test must remain invariant when it is moved from one test battery to another test battery.* The same principle can be stated as a fundamental requirement of a successful factorial method, that *the factorial description of a test must remain invariant when the test is moved from one battery to another which involves the same common factors.*† If a test with saturation on a factor were moved to another test battery in which that factor is absent, the factor would become a specific factor of the test in the second battery, and it would not be found by the factorial methods, which are limited to the common factors. This limitation was made in order to make the factorial problem determinate. This requirement is a criterion for the acceptance or rejection of factorial methods.

When a correlation matrix is factored, the result is a factor matrix with a set of orthogonal axes whose location in the test configuration is, in general, arbitrary and entirely dependent on the method of factoring. The first centroid axis is clearly dependent on the grouping of tests in the battery which is being analyzed. If there is a large number of verbal tests in the battery and only a few number tests and space tests, then it is evident that the

---

* *Ibid.*, p. 55.  † *Ibid.*, p. 120.

first centroid axis will lie close to the verbal tests. By changing the proportion of tests of different kinds, the first centroid axis can be moved about in the configuration. It is clear that the projection of a test vector on the first centroid axis will not be invariant when the test is moved from one battery to another battery. It will depend on the nature of the other tests with which it is combined in each battery. Hence the centroid axis should not be used for the interpretation of the factorial composition of any test. The same is true for all the centroid axes, and the same is also true for the principal axes whose location in the configuration is dependent on the concentration of tests of different kinds. Because this principle should be geometrically self-evident, it will not be demonstrated by numerical examples. If a

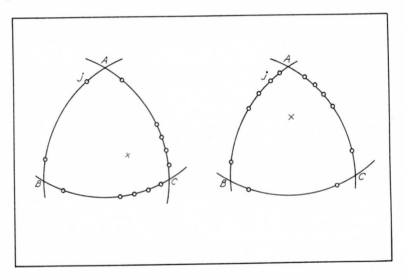

FIGURE 1

numerical demonstration were to be made, the maximum variation in factor loadings would be obtained by having marked variation in the proportions of different kinds of tests in the two batteries to be compared.

It was for the solution of this invariance problem that the simple-structure principle was introduced. In *Figure 1* we have represented two batteries of twelve tests with three common factors, $A$, $B$, and $C$. In the first battery there are eight tests near $C$ and only two tests each near $A$ and $B$. In the second battery there are eight tests heavily saturated with $A$ and only two each near $B$ and $C$. Let the two batteries have test $j$ in common. In each of the triangles we have indicated with an $x$ the approximate location of the first centroid axis or the major principal axis. It will be seen that test $j$ would have a low projection on the major principal axis in the first battery, while it would have a large projection on the major principal factor in the second battery. Test $j$ is far from the major principal axis in the first battery but close to the major principal axis in the second battery.

If these two test batteries were factored by any appropriate method and if a complete and determinate simple structure were found, as shown in the spherical triangles, then we should find in the first battery that test $j$ had a high saturation on the factor $A$, a small saturation on the factor $B$, and zero saturation on the factor $C$. The same result would be found in the second test battery, in spite of the fact that the two batteries differ markedly in the relative number of tests of each kind. *The factorial composition of a test in a set of primary factors that have been found in a complete and overdetermined simple structure remains invariant when the test is moved to another battery involving the same common factors and in which there are enough tests to make the simple structure complete and overdetermined.* This is one of the most important principles in multiple-factor analysis. It could happen that when a test is moved from one battery to another battery, one of the primary factors would be represented by only two tests. Theoretically, this would be a common factor, but the location of this doublet factor might be indeterminate in the configuration of the new battery. For this reason we state the principle with the specification that the simple structure should be complete and determinate in both of the test batteries before we can have assurance about invariance of factorial composition. If the simple structure is incomplete in one of the batteries, then the locations of the primary axes are, to that extent, uncertain, and then the factorial composition of the tests would also be uncertain.

### Types of factorial invariance

The simplest form of factorial invariance concerns the *metric invariance* of the factor matrix solution. This is the problem of ascertaining the conditions under which the numerical values of the factor matrix solution are invariant. Since there is infinite variation in the possible locations of the reference frame in the configuration, one should not expect any numerical invariance in the projections of the test vectors on the reference axes (the factor matrix), unless one imposes some restriction on the location of the reference frame. It has been shown that the initial reference frame and, consequently, the initial numerical values in the factor matrix are determined by the method of factoring which the author is free to choose to suit his convenience. If any particular method of factoring is specified in sufficient detail, then two authors would generally get the same numerical values in the factor matrix, but that sort of computing agreement is not of theoretical or scientific significance. If we impose the restrictions of simple structure on the reference frame and if such a frame can be found in any given test battery, then one can expect invariance of the numerical values in each row of the rotated factor matrix, even when a test is moved from one battery to another which also has a determinate simple structure in the same common factors. Other restrictions on the reference frame which give invariance of factorial composition of a test when it is moved from one battery to another can probably be found; but, so far, the simple-structure principle is the only restriction on the reference frame which has given this type of metric invariance.

A different type of factorial invariance appears in relation to the selection of subjects to whom a test battery is given. This is *configurational invariance*. The influence of selection on factorial results can be illustrated again with the boxes. The first diagram of *Figure 2* may represent the result of a factorial analysis of a set of measurements on a collection of boxes. The spherical triangle $XYZ$ represents the structure. The cosine of the angle

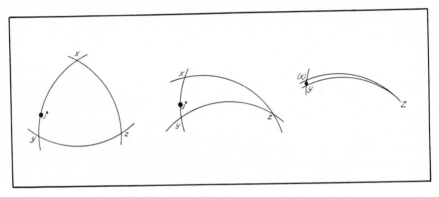

FIGURE 2

between the primary vectors $X$ and $Y$ is the correlation between the primary factors in the particular collection of boxes measured. A similar interpretation applies to the other two sides of the spherical triangle. Now suppose that the same set of measurements was made on another collection of boxes. Factorial analysis of the intercorrelations of measurements on the new box collection might give such a structure as is shown in the second diagram of *Figure 2*. Here the correlation between the two primary factors $X$ and $Y$ is much higher, as shown by the smaller angular separation between the two primary vectors in the second diagram. Both of the configurations are triangular because three primary factors are involved in both populations. The primary factors may be interpreted in the same way for the two populations, but their intercorrelations are different. This should not interfere seriously with the identification of each primary factor, which can be done independently for each analysis when the structure is overdetermined. It must be remembered that the identity of a factor, the box height, for example, is not affected by the fact that it correlates differently with other factors in different samples of boxes that may be chosen for measurement.

Confusion about this rather simple idea has been responsible for misinterpretation of factorial results.

In each of the two box collections the measurement $j$ was in both test batteries. In the first diagram of *Figure 2* one infers from the location of the measurement $j$ that it is a function of both $X$ and $Y$ and that it does not involve the parameter $Z$. Furthermore, the fact that the test vector $j$ is nearer $Y$ than $X$ makes it evident that the parameter $Y$ has greater influence on the variance of $j$ than does the parameter $X$. The score function $s_j$ might be some function like $(2y+x)$, which would lie closer to $Y$ than to $X$ because a greater part of the total variance of this score function would be attributable to $Y$ than to $X$. But notice also that the relative location of the measure $j$ is the same in the second diagram of *Figure 2*. This result is caused by the fact that, no matter what the correlation between the parameters $X$ and $Y$ happens to be in the particular population being analyzed, the score $j$ is a function of $X$ and $Y$ but not of the parameter $Z$. Hence it must lie in the side $XY$ of the spherical triangle. Furthermore, no matter what the correlation $r_{xy}$ happens to be, the score $j$ is closer to $Y$ than to $X$ because of the nature of the score function $s_j$. Here we have an example of *configurational invariance*. The factor loadings might change markedly from one population to another; but, if the same test battery is used on both populations, the configuration should be invariant. As a matter of fact, this is a far more important consideration in factor analysis than the invariance of the factor loadings. If the object is to identify a set of significant parameters for the description and understanding of a domain, it is more important to be able to make the identification as to the nature of the parameters than to ascertain that, in this particular collection of individuals that we happen to be studying, the correlations between the parameters have certain numerical values and that the saturations of some measure $j$ are such and such for this particular group of individuals. Later, when the nature of each primary factor becomes well understood, it may be a matter of great importance to ascertain the numerical values for particular groups of subjects in the form of practical norms and the like, but not at the exploratory stage of investigation for which factorial methods have been devised. At this stage we are groping for some set of concepts or parameters in terms of which the domain may be understood. The numerical values should then be regarded as being of three kinds, namely, those that are significantly positive, those that vanish or nearly vanish, and those that are significantly negative. Another way of stating the same idea is to point out that it is the *factor pattern* that is of importance rather than the *factor matrix* with its numerical entries. Configurational invariance can be represented algebraically by expressing the test vectors as linear combinations of the primary vectors. These relations will be described in *chapter xix*, with numerical examples of the results of univariate and multivariate selection in factor analysis.

Suppose, now, that a third collection of boxes is chosen for analysis, with the same set of measurements, and that all these boxes have the same height, $x$. The configuration would then collapse to the form shown in the third diagram of *Figure 2*. The factor $X$ disappears because it contributes nothing to the variances of the measurements, and the rank of the system is 2 instead of 3. The test vector $j$ is then identical with the parameter $Y$ because it is a function of $Y$. The contribution of $X$ is merely a constant in the score function with no contribution to the variance. The factor $X$ can hardly be expected to be identified when it is completely absent from the variances of the scores that are being analyzed. Of course, it does not follow that the factor $X$ is absent from the individual members of the population. It is equally present in all of them and therefore does not contribute to their individual differences.

Another case of factorial invariance is that in which two different test batteries are given to two populations. If the simple structures are complete in both batteries in the same common factors, factorial analyses should give the same configurations with different arrangements of the test vectors, unless some of these are common to the two batteries. The identification of the primary factors would be made independently for the two analyses, and it should generally be possible to identify the same primary factors in the two batteries, even if they have no tests in common. This type of result is the most convincing form of demonstration of the existence of primary mental abilities and their interpretation, especially if the factorial compositions of new tests are predicted at the time of their construction and later verified with factorial results. It is best in such studies to include several tests from previous studies as linkage, so as to make the demonstration of the identity and nature of the primary factors more convincing. It could happen in such studies that the new battery would reveal common factors not previously known. The result might be a reinterpretation of the older primary factors or the breakdown of a primary factor into several new primary factors. These results are dependent on the selection of test batteries, which are unlikely to be completely determinate for all the factors, especially in exploratory studies.*

One form of factorial invariance that has been legitimately demanded is that in which a small test battery is selected from a larger one that has been

---

* Some time ago the writer was disappointed to find that a certain new test, called "Designs," did not show large saturation on a certain perceptual factor which was the object of a factorial analysis. Later a possible explanation was found in the discovery of a new perceptual factor concerned with speed of closure. The old "Designs" test will be included in a study with other tests, such as the Gottschaldt Figures, in order to determine factorially whether this tentative explanation is sustained. If that is the case, then the interpretation of the perceptual closure factor can be made with a little more confidence. In this manner and as a result of a large amount of experimental work, we shall eventually know something about the mental faculties.

shown to have a complete simple structure. The analysis of the smaller battery could be made from a section of the larger correlation matrix. In such studies it should be expected that the smaller battery would show factorial invariance of the factor loadings if the smaller battery were selected so as to contain its own complete simple structure. If one of the hyperplanes is unstable in either the larger battery or the smaller one, or both, then factorial invariance cannot be expected, because there would then be no criterion for locating the reference frame which determines the numerical entries in the factor matrix.

## Rank order and the normalized scale

In most psychological tests the raw score is merely a numerical index of rank order. The reason for this interpretation of raw scores in psychological and educational tests is that there is no rational origin for the scale, and there is no defined unit of measurement which can in any fundamental sense be regarded as representing equal increments at the different parts of the scale. An exception is occasionally found in which all tests in a battery are scored in terms of time or of some natural spatial unit in which a rational origin can be used. The raw score interval from 20 to 30 points is not regarded as representing in any sense the same increment of ability or achievement as the interval from 80 to 90. The origin of the scale is quite arbitrary, being determined by the number of easy items, by the scoring formula which is more or less arbitrary, and by such arbitrary matters as the time limit. The increments at the different parts of a distribution can be modified to represent large or small increments in ability by the distribution of difficulty of the items selected for the test. The shape of a distribution of raw scores can be made normal or positively or negatively skewed, at will, by merely altering the time limits and the distribution of difficulty of the individual test items. Under these circumstances there is little justification for dealing with the raw scores as anything more than rank orders for the subjects in an experimental group.

The problem is sometimes raised as to whether the distribution of intelligence in the general population *is* normal, but such a question has little meaning unless it is modified. One can ask, for example, whether a scale exists such that the distributions of performances of successive age groups are normal on the same scale. That is the problem of absolute scaling, and it can be rather easily solved.* In dealing with the distribution of raw scores for a psychological test, one has the privilege of *defining* the scale so that a particular distribution of raw scores is normal, or one can define it so that the distribution takes any form one chooses. That is a question of definition. It is not a question of fact or a question to be determined experimentally.

* L. L. Thurstone, "A Method of Scaling Psychological and Educational Tests," *Journal of Educational Psychology*, Vol. XVI, No. 7 (October, 1925).

For example, an author has the privilege of defining his measure of stature as the logarithm of height in inches if he so chooses. The rank orders of his subjects remain the same. Similarly, one might decide to use the quartile range instead of the standard deviation as a measure of dispersion, or the co-efficient of alienation instead of the correlation coefficient. These are examples of monotonic functions.

If a transformation is made by which the distribution of raw scores becomes normal, then one has, in effect, merely altered the numerical values of the individual scores so as to retain the same rank order of the subjects. Such a scale is a monotonic function of the original raw scores. For any given frequency distribution of raw scores one could determine, by empirical curve-fitting, the monotonic function which transforms the given raw scores to a new set of scores for which the distribution is normal. This would be an awkward way to solve the problem. A simpler way is merely to tabulate the percentile ranks of the given raw scores and to assign to each raw score the standard score which corresponds to the percentile rank. This is determined directly from a probability table, such as the Kelley-Wood tables. The resulting scores are called *normalized standard scores* or simply *normalized scores*. They should not be confused with standard scores determined by a linear transformation, which represents merely a translation of the origin to the mean and a unit of measurement equal to the standard deviation of the distribution. This distribution of standard scores retains the shape of the original distribution of raw scores, whereas normalized scores give a normal distribution, no matter what the shape of the original distribution may be. In both cases the rank order of the subjects is retained.

It would be possible to carry out factor analysis with rank orders instead of scores, either the raw scores or the normalized scores. Such a procedure would probably be discouraged because, if the underlying distribution is assumed to be unimodal of any shape, then the rank orders in the middle range should represent smaller increments than the rank orders at the extremes of the distribution. Hence the procedure of using normalized scores in factoring is probably more appropriate than to use either rank orders or the arbitrary raw scores. These considerations make it a desirable practice to normalize the raw scores before the factor analysis is made.

The procedure of normalizing the raw scores before factoring introduces a form of invariance. All monotonic increasing functions of the raw scores retain the same rank order of the subjects. Hence *all monotonic increasing functions of the raw scores are factorially identical when the scores are normalized before factoring.* Empirical comparisons have been made between several methods of treating the original scores. These can be listed as follows:

1) Factoring the correlations obtained directly from the raw scores
2) Factoring the correlations of normalized scores

3) Factoring the correlations of new scores obtained with a separate arbitrary monotonic transformation for each test and without normalizing

4) Factoring the covariances of the raw scores

Comparisons of these different ways of treating the scores in factoring have shown that if the factor pattern is that of a complete simple structure, the different treatments of the scores in the factoring give essentially the same result. In general, the structure is retained in clearest form by the procedure of normalizing the raw scores before factoring, and that is the recommended procedure. The different treatments of the scores give different correlations or covariance entries in the correlation matrix, but the rotated factor matrix and the configuration determine whether the factorial results are the same.

## Invariance of factor loadings

A numerical example of the invariance of factor loadings will be described here. A later chapter will be devoted to the effects of selection on factorial results and to configurational invariance. In order to make this numerical example as concrete and direct as possible, it was designed as a three-dimensional box problem. Measurements of a random collection of thirty boxes were actually made in the Psychometric Laboratory and recorded for this numerical example. The three dimensions, $x$, $y$, and $z$, were recorded for each box. A list of 26 arbitrary score functions was then prepared. This is shown in the last column of *Table 2*, which shows, for example, that test 4 consisted of the area $xy$ of one side of the box.

The data were analyzed in several ways, but only the analysis for the normalized scores will be presented here. After the score functions had been computed for each of the thirty box shapes, the distributions were normalized so that normalized standard scores were used for the computation of correlation coefficients. The resulting correlations are shown in *Table 1*. It will be seen in the table of correlations that several pairs of columns are identical except for sign. This is the result of normalizing. For example, columns 15 and 16 in the correlation matrix are identical. Test 15 was defined as $x/z$, while test 16 was defined as $z/x$. The rank orders for these two formulae are identical except for direction, and consequently the correlations are identical except for sign. In the same way the score functions $x$ and $x^2$ would have been identical in the correlation if $x^2$ had been included in the battery.

The correlation matrix was factored by the group centroid method, and the resulting factor matrix is shown in *Table 2*. The last column of the factor matrix shows the communalities. A frequency distribution of the third-factor residuals is shown in *Table 3*, and it is seen that the average of the

## Table 1
### Correlation Matrix

| | 1 | 2 | 3 | 4 | 5 | 6 | 7 | 8 | 9 | 10 | 11 | 12 | 13 | 14 | 15 | 16 | 17 | 18 | 19 | 20 | 21 | 22 | 23 | 24 | 25 | 26 |
|---|---|---|---|---|---|---|---|---|---|---|---|---|---|---|---|---|---|---|---|---|---|---|---|---|---|---|
| 1 | | .24 | .26 | .75 | .76 | .26 | .90 | .55 | .89 | .61 | .24 | .26 | .59 | .59 | .59 | .59 | −.06 | .06 | .67 | .72 | .28 | .66 | .69 | .29 | .66 | .56 |
| 2 | | | .35 | .77 | .37 | .79 | .59 | .92 | .33 | .35 | .89 | .67 | −.60 | .60 | −.03 | .03 | .56 | .56 | .82 | .35 | .80 | .82 | .34 | .80 | .73 | .75 |
| 3 | | | | .38 | .80 | .82 | .37 | .40 | .63 | .90 | .68 | .91 | −.05 | .05 | −.58 | .58 | .52 | .52 | .36 | .81 | .82 | .37 | .81 | .79 | .74 | .74 |
| 4 | | | | | .67 | .67 | .95 | .93 | .73 | .56 | .72 | .58 | −.07 | .07 | −.35 | .35 | .38 | .38 | .97 | .64 | .68 | .95 | .62 | .68 | .87 | .83 |
| 5 | | | | | | .69 | .77 | .58 | .95 | .97 | .59 | .75 | .34 | .34 | .03 | .03 | .40 | .40 | .61 | .99 | .69 | .61 | .95 | .68 | .87 | .80 |
| 6 | | | | | | | .54 | .77 | .54 | .74 | .96 | .97 | −.43 | .43 | .42 | .42 | .02 | .02 | .68 | .69 | .99 | .68 | .68 | .97 | .88 | .90 |
| 7 | | | | | | | | .83 | .86 | .63 | .57 | .49 | .22 | .22 | .17 | .17 | .19 | .19 | .89 | .73 | .55 | .87 | .71 | .55 | .84 | .76 |
| 8 | | | | | | | | | .59 | .49 | .86 | .66 | .33 | .33 | −.21 | .21 | .47 | .47 | .93 | .54 | .78 | .91 | .52 | .78 | .85 | .81 |
| 9 | | | | | | | | | | .87 | .47 | .58 | .47 | .47 | .24 | .24 | .30 | .30 | .67 | .93 | .55 | .65 | .89 | .73 | .82 | .73 |
| 10 | | | | | | | | | | | .61 | .83 | .24 | .24 | .31 | .31 | .50 | .50 | .52 | .97 | .74 | .52 | .95 | .54 | .84 | .80 |
| 11 | | | | | | | | | | | | .90 | −.53 | .53 | .50 | .50 | .23 | .23 | .59 | .58 | .96 | .73 | .74 | .73 | .85 | .86 |
| 12 | | | | | | | | | | | | | .32 | .32 | .47 | .47 | .17 | .17 | .74 | .75 | .96 | .75 | .73 | .94 | .86 | .86 |
| 13 | | | | | | | | | | | | | | −1.00 | 1.00 | 1.00 | .57 | .57 | .16 | .33 | .42 | .15 | .30 | .93 | −.06 | .15 |
| 14 | | | | | | | | | | | | | | | .47 | .47 | .57 | .57 | .16 | .33 | .42 | .15 | .30 | −.40 | .06 | .15 |
| 15 | | | | | | | | | | | | | | | | 1.00 | .43 | .43 | .28 | .08 | .40 | .27 | −.09 | −.37 | −.06 | .12 |
| 16 | | | | | | | | | | | | | | | | | .43 | .43 | .28 | .08 | .40 | .27 | −.09 | −.37 | −.06 | .12 |
| 17 | | | | | | | | | | | | | | | | | | 1.00 | .43 | .44 | .03 | .42 | .42 | −.05 | −.03 | .04 |
| 18 | | | | | | | | | | | | | | | | | | | .43 | .44 | .03 | .42 | .42 | −.05 | −.03 | .04 |
| 19 | | | | | | | | | | | | | | | | | | | | .58 | .69 | .99 | .57 | .70 | .85 | .84 |
| 20 | | | | | | | | | | | | | | | | | | | | | .69 | .58 | .69 | .68 | .85 | .81 |
| 21 | | | | | | | | | | | | | | | | | | | | | | .69 | .69 | .69 | .88 | .91 |
| 22 | | | | | | | | | | | | | | | | | | | | | | | .56 | .57 | .85 | .86 |
| 23 | | | | | | | | | | | | | | | | | | | | | | | | .68 | .84 | .81 |
| 24 | | | | | | | | | | | | | | | | | | | | | | | | | .87 | .91 |
| 25 | | | | | | | | | | | | | | | | | | | | | | | | | | .96 |
| 26 | | | | | | | | | | | | | | | | | | | | | | | | | | |

absolute values of the residuals was .0116, which hardly justifies extracting another factor. The fact that the three factors were sufficient to account for the intercorrelations agrees with the fact that three parameters, $x$, $y$, and $z$, were used in writing the 26 score functions of this battery.

*Table 2*

Group Centroid Factor Matrix

| | I | II | III | $h^2$ |
|---|---|---|---|---|
| 1 | .65 | −.67 | .33 | .98 |
| 2 | .74 | .53 | .37 | .97 |
| 3 | .75 | .06 | −.64 | .98 |
| 4 | .87 | −.04 | .48 | .99 |
| 5 | .88 | −.40 | −.24 | .99 |
| 6 | .89 | .41 | −.20 | 1.00 |
| 7 | .84 | −.35 | .43 | 1.00 |
| 8 | .86 | .22 | .43 | .97 |
| 9 | .83 | −.55 | −.03 | .99 |
| 10 | .85 | −.26 | −.44 | .98 |
| 11 | .86 | .49 | −.01 | .98 |
| 12 | .87 | .29 | −.38 | .98 |
| 13 | −.07 | −.98 | −.09 | .97 |
| 14 | .07 | .98 | .09 | .97 |
| 15 | −.05 | −.55 | .80 | .99 |
| 16 | .05 | .55 | −.80 | .99 |
| 17 | .00 | .49 | .85 | .96 |
| 18 | .00 | −.49 | −.85 | .96 |
| 19 | .86 | .05 | .48 | .97 |
| 20 | .87 | −.39 | −.32 | 1.00 |
| 21 | .90 | .40 | −.19 | 1.00 |
| 22 | .85 | .05 | .47 | .94 |
| 23 | .86 | −.34 | −.32 | .96 |
| 24 | .89 | .39 | −.16 | .97 |
| 25 | .99 | −.01 | .01 | .98 |
| 26 | .96 | .10 | −.02 | .93 |

Factor Matrix after Rotation

| X | Y | Z | Variable |
|---|---|---|---|
| ·95 | .01 | .01 | $x$ |
| .02 | .92 | .01 | $y$ |
| .02 | .05 | .91 | $z$ |
| .59 | .64 | −.03 | $xy$ |
| .60 | .00 | .62 | $xz$ |
| −.04 | .60 | .58 | $yz$ |
| .81 | .38 | .01 | $x^2y$ |
| .35 | .79 | .01 | $xy^2$ |
| .79 | −.01 | .41 | $x^2z$ |
| .40 | −.02 | .79 | $xz^2$ |
| −.04 | .74 | .40 | $y^2z$ |
| .02 | .41 | .74 | $yz^2$ |
| .74 | −.77 | .06 | $x/y$ |
| −.74 | .77 | −.06 | $y/x$ |
| .74 | .02 | −.73 | $x/z$ |
| −.74 | −.02 | .73 | $z/x$ |
| −.07 | .80 | −.76 | $y/z$ |
| .07 | −.80 | .76 | $z/y$ |
| .51 | .70 | −.03 | $2x+2y$ |
| .56 | −.04 | .69 | $2x+2z$ |
| −.02 | .60 | .58 | $2y+2z$ |
| .50 | .69 | −.03 | $\sqrt{x^2+y^2}$ |
| .52 | −.01 | .68 | $\sqrt{x^2+z^2}$ |
| −.01 | .60 | .55 | $\sqrt{y^2+z^2}$ |
| .43 | .46 | .45 | $xyz$ |
| .31 | .51 | .46 | $\sqrt{x^2+y^2+z^2}$ |

*Table 3*

Third-Factor Residuals

| $\rho$ | $f$ |
|---|---|
| .05 | 1 |
| .04 | 4 |
| .03 | 9 |
| .02 | 37 |
| .01 | 75 |
| .00 | 84 |
| −.01 | 70 |
| −.02 | 30 |
| −.03 | 12 |
| −.04 | 2 |
| −.05 | |
| −.06 | 1 |

$$\frac{\Sigma|\rho|}{N} = .0116$$

The method of extended vectors was applied to the factor matrix of *Table 2*, and the resulting diagram is shown in *Figure 3*. The three planes are here immediately evident. All the points lie on or close to the sides of the triangle, except *25* and *26*. Referring to the list of score functions in *Table 2*, we see that these two test measures were the volume and the main diagonal of the box, respectively. Both of these measures are functions of all three of the parameters, and consequently the two points *25* and *26* should lie inside the configuration. Hence they do not contribute to the location of the coordinate planes of the simple structure. The list of score functions was so

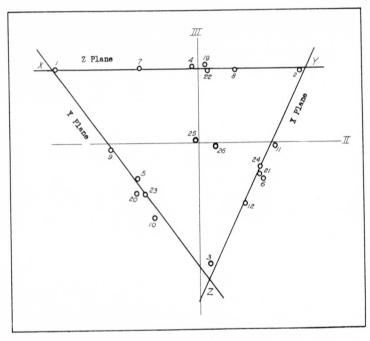

FIGURE 3

designed that most of the scores were functions of one or two parameters and only two of the scores were functions of all three of the parameters. Hence a simple structure was incorporated in the test battery. This is represented by the fact that all but two of the scores defined the triangular configuration of *Figure 3*. By the method of extended vectors the transformation Λ was determined, and the factor matrix after rotation is shown in *Table 2*. Diagrams for the two-dimensional sections are shown in *Figure 4*.

In *Table 4* we have the correlations of the three primary factors, $x$, $y$, and $z$, as determined from the battery of 26 measures. In the same table we have the correlations of the original dimensions of the thirty box shapes. The two sets of correlations agree closely.

When this analysis had been completed, a subbattery of 11 measures was selected from the longer list of 26 measures. The smaller list of 11 measures was made with the restriction that it should be balanced quite differently from the larger battery. The larger battery was equally balanced as to the three primary factors, $x$, $y$, and $z$. For the purpose of this demonstration the smaller battery was selected so as to contain a relatively large number of

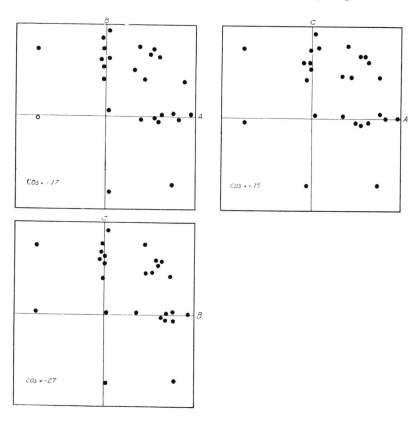

tests involving the primary factor $y$ and only a few tests of the other two factors. The second battery was also selected with the restriction that the simple structure should be complete and determinate. This selection could be easily made from the diagram of *Figure 3*. The smaller battery was then independently analyzed.

The smaller battery is shown in *Table 5*. The correlations were taken from the larger correlation matrix of *Table 1*. The group centroid method of factoring was used, but any appropriate factorial method could have been used. The mean absolute value of the third-factor residuals was .015, which

## Table 4

### Correlations between Primary Factors

|   | X | Y | Z |
|---|---|---|---|
| X | 1.00 | .22 | .21 |
| Y | .22 | 1.00 | .30 |
| Z | .21 | .30 | 1.00 |

|   | X | Y | Z |
|---|---|---|---|
| X | 1.00 | .26 | .23 |
| Y | .26 | 1.00 | .30 |
| Z | .23 | .30 | 1.00 |

## Table 5

| | Group Centroid Factor Matrix | | | | | Factor Matrix after Rotation | | |
|---|---|---|---|---|---|---|---|---|
| | I | II | III | $h^2$ | | X | Y | Z |
| 1 | .70 | −.26 | .58 | .90 | | .90 | .05 | .00 |
| 2 | .78 | −.12 | −.55 | .92 | | .04 | .88 | .01 |
| 3 | .61 | .66 | .03 | .81 | | .03 | .05 | .79 |
| 4 | .95 | −.31 | .01 | 1.00 | | .62 | .63 | −.06 |
| 6 | .82 | .43 | −.36 | .98 | | −.05 | .54 | .57 |
| 7 | .91 | −.29 | .32 | 1.00 | | .82 | .37 | −.01 |
| 8 | .92 | −.18 | −.26 | .95 | | .35 | .76 | .02 |
| 19 | .94 | −.32 | −.11 | .99 | | .53 | .71 | −.09 |
| 22 | .93 | −.31 | −.12 | .97 | | .52 | .71 | −.08 |
| 23 | .77 | .42 | .44 | .96 | | .52 | −.07 | .65 |
| 25 | .97 | .19 | .03 | .98 | | .42 | .43 | .43 |

## Table 6

### Correlation between Primary Factors

|   | X | Y | Z |
|---|---|---|---|
| X | 1.00 | .18 | .26 |
| Y | .18 | 1.00 | .37 |
| Z | .26 | .37 | 1.00 |

did not justify extraction of a fourth factor. The method of extended vectors was used in the centroid matrix of *Table 5*, and the resulting diagram is shown in *Figure 5*. The corresponding factor matrix after rotation is shown in the second part of *Table 5*. The figure and the rotated factor matrix show that a simple structure is present in the smaller battery, as was to be expected. The correlations between the three primary factors determined by

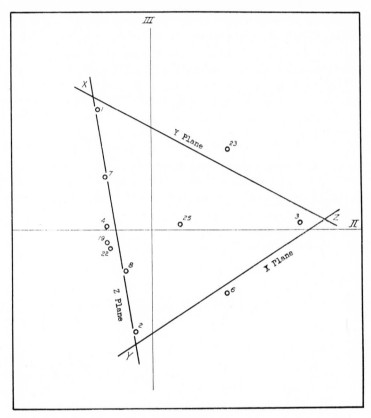

FIGURE 5

the smaller battery are shown in *Table 6*. The several tables can be seen to be very similar.

The invariance of the factor loadings can be seen by direct comparison of the factor matrices after rotation in *Tables 2* and *5*. It will be seen that the factor loadings for the overlapping tests are very similar. This numerical example should serve to illustrate the principle that the factorial composition of a test is invariant when it is moved from one test battery to another battery if the simple structure is determinate in both batteries. The invariance is independent of the proportions of tests which are heavily saturated with each primary factor, so long as the structure is defined in the same common factors.

A distinction must be observed in the discussion of factorial invariance between the characteristics of factorial methods and the characteristics of the data to be analyzed. In setting up a criterion for what is to constitute an acceptable factorial method, the chief concern is to insure that the method is adequate to discover what is determinate in the data. Factorial method has not been designed to guarantee the discovery of factors which are indeterminate in the data. If the purpose of a factorial investigation is to study a particular domain or a particular primary factor, then the test battery should be designed to fit a crucial experiment for the hypotheses to be examined. The investigator must use his ingenuity in covering the domain so as to make the structure determinate. Too often, factorial studies seem to be made on correlation matrices which just happen to be available, without reference to the likelihood that they will produce significant results. Occasionally, such studies do produce interesting findings, but it is safe to say that every such exploratory study will indicate the necessity for additional studies of test batteries specially designed to test the hypotheses that may appear in the exploratory study regarding the nature of the underlying parameters or factors.

# CHAPTER XVII

## ALTERNATIVE METHODS OF ROTATION

### The problem of finding an analytical criterion for the reference frame

The methods of locating a reference frame for a simple structure that have been described have all been graphical, and they have all depended on the selection of a subgroup of test vectors for defining each hyperplane. The graphical solutions in $n$-dimensional space are generally slow, and they require a considerable amount of labor. Ever since the simple-structure solution was found for the problem of locating a reference frame, there have been many attempts to arrive at the solution without the graphical procedures. Scores of proposed solutions have been tried on a variety of factorial problems, but, with a few exceptions, they have not been published. None of them, so far, has entirely satisfied the desire to find a routine method which can be applied to a set of data without calling for any judgment on the part of the computer. In this chapter we shall describe several procedures for locating the simple structure when it exists in the test battery. They all require considerably less labor than the graphical methods. They are not entirely automatic, in that one cannot do the computations blindfolded, as it were; but they are in some degree successful, in that a considerable portion of the work is done without plotting graphs. In fact, only a few graphs need be plotted, in comparison with either the method of two-dimensional sections or the method of extended vectors, which is really a method of taking three-dimensional sections. In the final acceptance or rejection of a simple-structure solution it is still the appearance of a set of graphs that determines the answer.

The problem of finding an analytical solution, for which many attempts have been made, can be briefly stated as follows: Let it be assumed that the correlation matrix has been factored so that a factor matrix of $r$ columns is available. Let it be assumed, further, that a simple structure exists in the test battery. It would be desirable to be able to write explicitly the direction cosines of the transformation $\Lambda$ in terms of the factor loadings and to be able to solve for this transformation directly.

The methods that have been tried consist generally of writing some function $\phi$ of the factor loadings and of the direction cosines of the transformation matrix $\Lambda$, which is to be maximized or minimized at the desired solution for each column of $\Lambda$. In effect, this general procedure consists in defining a subgroup of test vectors whose projections on one of the reference axes are to be minimized. These are the tests which have vanishing projections in a column of the oblique factor matrix $V$. Since the ideal solution is oblique, the solution for each reference vector is independent of the solutions for the other reference vectors. The choice of a subgroup for defining each hyperplane is usually done graphically, but this work can be done, at least in part, without graphical aid.

In practical work there frequently arise various forms of ambiguities that cannot be resolved by statistical methods if the structure is incomplete. Since it happens not infrequently that the structure of a test battery is unstable in one or more dimensions or else indeterminate as to the exact relation of one or more factors to the test battery, it is best for the author to present a set of primary axes as his interpretation of the data. Such interpretation can later be revised in the light of further information about the factors that appeared unstable in the initial studies. In some factorial problems the structure is complete and so convincing that it leaves little room for doubt in the location of the reference frame. It is for such test batteries that it would be useful to have a completely objective analytical procedure for locating the reference frame.

### A successive approximation method of rotation

The theory of the method will be given first, after which numerical examples will be given. In using this method one starts with a trial reference vector that will be denoted $\Lambda_q$ as in *Figure 1*. The projection of each test vector $j$ on the trial vector $\Lambda_q$ is computed. It is the scalar product $J\Lambda_q = v_{jq}$. These projections constitute, in a sense, a trial column of the oblique factor matrix $V$. A frequency distribution is made of the values of $v_{jq}$. A subgroup of tests is selected from this distribution whose projections on a new trial reference vector are to be minimized. In selecting a subgroup, one may take all tests whose projections are in a range of, say, $\pm.30$ or $\pm.20$, if a positive manifold is not to be imposed on the simple structure. If it is assumed that a positive simple structure exists, then a subgroup is selected which includes all negative projections, so that the range chosen would be, say, $+.30$ to $-1.00$.

The first trial vector may be selected by inspection of the correlation matrix. One selects a test whose correlations with the other tests satisfy two criteria, namely, (1) that its range of correlations is relatively large in comparison with those of other tests and (2) that there is an appreciable number of small projections $v_{jq}$ relative to those of other tests in the battery. Another good method of selecting trial reference vectors is to choose those tests which have highest projections on the centroid axes, although this method does not give a good choice with the first centroid axis. In *Table 1* we have a correlation matrix of seventeen tests, selected from one of the box problems, as an example. Inspection of the columns of that correlation matrix indicates that tests 1, 2, and 3 should be suitable trial vectors.

We choose one of these and normalize the test vector so that it is of unit length. This is the first trial vector $\Lambda_q$, which is shown in *Figure 1*.

In denoting the successive adjustments of a reference vector, we shall call its initial position $\Lambda_0$. After the first adjustment it will be denoted $\Lambda_1$, after the second adjustment $\Lambda_2$, and so on. In the computations for any one adjustment, the given position of a reference vector will be called $\Lambda_q$, and the

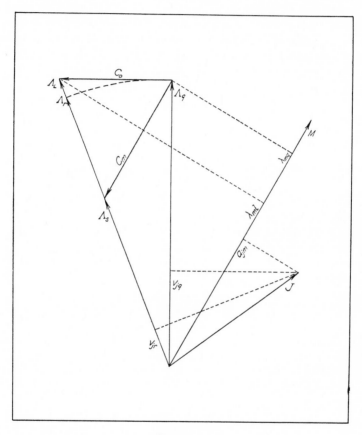

FIGURE 1

new position will be denoted $\Lambda_p$, which becomes $\Lambda_q$ for the next adjustment, and so on until a satisfactory solution has been found.

A correction vector $C_0$ is to be found, which is orthogonal to $\Lambda_q$, as shown in *Figure 1*. One such correction vector is found for each of the planes determined by the trial vector $\Lambda_q$ and one of the fixed orthogonal axes $M$ of the frame, defined by the given factor matrix. Hence there will be $r$ correction vectors $C_0$ to be determined in a common-factor space of $r$ dimensions. Let the unit vector $M$ in the figure be one of the centroid axes or one of the axes defined by factoring the correlation matrix. It is here drawn oblique to $\Lambda_q$ because, in general, the trial vector $\Lambda_q$ is oblique to the centroid axes. The projection of $\Lambda_q$ on $M$ is $\lambda_{mq}$, which is one of the $r$ direction cosines of $\Lambda_q$. *Figure 1* has been drawn to represent only one correction vector $C_0$ in the plane of $\Lambda_q$ and one of the fixed orthogonal axes $M$. Then

$$(1) \qquad \Lambda_q M = \lambda_{mq} .$$

In this discussion, vectors will be denoted by capital letters and scalars by lower-case letters except for the test vectors which have been discussed in other chapters with the notation $j$. Let $J$ be the projection of a test vector

*Table 1*

*Correlation Matrix*

| | 1 | 2 | 3 | 4 | 5 | 6 | 7 | 8 | 9 | 10 | 11 | 12 | 22 | 23 | 24 | 25 | 26 |
|---|---|---|---|---|---|---|---|---|---|---|---|---|---|---|---|---|---|
| 1 | | .24 | .26 | .75 | .76 | .26 | .90 | .55 | .89 | .61 | .24 | .26 | .66 | .69 | .29 | .66 | .56 |
| 2 | .24 | | .35 | .77 | .37 | .79 | .59 | .92 | .33 | .35 | .89 | .67 | .82 | .34 | .80 | .73 | .75 |
| 3 | .26 | .35 | | .38 | .80 | .82 | .37 | .40 | .63 | .90 | .68 | .91 | .37 | .81 | .79 | .74 | .74 |
| 4 | .75 | .77 | .38 | | .67 | .67 | .95 | .93 | .73 | .56 | .72 | .58 | .95 | .62 | .68 | .87 | .83 |
| 5 | .76 | .37 | .80 | .67 | | .69 | .77 | .58 | .95 | .97 | .59 | .75 | .61 | .95 | .68 | .87 | .80 |
| 6 | .26 | .79 | .82 | .67 | .69 | | .54 | .77 | .54 | .74 | .96 | .97 | .68 | .68 | .97 | .88 | .90 |
| 7 | .90 | .59 | .37 | .95 | .77 | .54 | | .83 | .86 | .63 | .57 | .49 | .87 | .71 | .55 | .84 | .76 |
| 8 | .55 | .92 | .40 | .93 | .58 | .77 | .83 | | .59 | .49 | .86 | .66 | .91 | .52 | .78 | .85 | .81 |
| 9 | .89 | .33 | .63 | .73 | .95 | .54 | .86 | .59 | | .87 | .47 | .58 | .65 | .89 | .54 | .82 | .73 |
| 10 | .61 | .35 | .90 | .56 | .97 | .74 | .63 | .49 | .87 | | .61 | .83 | .52 | .95 | .73 | .84 | .80 |
| 11 | .24 | .89 | .68 | .72 | .59 | .96 | .57 | .86 | .47 | .61 | | .90 | .73 | .58 | .94 | .85 | .86 |
| 12 | .26 | .67 | .91 | .58 | .75 | .97 | .49 | .66 | .58 | .83 | .90 | | .60 | .74 | .93 | .86 | .86 |
| 22 | .66 | .82 | .37 | .95 | .61 | .68 | .87 | .91 | .65 | .52 | .73 | .60 | | .56 | .70 | .85 | .86 |
| 23 | .69 | .34 | .81 | .62 | .95 | .68 | .71 | .52 | .89 | .95 | .58 | .74 | .56 | | .68 | .84 | .81 |
| 24 | .29 | .80 | .79 | .68 | .68 | .97 | .55 | .78 | .54 | .73 | .94 | .93 | .70 | .68 | | .87 | .91 |
| 25 | .66 | .73 | .74 | .87 | .87 | .88 | .84 | .85 | .82 | .84 | .85 | .86 | .85 | .84 | .87 | | .96 |
| 26 | .56 | .75 | .74 | .83 | .80 | .90 | .76 | .81 | .73 | .80 | .86 | .86 | .86 | .81 | .91 | .96 | |

$j$ on the plane of $\Lambda_q$ and $M$, the plane of the figure. The projection of $j$ on $M$ is $a_{jm}$, which is a cell entry in the given factor matrix $F$. Then, since $M$ is a unit vector,

$$(2) \qquad MJ = a_{jm} .$$

The projection of $j$ on $\Lambda_q$ is $v_{jq}$, one of the projections to be minimized by an adjustment in the position of the reference vector. Then, since $\Lambda_q$ is also a unit vector,

$$(3) \qquad J\Lambda_q = v_{jq} .$$

Applying the orthogonal correction vector $C_0$ to $\Lambda_q$ in the plane of $\Lambda_q$ and $M$, we have the long reference vector $\Lambda_L$, namely,

$$(4) \qquad \Lambda_q + C_0 = \Lambda_L .$$

The direction of $\Lambda_L$ can also be defined conveniently by a correction vector, $C_m$, which is collinear with $M$.* Let

$$(5) \qquad\qquad C_m = -sM .$$

Then

$$(6) \qquad\qquad \Lambda_s = \Lambda_q + C_m ,$$

where $\Lambda_s$ is collinear with $\Lambda_L$. We can write

$$(7) \qquad\qquad \Lambda_r = t\Lambda_s ,$$

where $\Lambda_r$ is a unit reference vector and $t$ is a stretching factor.

The projection of the test vector $j$ on the unit reference vector $\Lambda_r$ is $v_{jr}$. It is the scalar product

$$(8) \qquad\qquad J\Lambda_r = v_{jr} .$$

The length of the correction vector $C_m$ is to be determined so that the projections $v_{jr}$ of the tests in the selected subgroup are minimized. Substituting (7) in (8), we obtain

$$(9) \qquad\qquad tJ\Lambda_s = v_{jr} ,$$

and, by (6),

$$(10) \qquad\qquad tJ(\Lambda_q + C_m) = v_{jr} .$$

By (5)

$$(11) \qquad\qquad tJ(\Lambda_q - sM) = v_{jr} ,$$

which becomes

$$(12) \qquad\qquad tJ\Lambda_q - tsJM = v_{jr} .$$

By (2) and (3),

$$(13) \qquad\qquad tv_{jq} - tsa_{jm} = v_{jr} .$$

The problem now is to find the length $s$ of the vector $C_m$ so as to minimize the projections $v_{jr}$. Squaring both sides of (13), we get

$$(14) \qquad\qquad t^2 v_{jq}^2 - 2t^2 s v_{jq} a_{jm} + t^2 s^2 a_{jm}^2 = v_{jr}^2 .$$

---

* The vector $\Lambda_L$ is here defined with only one correction vector, $C_0$. It will later be defined with $r$ such correction vectors, one for each centroid axis $M$.

Summing for all tests in the selected subgroup, we have

$$(15) \qquad t^2 \sum_j v_{jq}^2 - 2t^2 s \sum_j v_{jq} a_{jm} + t^2 s^2 \sum_j a^2_m = \sum_j v_{jr}^2 \equiv u \,.$$

Writing the partial derivative of $u$ with respect to $s$ and setting it equal to zero, we obtain

$$(16) \qquad -2t^2 \sum v_{jq} a_{jm} + 2t^2 s \sum_j a_{jm}^2 = 0 \,,$$

from which

$$(17) \qquad s = \frac{\displaystyle\sum_j v_{jq} a_{jm}}{\displaystyle\sum a_{jm}^2} \,.$$

The values of $a_{jm}$ are known in the given factor matrix $F$, and the values of $v_{jq}$ are known, since they are the projections of the test vectors in the subgroup on the first trial reference vector $\Lambda_q$. Hence the length $s$ of the correction vector $C_m$ is known and also the direction of the vector $\Lambda_r$.

If the given projections $v_{jq}$ and $a_{jm}$ are plotted on rectangular cross-section paper with the axes $\Lambda_q$ and $M$, drawn at right angles, the termini of the test vectors $j$ will be represented by points. On such a graph the location of $\Lambda_r$ can be drawn so as to minimize the projections $v_{jr}$. The best-fitting line through the points, by the method of least squares, will be orthogonal to $\Lambda_r$ through the origin. The slope of the best-fitting line is $s$, which is also the length of the vector $C_m$, by which the projections of the test vectors in the subgroup on the vector $\Lambda_r$ are minimized.

With the $r$ correction vectors $C_m$ known, we proceed to add them to $\Lambda_q$ and thereby determine a vector to be denoted $\Lambda_u$, which, when normalized, becomes the new unit reference vector $\Lambda_p$. The vector $\Lambda_L$ is defined by the equation

$$(18) \qquad \Lambda_L = k\Lambda_s \,,$$

where $k$ is a stretching factor by which $k\Lambda_s$ has unit projection on $\Lambda_q$. By (5) and (6) we have

$$(19) \qquad k(\Lambda_q - sM) = \Lambda_L \,.$$

Since $\Lambda_L$ has unit projection on $\Lambda_q$ and since $\Lambda_q$ is a unit vector, we have

$$(20) \qquad \Lambda_L \Lambda_q = 1 \,,$$

or, by (19) and (20),

(21) $$k(\Lambda_q - sM)\Lambda_q = 1 \, ,$$

which becomes

(22) $$k\Lambda_q^2 - ksM\Lambda_q = 1 \, .$$

By (1), and since $\Lambda_q^2 = 1$, we get

(23) $$k - ks\lambda_{mq} = 1 \, ,$$

so that

(24) $$k = \frac{1}{1 - s\lambda_{mq}} \, .$$

One of the direction numbers of $\Lambda_L$ is represented in *Figure 1* by the projection of $\Lambda_L$ on $M$. This is $\lambda_{ml}$. The value of $\lambda_{ml}$ can be written

(25) $$\Lambda_L M = \lambda_{ml} \, .$$

By (19) and (25) we have

(26) $$k(\Lambda_q - sM)M = \lambda_{ml} \, ,$$

or

(27) $$k\Lambda_q M - ksM^2 = \lambda_{ml} \, ;$$

and by (1) this becomes

(28) $$k(\lambda_{mq} - s) = \lambda_{ml} \, .$$

Substituting (24) in (28), we get

(29) $$\lambda_{ml} = \frac{\lambda_{mq} - s}{1 - s\lambda_{mq}} \, ,$$

which determines the direction numbers $\lambda_{ml}$. Equation (29) is evaluated. separately for each of the $r$ direction numbers $\lambda_{ml}$ of $\Lambda_L$. The direction cosines $\lambda_{mq}$ of the trial reference vector $\Lambda_q$ are known, and the vector length $s$ of $C_m$ is determined by (17) for each of the $r$ columns of the factor matrix $F$.

When the direction numbers $\lambda_{ml}$ of $\Lambda_L$ have been computed, this vector can be normalized to unit length, and it can then be used as a new trial reference vector $\Lambda_t$. Its direction cosines are then given by

$$(30) \qquad \lambda_{mt} = \frac{1}{\sqrt{\sum_m \lambda_{ml}^2}} \, .$$

It has been found that this method of locating the co-ordinate hyperplanes is more rapidly convergent if the vector $\Lambda_t$ is adjusted so as to be orthogonal to the centroid vector $\Lambda_c$ of the subgroup $s$. The adjustment can be made on the vector $\Lambda_t$ in the plane of $\Lambda_t$ and $\Lambda_c$ so that its adjusted position $\Lambda_u$ is orthogonal to $\Lambda_c$. The adjustment vector may be denoted $E$, so that

$$(31) \qquad \Lambda_t + E = \Lambda_u \, ;$$

and, since $\Lambda_u$ is orthogonal to $\Lambda_c$, we have

$$(32) \qquad \Lambda_u \Lambda_c = 0 \, .$$

By (31) we have

$$(33) \qquad (\Lambda_t + E)\Lambda_c = 0 \, .$$

The adjustment vector $E$ can be written as a fraction of $\Lambda_c$, so that

$$(34) \qquad E = b\Lambda_c \, ,$$

where $b$ is a scalar. Then

$$(35) \qquad (\Lambda_t + b\Lambda_c)\Lambda_c = 0 \, ,$$

or

$$(36) \qquad \Lambda_t \Lambda_c + b\Lambda_c^2 = 0 \, ,$$

so that

$$(37) \qquad b = -\frac{\Lambda_t \Lambda_c}{\Lambda_c^2} \, .$$

Then, with $b$ known, we can write, from (31), (34), and (35),

$$(38) \qquad \Lambda_u = \Lambda_t - \frac{\Lambda_t \Lambda_c}{\Lambda_c^2} \Lambda_c \, ,$$

which defines the vector $\Lambda_u$.

Equation (38) can be written in terms of the $r$ components of $\Lambda_u$. We then have

$$(39) \qquad \lambda_{mu} = \lambda_{ml} - \frac{\displaystyle\sum_m \lambda_{ml}\lambda_{mc}}{\displaystyle\sum_m \lambda_{mc}^2}\, \lambda_{mc} ,$$

where $\lambda_{mu}$ are the direction numbers of $\Lambda_u$, and $\lambda_{mc}$ are the direction numbers of the centroid vector $\Lambda_c$. The components of $\Lambda_c$ can be determined from simple summation in the factor matrix $F$ over the subgroup $s$. We then have

$$(40) \qquad \lambda_{mc} = \sum_s a_{sm} ,$$

which may be denoted briefly $\displaystyle\sum_s a$ on the computing forms.

The scalar product $\Lambda_t\Lambda_c$ can be written in summational notation as

$$(41) \qquad \Lambda_t\Lambda_c = \sum_m \lambda_{ml}\lambda_{mc} ,$$

and the denominator $\Lambda_c^2$ can be similarly written as

$$(42) \qquad \Lambda_c^2 = \sum_m \lambda_{mc}^2 = \sum_m \left(\sum_s a_{sm}\right)^2 .$$

If we let

$$(43) \qquad b = \frac{\Lambda_t\Lambda_c}{\Lambda_c^2} ,$$

we can write the computing formula as

$$(44) \qquad \lambda_{mu} = \lambda_{ml} - b\lambda_{mc} .$$

When the vector $\Lambda_u$ has been determined, it is normalized and then becomes the new reference vector $\Lambda_p$. If this unit reference vector is to be adjusted again, it becomes the starting-point, $\Lambda_q$, for the next trial.

This method is simple as to the numerical work, which can be easily done by a clerk without instruction in factorial theory. The computational work will now be illustrated by numerical examples.

*Numerical example No. 1.*

For the numerical example of this method of locating the co-ordinate hyperplanes of a simple structure we shall use a seventeen-variable box problem selected from the numerical example of the previous chapter. This battery represents a three-factor positive structure. The correlation coefficients are shown in *Table 1*. A corresponding factor matrix *F* is shown in *Table 2*. The computations are shown here without the summational checks which are essential in practical work.

In *Table 3* we have the same factor matrix recorded with only the first digit. It is used in some of the cross products in order to simplify the com-

| | Table 2 | | | | Table 3 | | |
|---|---|---|---|---|---|---|---|
| | *Factor Matrix* F | | | | *Factor Matrix* $F_1$ *(One Decimal)* | | |
| | I | II | III | | I | II | III |
| 1 | .65 | −.67 | .33 | 1 | .6 | −.6 | .3 |
| 2 | .74 | .53 | .37 | 2 | .7 | .5 | .3 |
| 3 | .75 | .06 | −.64 | 3 | .7 | .0 | −.6 |
| 4 | .87 | −.04 | .48 | 4 | .8 | .0 | .4 |
| 5 | .88 | −.40 | −.24 | 5 | .8 | −.4 | −.2 |
| 6 | .89 | .41 | −.20 | 6 | .8 | .4 | −.2 |
| 7 | .84 | −.35 | .43 | 7 | .8 | −.3 | .4 |
| 8 | .86 | .22 | .43 | 8 | .8 | .2 | .4 |
| 9 | .83 | −.55 | −.03 | 9 | .8 | −.5 | .0 |
| 10 | .85 | −.26 | −.44 | 10 | .8 | −.2 | −.4 |
| 11 | .86 | .49 | −.01 | 11 | .8 | .4 | .0 |
| 12 | .87 | .29 | −.38 | 12 | .8 | .2 | −.3 |
| 22 | .85 | .05 | .47 | 22 | .8 | .0 | .4 |
| 23 | .86 | −.34 | −.32 | 23 | .8 | −.3 | −.3 |
| 24 | .89 | .39 | −.16 | 24 | .8 | .3 | −.1 |
| 25 | .99 | −.01 | .01 | 25 | .9 | .0 | .0 |
| 26 | .96 | .10 | −.02 | 26 | .9 | .1 | .0 |

putations, since one significant figure for the weights is sufficient for the purposes of this method.

When the factor matrices have been written as in *Tables 2* and *3*, a data sheet is prepared as shown in *Table 4*. The first step is to select as many independent test vectors as there are common factors to be normalized and used as the initial trial reference vectors. These trial vectors are to be adjusted by successive approximation until we find a set of reference vectors that defines a simple structure if it exists in the data.

Tests 1, 2, and 3 satisfy the criteria of having a wide range of correlation coefficients in their respective columns of the correlation matrix and also an appreciable number of relatively low coefficients. These three test vectors will be used as starting-points for the computations. The first section of *Table 4* shows the factor loadings of these three tests, copied from *Table 2*. These three test vectors are normalized, and the resulting direction cosines are shown in the columns $\Lambda_A$, $\Lambda_B$, $\Lambda_C$ of the transformation mat ix $\Lambda_0$. These three unit vectors are the normals which define the three trial planes, $A$, $B$, and $C$.

In the matrix $V_0$ of *Table 4* we have the projections of the normal-length test vectors on these three reference axes. These are obtained by the computations $F\Lambda_0 = V_0$. In the same table we also have three frequency distributions of these projections, one for each of the three trial vectors. The

*Table 4*

*Example 1. Initial Vectors*

| | Trial Test Vectors | | | | Matrix $\Lambda_0$ | | | | $C = \Lambda'\Lambda$ | | |
|---|---|---|---|---|---|---|---|---|---|---|---|
| | Test 1 | Test 2 | Test 3 | | $\Lambda_A$ | $\Lambda_B$ | $\Lambda_C$ | | $\Lambda_A$ | $\Lambda_B$ | $\Lambda_C$ |
| I | .65 | .74 | .75 | I | .66 | .75 | .76 | $\Lambda_A$ | 1.01 | .25 | .25 |
| II | −.67 | .53 | .06 | II | −.68 | .54 | .06 | $\Lambda_B$ | .25 | 1.00 | .36 |
| III | .33 | .37 | −.64 | III | .33 | .38 | −.65 | $\Lambda_C$ | .25 | .36 | 1.00 |

| | Matrix $V_0$ | | | | Distribution $D_0$ | | |
|---|---|---|---|---|---|---|---|
| | $A$ | $B$ | $C$ | | $A$ | $B$ | $C$ |
| 1 | .99 | .25 | .24 | .9 | 3 | 3 | 3 |
| 2 | .25 | .98 | .35 | .8 | | 4 | 4 |
| 3 | .24 | .35 | .99 | .7 | 2 | 2 | 2 |
| 4 | .76 | .81 | .35 | .6 | 3 | 2 | 2 |
| 5 | .77 | .35 | .80 | .5 | 3 | | |
| 6 | .24 | .81 | .83 | .4 | | | |
| 7 | .93 | .60 | .34 | .3 | — | 5 | 5 |
| 8 | .56 | .93 | .39 | .2 | 6 | 1 | 1 |
| 9 | .91 | .31 | .62 | .1 | | | |
| 10 | .59 | .33 | .92 | +.0 | | | |
| 11 | .23 | .91 | .69 | −.0 | | | |
| 12 | .25 | .66 | .93 | | | | |
| 22 | .68 | .84 | .34 | | | | |
| 23 | .69 | .34 | .84 | | | | |
| 24 | .27 | .82 | .80 | | | | |
| 25 | .66 | .74 | .75 | | | | |
| 26 | .56 | .77 | .75 | | | | |

lowest six test vectors are designated by their projections in each distribution as constituting a subgroup $s$. Each of the three subgroups is to be used for defining a plane.

Finally, we record the matrix $C$, which shows the cosines of the angles between the three trial reference axes. Inspection of this matrix shows that no two of them are sufficiently close together to define the same plane.

When the computations of *Table 4* have been completed, a data sheet is prepared like *Table 5*. The top section of this table shows the computations for the adjustment of the $A$-plane, and it will be described in some detail. A strip is prepared for the six tests in the subgroup for plane $A$. In the distribution of *Table 4* we see that the subgroup for the *A*-plane contains all projections below .30. In column *A* of the matrix $V_0$ we find that these six tests are 2, 3, 6, 11, 12, and 24. The factor loadings of these six tests are copied from column *A* of $V_0$, and they are recorded near the edge of the strip in the proper position to match the factor matrix of *Table 3*. The cross products, $\Sigma va$, are then computed. In doing this, one places the strip

*Table 5*

*Example 1. First Trial*

**A-Plane**

| | 1 | 2 | 3 | 4 | 5 | 6 | 7 | 8 | 9 |
|---|---|---|---|---|---|---|---|---|---|
| | $\Sigma va$ | $\Sigma a^2$ | $\lambda_{mq}$ | $s$ | $(1-s\lambda_{mq})$ | $\lambda_{ml}$ | $\lambda_{mc}$ | $\lambda_{mu}$ | $\lambda_{mp}$ |
| I | 1.135 | 3.54 | .66 | .32 | .79 | .43 | 5.00 | .51 | .43 |
| II | .444 | .70 | − .68 | .63 | 1.43 | − .92 | 2.17 | − .89 | − .75 |
| III | − .219 | .59 | .33 | − .37 | 1.12 | .63 | −1.02 | .61 | .51 |

**B-Plane**

| | | | | | | | | | |
|---|---|---|---|---|---|---|---|---|---|
| I | 1.459 | 3.41 | .75 | .43 | .68 | .47 | 4.82 | .59 | .46 |
| II | − .613 | .90 | .54 | − .68 | 1.37 | .89 | −2.16 | .84 | .65 |
| III | − .439 | .74 | .38 | − .59 | 1.22 | .80 | −1.34 | .77 | .60 |

**C-Plane**

| | | | | | | | | | |
|---|---|---|---|---|---|---|---|---|---|
| I | 1.525 | 3.41 | .76 | .45 | .66 | .47 | 4.81 | .50 | .46 |
| II | .007 | .74 | .06 | .01 | 1.00 | .05 | − .26 | .05 | .05 |
| III | .745 | .82 | − .65 | .91 | 1.59 | − .98 | 2.51 | − .96 | − .89 |

*Matrix* $V_1$

| | A | B | C |
|---|---|---|---|
| 1 | .95 | .06 | − .03 |
| 2 | .11 | .91 | .04 |
| 3 | − .05 | .00 | .92 |
| 4 | .65 | .66 | − .03 |
| 5 | .56 | .00 | .60 |
| 6 | − .03 | .56 | .61 |
| 7 | .84 | .42 | − .01 |
| 8 | .42 | .80 | .02 |
| 9 | .75 | .01 | .38 |
| 10 | .34 | − .04 | .77 |
| 11 | − .00 | .71 | .43 |
| 12 | − .04 | .36 | .75 |
| 22 | .57 | .71 | − .02 |
| 23 | .46 | − .02 | .66 |
| 24 | .01 | .57 | .57 |
| 25 | .44 | .45 | .45 |
| 26 | .33 | .49 | .46 |

*Distribution* $D_1$

| | A | B | C |
|---|---|---|---|
| .9 | 1 | 1 | 1 |
| .8 | 1 | 1 | |
| .7 | 1 | 2 | 2 |
| .6 | 1 | 1 | 3 |
| .5 | 2 | 2 | 1 |
| .4 | 3 | 3 | 3 |
| .3 | 2 | 1 | 1 |
| .2 | | | |
| .1 | 1 | | |
| +.0 | 1 | 4 | 2 |
| −.0 | 4 | 2 | 4 |

*Coefficient* b

| | A | B | C |
|---|---|---|---|
| $\Sigma\lambda_{ml}\lambda_{mc}$ | − .4890 | − .7290 | − .2121 |
| $\Sigma\lambda_{mc}^2$ | 30.7493 | 29.6936 | 29.5038 |
| b | − .0159 | − .0246 | − .0072 |

$\Lambda_1$                              $\Lambda_1'\Lambda_1 = C$

| | A | B | C |
|---|---|---|---|
| I | .43 | .46 | .46 |
| II | − .75 | .65 | .05 |
| III | .51 | .60 | − .89 |

| | A | B | C |
|---|---|---|---|
| A | 1.01 | .02 | − .29 |
| B | .02 | .99 | − .29 |
| C | − .29 | − .29 | 1.01 |

adjacent to columns I, II, and III of *Table 3*. The cross products are recorded in column 1 of *Table 5*.

In the same manner the sum of the squares of the six factors loading of each column of *Table 3* are computed and recorded in the second column of *Table 5*.

The values of *s* are determined by equation (17). This is, computationally, merely dividing the entry of the first column by that of the second column. The ratio *s* is recorded in column 4.

In column 3 are recorded the direction cosines of the trial reference vector for the $A$-plane from the first column of $\Lambda_0$.

Column 5 is self-explanatory. The entries of column 6 are determined by equation (29), and they are computed from columns 3, 4, and 5.

Column 7 is computed by equation (40). These entries are merely the sums of the factor loadings in the three columns of *Table 2*, the summation being taken only for the subgroup.

The entries of column 8 are determined by equation (39). The coefficient $b$ is computed as shown in the fourth section of *Table 5*. Its value for the $A$-plane is $-.0159$ as shown.

The entries in column 8 are normalized to give the direction cosines of column 9. These values are also recorded in the new transformation matrix, which is denoted $\Lambda_1$ in *Table 5*. Matrix $C$ is also computed as shown, and it is seen that the three reference vectors are independent, since none of the side entries approach unity. In higher dimensions this fact is not a guarantee of linear independence, but it is usually a safe assumption.

The same computational procedure is followed 'or the adjustment in the normals for the $B$-plane and the $C$-plane, as shown in the corresponding sections of *Table 5*. The given factor matrix of *Table 2* is now multiplied by the new transformation matrix, $\Lambda_1$ of *Table 5*, and the result is the new oblique factor matrix $V_1$ of *Table 5*. The frequency distribution of factor loadings in each of the three columns is shown in *Table 5*, and a subgroup is indicated in each distribution. It is a matter of judgment how large to take a subgroup. If it is taken too large, the corresponding factor loadings cannot be made vanishingly small. If it is taken too small, an indeterminate solution may be obtained which is revealed in the final graphs. In the present case the lowest six tests in each distribution were taken to constitute the subgroup for the next adjustment. It is, of course, not at all necessary to have the same number of tests in each subgroup. The size of the subgroup usually varies from one plane to another, and it depends entirely on the factorial compositions of the several tests in the battery.

In *Table 6* we have the same type of computations for the next adjustment of the reference vectors, and it is seen in the frequency distributions of this table that the reference axes have been so adjusted that all the tests in each subgroup have projections that are close to zero for their respective reference axes.

The next step is to plot the three graphs $AB$, $AC$, and $BC$. These are shown in *Figure 2*, and it is seen that the positive simple structure is here evident and is complete in all three of the common-factor dimensions. These graphs are plotted from pairs of columns of the matrix $V_2$ of *Table 6*. One more adjustment of the reference vectors would bring the configuration even closer to perfection, but the appearance of the three graphs hardly justifies any additional refinement.

*Numerical example No. 2*

The first numerical example started with three trial vectors that constituted a good choice so that the simple structure was readily identified without graphical assistance except for the final set of three graphs in *Figure 2*, by which the structure was accepted as complete in all three of the dimensions. In the present example we shall start with a bad choice for the third

Table 6

*Example 1. Second Trial*

A-*Plane*

| | 1 | 2 | 3 | 4 | 5 | 6 | 7 | 8 | 9 |
|---|---|---|---|---|---|---|---|---|---|
| | $\Sigma va$ | $\Sigma a^2$ | $\lambda_{mq}$ | $s$ | $(1-s\lambda_{mq})$ | $\lambda_{ml}$ | $\lambda_{mc}$ | $\lambda_{mu}$ | $\lambda_{mp}$ |
| I | −.006 | 3.54 | .43 | −.00 | 1.00 | .43 | 5.00 | .42 | .44 |
| II | .038 | .70 | −.75 | .05 | 1.04 | −.77 | 2.17 | −.77 | −.80 |
| III | .080 | .59 | .51 | .14 | .93 | .40 | −1.02 | .40 | .41 |

B-*Plane*

| | | | | | | | | | |
|---|---|---|---|---|---|---|---|---|---|
| I | −.004 | 3.41 | .46 | −.00 | 1.00 | .46 | 4.82 | .46 | .46 |
| II | −.027 | .90 | .65 | −.03 | 1.02 | .67 | −2.16 | .67 | .67 |
| III | .040 | .74 | .60 | .05 | .97 | .57 | −1.34 | .57 | .57 |

C-*Plane*

| | | | | | | | | | |
|---|---|---|---|---|---|---|---|---|---|
| I | −.022 | 3.41 | .46 | −.01 | 1.00 | .47 | 4.81 | .47 | .47 |
| II | .045 | .74 | .05 | .06 | 1.00 | −.01 | −.26 | −.01 | −.01 |
| III | −.013 | .82 | −.89 | −.02 | .98 | −.89 | 2.51 | −.89 | −.88 |

*Matrix* V₂

| | A | B | C |
|---|---|---|---|
| 1 | .96 | .04 | .02 |
| 2 | .05 | .91 | .02 |
| 3 | .02 | .02 | .92 |
| 4 | .61 | .65 | −.01 |
| 5 | .61 | .00 | .63 |
| 6 | −.02 | .57 | .59 |
| 7 | .83 | .40 | .02 |
| 8 | .38 | .79 | .02 |
| 9 | .79 | −.00 | .42 |
| 10 | .40 | −.03 | .79 |
| 11 | −.02 | .72 | .41 |
| 12 | −.01 | .38 | .74 |
| 22 | .53 | .69 | −.01 |
| 23 | .52 | −.01 | .69 |
| 24 | .01 | .58 | .56 |
| 25 | .45 | .45 | .46 |
| 26 | .33 | .50 | .47 |

*Distribution* D₂

| | A | B | C |
|---|---|---|---|
| .9 | 1 | 1 | 1 |
| .8 | 1 | | |
| .7 | 1 | 2 | 2 |
| .6 | 2 | 2 | 2 |
| .5 | 2 | 2 | 2 |
| .4 | 2 | 2 | 4 |
| .3 | 2 | 1 | |
| .2 | | | |
| .1 | | | |
| +.0 | 3 | 3 | 4 |
| −.0 | 3 | 3 | 2 |

| | A | B | C |
|---|---|---|---|
| $\Sigma\lambda_{ml}\lambda_{mc}$ | .0711 | .0062 | .0294 |
| $\Sigma\lambda^2_{mc}$ | 30.7493 | 29.6936 | 29.5038 |
| $b$ | .0023 | .0002 | .0010 |

Λ₂

| | A | B | C |
|---|---|---|---|
| I | .44 | .46 | .47 |
| II | −.80 | .67 | −.01 |
| III | .41 | .57 | −.88 |

Λ'₂Λ₂

| | A | B | C |
|---|---|---|---|
| A | 1.00 | −.10 | −.15 |
| B | −.10 | .99 | −.29 |
| C | −.15 | −.29 | 1.00 |

trial vector $C$ in order to illustrate how to alter the subgroups with graphical aids so as to arrive at the desired planes with a minimum of computation. It will be seen that, even with a bad initial choice of trial vector, the desired solution can be found.

Instead of starting with the test vectors 1, 2, and 3, as in the p evious example, we start here with the test vectors 1, 2, and 5. At the top of *Table 7* the factor loadings of these three vectors are listed, and in the adjacent matrix $\Lambda_0$ we have the same three vectors normalized to constitute the ini-

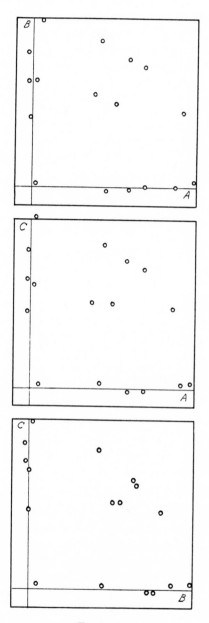

FIGURE 2

tial reference vectors $\Lambda_A$, $\Lambda_B$, $\Lambda_C$. In the next matrix, $C$, we have the cosines of the angles between the three trial vectors. Here we notice at once that the cosine of the angle between $A$ and $C$ is .77, which is unusually high. In the matrix $V_0$ we have the projections of the test vectors on the three trial reference vectors, and we also have in *Table 7* a frequency distribution of the projections. In columns $A$ and $B$ the lowest six tests were chosen for subgroups, and in column $C$ the lowest seven tests were chosen as a subgroup.

*Table 7*

*Example 2. Initial Vectors*

Trial Vectors

| | Test 1 | Test 2 | Test 5 |
|---|---|---|---|
| I | .65 | .74 | .88 |
| II | −.67 | .53 | −.40 |
| III | .33 | .37 | −.24 |

Matrix $\Lambda_0$

| | $\Lambda_A$ | $\Lambda_B$ | $\Lambda_C$ |
|---|---|---|---|
| I | .66 | .75 | .88 |
| II | −.68 | .54 | −.40 |
| III | .33 | .38 | −.24 |

$C = \Lambda'\Lambda$

| | $\Lambda_A$ | $\Lambda_B$ | $\Lambda_C$ |
|---|---|---|---|
| $\Lambda_A$ | 1.01 | .25 | .77 |
| $\Lambda_B$ | .25 | 1.00 | .35 |
| $\Lambda_C$ | .77 | .35 | .99 |

Matrix $V_0$

| | $A$ | $B$ | $C$ |
|---|---|---|---|
| 1 | .99 | .25 | .76 |
| 2 | .25 | .98 | .35 |
| 3 | .24 | .35 | .79 |
| 4 | .76 | .81 | .67 |
| 5 | .77 | .35 | .99 |
| 6 | .24 | .81 | .67 |
| 7 | .93 | .60 | .78 |
| 8 | .56 | .93 | .57 |
| 9 | .91 | .31 | .96 |
| 10 | .59 | .33 | .96 |
| 11 | .23 | .91 | .56 |
| 12 | .25 | .66 | .74 |
| 22 | .68 | .84 | .62 |
| 23 | .69 | .34 | .97 |
| 24 | .27 | .82 | .67 |
| 25 | .66 | .74 | .87 |
| 26 | .56 | .77 | .81 |

Distribution $D_0$

| | $A$ | $B$ | $C$ |
|---|---|---|---|
| .9 | 3 | 3 | 4 |
| .8 | | 4 | 2 |
| .7 | 2 | 2 | 4 |
| .6 | 3 | 2 | 4 |
| .5 | 3 | | 2 |
| .4 | | | |
| .3 | | 5 | 1 |
| .2 | 6 | 1 | |
| .1 | | | |
| +.0 | | | |
| −.0 | | | |

The computations of this example were made without plotting pairs of columns of $V_0$, but in practice this would be preferable. In *Figure 3* we have two of these plots, namely, $AB$ and $AC$. In these plots the subgroups $A$ and $B$ have been circled, and they agree with the subgroups chosen in the frequency distribution of *Table 7*. In the diagram $AC$ we would choose the subgroup that has been circled. It is not the same as the subgroup chosen in the frequency distribution for $C$ in *Table 7*. If the subgroup had been chosen from the plot of *Figure 3*, then the solution would have been obtained in the present example in one less trial. Ignoring *Figure 3*, we take the subgroups marked in the frequency distributions of *Table 7*

The computations for the first trial are shown in *Table 8*, and they were

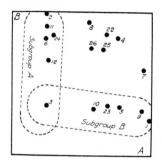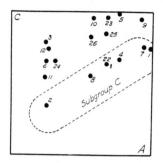

FIGURE 3

## Table 8

### Example 2. First Trial

#### A-Plane

| | 1 | 2 | 3 | 4 | 5 | 6 | 7 | 8 | 9 |
|---|---|---|---|---|---|---|---|---|---|
| | $\Sigma va$ | $\Sigma a^2$ | $\lambda_{mq}$ | $s$ | $(1-s\lambda_{mq})$ | $\lambda_{ml}$ | $\lambda_{mc}$ | $\lambda_{mu}$ | $\lambda_{mp}$ |
| I | 1.135 | 3.54 | .66 | .32 | .79 | .43 | 5.00 | .51 | .43 |
| II | .444 | .70 | − .68 | .63 | 1.43 | − .92 | 2.17 | − .89 | − .75 |
| III | − .219 | .59 | .33 | − .37 | 1.12 | .63 | −1.02 | .61 | .51 |

#### B-Plane

| I | 1.459 | 3.41 | .75 | .43 | .68 | .47 | 4.82 | .59 | .46 |
|---|---|---|---|---|---|---|---|---|---|
| II | − .613 | .90 | .54 | − .68 | 1 37 | .89 | −2.16 | .84 | .65 |
| III | − .439 | .74 | .38 | − .59 | 1.22 | .80 | −1.34 | .77 | .60 |

#### C-Plane

| I | 3.253 | 4.33 | .88 | .75 | .34 | .38 | 5.96 | .60 | .38 |
|---|---|---|---|---|---|---|---|---|---|
| II | .982 | .70 | − .40 | 1.40 | 1.56 | −1.15 | 2.05 | −1.08 | − .68 |
| III | .648 | .62 | − .24 | 1.05 | 1.25 | −1.03 | 1.38 | − .98 | − .62 |

#### Coefficient b

| | A | B | C |
|---|---|---|---|
| $\Sigma\lambda_{ml}\lambda_{mc}$ | − .4890 | − .7290 | − 1.5141 |
| $\Sigma\lambda_{mc}^2$ | 30.7493 | 29.6936 | 41.6285 |
| $b$ | − .0159 | − .0246 | − .0364 |

#### $\Lambda_1$

| | A | B | C |
|---|---|---|---|
| I | .43 | .46 | .38 |
| II | − .75 | .65 | − .68 |
| III | .51 | .60 | − .62 |

#### $\Lambda_1'\Lambda_1 = C$

| | A | B | C |
|---|---|---|---|
| A | 1.01 | .02 | .36 |
| B | .02 | .99 | − .64 |
| C | .36 | − .64 | .99 |

#### Matrix $V_1$

| | A | B | C |
|---|---|---|---|
| 1 | .95 | .06 | .50 |
| 2 | .11 | .91 | − .31 |
| 3 | − .05 | .00 | .64 |
| 4 | .65 | .66 | .06 |
| 5 | .56 | .00 | .76 |
| 6 | − .03 | .56 | .18 |
| 7 | .84 | .42 | .29 |
| 8 | .42 | .80 | − .09 |
| 9 | .75 | .01 | .71 |
| 10 | .34 | − .04 | .77 |
| 11 | − .00 | .71 | − .00 |
| 12 | − .04 | .36 | .37 |
| 22 | .57 | .71 | − .00 |
| 23 | .46 | − .02 | .76 |
| 24 | .01 | .57 | .17 |
| 25 | .44 | .45 | .38 |
| 26 | .33 | .49 | .31 |

#### Distribution $D_1$

| | A | B | C |
|---|---|---|---|
| .9 | 1 | 1 | |
| .8 | 1 | 1 | |
| .7 | 1 | 2 | 4 |
| .6 | 1 | 1 | 1 |
| .5 | 2 | 2 | 1 |
| .4 | 3 | 3 | |
| .3 | 2 | 1 | 3 |
| .2 | | | 1 |
| .1 | 1 | | 2 |
| +.0 | 1 | 4 | 1 |
| −.0 | 4 | 2 | 3 |
| −.1 | | | |
| −.2 | | | |
| −.3 | | | 1 |

carried out according to the plan described for the first example. The result was a new set of trial reference vectors, as shown in the matrix $\Lambda_1$, whose angular separations are shown by the cosines in the matrix $C$. The projections of the test vectors on the new trial reference vectors are shown in the oblique factor matrix $V_1$, and the frequency distributions of these projections are also tabulated. At this point graphs are made, and we show in *Figure 4* the graph for columns $A$ and $C$ of $V_1$. The subgroup $A$ is the same as in the frequency distribution of *Table 8*, but the subgroup $C$, which is circled in the graph, is not indicated by the distribution. A new subgroup $C$ is chosen from *Figure 4*. It consists of the tests *2, 8, 22, 4, 7*, and *1*. With these sub-

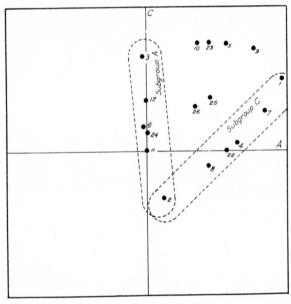

FIGURE 4

groups we proceed to the second trial with computations as shown in *Table 9*.

The result of the second trial computations of *Table 9* gives a new set of trial vectors in the columns of matrix $\Lambda_2$, with angular separation as shown by their cosines in matrix $C$. The projections of the test vectors on these trial vectors are shown in the oblique factor matrix $V_2$, below which we have the frequency distributions of the projections.

A plot of columns $A$ and $C$ of $V_2$ is shown in *Figure 5*, where the subgroup $C$ has been circled. It is the same subgroup as determined in the previous trial of *Figure 4*, and hence the same subgroup $C$ is retained for the third trial with the computations of *Table 10*. Note that the $s$ values are all small, except for the reference vector $C$, which has an appreciable adjustment in this trial. A plot of the pairs of columns of $V_3$ in *Table 10* shows the same structure as in *Figure 2*, which was accepted as final in the first numerical example. Note also that the matrix $\Lambda_3$ of *Table 10* is practically the same as the matrix $\Lambda_2$ of *Table 6*, which terminated the first numerical example.

This second example has been arranged primarily to show how the subgroup can be altered by graphs, which may be plotted for each trial. This

Table 9

*Example 2. Second Trial*

A-*Plane*

| | 1 | 2 | 3 | 4 | 5 | 6 | 7 | 8 | 9 |
|---|---|---|---|---|---|---|---|---|---|
| | $\Sigma va$ | $\Sigma a^2$ | $\lambda_{mq}$ | $s$ | $(1-s\lambda_{mq})$ | $\lambda_{ml}$ | $\lambda_{mc}$ | $\lambda_{mu}$ | $\lambda_{mp}$ |
| I | $-.006$ | 3.54 | .43 | $-.00$ | 1.00 | .43 | 5.00 | .42 | .44 |
| II | .038 | .70 | $-.75$ | .05 | 1.04 | $-.77$ | 2.17 | $-.77$ | $-.80$ |
| III | .080 | .59 | .51 | .14 | .93 | .40 | $-1.02$ | .40 | .41 |

B-*Plane*

| | | | | | | | | | |
|---|---|---|---|---|---|---|---|---|---|
| I | $-.004$ | 3.41 | .46 | $-.00$ | 1.00 | .46 | 4.82 | .46 | .46 |
| II | $-.027$ | .90 | .65 | $-.03$ | 1.02 | .67 | $-2.16$ | .67 | .67 |
| III | .040 | .74 | .60 | .05 | .97 | .57 | $-1.34$ | .57 | .57 |

C-*Plane*

| | | | | | | | | | |
|---|---|---|---|---|---|---|---|---|---|
| I | .291 | 3.41 | .38 | .09 | .97 | .30 | 4.81 | .37 | .46 |
| II | $-.560$ | .74 | $-.68$ | $-.76$ | .48 | .17 | $-.26$ | .17 | .21 |
| III | .161 | .82 | $-.62$ | .20 | 1.12 | $-73$ | 2.51 | $-.69$ | $-.86$ |

*Coefficient* b

| | A | B | C |
|---|---|---|---|
| $\Sigma\lambda_{ml}\lambda_{mc}$ | .0711 | .0062 | $-.4335$ |
| $\Sigma\lambda_{mc}^2$ | 30.7493 | 29.6936 | 29.5038 |
| $b$ | .0023 | .0002 | $-.0147$ |

$\Lambda_2$

| | A | B | C |
|---|---|---|---|
| I | .44 | .46 | .46 |
| II | $-.80$ | .67 | .21 |
| III | .41 | .57 | $-.86$ |

$\Lambda_2'\Lambda_2 = C$

| | A | B | C |
|---|---|---|---|
| A | 1.00 | $-.10$ | $-.32$ |
| B | $-.10$ | .99 | $-.14$ |
| C | $-.32$ | $-.14$ | 1.00 |

*Matrix* $V_2$

| | A | B | C |
|---|---|---|---|
| 1 | .96 | .04 | $-.13$ |
| 2 | .05 | .91 | .13 |
| 3 | .02 | .02 | .91 |
| 4 | .61 | .65 | $-.02$ |
| 5 | .61 | .00 | .53 |
| 6 | $-.02$ | .57 | .67 |
| 7 | .83 | .40 | $-.06$ |
| 8 | .38 | .79 | .07 |
| 9 | .79 | $-.00$ | .29 |
| 10 | .40 | $-.03$ | .71 |
| 11 | $-.02$ | .72 | .51 |
| 12 | $-.01$ | .38 | .79 |
| 22 | .53 | .69 | $-.00$ |
| 23 | .52 | $-.01$ | .60 |
| 24 | .01 | .58 | .63 |
| 25 | .45 | .45 | .44 |
| 26 | .33 | .50 | .48 |

*Distribution* $D_2$

| | A | B | C |
|---|---|---|---|
| .9 | 1 | 1 | 1 |
| .8 | 1 | | |
| .7 | 1 | 2 | 2 |
| .6 | 2 | 2 | 3 |
| .5 | 2 | 3 | 2 |
| .4 | 2 | 2 | 2 |
| .3 | 2 | 1 | |
| .2 | | | 1 |
| .1 | | | 1 |
| $+.0$ | 3 | 3 | 1 |
| $-.0$ | 3 | 3 | 3 |
| $-.1$ | | | 1 |

method of successive approximation can be used for factorial problems in which the assumption of a positive manifold is not imposed. The principal reason why the computational labor is reduced is that each trial vector is adjusted in all the dimensions of the common-factor space in each trial instead of being adjusted in only a few dimensions from the graphs in each trial. Hence the total number of trials is reduced. The successful selection of the subgroup of test vectors which is to determine each hyperplane is best made by graphical inspection. It must also be remembered that the final acceptance of a simple-structure solution for a test battery depends on the appearance of the graphs. The various criteria by which a set of graphs are interpreted have been discussed in a previous chapter on configurations and factor patterns.

## The method of minimizing weighted sums

*Theory of the method*

One of the simplest methods of solving the rotational problem in multiple-factor analysis is that of locating each reference vector so that the absolute

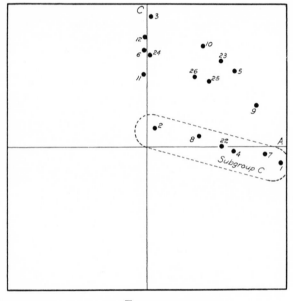

FIGURE

sum of test projections is a minimum for those tests that lie in or near the hyperplane that is defined by the reference vector. If that group of tests were known beforehand, then the rotational problem would be easily solved, but it will be shown that the desired solution can also be reached with successive approximation.

Suppose that a unit trial reference vector $\Lambda_q$ is located quite arbitrarily in the common-factor space and that the projections $v_{jq}$ are computed. It is desired to move this trial vector $\Lambda_q$ in successive steps to the position of a primary reference vector. Here we shall differentiate between two assumptions that the investigator can make, namely, that the nearest primary reference axis is bipolar or that it is positive. The computational outcome is not affected by a wrong assumption as to whether the nearest primary reference vector is bipolar or positive, but the solution is reached more quickly if the assumption is correct in this regard. If the original correlations are all positive or zero, it is a fairly safe assumption that the structure is a positive manifold. If the original correlations are both positive and negative, then some of the primary reference vectors may be positive while some are bipolar, or they might all be bipolar.

### Table 10

### Example 2. Third Trial

#### A-Plane

|     | 1 | 2 | 3 | 4 | 5 | 6 | 7 | 8 | 9 |
|-----|-----|-----|-----|-----|-----|-----|-----|-----|-----|
|     | $\Sigma va$ | $\Sigma a^2$ | $\lambda_{mq}$ | $s$ | $(1-s\lambda_{mq})$ | $\lambda_{ml}$ | $\lambda_{mc}$ | $\lambda_{mu}$ | $\lambda_{mp}$ |
| I   | .017 | 3.54 | .44 | .00 | 1.00 | .44 | 5.00 | .43 | .44 |
| II  | .010 | .70 | −.80 | .01 | 1.01 | −.80 | 2.17 | −.80 | −.81 |
| III | .009 | .59 | .41 | .02 | .99 | .39 | −1.02 | .39 | .39 |

#### B-Plane

| I   | .006 | 3.41 | .46 | .00 | 1.00 | .46 | 4.82 | .46 | .46 |
|-----|-----|-----|-----|-----|-----|-----|-----|-----|-----|
| II  | −.015 | .90 | .67 | −.02 | 1.01 | .68 | −2.16 | .68 | .68 |
| III | .015 | .74 | .57 | .02 | .99 | .56 | −1.34 | .56 | .56 |

#### C-Plane

| I   | .005 | 3.41 | .46 | .00 | 1.00 | .46 | 4.81 | .45 | .46 |
|-----|-----|-----|-----|-----|-----|-----|-----|-----|-----|
| II  | .175 | .74 | .21 | .24 | .95 | −.03 | −.26 | −.03 | −.03 |
| III | −.004 | .82 | −.86 | −.00 | 1.00 | −.86 | 2.51 | −.87 | −.89 |

#### Matrix $V_3$

|     | A | B | C |
|-----|-----|-----|-----|
| 1  | .96 | .03 | .03 |
| 2  | .04 | .91 | −.00 |
| 3  | .03 | .03 | .91 |
| 4  | .60 | .64 | −.03 |
| 5  | .62 | −.00 | .63 |
| 6  | −.02 | .58 | .58 |
| 7  | .82 | .39 | .01 |
| 8  | .37 | .79 | .01 |
| 9  | .80 | −.01 | .43 |
| 10 | .41 | −.03 | .79 |
| 11 | −.02 | .72 | .39 |
| 12 | −.00 | .38 | .73 |
| 22 | .52 | .69 | −.03 |
| 23 | .53 | −.01 | .69 |
| 24 | .01 | .59 | .54 |
| 25 | .45 | .45 | .45 |
| 26 | .33 | .50 | .46 |

#### Distribution $D_3$

|     | A | B | C |
|-----|-----|-----|-----|
| .9  | 1 | 1 | 1 |
| .8  | 2 |   |   |
| .7  |   | 2 | 2 |
| .6  | 2 | 2 | 2 |
| .5  | 2 | 3 | 2 |
| .4  | 2 | 1 | 3 |
| .3  | 2 | 2 | 1 |
| .2  |   |   |   |
| .1  |   |   |   |
| +.0 | 3 | 2 | 3 |
| −.0 | 3 | 4 | 3 |

#### Coefficient b

|     | A | B | C |
|-----|-----|-----|-----|
| $\Sigma\lambda_{ml}\lambda_{mc}$ | .0662 | − .0020 | .0618 |
| $\Sigma\lambda^2_{mc}$ | 30.7493 | 29.6936 | 29.5038 |
| $b$ | .0022 | − .0001 | .0021 |

#### $\Lambda_3$

|     | A | B | C |
|-----|-----|-----|-----|
| I   | .44 | .46 | .46 |
| II  | − .81 | .68 | − .03 |
| III | .39 | .56 | − .89 |

#### $\Lambda'_3\Lambda_3 = C$

|     | A | B | C |
|-----|-----|-----|-----|
| A | 1.00 | − .13 | − .12 |
| B | − .13 | .99 | − .31 |
| C | − .12 | − .31 | 1.00 |

Let it be assumed that the projections $v_{jq}$ cover a wide range of both positive and negative values. If it is assumed that the nearest primary reference vector is positive, then we should want to move the trial reference vector so that, in general, the negative projections will rise toward zero, so that the small positive projections will fall toward zero, and so that the high positive projections will remain high, or rise still higher, to identify the factor. This adjustment would be accomplished by moving the trial vector $\Lambda_q$ so as to increase the algebraic sum of the projections except for the small positive projections which should be decreased.

Let it be assumed, next, that the nearest primary reference vector is bipolar. Then we should want to move $\Lambda_q$ so that the strong positive projections rise and the strong negative projections fall, thus identifying the tests with high variance on the factor. The small projections should move toward zero. Here we want $\Lambda_q$ to move so as to let all projections rise except the small positive and the strong negative ones, which should decrease algebraically.

If it is desired to locate a residual plane, then the trial reference vector $\Lambda_q$ should be adjusted so that all its projections approach zero. Then all positive projections should fall, and all negative projections should rise.

These three cases can be summarized for convenience in *Table 11*. The positive and negative signs in this table indicate for each case whether the

*Table 11*

| Values of Projections | For Locating Positive Reference Vector | For Locating Bipolar Reference Vector | For Locating Residual Reference Vector |
|---|:---:|:---:|:---:|
| Strong positive...... | + | + | − |
| Small positive....... | − | − | − |
| Small negative...... | + | + | + |
| Strong negative..... | + | − | + |

adjustment of the trial vector should be made so as to make the projections $v_{jq}$ rise or fall, i.e., to increase or decrease algebraically.

In *Figure 6* we have arbitrary trial vector $\Lambda_q$ of unit length and with direction cosines $\lambda_{mq}$. The subscript $m$ refers to the axis of the fixed orthogonal reference frame. The test vector $J$ has the direction numbers $a_{jm}$, so that the projection $v_{jq}$ then becomes

$$(45) \qquad v_{jq} = \sum_m a_{jm} \lambda_{mq} .$$

The algebraic sum of the projections of all the $n$ tests on $\Lambda_q$ then is

$$(46) \qquad \sum_j v_{j} = \sum_m \lambda_{mq} \sum_j a_{jm} .$$

Let one of the test vectors be denoted $J$, as in the figure, with projection $v_{jq}$ on $\Lambda_q$, as shown. Let $K$ be another test vector with negative projection $v_{jq}$ on $\Lambda_q$, as shown in the figure. If it is desired to move $\Lambda_q$ so that both these projections approach zero, then it is necessary to increase $v_{kq}$ and to decrease $v_{jq}$. The same object can be attained by dealing with $J$ and $-K$ in which the direction numbers $a_{km}$ have been reversed. Then the desired adjustment of $\Lambda_q$ is such as to decrease both $v_{jq}$ and $v_{kq}$. Let us denote the vectors whose projections are to be increased or decreased by $w_j J$, where $w_j$ takes the values $+1$ or $-1$, depending on whether the test vector is reversed.

Further, let $\phi$ denote the algebraic sum of projections of all the test vectors $w_j J$ on $\Lambda_q$. This sum is the criterion which is to be maximized or minimized as the case may be. Then we have for this criterion

$$(47) \qquad \phi_p = \sum_m \lambda_{mq} \sum_j w_j a_{jm} ,$$

where the subscript $p$ defines the hyperplane $\Lambda_p$, which is to be located by adjusting the trial vector $\Lambda_q$.

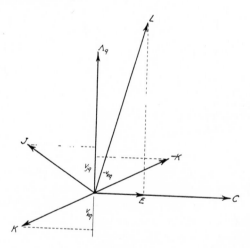

FIGURE 6

The adjustment of the trial vector can be made in the direction determined by the maximum rate of change in the criterion $\phi_p$. This is determined by the partial derivatives of $\phi_p$ with respect to the direction cosines $\lambda_{mq}$. We then have

$$(48) \qquad \frac{\partial \phi_p}{\partial \lambda_{mq}} = \sum_j w_j a_{jm} = l_{mq} ,$$

where $l_{mq}$ are the direction numbers of a vector $L$, as shown in the figure. The numerical values of $l_{mq}$ are merely the sums of columns of the original factor matrix $F$ with positive or negative signs as defined by $w_j$. The adjustment of $\Lambda_q$ should then be made in the plane of $\Lambda_q$ and $L$, either toward

$L$ or away from it; but we have, so far, no measure of how large the displacement of $\Lambda_q$ should be in this plane.

In order to obtain a simple graphical method of determining the amount of displacement of $\Lambda_q$, we determine the vector $E$ in the plane of $\Lambda_q$ and $L$, where $E$ is orthogonal to $\Lambda_q$. Then $E$ is evidently a linear combination of the given trial vector $\Lambda_q$ and the vector $L$. We then have

$$(49) \qquad\qquad E = L - s\Lambda_q ,$$

where the parameter $s$ is to be determined. Since $\Lambda_q$ and $E$ are to be orthogonal, we set

$$(50) \qquad\qquad \Lambda_q E = 0$$

or, by (49),

$$(51) \qquad\qquad \Lambda_q(L - s\Lambda_q) = 0 ,$$

and hence

$$(52) \qquad\qquad \Lambda_q L = s\Lambda_q^2 .$$

But since $\Lambda_q$ is a unit vector, we have simply

$$(53) \qquad\qquad s = \Lambda_q L ,$$

so that $s$ is numerically determined as merely the scalar product of $\Lambda_q$ and $L$. By (49) and (53) the vector $E$ is then located with direction numbers $e_{mq}$. Let $C$ be defined as the vector $E$ normalized with direction cosines $c_{mq}$. We then have $\Lambda_q$ and $C$ as two orthogonal unit vectors.

The projections $c_{jq}$ are next computed from

$$(54) \qquad\qquad c_{jq} = \sum_m a_{jm} c_{mq} ,$$

and a plot is made of $v_{jq}$ against $c_{mq}$. From this plot the displacement of $\Lambda_q$ is determined. When $\Lambda_q$ has been adjusted to a new position, it can again be regarded as a trial vector to be adjusted. It has been found that each primary reference vector can be located approximately in five or six adjustments of this kind. The fine adjustments should be made by a whole set of plots of pairs of columns of $v_{jp}$, which are the elements in the oblique factor matrix $V$. The present method will locate some, or perhaps most, of the primary reference vectors, while some of them may need final adjustment by the complete set of diagrams from the columns of $V$. The present method seems to save a great deal of labor in solving the rotational problem.

*Outline of computations*

(1) When a correlation matrix has been factored into a factor matrix $F$, the rotational problem can be solved by the present method. A useful way to start is to select a test vector. Normalizing this test vector gives the unit trial vector $\Lambda_q$.

(2) Find the test projections $v_{jq}$ on $\Lambda_q$ and tabulate them.

(3) Place a strip adjacent to the column of projections $v_{jq}$ and mark on this strip negative signs for all tests which are to be reversed in sign according to the plan of *Table 11*. In the interpretation of this table one must make some decision as to what are to be regarded as large or small projections. In the first few trials these bands should ordinarily be rather wide, but in the last few trials the bands may be narrower so that a projection is regarded as small if it is numerically smaller than .20.

(4) Place this strip of signs adjacent to each column of $F$ and determine the weighted sums (equation [48]),

$$\sum_{j} w_j a_{jm} = l_{mq} .$$

(5) Find the scalar product (equation [53]),

$$s = \Lambda_q L = \sum_{m} \lambda_{mq} l_{mq} .$$

(6) Find the direction numbers $e_{mq}$ of the vector $E$ (equation [49]),

$$E = L - s\Lambda_q .$$

(7) Normalize $E$ to find direction cosines $c_{mq}$ of the unit vector $C$.

(8) Check orthogonality by the relation $\Lambda_q C = 0$.

(9) Find projections $c_{jm}$ of the test vectors on $C$.

(10) Plot $v_{jq}$ against $c_{jm}$.

(11) Locate a new trial vector as a linear combination of $\Lambda_q$ and $C$, as in the two-dimensional rotations.

(12) Find the projections on the new trial vector, and repeat the process if necessary.

In the interpretation of *Table 11* it may be useful occasionally to assign positive or negative signs to the extremes and to ignore some of the test vectors that are already in the hyperplane. These test vectors that are in or near the hyperplane are then given weights, $w_j = 0$. When this is done, there are three weights for $w_j$, namely, $+1$, $-1$, or 0.

When one or more residual planes are to be located, it is probably best to choose one of the last few centroid axes as trial vector. When a primary reference axis is to be located, it is convenient to choose a normalized test vector as the trial vector. The trial vector for the next plane should be a normalized test vector chosen from the tests that have near-zero projections on the reference axes that have already been determined. In this manner one can avoid starting with a trial vector that moves into the position of one of the reference vectors already located.

*Numerical example*

In order to illustrate the method we shall use actual data. *Table 12* is reproduced from "Psychometric Monograph," No. 2, page 91.* This is a factor matrix for twenty-one tests and eight orthogonal factors, computed by the centroid method.

*Table 12*

*Factor Matrix* $F_0$

| | I | II | III | IV | V | VI | VII | VIII | $h^2$ |
|---|---|---|---|---|---|---|---|---|---|
| 1 | .51 | −.27 | −.26 | .11 | −.13 | −.09 | −.25 | .10 | .5102 |
| 2 | .62 | −.31 | .12 | .06 | −.16 | .12 | −.27 | −.07 | .6163 |
| 3 | .63 | −.09 | −.10 | −.09 | −.09 | .08 | −.21 | .17 | .5106 |
| 4 | .47 | .28 | .08 | −.14 | −.33 | −.17 | .17 | −.10 | .5020 |
| 5 | .38 | .06 | .22 | −.14 | −.23 | .10 | −.11 | −.17 | .3199 |
| 6 | .40 | .19 | .15 | −.19 | −.34 | −.28 | .14 | −.07 | .4732 |
| 7 | .66 | .40 | .11 | .39 | .22 | −.10 | −.09 | .13 | .8432 |
| 8 | .69 | .43 | .12 | .27 | .23 | −.19 | −.09 | .06 | .8490 |
| 9 | .70 | .28 | .26 | .27 | .28 | −.10 | −.10 | −.08 | .8137 |
| 10 | .63 | .26 | −.29 | −.31 | .19 | .04 | −.17 | −.10 | .7213 |
| 11 | .59 | .22 | −.26 | −.34 | .23 | .07 | −.03 | −.09 | .6465 |
| 12 | .53 | .29 | −.19 | −.19 | .20 | −.15 | −.09 | .04 | .5094 |
| 13 | .48 | −.44 | .29 | −.18 | .16 | .16 | .16 | −.08 | .6237 |
| 14 | .40 | −.50 | .41 | −.25 | .17 | .18 | .11 | .08 | .7204 |
| 15 | .46 | −.47 | .42 | −.22 | .12 | .12 | .08 | .13 | .7094 |
| 16 | .57 | −.26 | −.32 | .19 | −.05 | −.23 | .17 | −.12 | .6297 |
| 17 | .58 | −.21 | −.42 | .21 | −.08 | −.24 | .18 | −.08 | .7038 |
| 18 | .64 | −.21 | −.14 | .18 | .04 | .03 | .18 | −.13 | .5575 |
| 19 | .69 | .13 | −.08 | .15 | −.15 | .29 | .19 | .10 | .6746 |
| 20 | .65 | .23 | .06 | .21 | −.13 | .23 | .08 | .07 | .6042 |
| 21 | .65 | .04 | −.16 | .07 | −.10 | .26 | .09 | .14 | .5599 |

Trial 1 is represented by one of the sections of *Table 13*. We start with one of the test vectors, chosen arbitrarily. This is test 14 in the present battery. Its direction numbers are recorded in the first column in *Table 13*. This vector is normalized by the multiplying constant, as shown at the bottom of the first column, and we then have the direction cosines of the first trial vector, $\Lambda$, as shown in the next column. The projections of the test vectors on this trial vector are listed in column $V$, trial 1, of *Table 14*. Here it will be assumed that the structure is a positive manifold, and hence the primary reference axes are assumed to be positive rather than bipolar. Ac-

* L. L. Thurstone and Thelma Gwinn Thurstone, *Factorial Studies of Intelligence* (Chicago: University of Chicago Press, 1941).

cording to *Table 11*, we should reverse the signs of the test vectors with small positive projections in this column *V*. We do this by reversing the signs of all test vectors whose positive projections in this column are less than .20. The reversals are indicated by the negative signs in the column adjacent to the projections *v*.

Table 13

Trial 1

| | Test 14 | Λ | L | e | c |
|---|---|---|---|---|---|
| I | .40 | .47 | − .63 | −2.20 | − .68 |
| II | −.50 | − .59 | −3.07 | −1.10 | − .34 |
| III | .41 | .48 | 2.46 | .86 | .27 |
| IV | −.25 | − .29 | − .36 | .61 | .19 |
| V | .17 | .20 | .03 | − .64 | − .20 |
| VI | .18 | .21 | 2.35 | 1.65 | .51 |
| VII | .11 | .13 | .10 | − .33 | − .10 |
| VIII | .08 | .09 | .25 | − .05 | − .02 |
| Norm | 1.178184 | | | .310009 | |
| S | 3.3354 | | | | |

Trial 2

| | Λe | Λ | L | e | c |
|---|---|---|---|---|---|
| I | .35 | .34 | − .89 | −1.22 | − .56 |
| II | −.65 | − .65 | − .59 | .04 | .02 |
| III | .53 | .52 | 1.28 | .77 | .35 |
| IV | −.26 | − .26 | − .78 | − .53 | − .24 |
| V | .16 | .16 | 1.39 | 1.23 | .57 |
| VI | .30 | .30 | − .59 | − .88 | − .40 |
| VII | .11 | .11 | − .16 | − .27 | − .12 |
| VIII | .09 | .09 | .09 | .00 | .00 |
| Norm | .985664 | | | .460092 | |
| S | .9793 | | | | |

Trial 3

| | Λe | Λ | L | e | c |
|---|---|---|---|---|---|
| I | .26 | .26 | − .09 | − .41 | − .20 |
| II | −.64 | − .63 | − .21 | .58 | .28 |
| III | .57 | .56 | 1.58 | .88 | .43 |
| IV | − .30 | − .30 | −1.16 | − .79 | − .39 |
| V | .25 | .25 | .71 | .40 | .20 |
| VI | .24 | .24 | −1.15 | −1.45 | − .71 |
| VII | .09 | .09 | .12 | .01 | .00 |
| VIII | .09 | .09 | − .05 | − .16 | − .08 |
| Norm | .986095 | | | .488462 | |
| S | 1.2495 | | | | |

Trial 4

| | Λe | Λ | L | e | c |
|---|---|---|---|---|---|
| I | .22 | .21 | − .25 | 4.96 | .94 |
| II | −.57 | − .56 | − .85 | − .09 | − .02 |
| III | .65 | .64 | − .24 | −1.11 | − .21 |
| IV | − .38 | − .37 | .68 | 1.18 | .22 |
| V | .29 | .28 | .27 | − .11 | − .02 |
| VI | .10 | .10 | .33 | .19 | .04 |
| VII | .09 | .09 | .40 | .28 | .05 |
| VIII | .07 | .07 | .67 | .57 | .11 |
| Norm | .977157 | | | .190052 | |
| S | 1.3648 | | | | |

Trial 5

| | Λe | Λ | L | e | c |
|---|---|---|---|---|---|
| I | .28 | .28 | 3.81 | 3.01 | .85 |
| II | −.56 | − .56 | − .51 | 1.09 | .31 |
| III | .63 | .63 | 1.76 | − .03 | − .01 |
| IV | − .35 | − .35 | − .34 | .66 | .19 |
| V | .28 | .28 | 1.39 | .59 | .17 |
| VI | .10 | .10 | − .37 | − .65 | − .18 |
| VII | .09 | .09 | − .64 | − .90 | − .25 |
| VIII | .08 | .08 | − .33 | − .56 | − .16 |
| Norm | .992925 | | | .281954 | |
| S | 2.8484 | | | | |

These negative signs are now copied at the edge of a strip which is placed adjacent to each column of the factor matrix in *Table 12*, and the weighted sums are determined. These weighted sums are recorded in column $L$ of *Table 13*, trial 1. The scalar product $s$ is next computed and recorded as shown. This enables us to compute the direction numbers $e$ of the vector $E$, as shown in the next column. The normalizing constant for this vector is shown at the bottom of column $e$, and then we have the direction cosines of the unit vector $C$, as shown in the last column for this trial. It is useful to check the computations to make sure that the vectors $C$ and $\Lambda$ are orthogonal by computing their scalar product, which should vanish.

*Table 14*

| Tests | Trial 1 | | | Trial 2 | | | Trial 3 | | | Trial | | | Trial 5 | | |
|---|---|---|---|---|---|---|---|---|---|---|---|---|---|---|---|
| | $C$ | $V$ | $\pm$ | $C$ | $V$ | $\pm$ | $C$ | $V$ | $\pm$ | $C$ | $V$ | $\pm$ | $C$ | $V$ | $\pm$ |
| 1 | −.30 | .17 | − | −.42 | .12 | − | −.30 | .06 | − | .56 | −.01 | | .41 | .03 | − |
| 2 | −.15 | .47 | | −.43 | .43 | | −.29 | .36 | | .56 | .30 | | .47 | .34 | |
| 3 | −.37 | .26 | | −.43 | .25 | − | −.25 | .18 | − | .61 | .13 | − | .49 | .17 | |
| 4 | −.46 | .05 | − | −.34 | −.04 | | .17 | −.11 | | .39 | −.06 | | .41 | −.03 | |
| 5 | −.13 | .23 | | −.26 | .21 | | −.01 | .17 | − | .26 | .16 | − | .31 | .18 | |
| 6 | −.42 | .09 | − | −.22 | .01 | − | .25 | −.02 | | .29 | .03 | − | .33 | .05 | − |
| 7 | −.57 | .04 | − | −.24 | −.07 | | −.02 | −.10 | | .68 | −.11 | | .82 | −.05 | |
| 8 | −.67 | .05 | − | −.18 | −.04 | | .10 | −.10 | | .66 | −.08 | | .86 | −.02 | |
| 9 | −.55 | .23 | | −.15 | .12 | − | .08 | .10 | − | .63 | .11 | − | .83 | .16 | |
| 10 | −.65 | .11 | − | −.26 | −.01 | | −.04 | −.04 | | .56 | −.05 | | .64 | −.01 | |
| 11 | −.62 | .17 | − | −.23 | .06 | − | −.03 | .03 | − | .52 | .02 | − | .56 | .06 | − |
| 12 | −.65 | .04 | | −.13 | −.07 | | .11 | −.08 | | .48 | −.07 | | .58 | −.03 | |
| 13 | −.10 | .76 | | −.12 | .73 | | −.10 | .70 | | .36 | .67 | | .21 | .70 | |
| 14 | .01 | .85 | | −.02 | .83 | | −.05 | .83 | | .26 | .80 | | .09 | .82 | |
| 15 | −.01 | .83 | | −.06 | .81 | | −.03 | .79 | | .33 | .77 | | .16 | .80 | |
| 16 | −.47 | .17 | − | −.44 | .08 | − | −.24 | .01 | − | .64 | −.04 | | .45 | .01 | − |
| 17 | −.52 | .08 | − | −.50 | −.01 | | −.28 | −.08 | | .68 | −.14 | | .47 | −.09 | |
| 18 | −.38 | .33 | | −.47 | .26 | − | −.32 | .19 | − | .67 | .12 | − | .49 | .17 | |
| 19 | −.35 | .23 | | −.67 | .16 | − | −.44 | .07 | − | .73 | −.02 | | .51 | .03 | |
| 20 | −.33 | .18 | − | −.56 | .11 | − | −.32 | .03 | − | .66 | −.03 | | .57 | .02 | − |
| 21 | −.34 | .24 | | −.61 | .18 | − | −.43 | .09 | − | .69 | .00 | | .47 | .05 | − |

The projections of the test vectors on the unit correction vector $C$ are next computed and recorded in column $C$, trial 1, of *Table 14*.

The projections $v$ are then plotted against the projections $c$, as shown in *Figure 7*. The new plane is located as shown in this graph by its trace through the origin. The normal to the trace defines the new extended trial vector, $\Lambda_e$. This new trial vector is a linear combination of the first trial vector, $\Lambda$, and the correction vector, $C$. The vector equation for the new trial vector is shown in each graph. The parameter .18 in this graph is determined readily when the plot is made on cross-section paper. The fine gradations of the cross-section paper are omitted in these diagrams.

The direction numbers of the new trial vector are recorded in the first

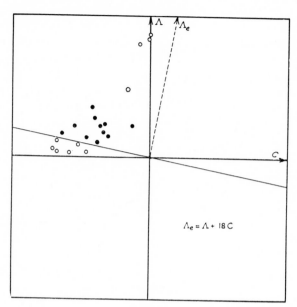

FIGURE 7

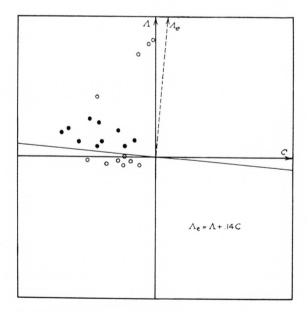

FIGURE 8

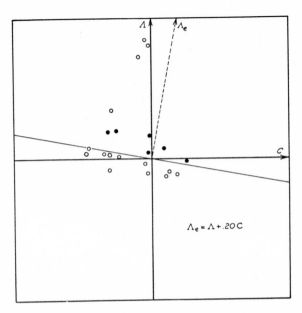

FIGURE 9

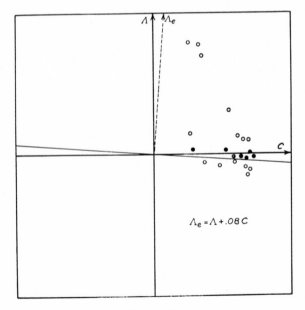

FIGURE 10

column of the next section of *Table 13*, trial 2. This vector is normalized by the normalizing constant at the bottom of this column, and we then have the new unit trial vector, $\Lambda$, whose direction cosines are listed in the next column. The notation $\Lambda_e$ represents the new trial vector, but it is longer than a unit vector. The first step in each trial is to reduce the new extended trial vector to unit length.

The calculations proceed here as before to the determination of the correction vector $C$ for trial 2. The projections of the test vectors on the trial vector $\Lambda$ and on the correction vector $C$ are computed and recorded in *Table 14*, trial 2. The plot is shown in *Figure 8*. The small positive projec-

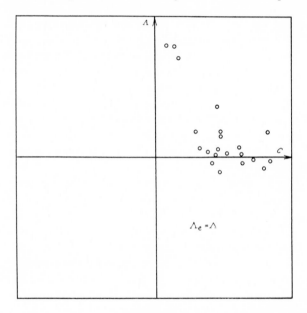

FIGURE 11

tions on the new trial vector which are to be reversed in sign for the weighted summation are shown in black on the previous graph, *Figure 7*. These reversals can be anticipated before the new trial vector is determined.

This procedure is repeated, as shown in *Figures 9* and *10*, until the fifth trial, which produces the graph in *Figure 11*. Since this graph does not indicate any improvement to be gained by moving the trial vector in the plane of $\Lambda$ and the correction vector $C$, we accept the trial vector $\Lambda$ for this trial as a close approximation to the desired reference vector.

It can be seen in *Figure 11*, as well as from the last column of *Table 14*, that there are three tests which are exceptionally high on this reference vector. These are the three space tests of the test battery in this experiment. In order to locate another primary reference vector, we should start by normalizing one of the test vectors, which have small projections as shown in the last column of *Table 14*.

The same procedure was used to locate the residual plane in this test battery. This was done by starting with the last centroid column of *Table 12* and by reversing the signs of all test vectors which had positive projections on the eighth centroid axis. This leads to an improved position for the residual reference vector. One trial with this method was sufficient to locate the residual reference axis for these data.

When the primary reference axes, as well as one or more residual reference axes, have been determined by this simple method, the final step is to plot the whole set of diagrams, one diagram for each pair of reference vectors. Since there are eight dimensions in this problem, the final set of diagrams will have twenty-eight graphs. Inspection of these graphs enables one to determine any further small adjustments that may be necessary to locate the best position for the simple structure. The present method should be regarded as adequate for obtaining an approximate location of the reference frame of a simple structure; but it should always be followed by a complete set of plots of pairs of columns of the oblique factor matrix, to make sure that the best location of the frame has been attained. The procedure here described is perhaps the simplest of the rotational methods so far devised, and it should serve to eliminate a very large part of the labor which has hitherto been necessary in locating a simple structure in multidimensional factor problems.

In the application of this method or similar methods to the rotational problem, it will be found that some configurations are dominated by the large variance of the first centroid as compared with subsequent factors and that this circumstance causes slow convergence in these solutions. In dealing with such configurations it may be found useful to extend the test vectors as in the method of extended vectors. The configuration is then unaltered except for the fact that all the test vectors are extended so as to have unit projection on the first centroid axis. The present method can be applied to such a configuration in the same manner as here described. In the location of the new trial vector, one has additional freedom, in that a streak of points on the diagram which are not radial can be brought into a hyperplane directly by expressing the next trial vector as a linear combination of three vectors, namely, the given trial vector, the new correction vector, and the unit reference vector along the first axis. All the test vectors have unit projection on the first centroid axis, and the new trial vector can then be determined in the same manner as in the method of extended vectors. This procedure gives the solution in two trials with the present example.

Another variant of the method here described is to weight each of the co-ordinates of the correction vector inversely as the absolute sum of the entries in the corresponding columns of the given factor matrix $F$. The same result can be attained by writing a new factor matrix in which the absolute sums of the columns are equal. This involves a distortion of the configuration, but the simple structure is nevertheless invariant under this kind of distortion. The disadvantage of this procedure on experimental data is that the axes on which the variance is very much extended become so distorted that the residual variance is more difficult to differentiate from the significant variance which is to be interpreted.

## A double-group method of rotation

It happens not infrequently in a plot of two columns of the oblique factor matrix that the points reveal a concentration which could be fitted by a line that does not pass through the origin. In previous chapters there have been a number of such cases. A few examples will be listed here to show the situation in which the double-group method is applicable. *Figure 3* of *chapter x* shows three such possibilities in the same diagram. In that figure there is a roughly linear arrangement of points that could be fitted by a straight line through points *1* and *3*. A second line could be drawn through points *2* and *3*, while a third line could be drawn through points *1* and *2*. All but two of the points in the figure would be near one or more of these three lines. Instead of locating the line through points *1* and *3*, we might choose the centroids of the two groups, *1, 13, 18,* and *3, 15, 20,* which would, in this case, give practically the same solution.

In *Figure 5* of *chapter x* we have another case. The two groups, *1, 13, 18,* and *3, 15, 20,* might be chosen in this diagram to define the next adjustment in plane $C$. In *Figure 5* of this chapter the plane $C$ might be defined by a vector that is set orthogonal to the two groups, *2, 8,* and *1, 7.*

The principle involved in this adjustment is to express the new vector $\Lambda_1$ as a linear combination of the given unit vector $\Lambda_0$ and the two centroid vectors $C_1$ and $C_2$ of the two groups chosen graphically. We start, then, with the following notation:

$$\Lambda_0 = \text{given unit reference vector},$$

$$\Lambda_1 = \text{new unit vector to be determined},$$

$$C_1 = \text{centroid vector for group 1},$$

$$C_2 = \text{centroid vector for group 2},$$

$$L_1 = k_1 C_1, \text{ where } L_1^2 = 1,$$

$$L_2 = k_2 C_2, \text{ where } L_2^2 = 1.$$

The vectors $L_1$ and $L_2$ are collinear with the corresponding centroid vectors. The new vector $\Lambda_1$ is expressed as the linear combination

(55) $$\Lambda_1 = \Lambda_0 + p_1 L_1 + p_2 L_2,$$

where $p_1$ and $p_2$ are scalars to be determined. The vector $\Lambda_1$ must satisfy the two requirements of orthogonality with $L_1$ and $L_2$. Then we have

$$(56) \qquad\qquad \Lambda_1 L_1 = 0$$

and

$$(57) \qquad\qquad \Lambda_1 L_2 = 0 \, .$$

Substituting the linear combination for $\Lambda_1$, we have

$$(58) \qquad\qquad (\Lambda_0 + p_1 L_1 + p_2 L_2) L_1 = 0 \, ,$$

from which we get

$$(59) \qquad\qquad \Lambda_0 L_1 + p_1 L_1^2 + p_2 L_1 L_2 = 0 \, .$$

$L_1$ is a unit vector, and hence

$$(60) \qquad\qquad L_1^2 = 1 \, .$$

Let $\Lambda_0 L_1 = s_1$ and let $L_1 L_2 = l$. Then

$$(61) \qquad\qquad s_1 + p_1 + p_2 l = 0 \, .$$

For the second condition of orthogonality, we have, similarly,

$$(62) \qquad\qquad (\Lambda_0 + p_1 L_1 + p_2 L_2) L_2 = 0 \, ,$$

from which we get

$$(63) \qquad\qquad s_2 + p_1 l + p_2 = 0 \, ,$$

where $s_2 = \Lambda_0 L_2$. Solving for $p_2$, we get

$$(64) \qquad\qquad p_2 = \frac{s_1 l - s_2}{1 - l^2}$$

and, by analogy,

$$(65) \qquad\qquad p_1 = \frac{s_2 l - s_1}{1 - l^2} \, .$$

When the parameters $p_1$ and $p_2$ are thus known numerically, the new vector $\Lambda_1$ can be determined. It is normalized to become the new unit reference vector, $\Lambda_p$. When the double-group method is graphically indicated, it is quite effective.

# CHAPTER XVIII

## SECOND-ORDER FACTORS

### First-order and second-order factors

Most of the work that has been done so far in the development of factorial theory has been concerned with the factors obtained from the test correlations with or without rotation of axes for the selection of a suitable reference frame. *Factors that are obtained from the test correlations will be called first-order factors,* whether they are selected so as to be orthogonal or oblique. We shall now consider the factors that may be determined from the correlations of the first-order factors. *Factors that are obtained from the correlations of the first-order factors will be called second-order factors.* Factors of this type seem to be of fundamental significance in the interpretation of correlated variables.

Analysis of second-order factors and their relations to those of first order can be presented in several different ways. We shall describe these two factorial domains in terms of a literal notation, a physical example, a diagrammatic representation, a geometrical example, and the matrix equations relating the two domains.

Consider, first, a reduced correlation matrix for the tests whose rank is, say, 5. The factoring of this correlation matrix determines five arbitrary orthogonal unit reference vectors which may be denoted $I$, $II$, $III$, $IV$ and $V$. This orthogonal reference frame is arbitrary in the sense that it is defined by the method of factoring which happens to be used. This reference frame will be regarded as fixed, and all other vectors will be defined in terms of this fixed orthogonal frame, which is designated by the subscript $m$. Let it be assumed that a complete simple structure can be found in the test configuration and let the corresponding primary vectors be denoted $A$, $B$, $C$, $D$, and $E$. (These are ordinarily denoted $T_A$, $T_B$, etc.). We shall assume that these primary traits are correlated in the experimental population. Then the primary vectors in the test configuration will be separated by oblique angles, whose cosines are the correlations between the primary traits in the particular group of subjects studied. Let these correlations be listed in a new correlation matrix of order $5 \times 5$, showing the correlations between primary factors. This correlation matrix defines the second-order domain just as the correlation matrix for the tests defines the first-order domain.

The simplest case is that in which the five primary factors are uncorrelated, in which case their correlation matrix is a unit matrix so that an analysis of a second-order domain is not immediately indicated. Next would be the case in which the reduced correlation matrix for the primary factors $A$, $B$, $C$, $D$, and $E$ is of unit rank. There are two types of interpretation for such a situation. The correlations between the primary factors in a particular experimental population may be due to conditions of selection of the subjects, and in this case the correlations would be of no more theoretical importance than the conditions of selection of the subjects. If, on the other hand, the five primary functions, $A$, $B$, $C$, $D$, and $E$, actually do have some parameter in common, then one would expect their intercorrelations to be of unit rank for different experimental groups of subjects that are selected in different ways. In other words, the mere fact that a set of variables or a set of factors is correlated does not imply any scientific obligation to find "the" factors that account for the correlations, because the factors, if found, might turn out to be as incidental in significance as the conditions by which the subjects happened to be selected. On the other hand, the fact that correlations between variables, or between factors, can be caused by scientifically trivial circumstances does not guarantee that all correlations between variables are of trivial significance. If the correlations between the five primary factors in the present example should turn out to be of unit rank, then this circumstance merits a closer look because such a simplification would not often happen by chance. If the correlations between the primary factors should turn out to be of unit rank for several different experimental groups, then we should have an obligation to ascertain the cause which must transcend the selective conditions.

Let it be assumed that the five primary factors do have a parameter $p$ in common. Then the five primaries could be expressed in the form

$$A = f(p, a) , \qquad\qquad D = f(p, d) ,$$
$$B = f(p, b) , \qquad\qquad E = f(p, e) ,$$
$$C = f(p, c) ,$$

where each primary function is defined in terms of a parameter such as $a$, $b$, $c$, $d$, or $e$, which is unique, and also in terms of another parameter, $p$, which it shares with the functions that define the other primaries. If there should happen to be conspicuous correlation between the parameters $a$, $b$, $c$, $d$, and $e$ in the particular group of subjects, then the unit rank of the second-order domain would be disturbed. If the correlations of the primaries show unit rank, then, in addition to the parameters $a$, $b$, $c$, $d$, and $e$, a second-order parameter or factor $p$ can be postulated. It should be noted that we now have six parameters, namely, $a$, $b$, $c$, $d$, $e$, and $p$; and, since the rank of the test correlations is 5, it follows that these six parameters are linearly dependent. In fact, the parameter $p$ is now a linear combination of the other five parameters. We can express these relations by a set of parameters such as $A$, $B$, $C$, $D$, $E$, and $p$, in which $p$ is a linear combination of the five primary parameters. The five primaries are parameters descriptive of the first-order domain, and the parameter or factor $p$ is descriptive of the second-order domain, which is of unit rank here. The second-order parameter is a linear combination of the five primaries that are defined by the original test correlations. If some degree of consistency can be found for these parameters for different groups of subjects, then all these parameters should represent some aspects of the underlying physical or mental functions.

Consider, next, a set of correlated primaries, $A$, $B$, $C$, $D$, and $E$, in which the parameter $p$ appears in the first order, as in the following example:

$$A = f(p, a) , \qquad\qquad D = f(p, d) ,$$

$$B = f(p, b) , \qquad\qquad E = f(p) .$$

$$C = f(p, c) ,$$

The rank of the reduced correlation matrix of the tests would now be 5. The five primaries listed above would be correlated and of unit rank. The second-order factor $p$ would be determined from the correlations of the primaries. In this case the communality for the primary factor $E$ would be near unity, thus showing that its total variance is common to the second-order factor $p$. Hence the primary factor $E$ of the first order and the factor $p$ of the second order would be identical. The presence, or absence, of the primary $E$ could be determined by including, or excluding, a few tests in the battery. We see, therefore, that the appearance of a factor in the first order or in the second order may depend on the battery of measurements taken. Hence a factor should not be considered as intrinsically different because it appears in the second order. This circumstance can be determined by the selection of the test battery.

On the other hand, a parameter which always appears in the measurements in association with some other function would not appear as in the primary $E$, and it would be discovered experimentally, nearly always in the second order. Such a limitation could be introduced by the physical nature of the attribute which the factor represents, so that in such a case the second-order factor would represent something fundamentally different from that of the first order. A single-factor study is not likely to reveal whether a second-order parameter is fundamentally different from the parameters of first order or whether the differentiation is caused merely by the selection of the test battery.

In the following example we have another combination of primaries:

$$A = f(p, a),\qquad\qquad D = f(p, d),$$

$$B = f(p, b),\qquad\qquad E = f(e).$$

$$C = f(p, c),$$

In this example the reduced rank of the test correlations would again be 5. The correlations of the primaries would show unit rank for $A$, $B$, $C$, and $D$. The factor $E$ would be orthogonal to the rest of the system, so that its row and column would have side correlations of zero. The correlations of primaries would not be of unit rank if we consider the whole table of order $5 \times 5$, but it would be of unit rank if we consider only the $4 \times 4$ table for $A$, $B$, $C$, and $D$. Relations of this kind can be found by inspection of the correlations of the primaries, and they may be indicative of the underlying order of the domain that is being investigated.

The principles of a second-order domain have been discussed here in terms of the simple case in which that domain is of unit rank, so that there is only one general second-order factor. It should be evident that the organization of the second-order parameters can be of any rank and complexity. For example, the rank may be higher than 1, and the second-order factors may extend to all the primaries or to only some of them. The possibility of third- and higher-order factors must be recognized; but their experimental identification is of increasing difficulty the higher the order, because of the instability of such a superstructure on practically feasible experimental data. The number of second-order factors that can be determined from a given number of linearly independent primary factors follows the same restrictive relations that govern the number of primary factors that can be determined from a given number of tests. Thus, for example, it is not to be expected that three second-order factors would be determinate from only five primary factors, for the same reason that three primary factors cannot be determined from five tests. Furthermore, it is entirely possible in the same data for the first-order domain to give clear interpretation of a set of primary factors and for the second-order domain to be indeterminate or ambiguous in the same data.

In order to avoid misunderstanding, perhaps it should be remarked that in factor analysis we are using the term *parameter* in its universal meaning in science. *A parameter is one of the measurements that are used for describing or defining an object or event.* In statistical theory the term *parameter* is frequently used in a more restricted sense as descriptive of the universe, as contrasted with a *statistic*, which is the corresponding measurement on a sample. We are not using the term in this restricted sense.

## The box example

In order to illustrate the nature of first- and second-order factors we shall make use of populations of simple objects or geometrical figures and their measurable properties instead of dealing with these factors merely as logical abstractions. We have used a population of rectangular boxes and their measurable attributes to illustrate the principles of correlated primary factors, and we can use them also for the present discussion.

A random collection of rectangular boxes was represented by the three measurements, length ($x$), width ($y$), and height ($z$) (*chapter vii*). A list of measurements was prepared which could be made on each box, such as the diagonal of the front face, the area of the top surface, the length of a vertical edge, and so on. Each of these measurements represented a test score, and each box represented an individual member of the statistical population. The correlations between the measurements were computed and analyzed factorially as if we did not know anything about their exact nature. Each measurement was treated as a test score of unknown factorial composition. As has been shown previously, the analysis revealed three factors in the correlations for the particular set of measurements used. The configuration showed a complete simple structure, and a set of primary vectors was determined by the configuration. These three primaries represented the three basic parameters in terms of which all the test measurements had been expressed.

The three primary vectors were separated by acute angles whose cosines represented the correlations between the three basic parameters that were used in setting up the box example. These three correlations could be assembled into a small correlation matrix of order $3 \times 3$. The physical interpretation of the positive correlations was that large boxes tend to have all their dimensions larger than those of small boxes. In other words, if one of the dimensions of a box shape is, say, 6 feet, the other dimensions of the box are not likely to be of the order of, say, 2 or 3 inches. The table of correlations of the three primary factors, $X$, $Y$, and $Z$, could be represented by a single common factor. This factor would be a second-order factor. It would, no doubt, be interpreted as a size factor in the box example. If this second-order size factor were denoted $s$, we should have four parameters for describing the box shapes, namely, the three dimensions $x$, $y$, and $z$ and the size factor $s$. These four parameters or factors would be linearly dependent because the rank of the correlation matrix of the tests was 3.

In the case of the box example, a size factor or parameter could be determined in the first order if desired. For this purpose we could use the first centroid axis, the major principal axis, or the volume vector, all of which can be easily defined in the first-order system of test vectors. The four parameters so chosen would also be linearly dependent. If we wanted to use only three linearly independent parameters, including a size factor, that could be done in the first order by choosing, say, the two ratios $x/y = r_1$ and $x/z = r_2$ as well as the volume vector $v$. These three factors would be linearly independent, but they would be correlated. The latitude with which we can choose simplifying parameters for the box example is determined in part by the fact that three factors can nearly always be represented by a common factor, whereas this is not the case when the rank is higher than 3.

## Diagrammatic representation

The relations between the first-order and the second-order domains can be represented diagrammatically as shown in *Figures 1, 2,* and *3.* In *Figure 1* we have a set of eight tests, whose correlations are accounted for by five

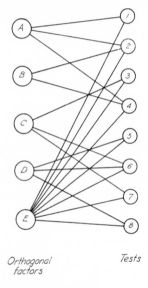

Orthogonal      Tests
factors

FIGURE 1

primary factors, $A$, $B$, $C$, $D$, and $E$, which are uncorrelated. The factor $A$, for example, is present in the common-factor variances of tests 1, 2, and 4. The primary factor $E$ is present in the common-factor variances of all the tests, and hence $E$ would be called a general factor for the particular battery. Since it is orthogonal to all the other primary factors, it would be called an *orthogonal general factor of the first order.* In order to determine the nature of the factor $E$ it would be necessary to study it in different test batteries so that one could predict with certainty when the factor would be present and when it would be absent from a test. Since the primary factors are here represented as uncorrelated, the matrix of correlations of the primary factors would be an identity matrix, and there would be no immediate provocation to investigate a second-order domain.

*In Figure 2* we have represented a set of tests and five primary factors, *A, B, C, D,* and *E*. (We are not here concerned as to whether the particular number of tests represented in this diagram is adequate for the determination of five primary factors. The purpose of these diagrams is merely to show the nature of the relations between the two domains.) The rank of the correlation matrix of the tests would here be 5, which corresponds to the number of linearly independent primary factors. In the present case we should find that the primary factors are themselves correlated. The matrix of correlations of these primaries would be of order $5 \times 5$, and it would be of unit rank. The correlations between the primary factors could therefore be

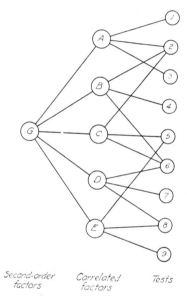

Second-order    Correlated    Tests
factors       factors

FIGURE 2

accounted for by a single general second-order factor that is denoted *G*. If both the first-order and the second-order factors were to be used for the description of the tests and the relations, we should have six parameters which would be linearly dependent because the rank of the correlations of the tests is only 5. In fact, the saturation of each test with the second-order factor *G* would be a linear combination of the saturations of the test with the five primaries of the first order. None of the primary factors are general factors in this figure.

In *Figure 3* we have a more complex relation, in that the correlation matrix for the primary factors would be of rank 2. One of the second-order factors is here shown to be common to all but one of the primary factors; one of the second-order factors is a factorial doublet, in that it represents additional correlation between the primaries $B$ and $D$; and the primary factor $A$ is orthogonal to the rest of the primaries, so that it does not participate in the second-order domain. This diagram is drawn merely to illustrate the variations in complexity that may be found in factorial studies.

The two types of general factors here shown in *Figures 1* and *2* have some interesting differences. The general factor $E$ of *Figure 1* is independent of the other primary factors, while the general factor $G$ in *Figure 2* is present in all the other factors. Hence we must conclude that a second-order gen-

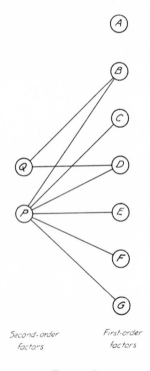

Second-order factors        First-order factors

FIGURE 3

eral factor is a part of, and must participate in, the definition of the other factors, while the orthogonal general factor $E$ of *Figure 1* is, by definition, independent of the other primary factors. It is evident, therefore, that a general second-order factor is likely to be of more fundamental significance for the domain in question than a general orthogonal first-order factor. An orthogonal general factor of the first order might operate in a test without any group factor, whereas a second-order general factor would operate, ordinarily, through the mechanism of some function that could be identified as a group factor, a primary factor, or a special ability.

The factor patterns corresponding to the relations shown diagrammatically in these figures are given in *Tables 1, 2,* and *3*. *Table 1* shows the factor pattern for *Figure 1*. Here the orthogonal general factor *E* is identified by the fact that all entries of its column are filled. *Table 2* shows the factor pattern for *Figure 2*. Here it is seen by the factor pattern that a group such as tests 1, 4, 5, and 7 have no primary factor in common and that hence their correlations would be determined only by the second-order general factor *G*. The determinant of the correlations for these four tests (the tetrad difference) would therefore vanish. The second-order factor matrix is also shown in this table with only one factor *G* to correspond to this example.

Table 1

Orthogonal Factors

|   | A | B | C | D | E |
|---|---|---|---|---|---|
| 1 | X |   |   |   | X |
| 2 | X | X |   |   | X |
| 3 |   |   | X |   | X |
| 4 | X | X |   |   | X |
| 5 |   |   |   | X | X |
| 6 |   |   | X | X | X |
| 7 |   |   | X |   | X |
| 8 |   |   |   | X | X |

Table 2

Correlated Factors

|   | A | B | C | D | E |
|---|---|---|---|---|---|
| 1 | X |   |   |   |   |
| 2 | X | X | X |   |   |
| 3 | X |   |   |   |   |
| 4 |   | X |   |   |   |
| 5 |   |   | X |   | X |
| 6 |   | X | X | X |   |
| 7 |   |   |   | X |   |
| 8 |   |   |   | X | X |
| 9 |   |   |   |   | X |

|   | G |
|---|---|
| A | X |
| B | X |
| C | X |
| D | X |
| E | X |

Table 3

Second-Order Domain of Figure 3

|   | P | Q |
|---|---|---|
| A |   |   |
| B | X | X |
| C | X |   |
| D | X | X |
| E | X |   |
| F | X |   |
| G | X |   |

The question might be raised as to whether both types of general factors could be present in the same battery. That seems possible. In that case a simple structure could define the primary factors *A, B, C,* and *D* but not *E* in the particular battery of *Figure 1*. This factor could be assumed arbitrarily to be orthogonal to the other factors, but then the line *GE* of *Figure 2* would be erased to correspond to the fact that *E* is orthogonal to the other factors. One or more second-order general factors could be found in the correlated primaries. If the correlations of *A, B, C,* and *D* were of unit rank, another alternative would be to set *E* in such a relation to the other primary vectors as to maintain the unit rank with the second-order general factor. It might then be found that the vector $E$ has non-vanishing projections on all the test vectors, in which case both types of general factor would be assumed to be a possible set of explanatory parameters for the battery in question. It must be remembered that these various locations of the reference frame for the explanatory parameters in both the first-order and the second-order domains have validity only in so far as they are suggestive of fruitful scientific interpretation. If this is not the purpose, then the factorial resolution might as well remain in the arbitrary orthogonal factors produced by factoring the given test correlations—or, better still, by not doing the factoring at all.

It might be asked how the correlations of a test battery can be resolved into a second-order domain of unit rank which is lower than the rank of the test correlations. The transitions can be regarded geometrically. The unit test vectors usually define a space of as many dimensions as there are tests. When the reduced correlation matrix is considered, its rank is frequently lower than its order. Hence the reduction from the number of tests $n$ to the number of primary factors $r$ represents a reduction from the total variance of the tests to the common-factor variance. The complete correlation matrix for the primary factors represents a set of $r$ unit vectors in as many dimensions, the dimensionality of the common-factor space. The reduced form of this matrix for the example of *Figure 2* would have unit rank because the side correlations are determined only by that which the primaries have in common, namely, the second-order general factor.

### Group factors and primary factors

In *Figure 4* we have a diagrammatic representation of a different kind of resolution of factors in the second-order domain and their relation to the primary factors. In this example the rank of the correlation matrix of tests is assumed to be five, as represented by as many primary factors, $A$, $B$, $C$, $D$, and $E$. Let it be assumed that the correlation matrix for these five primaries is of unit rank. The general second-order factor $G$ then accounts for the observed correlations of the primary factors. If the five linearly independent primary unit vectors and the second-order unit vector $G$ are to be represented in the same space, the dimensionality of this space must be six. It is possible to locate in this augmented space another set of unit vectors, $a$, $b$, $c$, $d$, and $e$, which are mutually orthogonal and which are also orthogonal to the unit vector $G$. Then we have the orthogonal reference frame $G$, $a$, $b$, $c$, $d$, and $e$, which defines the six dimensions of the first- and second-order factors but not the test space. The five linearly independent primary factors define a five-dimensional space corresponding to the rank of the test correlations, and this space is a part of the total six-dimensional space of this representation.

The unit vector $a$ is a linear combination of the unit vector $G$ and the primary vector $A$. The relation is similar for the other primary vectors. The primary vectors $A, B, C, D$, and $E$ are correlated and of unit rank, whereas the vectors $a, b, c, d$, and $e$ are arbitrarily set orthogonal to each other. In general, if the rank of the test correlations is $r$ and if the correlations of the primaries are of unit rank, then the primaries define a unit vector $G$ for a general second-order factor in an augmented space of dimensionality $(r+1)$ and also a set of $r$ mutually orthogonal unit vectors, each of which is in the plane of the second-order general factor and one of the primaries. These vectors are arbitrarily set orthogonal to the general second-order factor, and

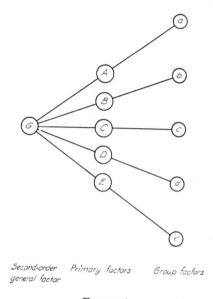

Second-order   Primary factors   Group factors
general factor

FIGURE 4

they are called *group factors*. In *Figure 4* the primary factors are denoted $A, B, C, D$, and $E$, and the group factors are denoted $a, b, c, d$, and $e$. With this resolution we have $(r+1)$ linearly dependent factors, which represent the test correlations of rank $r$. This type of resolution is preferred by some students, who use the reference frame $G, a, b, c, d$, and $e$ because it is orthogonal rather than the frame $G, A, B, C, D$, and $E$, which is oblique.

## A general second-order factor

The algebraic and computational relations between the first-order and the second-order domains will be shown for the case of a single general second-order factor because of the interest of this case for the psychological controversies of the past forty years about Spearman's general intellective factor. The algebraic and computational relations to be shown can be generalized to second-order domains of higher than unit rank. It must be remembered, however, that the restriction of our discussion to unit rank for the second-order domain does not in any way imply that such low rank is always to be expected. The methods of analysis can be readily extended to a second order of higher rank when the data indicate a determinate second-order configuration. In any case the second-order rank should be considerably lower than the rank $r$ of the first-order factors in order to justify interpretation.

The primary vectors constitute a set of $r$ linearly independent unit vectors that define a space of dimensionality equal to the rank of the test correlations. In order to represent a general second-order factor as a unit vector in the same configuration it is necessary to augment the dimensionality to $(r+1)$ dimensions. A second-order domain of rank 2 would thus require an augmented space of dimensionality $(r+2)$. The projections of the test vectors on these additional vectors in the augmented space can, however, be expressed as linear combinations of the test projections on the primary vectors or on any set of $r$ linearly independent vectors in the common-factor space. The procedures for determining these saturations will be shown without writing explicitly the $(r+1)$ co-ordinates of the second-order unit vectors in the augmented space.

The present discussion is confined to factorial data that satisfy two conditions, namely, (1) that a complete simple structure is revealed in the test configuration and (2) that the second-order correlation matrix is of unit rank. These methods can be adapted to the analysis of less than $r$ primary factors, and the methods can be adapted to higher second-order rank.

One of two objectives will be assumed, namely, (1) to determine the projections (saturations) of the tests on the second-order factor in addition to the projections on the primary reference vectors or (2) to determine the projections on the second-order factor and also on the orthogonal group factors. It will be convenient to discuss the algebraic relations under four cases because of the different computational routes that may be chosen. These four cases are as follows:

*Case 1. Transformation from* F *to* V, *including the column vector* G

This transformation is shown in rectangular notation in *Table 4* for the equation

$$(1) \qquad\qquad F_{jm}\Psi_{mp} = V_{jp} ,$$

in which the matrix $V_{jp}$ has an extra column for the second-order factor $G$ with elements $v_{jg}$, which may also be denoted $r_{jg}$ because these are the correlations between the tests $j$ and the general factor $G$. The transformation matrix $\Psi_{mp}$ is identical with $\Lambda_{mp}$ except for the added column $G$ with elements $\psi_{mg}$, which are to be determined. Consider the matrix $T$ as an extension of the factor matrix $F$. The rows of $T$ give the direction cosines of the primary vectors $T_t$ with elements $t_{tm}$. The same transformation gives

(2) $$T_{tm}\Psi_{mp} = V_{tp} ,$$

which is the diagonal matrix $D$ except for the first column. Applying the transformation $\Psi_{mg}$, we have

(3) $$T_{tm}\Psi_{mg} = r_{tg} ,$$

*Table 4*

*Case 1. Transformation from* F *to* V, *Including the Column Vector* G

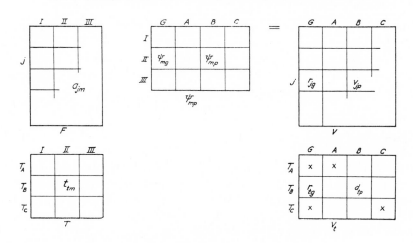

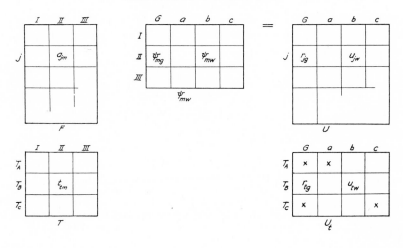

*Case 2. Transformation from* F *to* U, *Including the Group Factors and the Column Vector* G

where $r_{tg}$ is the first column of $V_t$ and its elements are the correlations of the primary factors with the general factor $G$. These are known from the factoring of the unit-rank correlation matrix for the primaries. Then

(4) $$\Psi_{mg} = T_{tm}^{-1} r_{tg} \; ;$$

and, since $T = D\Lambda^{-1}$, we have

(5) $$\Psi_{mg} = \Lambda D^{-1} r_{tg} \; ,$$

from which the first column of $\Psi_{mg}$ can be computed. Hence the column $G$ of the augmented oblique factor matrix $V$ becomes known.

*Case 2. Transformation from* F *to* U, *including group factors and general factor* G

Here the computation starts again with the orthogonal factor matrix $F$, and the objective is to determine the saturations of the tests $j$ with the $r$ group factors and the second-order general factor $G$. This transformation is also shown in *Table 4* in rectangular notation by the equation

(6) $$F_{jm}\Psi_{mw} = U_{jw} \; ,$$

where $U$ is the factor matrix, showing the projections of tests $j$ on group factors and general factor $G$. These $(r+1)$ mutually orthogonal factors will be designated by the subscript $w$. The first column of this matrix is again the column of correlations $r_{jg}$. If the same transformation is applied to the matrix $T$ for the primary vectors, we have

(7) $$T_{tm}\Psi_{mw} = U_{tw,}$$

which is also a diagonal matrix except for the first column, which contains the correlations $r_{tg}$ between the primary factors and the second-order general factor $G$. These saturations can be determined from the unit-rank correlation matrix $TT' = R_t$ for the primary factors.* Consider the first row of $U_t$. The two entries in this row show the direction cosines of $T_A$ in terms of the orthogonal frame $G$, $a$, $b$, and $c$. The primary vector $T_A$ is a linear combination of the two orthogonal unit vectors $G$ and $a$. Hence, when $r_{1g}$ is known, we have

(8) $$r_{1g}^2 + u_{12}^2 = 1$$

* Elsewhere we have denoted this matrix $R_{pq}$, but we are here using the subscript $t$ for the primary vectors $T_t$ and reserving the subscripts $p$ and $q$ for the primary reference vectors $A$, $B$, and $C$. Hence the correlations of the primary factors are here denoted $R_t$ instead of $R_{pq}$.

or

(9) $$r_{Ag}^2 + u_{Aa}^2 = 1 ,$$

so that the element $u_{Aa}$ is known. The other diagonal elements of $U_t$ are determined in the same way, so that, for example,

(10) $$r_{Bg}^2 + u_{Bb}^2 = 1 .$$

When the matrix $U_t$ is known, we have, by (7),

(11) $$\Psi_{mw} = T^{-1}U_t$$

or

(12) $$\Psi_{mw} = \Lambda D^{-1}U_t ,$$

so that the transformation $\Psi_{mw}$ is known. The saturations of tests $j$ on the second-order general factor $G$ and the group factors $w$ can then be computed.

The transformation matrix $\Psi_{mw}$ represents a rigid rotation from one orthogonal frame to another orthogonal frame, and hence this transformation matrix must be orthogonal by rows. A fourth row could be added to $\Psi_{mw}$ for a fourth orthogonal unit vector $IV$ with cell entries which normalize each column. Then we should have an orthogonal matrix of order $4 \times 4$.

*Case 3. Transformation from* V *to* U, *including the group factors and column vector* G

Here it is assumed that the computations are to be made from the oblique factor matrix $V$. In *Table 5* we have the transformation equation in rectangular notation, namely,

(13) $$V_{jp}\Psi_{pw} = U_{jw} ,$$

which gives the saturations of the tests $j$ on the group factors and on the general factor. If the factor matrix $V$ is extended to include the primary vectors $T_t$, we have the diagonal matrix $D$. Applying the same transformation to $D$, we have

(14) $$D_{tp}\Psi_{pw} = U_t,$$

so that

(15) $$\Psi_{pw} = D^{-1}U_t .$$

When the elements of $U_t$ have been determined as for Case 2, the transformation $\Psi_{pw}$ can be written by merely adjusting the rows of $U_t$ by the multipliers of $D_{tp}^{-1}$. The transformation $\Psi_{pw}$ is then known.

Table 5

Case 3. Transformation from V to U, Including
the Group Factors and the Column Vector G

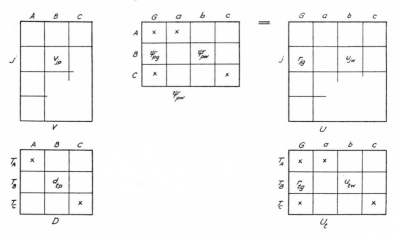

Case 4. Transformation from V to Column Vector G

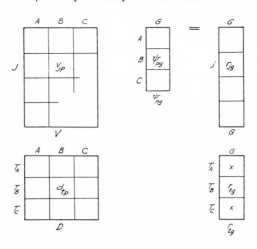

*Case 4. Transformation from V to column vector G*

This is the simplest case and perhaps the most useful as regards the second-order domain. The matrix $V$ is known in determining the simple structure and the primaries. The saturations of the tests $j$ on the second-order general factor $G$ are of interest, and these can be determined as linear combinations of the columns of $V$. Here we have the transformation shown in *Table 5*, namely,

$$V_{jp}\Psi_{pg} = r_{jg} .$$ (16)

Applying the same transformation to $D_{tp}$, we have

$$D_{tp}\Psi_{pg} = r_{tg} .$$ (17)

The elements of the column vector $r_{tg}$ are known from the correlation matrix $TT' = R_t$ of the primaries. Then

$$\Psi_{pg} = D_{tp}^{-1} r_{tg} ,$$ (18)

and hence the column vector $\Psi_{pg}$ is known. In computing, it is necessary only to multiply the elements $r_{tg}$ by the corresponding diagonal elements of $D_{tp}^{-1}$ to determine $\Psi_{pg}$. The desired column vector, $r_{jg}$, can then be determined.

### A trapezoid population

In previous studies of factorial theory it has been found useful to illustrate the principles by means of a population of simple physical objects or geometrical figures. The box population was used to illustrate three correlated factors and their physical interpretation. In the present case we want four factors in the first-order domain, which, by their correlations of unit rank, determine a general second-order factor. The correlations of three variables can nearly always be accounted for by a single factor, and hence it seems better to choose a four-dimensional system in which the existence of a second-order general factor is more clearly indicated by the unit rank of the correlations of four primary factors. For the present physical illustration we have chosen a population of trapezoids whose shapes are determined by four primary parameters or factors.

The measurements on the trapezoids are indicated in *Figure 5*. The base line is bisected, and the length of each half is denoted by the parameter $c$. An ordinate is erected at this mid-point, and its length is $h$. This ordinate divides the top section into two parts, which are denoted $a$ and $b$ as shown. These four parameters, $a$, $b$, $c$, and $h$, completely determine the figure. The test battery was represented by sixteen measurements, which are drawn in the figure. The parameters $a$, $b$, $c$, and $h$ are given code numbers *1*, *2*, *3*, and *4*, respectively. Variables *(12)* and *(13)* are the two areas as shown. The sum of *(12)* and *(13)* equals the total area of the trapezoid. In general, each of these measurements is a function of two or three of the parameters but not of all four of them, and hence we should expect a simple structure in this set of measurements. There is a rather general impression that a simple structure is necessarily confined to the positive manifold. In order to offset this impression we included here three additional measures, which extend the simple structure beyond the positive manifold. These three additional measures are as follows:

$$14 = (1)/(2) = a/b\,, \quad 15 = (2)/(3) = b/c\,, \quad 16 = (1)/(3) = a/c\,.$$

These three measures will necessarily introduce negative saturations on some of the basic factors.

In *Table 6* we have a list of dimensions for a set of thirty-two trapezoids. These will constitute the trapezoid population. Each figure was drawn to

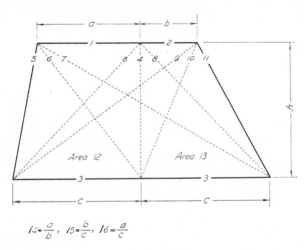

FIGURE 5

scale on cross-section paper, and then the sixteen measurements were made on each figure. These constituted the test scores for the present example. In setting up the dimensions of *Table 6* the numbers were not distributed entirely at random. To do so would tend to make the correlations between the four basic parameters, *a*, *b*, *c*, and *h*, approach zero, and this would lead to an orthogonal simple structure in which there would be no provocation to investigate a second-order domain. The manner in which the generating conditions of the objects determine the factorial results will be discussed in a later section. *Table 6* was so constructed that, in addition to the four basic parameters, there was also a size factor, which functioned as a second-order parameter in determining correlation between the four primary factors in generating the figures.

The product-moment correlations between the sixteen measurements for the thirty-two objects were computed, and these are listed in *Table 7*. This correlation matrix was factored by the group centroid method, and the resulting factor matrix $F$ is shown in *Table 8*. The fourth-factor residuals are listed in *Table 9*, which indicates that the residuals are vanishingly small. Applying the rotational methods to the configuration, we found the transformation matrix $\Lambda$ of *Table 10*, which produced the oblique factor matrix $V$ of *Table 11*. In this matrix we are now concerned with all but the last col-

*Table 6*

*Trapezoid Parameters*

|  | $a$ | $b$ | $c$ | $h$ |
|---|---|---|---|---|
| 1 | 1 | 2 | 1 | 2 |
| 2 | 1 | 2 | 1 | 4 |
| 3 | 1 | 2 | 3 | 2 |
| 4 | 1 | 2 | 3 | 4 |
| 5 | 1 | 3 | 1 | 2 |
| 6 | 1 | 3 | 1 | 4 |
| 7 | 1 | 3 | 3 | 2 |
| 8 | 1 | 3 | 3 | 4 |
| 9 | 2 | 2 | 1 | 2 |
| 10 | 2 | 2 | 1 | 4 |
| 11 | 2 | 2 | 3 | 2 |
| 12 | 2 | 2 | 3 | 4 |
| 13 | 2 | 3 | 1 | 2 |
| 14 | 2 | 3 | 1 | 4 |
| 15 | 2 | 3 | 3 | 2 |
| 16 | 2 | 3 | 3 | 4 |
| 17 | 2 | 3 | 3 | 3 |
| 18 | 2 | 3 | 3 | 5 |
| 19 | 2 | 3 | 5 | 3 |
| 20 | 2 | 3 | 5 | 5 |
| 21 | 2 | 4 | 3 | 3 |
| 22 | 2 | 4 | 3 | 5 |
| 23 | 2 | 4 | 5 | 3 |
| 24 | 2 | 4 | 5 | 5 |
| 25 | 3 | 3 | 3 | 3 |
| 26 | 3 | 3 | 3 | 5 |
| 27 | 3 | 3 | 5 | 3 |
| 28 | 3 | 3 | 5 | 5 |
| 29 | 3 | 4 | 3 | 3 |
| 30 | 3 | 4 | 3 | 5 |
| 31 | 3 | 4 | 5 | 3 |
| 32 | 3 | 4 | 5 | 5 |

umn. When pairs of columns of the factor matrix $V$ are plotted, we have the configuration shown in the diagrams of *Figure 6*, in which a simple structure is clearly indicated. The cosine of the angle between the reference vectors is indicated on each diagram of *Figure 6*. These cosines were obtained from the relation $C = \Lambda'\Lambda$, as shown in *Table 12*.

So far in the analysis we have found that four primary factors account for the correlations, and this corresponds to the fact that we used four parameters in setting up the trapezoid figures. The four primary factors are correlated, as indicated by the obliqueness of the reference axes in the dia-

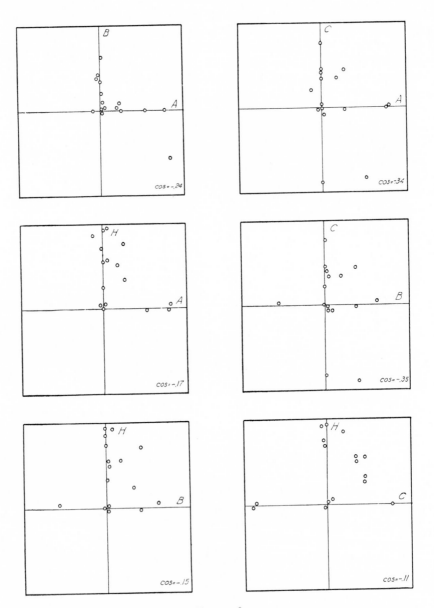

FIGURE 6

## Table 7

### Correlation Matrix

| | 1 | 2 | 3 | 4 | 5 | 6 | 7 | 8 | 9 | 10 | 11 | 12 | 13 | 14 | 15 | 16 |
|---|---|---|---|---|---|---|---|---|---|---|---|---|---|---|---|---|
| 1 | 1.00 | .50 | .50 | .32 | .29 | .58 | .72 | .49 | .58 | .45 | .31 | .66 | .53 | .76 | −.35 | −.11 |
| 2 | .50 | 1.00 | .50 | .32 | .36 | .42 | .57 | .49 | .74 | .67 | .33 | .54 | .64 | .16 | −.14 | −.23 |
| 3 | .50 | .50 | 1.00 | .32 | .52 | .42 | .88 | .82 | .90 | .45 | .30 | .78 | .75 | .19 | −.84 | −.72 |
| 4 | .32 | .32 | .32 | 1.00 | .95 | .96 | .65 | .80 | .61 | .91 | .98 | .78 | .82 | .12 | −.22 | −.15 |
| 5 | .29 | .36 | .52 | .95 | 1.00 | .90 | .75 | .90 | .75 | .90 | .94 | .84 | .89 | .05 | −.37 | −.31 |
| 6 | .58 | .42 | .42 | .96 | .90 | 1.00 | .78 | .83 | .70 | .92 | .94 | .86 | .86 | .34 | −.29 | −.09 |
| 7 | .72 | .57 | .88 | .65 | .75 | .78 | 1.00 | .95 | .95 | .74 | .64 | .95 | .91 | .39 | −.69 | −.46 |
| 8 | .49 | .49 | .82 | .80 | .90 | .83 | .95 | 1.00 | .93 | .83 | .78 | .94 | .95 | .19 | −.64 | −.52 |
| 9 | .58 | .74 | .90 | .61 | .75 | .70 | .95 | .93 | 1.00 | .79 | .60 | .90 | .93 | .11 | −.64 | −.57 |
| 10 | .45 | .67 | .45 | .91 | .90 | .92 | .74 | .83 | .79 | 1.00 | .90 | .83 | .90 | .01 | −.22 | −.21 |
| 11 | .31 | .33 | .30 | .98 | .94 | .94 | .64 | .78 | .60 | .90 | 1.00 | .77 | .80 | .11 | −.12 | −.09 |
| 12 | .66 | .54 | .78 | .78 | .84 | .86 | .95 | .94 | .90 | .83 | .77 | 1.00 | .97 | .34 | −.59 | −.39 |
| 13 | .53 | .64 | .75 | .82 | .89 | .86 | .91 | .95 | .93 | .90 | .80 | .97 | 1.00 | .12 | −.52 | −.44 |
| 14 | .76 | .16 | .19 | .12 | .05 | .34 | .39 | .19 | .11 | .01 | .11 | .34 | .12 | 1.00 | −.28 | −.34 |
| 15 | −.35 | −.14 | −.84 | −.22 | −.37 | −.29 | −.69 | −.64 | −.64 | −.22 | −.12 | −.59 | −.52 | −.28 | 1.00 | .76 |
| 16 | −.11 | −.23 | −.72 | −.15 | −.31 | −.09 | −.46 | −.52 | −.57 | −.21 | −.09 | −.39 | −.44 | −.34 | .76 | 1.00 |

grams of *Figure 6*. The next step is to determine the correlations between the primary factors that correspond to the primary reference axes. For this purpose the inverse of the matrix $C$ is computed, as shown in *Table 12*. From the diagonal values of this matrix are found the numerical values of the diagonal matrix $D$, which is also shown in *Table 12*. The inverse of this diagonal matrix is also listed. These numerical values are merely the reciprocals of the entries in $D$.

<table>
<tr><td colspan="5">Table 8</td></tr>
<tr><td colspan="5">Orthogonal Factor Matrix F</td></tr>
<tr><td></td><td>I</td><td>II</td><td>III</td><td>IV</td></tr>
<tr><td>1</td><td>.57</td><td>.44</td><td>.63</td><td>.16</td></tr>
<tr><td>2</td><td>.59</td><td>−.03</td><td>−.01</td><td>.59</td></tr>
<tr><td>3</td><td>.79</td><td>−.46</td><td>.38</td><td>.03</td></tr>
<tr><td>4</td><td>.81</td><td>.35</td><td>−.42</td><td>−.25</td></tr>
<tr><td>5</td><td>.88</td><td>.13</td><td>−.38</td><td>−.24</td></tr>
<tr><td>6</td><td>.87</td><td>.46</td><td>−.14</td><td>−.12</td></tr>
<tr><td>7</td><td>.96</td><td>−.02</td><td>.30</td><td>.00</td></tr>
<tr><td>8</td><td>.98</td><td>−.07</td><td>−.02</td><td>−.10</td></tr>
<tr><td>9</td><td>.95</td><td>−.19</td><td>.10</td><td>.27</td></tr>
<tr><td>10</td><td>.88</td><td>.25</td><td>−.36</td><td>.17</td></tr>
<tr><td>11</td><td>.78</td><td>.39</td><td>−.44</td><td>−.14</td></tr>
<tr><td>12</td><td>.97</td><td>.09</td><td>.10</td><td>−.05</td></tr>
<tr><td>13</td><td>.98</td><td>.01</td><td>−.09</td><td>.06</td></tr>
<tr><td>14</td><td>.21</td><td>.47</td><td>.65</td><td>−.38</td></tr>
<tr><td>15</td><td>−.60</td><td>.50</td><td>−.44</td><td>.37</td></tr>
<tr><td>16</td><td>−.46</td><td>.77</td><td>.02</td><td>.08</td></tr>
</table>

**Table 9**

Distribution of Residuals

| Dev. | $f$ |
|------|-----|
| .00 | 50 |
| .01 | 94 |
| .02 | 46 |
| .03 | 30 |
| .04 | 8 |
| .05 | 2 |
| .06 | 2 |
| .07 | 0 |
| .08 | 4 |
| .09 | 2 |
| .10 | 2 |

$N = 240$

**Table 10**

Transformation Matrix $\Lambda$

|      | A | B | C | H |
|------|-----|-----|-----|-----|
| I | .07 | .12 | .39 | .53 |
| II | .70 | −.01 | −.81 | .35 |
| III | .71 | −.32 | .28 | −.64 |
| IV | −.01 | .94 | −.34 | −.44 |

**Table 11**

Oblique Factor Matrix V

|    | A | B | C | H | G |
|----|-----|-----|-----|-----|-----|
| 1 | .79 | .01 | −.01 | −.02 | .68 |
| 2 | .01 | .63 | .05 | .05 | .63 |
| 3 | .00 | .01 | .78 | .00 | .73 |
| 4 | .01 | −.01 | .00 | .93 | .46 |
| 5 | −.11 | .00 | .21 | .86 | .52 |
| 6 | .28 | .03 | −.03 | .76 | .62 |
| 7 | .27 | .02 | .47 | .31 | .84 |
| 8 | .01 | .03 | .47 | .55 | .74 |
| 9 | .00 | .34 | .46 | .25 | .85 |
| 10 | −.02 | .38 | −.02 | .71 | .64 |
| 11 | .02 | .10 | −.09 | .91 | .47 |
| 12 | .20 | .04 | .35 | .50 | .78 |
| 13 | .01 | .20 | .33 | .55 | .76 |
| 14 | .81 | −.54 | .01 | .03 | .27 |
| 15 | −.01 | .41 | −.89 | −.02 | −.49 |
| 16 | .52 | .01 | −.82 | −.02 | −.31 |

In *Table 13* we have the correlation matrix $R_t$, showing the correlations between the primary factors. These are the cosines of the angles between the primary vectors. It can be seen by inspection that this matrix is close to unit rank, which indicates that a single general second-order factor can be postulated to account for the correlations between the primary factors. The saturation of each primary factor with this second-order general factor was determined by one of the special formulae for unit rank, and the satura-

Table 12

Matrix $C = \Lambda'\Lambda$

|   | A | B | C | H |
|---|---|---|---|---|
| A | 1.00 | − .24 | − .34 | − .17 |
| B | − .24 | 1.00 | − .35 | − .15 |
| C | − .34 | − .35 | 1.00 | − .11 |
| H | − .17 | − .15 | − .11 | 1.00 |

Matrix $D_{tp}$

|   | A | B | C | H |
|---|---|---|---|---|
| $T_A$ | .808 |  |  |  |
| $T_B$ |  | .808 |  |  |
| $T_C$ |  |  | .786 |  |
| $T_H$ |  |  |  | .912 |

Matrix $C^{-1}$

|   | A | B | C | H |
|---|---|---|---|---|
| A | 1.53 | .73 | .83 | .46 |
| B | .73 | 1.53 | .84 | .44 |
| C | .83 | .84 | 1.62 | .45 |
| H | .46 | .44 | .45 | 1.19 |

Matrix $D_{tp}^{-1}$

|   | $T_A$ | $T_B$ | $T_C$ | $T_H$ |
|---|---|---|---|---|
| A | 1.237 |  |  |  |
| B |  | 1.237 |  |  |
| C |  |  | 1.273 |  |
| H |  |  |  | 1.091 |

Table 13

Correlation Matrix $R_t = D_{tp}C_{pq}^{-1}D_{pt}$

|   | $T_A$ | $T_B$ | $T_C$ | $T_H$ |
|---|---|---|---|---|
| $T_A$ | 1.00 | .48 | .53 | .34 |
| $T_B$ | .48 | 1.00 | .53 | .33 |
| $T_C$ | .53 | .53 | 1.00 | .32 |
| $T_H$ | .34 | .33 | .32 | 1.00 |

Column Vector $r_{tg}$

|   | $r_{tg}$ |
|---|---|
| $T_A$ | .71 |
| $T_B$ | .70 |
| $T_C$ | .73 |
| $T_H$ | .45 |

Residuals $= R_t - r_{tg}r_{tg}'$

|   | $T_A$ | $T_B$ | $T_C$ | $T_H$ |
|---|---|---|---|---|
| $T_A$ | .50 | − .02 | .01 | .02 |
| $T_B$ | − .02 | .51 | .02 | .01 |
| $T_C$ | .01 | .02 | .47 | − .01 |
| $T_H$ | .02 | .01 | − .01 | .80 |

Column Vector
$\Psi_{pg} = D_{tp}^{-1}r_{tg}$

|   | $G$ |
|---|---|
| A | .878 |
| B | .866 |
| C | .929 |
| H | .491 |

tions are listed in the column vector $r_{tg}$. The interpretation is, for example, that the primary factor $A$ has a correlation of .71 with the second-order general factor $G$. The closeness of the correlation matrix to unit rank is shown by the small side correlations in the residual matrix of *Table 13*. The diagonal values of the residual matrix show that part of the total variance of each primary factor which it does not share with the general second-order factor. If the diagonals of this matrix vanished completely, then the primaries would have their total variance in common, and the original reduced correlation matrix for the tests would have been of unit rank.

The saturation of each test with the second-order general factor was determined as a linear combination of the columns of the oblique factor matrix $V$ of *Table 11*. The transformation of equation (18) was used, and the numerical values of $\Psi_{pg}$ were listed in *Table 13*. Column $G$ of *Table 11* was then computed by equation (16).

The second-order general factor $G$ can be interpreted in this example as a size factor, and it also indicates that, in generating the thirty-two figures, the four parameters $a$, $b$, $c$, and $h$ were not allowed to take entirely independent values. In other words, either the extreme forms of figures did not occur, or else they were used only occasionally. If the four parameters had been allowed to take entirely independent values, then there would have been an appreciable number of figures in which one of these parameters had an unusually small value, while some other parameter had some unusually large value. This interpretation of the second-order general factor leads to a consideration of what we shall call *generating parameters*. The present geometrical example illustrates the type of factorial organization that is represented diagrammatically in *Figure 2*. The problem of interpreting the four primary factors can be solved in this case without investigating the second-order domain. But if the correlations between the primary factors show unexpectedly low rank, then this fact can be utilized factorially in gaining further insight into the conditions under which the objects were generated. The four primary factors here identified by the simple structure were the four parameters that were used in setting up the problem.

### Generating parameters

In addition to the principle of simple structure for the description of each individual object, we may consider an extension of this principle to the problem of describing the manner in which the measured objects were generated. Other things being equal, we should prefer a set of descriptive parameters that give some indication of the conditions that were operative in producing the objects. To the extent that a factor analysis can throw some light on the conditions that were responsible for producing the objects and their measurable characteristics in addition to the description of each individual object, both by some simplifying set of parameters representing causative factors, the factorial methods become even more useful as tools in scientific work.

The numerical values of the trapezoid parameters in *Table 6* defined thirty-two figures of various shapes. The method of constructing the table of four measures for each figure determined whether one or more second-order factors would be present and also whether each of the primaries would be equally or differently represented in the second-order factor. The factorial result could be altered indefinitely by the manner in which the objects were generated in constructing *Table 6*. Since it is the object of factor analysis to reveal the underlying order in the domain, it is an essential part of the numerical example to show that there is a relation between the generating principles and the factorial results.

The first column of the table contains the three linear measurements 1, 2, and 3. Suppose that these were inserted in the column entirely at random. Assume that each column was similarly constructed by distributing a set of measurements entirely at random. Then we should expect zero correlations between the four primaries, $T_A$, $T_B$, $T_C$, and $T_H$. The correlation matrix for the four primary factors would be an identity matrix, and it would not be factored because the primary factors would be statistically independent. There would be no second-order factor present.

If, for each one of these thirty-two figures with uncorrelated primaries, we should draw another one similar in proportions but with twice the area and another one with similar proportions but three times the area, then we should have a set of ninety-six figures, consisting of three sets that have similar shapes but different sizes. If this new set of ninety-six figures were analyzed factorially with the same battery of sixteen measurements, we should find the same primary factors, but they would be correlated. Furthermore, the correlations of the primary factors would all be the same, so that we should have a correlation matrix for the primary factors with uniform side correlations. The reduced correlation matrix would have unit rank, and all the four primaries would have the same saturation on the second-order general factor. This would be a situation with a second-order general factor which has a uniform effect on all the primaries. Here, again, the factorial result would be determined by the manner in which the objects were generated.

Suppose that a group of persons was asked to draw some trapezoids of arbitrary shapes and that these trapezoids were assembled as a population of figures to be measured and analyzed factorially. Then we should almost certainly introduce a second-order size factor because our subjects would probably unwittingly draw the figures so that the several dimensions of each figure would be at least roughly of the same general order of magnitude. Some of the subjects might draw trapezoids of the general size, of say, 5 or 6 inches, while other subjects might draw figures only 1 or 2 inches across.

Very few would produce trapezoids that are 1 or 2 inches wide and 10 inches tall. In other words, since some subjects would draw big figures and others small ones and since they would probably produce very few extreme figures, there would be strong correlation between the primary factors, and these, in turn, could be analyzed factorially into secondary factors. In this situation the rank of the correlations of the primary factors would probably not be exactly 1, but the inference could certainly be drawn from the factorial result that secondary factors were operative to produce some big figures and some small ones in addition to the primary parameters that define the individual figures.

The interpretation of the second-order factor as a size factor in the trapezoid example should be distinguished from the size factor that could be chosen as a parameter in the first-order domain. If one of the measurements had been the total area of the trapezoid, it would have been represented by a test vector in the middle of the configuration, since it would be affected by all four of the generating parameters that were used and which appeared in the simple structure. The total-area test vector could be normalized to a unit vector, and it could be used as one of the parameters for describing the trapezoids. It would not be identical with the second-order size factor, but they would be closely related. Whether a size factor appears as a first-order or a second-order factor depends on the restrictive conditions under which the figures or objects are produced or selected and also on the selection of measurements for the test battery. It is interesting to note that here the results would indicate either that the thirty-two trapezoids had been systematically selected by some restrictive conditions or else that the objects themselves had been generated under some restrictive conditions.

When the factorial results are clear in both the first-order and the second-order domains, inferences can sometimes be drawn concerning the generating conditions that produced the individual parts of the objects. Such inferences can be the basis for formulating hypotheses that can be investigated further either by factorial methods or by more directly controlled experiments.

### Incidental parameters

So far we have considered the primary factors determined by a simple structure as representing parameters that can be given some scientific interpretation in terms of concepts that are fundamental for the domain in question. In using the simple-structure solution, which leads sometimes to the second-order domain, we have tried to avoid using arbitrary parameters whose only merit is that they serve in the condensation of numerical data. We have tried to find in the primary factors a set of parameters which not only describe the individual measurements but also reveal something about the underlying order in the domain. In looking for meaningful parameters of this kind it would be an error to assume that all the factors have significance that transcends the particular experiment or the particular group of subjects. It would be strange indeed if factor analysis were immune from the distracting circumstances of the particular occasion. The experimenter must try to distinguish that which is invariant and which transcends the particular experimental arrangement or the particular experimental group of subjects from that which is local and incidental to the particular occasion. In factor analysis we are not relieved of this difficult task any more than in other forms of scientific experimentation. In order to focus attention on this circumstance, it might be well to distinguish the primary factors which represent the invariants for which we are really looking from those primary factors which, though genuine as regards the explanation of the test variances, are local and of significance only for the experimental group or the particular occasion. *Primary factors which characterize only a particular experimental group or a particular situation may be called **incidental factors** to distinguish them from the invariants which are normally the object of scientific experimentation.* Incidental factors may appear in the first-order or in the second-order domain.

A few examples will serve to illustrate the manner in which incidental factors may appear as primaries in factorial analysis. In addition to the primary factors that would be found in different groups of subjects, we might find primary factors that are unique for the particular occasion. Suppose that an exceptionally good examiner who is skilled in obtaining good rapport with the subjects should give a part of the test battery to a part of the experimental group. A primary factor might appear for this group of tests, and the investigator might be at a loss to explain it because he would be thinking about the nature of the tests and he would try to find something common in the psychological nature of these tests. It might not occur to him that this is the very group of tests that was administered by the experienced examiner. Such a factor would probably be left without interpretation in the final results, or the interpretation might be one that would not be sustained in a subsequent experiment with different subjects and different examiners. Incidental factors are almost certainly present in every study. Hence the investigator should feel free to leave without interpretation those primary factors which do not lend themselves to rather clear scientific interpretation. Even then the interpretation should, at first, be in the nature of a hypothesis to be sustained, if possible, by subsequent factorial studies. The fact that all the variances are not adequately accounted for in the interpretation has led some students to conclude that the whole result should be discarded, but that is not the case. It is quite possible to make an important discovery concerning the primary factors that are operative in an experiment, even though the major part of the common-factor variances remains unexplained. It is assumed, of course, that such a finding could be sustained by the construction of new tests with prediction as to how they should behave factorially in new groups of differently selected subjects.

In one factorial study it was found that a primary factor was common to a set of tests that were given by the projector method with individual timing for each response. The interpretation of such a factor was uncertain. Some psychological function might be involved in the projector tests which was absent from the other tests; but the explanation might also be that some motivational condition was common to the projector tests that was absent from the other tests and which would be of only incidental significance as far as the major purposes were concerned.

Suppose that one of the examiners misunderstands the time limits for a set of tests and that he gives the shorter time limits to a part of the group of subjects for some of the tests. A factor might appear under certain circumstances that would be incidental and of no fundamental significance, but the primary factors that are significant might still be revealed. An unexpected interruption in a school examination, such as fire drill, a street parade, or the anticipation of an important school event, may act to introduce incidental factors.

One of the most important sources of incidental factors is to be found in the selective conditions. If a group of subjects is selected because of qualification in a composite of two or more tests, the unique variances of such selective tests combine to form one or more incidental common factors which would have remained a part of the unique variance if the selective conditions had not been imposed. The correlations between the factors are determined in large part by the selective conditions. If a group of subjects is selected because of certain test qualifications, it is to be expected that the primary factors will show correlations between factors that are different from the correlations between the same factors in an unselected population. It must not be assumed that the factors are different just because they correlate differently in different populations. This effect is well known with physical measurements—height and weight with intelligence, for example—whose intercorrelations are determined in large part by the selective conditions. These changes do not affect the identity of the factors. An incidental factor which is introduced by conditions of selection may be trivial or it may be significant, depending on the nature of the unique variances which are introduced into the common factors by the selective conditions.

It should be remarked that in a well-planned factorial experiment the incidental factors are usually of secondary importance in comparison with the variance that is assignable to the principal primary factors for which an experiment was planned. When one or more primary factors have relatively small variance and do not seem to lend themselves to clear interpretation, they should be reported without interpretation. Some reader of such a report may find a fruitful hypothesis for it, or the factor may be of only incidental significance.

These few examples will serve to call attention to the fact that not all the primary factors can be expected to have meaning in the fundamental sense of representing functional unities whose identity transcends the particular occasion. It does not follow that incidental factors are in any sense artifacts. They may represent genuine factors that were operating to produce the observed individual differences, but their significance may not extend beyond the particular occasion. In that sense they are irrelevant to the purposes of the experimenter, even though they are valid as factors which can sometimes be identified.

An interesting application of second-order factors is an attempt to reconcile three theories of intelligence, namely, Spearman's theory of a general intellective factor; Godfrey Thomson's sampling theory, with what he calls "sub-pools"; and our own theory of correlated multiple factors, which are interpreted as distinguishable cognitive functions. The tetrad differences vanish when there are no primary factors common to the four tests of each tetrad, the correlations being determined only by the general second-order factor.

# CHAPTER XIX

## THE EFFECTS OF SELECTION

### Types of selection

Factorial results are affected by selection of subjects and by selection of tests. It will be shown that the addition of one or more tests which are linear combinations of tests already in a battery causes the addition of one or more incidental factors. If the given test battery reveals a simple structure, the addition of tests which are linear combinations of the given tests leaves the structure unaffected, unless the number of incidental factors is so large that the common factors become indeterminate. Such a situation violates the restrictive relation between the number of tests $n$ and the number of common factors $r$.

When a factor analysis has been completed for a test battery on one group of subjects, the administration of the same battery to a differently selected group of subjects will give a different factorial result if the second group is selected by any criterion in the common factors. If a simple structure is found for the first group of subjects, the same structure will be found for the second group, but the correlations between the primary factors will be different. Incidental factors are added to the common factors under certain conditions of selection of the subjects. It will be shown that, under these various conditions of selection of tests and subjects, a simple structure remains invariant. It will also be shown that the physical interpretation of each primary factor remains the same for wide variations in selection of both subjects and tests but that their intercorrelations are altered by selection of subjects. It can readily be seen that these considerations are of fundamental significance for factor analysis as a scientific method.

These principles will be illustrated by numerical examples with the box problem. The box dimensions, $x$, $y$, and $z$, may have low correlations in one group of boxes, but these correlations may be quite different if the analysis is repeated on another group of boxes so selected that they are all, say, relatively low and squatty. Then the $x$-variance is reduced, and the correlations may be altered. Of course, these altered correlations of the primary factors do not deny the identity of the parameters, length, height, and width, for describing the box measurements in both box populations. The factors are the same and their physical interpretations are the same in both populations, even though their intercorrelations alter from one experimental population to another. This simple principle will be illustrated in numerical examples.

440

### Experimental dependence

One of the most important sources of incidental factors which are extraneous to the purposes of a factorial study is what we have called *experimental dependence*. In earlier studies with the factorial methods this source of factors was not recognized, but for a number of years this principle has been applied in the preparation of test batteries in the Psychometric Laboratory at the University of Chicago.* In *Table 1* we have the factor pattern for a set of five tests (1, 2, 3, 4, and 5) with two common factors, $A$ and $B$. The reduced correlation matrix of this battery would be of rank 2, corresponding to the number of common factors. For each of these five tests there is also indicated in the factor pattern a unique variance. Now suppose that the performance from which the score of test 1 was derived is also used to derive

*Table 1*

| | $A$ | $B$ | Unique Factors | | | |
|---|---|---|---|---|---|---|
| 1 | ✕ | ✕ | ✕ | | | |
| 2 | ✕ | ✕ | | ✕ | | |
| 3 | ✕ | ✕ | | | ✕ | |
| 4 | ✕ | ✕ | | | | ✕ |
| 5 | ✕ | ✕ | | | | |
| 1*a* | ✕ | ✕ | ✕ | | | |

another score, 1*a*. Then we have two test scores derived from the same performance, and they are quite likely to share some of the uniqueness of that particular performance. This fact is indicated in the factor pattern by the two $x$'s in the third column. Tests 1 and 1*a* share the same uniqueness. In addition, the two tests 1 and 1*a* may also have unique factors that are not shared, but these are not indicated in the factor pattern of *Table 1*.

A simple example of this manner of constructing a test battery would be to record speed and accuracy as two scores from the same test performance in the attempt to cover all aspects of the domain that is being investigated. The new factor pattern, after adding test 1*a*, has three common factors. The third common factor has saturations in only 1 and 1*a*. It should be noted that the rank of the reduced correlation matrix has been raised from 2 to 3 by this manner of assembling the test battery. In factoring the test battery it would be necessary to extract one additional factor from the correlation matrix before the residuals vanish. After rotation of axes, a third common factor would be found on which only two tests have significant saturations, namely, 1 and 1*a*. Upon examination of their nature it would be found that these two tests derive from the same test performance. Such a factor on which two variant scores of the same performance have satura-

* The importance of experimental dependence in factor analysis was first pointed out by Ledyard Tucker.

tions is called a *doublet factor*, and it is ignored in interpretation. It rarely gives any leverage on the problem of interpreting what the factor might represent, except that it is something concerned with that test performance —a fact that was known before the factoring was begun. For this reason it is best to avoid inserting in a test battery two or more measures that are taken from the same test performance.

If we push this effect to an extreme by adding a duplicate form of each test to the battery, or by using each test and a parallel form of it, then we have a battery of ten tests instead of the five tests with which we started. If there is a unique variance for each test, then the factor pattern of *Table 1* is altered by introducing five new common factors so that there are seven common factors in all, the two factors common to the five original tests and the five unique variances which have now become common factors. It is doubtful whether a useful resolution of the correlation matrix into common factors is then possible. The unique variances have been made into common variances by the inclusion of a parallel form of each test, and the common factors that might be significant would be obscured by the addition of five common factors that may make the factor problem insoluble.

It is good practice to inspect a test battery for experimental dependence before factoring is begun. One of the most common forms of experimental dependence is that in which some kind of total score is added to a test battery to be factored. A mental age, for example, is essentially a summation score. It is known before the analysis is begun that the total score will be represented by a test vector that is in the middle of the configuration and that hence it contributes nothing to the identification of the primary vectors which are at the corners or intersections of the configuration. Nor does it contribute to the identification of a second-order general factor which is defined by the correlations of the primaries. However, a total score may be found to have higher saturation on the second-order general factor than on any one of the primaries. The best procedure is to investigate the structure of the domain without the summation score and to investigate the characteristics of the summation separately.

### Linearly dependent tests

The summation score is an example of both experimental dependence and linear dependence of scores. If we add to a test battery a new test score which is merely some linear combination of test scores from the battery, we have linear dependence which generally introduces a new common factor. An exception is that in which the tests that are combined have no unique variance—a situation that arises only rarely. The introduction of a new test which is a linear combination of tests already in the battery is represented by the factor pattern of *Table 2*. Here we represent five tests (1, 2, 3, 4, and 5) with two common factors and five unique factors. If a new test were added by merely taking the sum of the test scores 1 and 2, we should have the test denoted $(1+2)$. This test is indicated as participating in the two common factors $A$ and $B$ and in the uniqueness which adds two more common factors.

## Univariate and multivariate selection of subjects

When a factor study has been done on a particular group of subjects with a given test battery, it is of fundamental interest to know how the factorial results would be altered if the analysis were repeated on another group of subjects differently selected. Here we are not interested in whether one of the groups is in any way representative of a universe while the other group is not so representative. For our purposes the two groups are coordinate, but they are differently selected so that they differ in homogeneity in one or more factors. The results for either group are assumed to be known, and we want to be able to predict the factorial results when we know how the second group was selected in comparison with the first group.

*Table 2*

|       | $A$ | $B$ | 1 | 2 | 3 | 4 | 5 |
|-------|-----|-----|---|---|---|---|---|
| 1     | ×   | ×   | × |   |   |   |   |
| 2     | ×   | ×   |   | × |   |   |   |
| 3     | ×   | ×   |   |   | × |   |   |
| 4     | ×   | ×   |   |   |   | × |   |
| 5     | ×   | ×   |   |   |   |   | × |
| $(1+2)$ | × | ×   | × | × |   |   |   |

Consider the selection of a second group of subjects so that they are more homogeneous, or less, in one of the tests in the battery. This test will be called the *selection test*, and it will be denoted $l$. The variances of all the tests have been arbitrarily reduced to unity by standardizing the scores for the first group so that in that group $\sigma_j = 1$ and, in particular, so that $\sigma_l = 1$. Let the new group be selected so as to have a different standard deviation in the selection test $l$, and let it be denoted $s_l \neq 1$. The new group of subjects will have different standard deviations in all the tests that have correlation with the selection test $l$. These new standard deviations will be denoted $s_j$. The problem then is to estimate the new test correlations and the new factorial results for the second group. The selection of a new group on the basis of their homogeneity in one of the tests has been called *univariate selection* by Godfrey Thomson, who has investigated this problem and whose results will be summarized here. Univariate selection can be either *complete* or *partial*. If the new group of subjects is so selected that all the subjects have the same score in the selection test $l$ ($\sigma_l = 0$), then we have *complete univariate selection*. If the new group is selected so that $\sigma_l \neq 0$, then the selection will be called *partial univariate selection* as to the selection variable $l$. It will be shown that interesting differences in the factorial results are determined by univariate selection when $\sigma_l > 0$ and when $\sigma_l = 0$, which represents complete homogeneity in the selection test. Further, it will be shown that the factorial results are also affected by the communality of the selection test $l$, so that the results differ according to whether $h_l^2 = 1$ or $h_l^2 < 1$.

When the selection of a second group of experimental subjects is determined by more than one selection test, we have *multivariate selection*. The principles of multivariate selection can be illustrated in terms of two selection tests, denoted $l$ and $m$. Such a situation can be analyzed as two *successive univariate selections*. In multivariate selection one is likely to be dealing with a composite selection test, $c = f(l,m)$. This is the case of multivariate selection that has been studied by Godfrey Thomson and by Walter

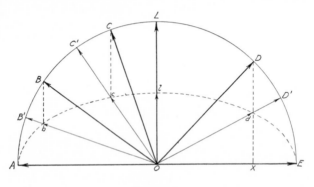

FIGURE 1

Ledermann. Here, also, the factorial results are affected by complete and partial selection in the composite criterion of selection and by the communalities of the selection variables. The theory of univariate and multivariate selection will be described and numerically illustrated, and a comparison will be made of the psychological interpretations of the resulting factors.

## Geometrical representation

Before writing the vector equations which represent the effects of univariate selection on the standard deviations and on the test correlations, we shall consider the geometrical interpretation of selection in terms of the test configuration. In *Figure 1* we have a set of six unit test vectors in a configuration of two dimensions. At the start the problem will be simplified by letting all six of these test vectors be of unit communality in the space of the two common factors, so that the diagram represents the total test space as well. The standard deviations of the tests are represented by the unit length of the test vectors, which corresponds to the fact that $\sigma_j = 1$ for all the tests. The test correlations are represented by the scalar products of pairs of test vectors. In $n$ dimensions we should have a test configuration which is spherical, in that the dispersions have all been normalized by reducing the scores to standard scores. The correlations are unaffected by this standardization.

Now let another group of experimental subjects be selected so that they show less variability in the direction of a selection test, $L$. The effect will be to alter the shape of the test configuration, so that it is narrower in the direction of the selection test. In fact, the configuration will have an ellipsoidal shape, so that the configuration of two dimensions in *Figure 1* will be an ellipse determined by the termini of the test vectors. Since the new group is selected so as to be more homogeneous in test $L$, it follows that the components in this direction of all the other tests will be affected proportionally. If the factor of test $L$ is reduced in dispersion, the same factor is also reduced proportionally in all the other tests in which this factor enters as a component.

*Figure 1* has been drawn to represent a reduction of one-half in the dispersion of test $L$. The $L$-component of the other tests is then also reduced by one-half, so that the new test vectors are depressed in the direction parallel to test $L$, as shown in the diagram. The termini of the new test vectors now define an ellipse instead of the circle. It should be noted that tests $A$ and $E$ are unaffected by the selection because these tests are orthogonal (uncorrelated) to the selection test.

The scalar product of the unit vectors $L$ and $D$ is the given correlation $r_{LD}$. This correlation is also the cosine of the angle $LOD$, and it is the projection of the vector $D$ on the vector $L$. This is the distance $DX$. It is the component of $D$ in the direction of $L$. Reducing this component by one-half, we have the new test vector $d$ as shown. The length of this vector is the standard deviation of test $D$ in the selected group. The new vector for test $L$ is $l$, which is collinear with $L$ but only half as long. The cross product $ld$ is the covariance of tests $L$ and $D$ in the new group. If each of these shortened vectors, $l$ and $d$, is extended to unit length, we have the vectors $L'$ and $D'$. It should be noted that the vectors $L$ and $L'$ are identical, whereas $D$ and $D'$ are not the same vectors. The correlation between two tests, such as $C$ and $D$, is changed by the selection to a value which is the scalar product of the new vectors $C'$ and $D'$.

## The correlations after selection

The effect of univariate selection on the test correlations can be shown vectorially. In *Figure 2* let $L$ be a unit vector representing the selection test in the total test space. Let $J$ be a unit vector representing any other test in the battery. The components of $J$ may be considered to be $OX$, which is orthogonal to $L$, and $XJ$, which is collinear with $L$. When selection is made on the basis of dispersion in $L$, the component $OX$ of $J$ will be unaffected, whereas the component $XJ$ will be affected.

Let the selection alter the dispersion of $L$ so that its standard deviation is altered from $\sigma_l = 1$ to $s_l = p$. The test $L$ is then represented by the test vector $l$, whose length is $s_l = p$. The new test vector $l$ can be written in the form

$$(1) \qquad\qquad l = L - tL ,$$

where

$$(2) \qquad\qquad t \equiv 1 - p .$$

The component $XJ$ of $J$ is the projection of $J$ on $L$, and it is also the corre-

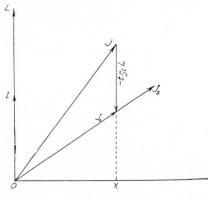

FIGURE 2

lation $r_{jl}$. Since the effect of selection on the test vector $J$ is proportional to its component collinear with $L$, we have

$$(3) \qquad\qquad J_0 = J - tr_{jl}L ,$$

where $J_0$ is the new vector for test $J$. Its new standard deviation is the length of the vector $J_0$. Squaring (3), we have

$$(4) \qquad\qquad J_0^2 = (J - tr_{jl}L)^2$$

or

$$(5) \qquad\qquad J_0^2 = s_j^2 = J^2 - 2tr_{jl}LJ + t^2r_{jl}^2L^2 .$$

The scalar product $JL$ is the correlation $r_{jl}$ and the scalar product $L^2 = J^2 = 1$. Hence

$$(6) \qquad\qquad s_j^2 = 1 - 2tr_{jl}^2 + t^2r_{jl}^2$$

which becomes

(7)
$$s_j^2 = 1 - r_{jl}^2(2t - t^2) \, .$$

For convenience let $q^2 \equiv 1 - p^2$. From (2) we then have

(8)
$$2t - t^2 = q^2 \, ,$$

so that the new variance $s_j^2$ can be written as

(9)
$$s_j^2 = 1 - q^2 r_{jl}^2 \, ,$$

by which the new standard deviation becomes

(10)
$$s_j = \sqrt{1 - q^2 r_{jl}^2} \, .$$

The numerical values of $s_j$ can then be computed, since the correlations $r_{jl}$ and the constants $p$ and $q$ are assumed to be known.

By analogy with (3) we can write the corresponding vector equation for test $K$, and we then have

(11)
$$K_0 = K - tr_{kl}L \, .$$

The new covariance $c_{jk}$ can be expressed as the scalar product $J_0K_0$, which by (3) and (11) is

(12)
$$c_{jk} = J_0K_0 = (J - tr_{jl}L)(K - tr_{kl}L) \, ;$$

and this becomes

(13)
$$c_{jk} = JK - tr_{kl}JL - tr_{jl}KL + t^2 r_{jl} r_{kl}L^2 .$$

Recalling that the scalar products $JK = r_{jk}$, $JL = r_{jl}$, $KL = r_{kl}$, and $L^2 = 1$, we get

(14)
$$c_{jk} = r_{jk} - tr_{jl}r_{kl} - tr_{jl}r_{kl} + t^2 r_{jl} r_{kl} \, .$$

Collecting terms, we obtain

(15)
$$c_{jk} = r_{jk} - r_{jl}r_{kl}(2t - t^2) \, ,$$

which, by (8), becomes

(16)
$$c_{jk} = r_{jk} - q^2 r_{jl} r_{kl} \, .$$

This equation enables us to compute the new covariances to be expected by selection on test $L$.

The new correlations can be obtained by the stretching factor, which merely reduces the new scores to standard scores. Vectorially, this stretching factor is represented by normalizing the new test vectors $J_0$ and $K_0$ to unit length. Since the lengths of these vectors are known to be their standard deviations as given by equation (10), we have for the new correlations

$$(17) \qquad {}_sr_{jk} = \frac{c_{jk}}{s_j s_k}$$

or, in more complete form,

$$(18) \qquad {}_sr_{jk} = \frac{r_{jk} - q^2 r_{jl} r_{kl}}{s_j s_k} ,$$

where ${}_sr_{jk}$ denotes the test correlations after selection. This is Godfrey Thomson's equation for the new correlations after selection.* In computing the new correlations, ${}_sr_{jk}$, it should be recalled that $r_{jj} = r_{ll} = 1$, because the present problem is concerned with the total variances of the tests. It is not limited to the common factors. The diagonals of the given correlations $r_{jk}$ are unity.

In general, the dimensionality of the test configuration in the total test space is equal to the number of tests $n$. When the test scores are normalized, each test vector is of unit length in the total test space, and the surface determined by the test vector termini is a sphere in $n$ dimensions. After selection on one of the tests so as to reduce the variance of the selection test $L$, we have an ellipsoid determined by the test vector termini. If the selection on test $L$ is complete so that all subjects in the new group have the same score in test $L$, then we should expect to lose one dimension. The surface determined by the test vector termini would then be a sphere of dimensionality $(n-1)$. If $n=3$, the spherical surface becomes a round pancake when $p$ is small and a plane when $p$ is zero.

When $s_l = p = 0$ so that $t = 1$, the selection on test $L$ is complete. The dimensionality is then reduced to $(n-1)$, and equation (18) becomes

$$(19) \qquad {}_sr_{jk} = r_{jk.l} = \frac{r_{jk} - r_{jl} r_{kl}}{\sqrt{1 - r_{jl}^2} \; \sqrt{1 - r_{kl}^2}} ,$$

---

* Godfrey H. Thomson, "The Influence of Univariate Selection on the Factorial Analysis of Ability," *British Journal of Psychology* (Gen. Sec.), Vol. XXVIII (April, 1938), Part IV; Walter Ledermann, "Note on Professor Godfrey H. Thomson's Article 'The Influence of Univariate Selection on Factorial Analysis of Ability,'" *British Journal of Psychology* (Gen. Sec.), Vol. XXIX (July, 1938), Part I; Godfrey H. Thomson and Walter Ledermann, "The Influence of Multivariate Selection on the Factorial Analysis of Ability," *British Journal of Psychology* (Gen. Sec.), Vol. XXIX (January, 1939), Part III; and Godfrey H. Thomson, *The Factorial Analysis of Human Ability* (New York: Houghton Mifflin Co., 1939), chaps. xi and xii.

which is the familiar partial correlation formula. If the three-dimensional configuration has been represented on the surface of a sphere and if the selection is complete on test $L$, the resulting two-dimensional configuration can be visualized by looking at the spherical model with test vector $L$ in the line of regard. The resulting two-dimensional configuration is then directly seen. The partial correlations would then be represented by the scalar products of pairs of these vectors after they have been normalized in the two dimensions that would be seen on a photograph of the sphere with test $L$ at the center of the picture.

It has been pointed out by Godfrey Thomson that the well-known Otis-Kelley formula for the effect of restricted selection on the correlation coefficient is a special case of equation (18). In this case $s_j = s_k$ because both variables are then assumed to be subject to the same restricted selection. Equation (18) then becomes

$$(20) \qquad {}_sr_{jk} = \frac{r_{jk} - q^2 r_{jl} r_{kl}}{s_j^2} .$$

By (10) we have, when $s_j = s_k$,

$$(21) \qquad 1 - q^2 r_{jl}^2 = 1 - q^2 r_{kl}^2 ,$$

so that

$$(22) \qquad r_{jl} = r_{kl} ;$$

and hence (20) becomes

$$(23) \qquad {}_sr_{jk} = \frac{r_{jk} - q^2 r_{jl}^2}{s_j^2} .$$

From (9) we have

$$(24) \qquad q^2 r_{jl}^2 = 1 - s_j^2 ,$$

so that (23) becomes

$$(25) \qquad {}_sr_{jk} = \frac{r_{jk} - (1 - s_j^2)}{s_j^2} ;$$

and hence

$$(26) \qquad {}_sr_{jk} s_j^2 = r_{jk} - 1 + s_j^2 ,$$

so that

$$(27) \qquad s_j^2 (1 - {}_sr_{jk}) = 1 - r_{jk} ,$$

from which we have

$$(28) \qquad \frac{1 - r_{jk}}{1 - {}_s r_{jk}} = s_j^2 = \frac{s_j^2}{\sigma_j^2},$$

which is the Otis-Kelley formula. These estimates of the effects of selection are, of course, in the nature of expected averages, from which the selected samples would show random deviations.

### The communalities

So far we have considered the effect of selection on the dispersions and correlations which imply the total test space. When the communalities are known in one correlation matrix, the new communalities can be found by a slight adaptation of equation (18). The diagonal correlations are then written $r_{jj} = h_j^2$ instead of unity. Since the selection is assumed to be made by the test scores, it follows that the uniqueness of the selection test, as well as its common-factor variance, must be involved in the result.

Writing equation (18) for the communalities, where $r_{jj} = h_j^2$, we have

$$(29) \qquad {}_s r_{jj} = {}_s h_j^2 = \frac{h_j^2 - q^2 r_{jl}^2}{1 - q^2 r_{jl}^2} \qquad (j \neq l),$$

where the denominator is written by equation (10). It should be noted that equation (29) applies to the computation of all the communalities, except for the selection test. Hence the restriction for equation (29) that $j \neq l$.

When $j = l$, we can write this equation in the modified form

$$(30) \qquad {}_s r_{ll} = {}_s h_l^2 = \frac{h_l^2 - q^2 \cdot r_{ll} \cdot h_l^2}{1 - q^2 r_{ll} h_l^2},$$

where one of the correlations $r_{ll}$ is unity and the other is $h_l^2$. Then

$$(31) \qquad {}_s h_l^2 = \frac{h_l^2 (1 - q^2)}{1 - q^2 h_l^2} = \frac{h_l^2 p^2}{1 - q^2 h_l^2},$$

by which the new communality of the selection test can be computed. Equation (31) may be derived vectorially as follows:

Let $L$ in *Figure 3* be the selection test vector in the total test space, and let $L_c$ and $L_u$ be the common-factor component and the unique component of $L$, so that $L = L_c + L_u$. By selection the configuration of test vectors is first contracted by the proportion $p$ in the direction of $L$ and then normalized. Contracting $L$ to $pL$ and then normalizing reproduces $L$ again. Hence the selection vector $L$ is not altered by selection, except, of course, when

$p = 0$, in which case $pl$ becomes a null vector and the configuration is reduced to dimensionality $(r - 1)$.

The length of the common factor component $L_c$ is $h_l$, and the projection of $L_c$ on $L$ is $pL$, whose length is $h_l^2$. The correction vector for $L_c$, which is introduced by selection, is therefore $-th_l^2\,L$, as shown in *Figure 3*. The altered vector $L_c$ can now be written as

(32) $$ {}_sL_c' = L_c - th_l^2 L , $$

where ${}_sL_c'$ represents the distortion of $L_c$ that is introduced by compressing the configuration in the direction of $L$ before the vectors are finally normalized again.

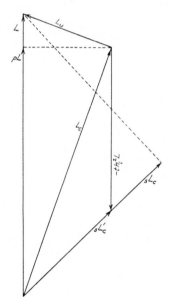

In order to find the length of ${}_sL_c'$ we write

(33) $$ ({}_sL_c')^2 = L_c^2 - 2th_l^2 L_c L + t^2 h_l^4 L^2 . $$

Since $L^2 = 1$, $L_c^2 = h_l^2$; and, since the scalar product $L_c L = h_l$, equation (33) becomes

(34) $$ ({}_sL_c')^2 = h_l^2 - 2th_l^4 + t^2 h_l^4 , $$

which, by (8), reduces to

(35) $$ ({}_sL_c')^2 = h_l^2(1 - q^2 h_l^2) . $$

The scalar product of $_sL'_c$ and $L$ in *Figure 3* can be written either as a product from equation (32) or as the product of the lengths of $L$ and $_sL'_c$ and the cosine of their angular separation. The length of $L$ is unity, the length of $_sL'_c$ is $h_l\sqrt{1-q^2h_l^2}$ ; and, since the cosine of the angular separation is also the projection of $L$ on the new common-factor space, namely, $_sh_l$, we have

$$(36) \qquad _sL'_cL = {}_sh_l \cdot h_l\sqrt{1 - q^2h_l^2} \,.$$

The same scalar product can be written by equation (32)

$$(37) \qquad _sL'_cL = LL_c - th_l^2L^2 \,,$$

which becomes

$$(38) \qquad _sL'_cL = h_l^2 - th_l^2$$

or

$$(39) \qquad _sL'_cL = h_l^2p \,.$$

Equating (36) and (39), we get

$$(40) \qquad h_l^2p = {}_sh_lh_l\sqrt{1 - q^2h_l^2} \,;$$

and writing this explicitly for the new communality of the selection test, we have

$$(31) \qquad _sh_l^2 = \frac{h_l^2p^2}{1 - q^2h_l^2} \,,$$

as previously written. By this equation the new communality of the selection test can be computed.

In solving a complete problem of this kind it is convenient to use Godfrey Thomson's equation (18) for all the new correlations, including the communalities, except that of the selection test, for which equation (31) applies.

### Computational sequence

The problem of determining the effects of univariate selection starts with the correlation matrix and the communalities, as well as the degree of selection on the selection test, which is denoted $L$ with subscript 1. It is assumed that the given scores have been standardized so that $\sigma_j = 1$ for all tests. The selection of a new group is such that the standard deviation of the selection test is changed from the given value $\sigma_l = 1$ to a new value, $s_l$, which is known. The ratio of the standard deviations is

$$\frac{s_l}{\sigma_l} = s_l = p ,$$

where $p$ is a parameter that determines the new factorial results. The following convenient constants are then computed: $p^2$, $q^2 = 1 - p^2$, and $q$.

The given correlation matrix is written with unity in the diagonals. Equation (18) can be written in the form

$$(41) \qquad R_s = MCM = M(R - UU')M ,$$

where $R_s$ denotes the expected correlation matrix after univariate selection. The matrix $U$ is a column vector with elements $u_j = qr_{jl}$, and the matrix $M$

Table 3

Given Correlation Matrix $R_1$

|   | 1 | 2 | 3 | 4 | 5 | 6 | 7 | 8 | 9 | 10 |
|---|---|---|---|---|---|---|---|---|---|----|
| 1 | 1.000 | .000 | .000 | .350 | .606 | .350 | .606 | .000 | .000 | .404 |
| 2 | .000 | 1.000 | .000 | .606 | .350 | .000 | .000 | .350 | .606 | .404 |
| 3 | .000 | .000 | 1.000 | .000 | .000 | .606 | .350 | .606 | .350 | .404 |
| 4 | .350 | .606 | .000 | 1.000 | .606 | .175 | .303 | .303 | .525 | .552 |
| 5 | .606 | .350 | .000 | .606 | 1.000 | .303 | .525 | .175 | .303 | .552 |
| 6 | .350 | .000 | .606 | .175 | .303 | 1.000 | .606 | .525 | .303 | 552 |
| 7 | .606 | .000 | .350 | .303 | .525 | .606 | 1.000 | .303 | .175 | .552 |
| 8 | .000 | .350 | .606 | .303 | .175 | .525 | .303 | 1.000 | .606 | .552 |
| 9 | .000 | .606 | .350 | .525 | .303 | .303 | .175 | .606 | 1.000 | .552 |
| 10 | .404 | .404 | .404 | .552 | .552 | .552 | .552 | .552 | .552 | 1.000 |

is a diagonal matrix with elements $d_j = 1/s_j$. Equation (41) indicates the computational order. One may compute, first, the column vector $U$, then the covariance matrix $C = UU'$ of order $n \times n$, and, finally, $R_s$. The correlation matrix $R_s$ is, of course, symmetric, and it also has unity in the diagonals.

When the correlation matrix $R_s$ has been computed, the communalities may be computed separately by equation (36), where it must be remembered that $r_{ll}$ is written as $h_l$.

### Examples of univariate selection

The principles of the preceding sections will be illustrated by a numerical example with a physical model. A variant of the box problem will be used. The factor matrix of Table 4 represents ten measures of the box problem, including the basic parameters, height, width, and length, and such other box measurements as the diagonal of each face, the area of each face, and one complex measure, such as the volume. In order to illustrate the effects of selection, the given example in *Table 4* is arranged to represent the situation in which the three basic parameters are uncorrelated. Further, in order to show the effect of selection on the communalities, these have been arranged in the factor matrix as markedly below unity, namely, .70 for all ten measures. The corresponding correlation matrix is shown in *Table 3*. These are the given data.

*Table 4*

*Given Factor Matrix* $F_0$

|  | I | II | III |
|---|---|---|---|
| 1 | .265 | − .270 | .546 |
| 2 | .542 | .632 | .047 |
| 3 | .542 | − .424 | − .473 |
| 4 | .620 | .448 | .313 |
| 5 | .566 | .116 | .555 |
| 6 | .620 | − .519 | − .165 |
| 7 | .566 | − .514 | .257 |
| 8 | .740 | − .051 | − .386 |
| 9 | .740 | .336 | − .195 |
| 10 | .815 | − .024 | .047 |

*Table 5*

*Computation of* $s_j$

|  | $r_{jl}$ | $qr_{jl}$ | $q^2r_{jl}^2$ | $s_j$ | $s_j$ | $m_j$ |  |
|---|---|---|---|---|---|---|---|
| 1 | 1.000 | .800 | .640 | .360 | .600 | 1.667 | $p = .60$ |
| 2 | .000 | .000 | .000 | 1.000 | 1.000 | 1.000 | $p^2 = .36$ |
| 3 | .000 | .000 | .000 | 1.000 | 1.000 | 1.000 | $q^2 = .64$ |
| 4 | .350 | .280 | .078 | .922 | .960 | 1.042 | $q = .80$ |
| 5 | .606 | .485 | .235 | .765 | .875 | 1.144 | $t = .40$ |
| 6 | .350 | .280 | .078 | .922 | .960 | 1.042 | $t^2 = .16$ |
| 7 | .606 | .485 | .235 | .765 | .875 | 1.144 | $s_j^2 = 1 - q^2r_{jl}^2$ |
| 8 | .000 | .000 | .000 | 1.000 | 1.000 | 1.000 | $q^2 = 1 - p^2$ |
| 9 | .000 | .000 | .000 | 1.000 | 1.000 | 1.000 | $t = 1 - p$ |
| 10 | .404 | .323 | .105 | .896 | .946 | 1.057 | $u_j = qr_{jl}$ |
|  |  |  |  |  |  |  | $m_j = 1/s_j$ |

It will now be supposed that a new collection of boxes is measured which is more homogeneous in the measurement of test 1, so that its standard deviation is .60 in the new population instead of unity, as in the given population. The problem is now to investigate the effects of such selection on the correlations and on the simple structure. The reduced standard deviation is the parameter $p$ of *Table 5*, and from this value are determined the other parameters, such as $q$, $t$, and the new standard deviations $s_j$ of the other measures that are correlated with test 1. These are all listed in *Table 5*.

In the same table we have the detailed computations for the new standard deviations $s_j$ and the reciprocal $m_j$. The computations of this table are determined by equations (9) and (10).

The new covariances after selection are determined by equation (16), which can also be written in matrix form, as shown in *Table 6*. The entries in this table are the cross products of the new scores, whose standard deviations have been depressed. Hence these entries are not correlation coefficients. The diagonal entries are the new variances of the tests. The corre-

*Table 6*

Covariance Matrix $C_s = R_1 - UU'$ *or* $c_s = r_{jk} - u_j u_k$

|    | 1 | 2 | 3 | 4 | 5 | 6 | 7 | 8 | 9 | 10 |
|----|------|------|------|------|------|------|------|------|------|------|
| 1  | .360 | .000 | .000 | .126 | .218 | .126 | .218 | .000 | .000 | .146 |
| 2  | .000 | 1.000 | .000 | .606 | .350 | .000 | .000 | .350 | .606 | .404 |
| 3  | .000 | .000 | 1.000 | .000 | .000 | .606 | .350 | .606 | .350 | .404 |
| 4  | .126 | .606 | .000 | .922 | .470 | .097 | .167 | .303 | .525 | .462 |
| 5  | .218 | .350 | .000 | .470 | .765 | .167 | .290 | .175 | .303 | .395 |
| 6  | .126 | .000 | .606 | .097 | .167 | .922 | .470 | .525 | .303 | .462 |
| 7  | .218 | .000 | .350 | .167 | .290 | .470 | .765 | .303 | .175 | .395 |
| 8  | .000 | .350 | .606 | .303 | .175 | .525 | .303 | 1.000 | .606 | .552 |
| 9  | .000 | .606 | .350 | .525 | .303 | .303 | .175 | .606 | 1.000 | .552 |
| 10 | .146 | .404 | .404 | .462 | .395 | .462 | .395 | .552 | .552 | .896 |

*Table 7*

New Correlation Matrix $R_s = MC_sM$

|    | 1 | 2 | 3 | 4 | 5 | 6 | 7 | 8 | 9 | 10 |
|----|-------|-------|-------|-------|-------|-------|-------|-------|-------|-------|
| 1  | 1.000 | .000 | .000 | .219 | .416 | .219 | .416 | .000 | .000 | .256 |
| 2  | .000 | 1.000 | .000 | .632 | .400 | .000 | .000 | .350 | .606 | .427 |
| 3  | .000 | .000 | 1.000 | .000 | .000 | .632 | .400 | .606 | .350 | .427 |
| 4  | .219 | .632 | .000 | 1.000 | .560 | .105 | .199 | .316 | .547 | .508 |
| 5  | .416 | .400 | .000 | .560 | 1.000 | .199 | .379 | .200 | .347 | .478 |
| 6  | .219 | .000 | .632 | .105 | .199 | 1.000 | .560 | .547 | .316 | .508 |
| 7  | .416 | .000 | .400 | .199 | .379 | .560 | 1.000 | .347 | .200 | .478 |
| 8  | .000 | .350 | .606 | .316 | .200 | .547 | .347 | 1.000 | .606 | .583 |
| 9  | .000 | .606 | .350 | .547 | .347 | .316 | .200 | .606 | 1.000 | .583 |
| 10 | .256 | .427 | .427 | .508 | .478 | .508 | .478 | .583 | .583 | 1.000 |

sponding correlation coefficients are shown in *Table 7*, and these represent Godfrey Thomson's equation (18) with unit diagonals. They can be obtained from the covariances of *Table 6* by the stretching factors $m_j = 1/s_j$, which are the elements of the diagonal matrix $M$. This matrix is identical with the table of covariances, except for the fact that the standard deviations have been stretched to unity.

The new communalities are determined by the detailed calculations shown in *Table 8* from (36), in which $r_{ll}$ is written as $h_l$. Finally, when the new correlation matrix with communalities in the diagonal cells is factored, we get the new factor matrix $F_s$, as shown in *Table 9*. Here the number of factors is again three, as in the given correlation matrix, thus verifying Godfrey Thomson's theorem that the rank of the correlation matrix with communalities remains unaltered with univariate selection. However, an exception should be mentioned. In complete or total univariate selection on a factor or its equivalent—a test with perfect communality—the new standard deviation of the selection test or factor is zero, and the rank of the new correlation matrix has then been reduced by 1. In the present example the rank of the new correlation matrix, after complete selection by a factor or by a perfect test, is reduced to 2. Several examples of this type will also be shown.

Perhaps the most important consideration in this problem is to ascertain what happens to the identification of the primary factors. In *Figure 4* we

Table 8

New Communalities: $_sh_j^2 = \dfrac{h_j^2 - q^2 r_{jl}^2}{1 - q^2 r_{jl}^2}$

Table 9

New Factor Matrix $F_s$

| | $h_j^2$ | $r_{jl}$ | $r_{jl}^2$ | $q^2 r_{jl}^2$ | Num. | Denom. | $_sh_j^2$ |
|---|---|---|---|---|---|---|---|
| 1 | .700 | .837 | .700 | .448 | .252 | .552 | .457 |
| 2 | .700 | .000 | .000 | .000 | .700 | 1.000 | .700 |
| 3 | .700 | .000 | .000 | .000 | .700 | 1.000 | .700 |
| 4 | .700 | .126 | .016 | .010 | .690 | .990 | .697 |
| 5 | .700 | .218 | .048 | .031 | .670 | .970 | .691 |
| 6 | .700 | .126 | .016 | .010 | .690 | .990 | .697 |
| 7 | .700 | .218 | .048 | .031 | .670 | .970 | .691 |
| 8 | .700 | .000 | .000 | .000 | .700 | 1.000 | .700 |
| 9 | .700 | .000 | .000 | .000 | .700 | 1.000 | .700 |
| 10 | .700 | .146 | .021 | .014 | .686 | .986 | .696 |

| | I | II | III |
|---|---|---|---|
| 1 | .334 | −.340 | .688 |
| 2 | .544 | .634 | .048 |
| 3 | .543 | −.425 | −.474 |
| 4 | .638 | .379 | .385 |
| 5 | .561 | .023 | .619 |
| 6 | .637 | −.538 | −.067 |
| 7 | .561 | −.507 | .359 |
| 8 | .742 | −.051 | −.387 |
| 9 | .742 | .337 | −.196 |
| 10 | .820 | −.075 | .151 |

have the configuration of test vectors before and after selection on test *1*. In this diagram the test vectors are represented by the method of extended vectors, so that the three-dimensional configuration can be seen in a plane. The given positions of the test vectors are denoted $a$, and the new positions by $b$. A glance at this figure shows that the position of the selection variable *1* remains unaltered. So do also the tests which are uncorrelated with the selection test. These are tests *2*, *3*, *8*, and *9*. These remain unaltered. The other test vectors—*4*, *5*, *6*, *7*, and *10*—move in a direction radially from the selection vector, so that the triangular configuration is still retained. In the present example the actual dimensions of the triangle even remain unaltered. We see, then, that in this example of partial univariate selection the simple structure remains invariant. If two investigators started with the two correlation matrices, one with the first group of objects and the other with the specially selected group of objects, they would arrive at the same simple structure, and they would identify the same primary factors or parameters. But their results would differ as to the correlations between the measurements with which they started. In the present example the correlations between the primary factors would remain the same for the two groups of objects. Variations of these principles will be shown in additional examples.

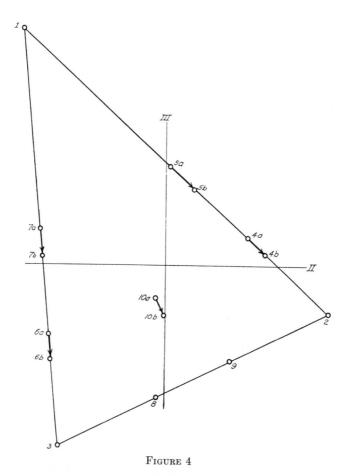

FIGURE 4

The most important principle to be drawn from analyzing the effects of selection on factorial results is that under wide variations in the conditions of selection the simple structure is invariant, so that the primary factors or parameters are the same. The correlations of primary factors are altered from one selected group to another. A simple example will serve to illustrate this principle, which is well known in other contexts. The correlations between height, weight, and intelligence can be made to take widely different values, depending on the selection of the experimental group. If children of all ages and statures are included, then the correlation between stature and intelligence will be found to be appreciable. This correlation is not spurious. It is correct to say that there actually is a high correlation between intelligence and stature for any experimental population of children with a wide range in chronological age. The taller children are generally older, and they score higher on the tests. If the experimental population is limited to point age, the correlation between stature and intelligence vanishes, or nearly so. The interpretation is not to deny the meaning of the variables or the factors. These are the same measurements of stature and test score for the two groups. It is the correlations between the factors that are altered by the selective conditions. In the box example it will be seen that the correlations between height, width, and length of the boxes can be altered by the selection of each collection of boxes, but the physical interpretation of the three parameters remains precisely the same in the several box collections. We dwell on this point in detail because it is the source of misunderstanding of the factorial methods, in that some critics are inclined to deny the validity of the physical interpretation of factors merely because their correlations are altered by conditions of selection.*

We turn now to several other examples of univariate selection with the same box problem. The detailed computations will not be repeated because the principles were illustrated with the first numerical example. The next few examples have been prepared to show the effects of univariate selection of *factors*, as distinguished from selection by *tests*. The three primary factors for the box problem may be denoted $P_1$, $P_2$, and $P_3$. These may be regarded as unit vectors determined by the first three measures, *1*, *2*, and *3*, in the battery. *Figure 5* has been drawn to show the effects of univariate selection on the factor $P_1$. In this set of diagrams—*Figures 5–10*, inclusive—the selection variable is denoted $S$. The method of extended vectors has been used to show the entire three-dimensional configuration in a single diagram in the plane of the paper. The given positions of the test vectors are shown by their numerical identification—*1*, *2*, *3*, etc. The new positions

---

* Godfrey Thomson, who has contributed fundamental theory on the problem of univariate and multivariate selection in relation to factor analysis, has expressed doubt as to whether the primary factors can be interpreted as basic and identifiable psychological processes. His reason is mainly that the correlations between the primary factors of a simple structure are altered and determined in part by the conditions of selection and, further, that incidental factors can be added by certain conditions of multivariate selection. Our interpretation is that the primary factors represent the same basic processes in different conditions of selection and that it is the correlations between these parameters that are altered rather than the fundamental meaning of the parameters themselves. The incidental factors can be classed with the residual factors, which reflect the conditions of particular experiments. These extraneous factors do not show the invariant characteristics that have been shown for the more basic primary factors. In presenting Godfrey Thomson's theoretical work on the selection problem, we are giving a less pessimistic interpretation of the factorial results.

are denoted *1x*, *2x*, *3x*, etc. This set of six diagrams was designed by Led-yard Tucker to show graphically the effects of various conditions of uni-variate selection on the test configuration.

*Figure 5* shows the effect of partial selection on the factor $P_:$. Note that the position of the selection variable $S = 1 = 1x$ remains unaltered. The positions of the test vectors *2*, *3*, *8*, and *9* remain the same because they are uncorrelated with the factor $P_1$. The other test vectors move radially from the selection variable *S*, as shown in the triangular configuration. The simple structure is unaltered. In the same figure we have a diagram showing the effect of total selection on $P_1$. This means that all the boxes in the new box population have the same height. The individual box shapes will be determined by only two parameters, since one of the parameters has become a constant and does not affect the individual differences among the

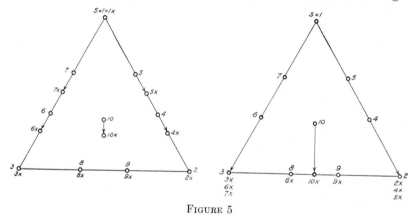

FIGURE 5

objects. Therefore, we expect the factorial result after selection to be of rank 2. This is verified in the diagram, which was plotted after making the computations that have been explained. The variable *1* disappears from the second analysis because it is a null vector. This is what happens occasionally when the communality of a variable turns out to be vanishingly small. It usually happens when the corresponding correlations are also small. The new configuration lies entirely in the base line of the figure, which represents only two dimensions.

If an investigator were to make a factor analysis of such a collection of boxes, he would find only two factors. If he were to plot the resulting configuration, he would get a simple structure, as shown in *Figure 6*. Here we see that, even though one of the three factors has been entirely eliminated from the individual differences and from the analysis, the same simple structure is identified for the remaining two factors. The interpretation of the two primary factors, width and length of boxes, is the same in the two box populations.

*Figure 7* was drawn to show the effect of univariate selection on the composite variable $(P_2+P_3)$. The first diagram shows the effect of partial selection on this composite variable, which is denoted $S$. The given configuration of ten vectors is shown on the inside triangle, which is identical with that of *Figure 5*. The effect of selection is to move the termini of the test vectors radially from the selection vector to the new positions, denoted *1x*, *2x*, *3x*, etc. The variable *1 = 1x* is unaltered because it is orthogonal to the composite variable $S$. The others move as shown by the radial lines from $S$. The new configuration shows the same simple structure as before, with the same primary factors in the tests *1*, *2*, *3*. Hence the interpretation of the primary factors would be the same as before selection. The correlations between the primary factors have been altered.

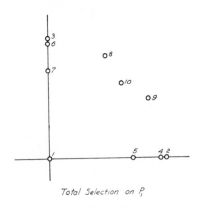

Total Selection on $P_1$

FIGURE 6

In the second diagram of *Figure 7* we have the effect of total selection on the composite variable $S = (P_2+P_3)$. Here we start, as before, with the given triangular configuration of ten test vectors extended to the tangent plane. The new configuration, after selection on $S$, is of two dimensions, as is to be expected after complete selection on a factor. The new configuration is indicated along the upper horizontal line of the diagram. Tests *2x* and *9x* are orthogonal to test *1*, and so are also tests *3x* and *8x*. If an investigator were to start with the selected box population and proceed with a factor analysis, he would find only two factors in this case. The configuration that he would find is shown in *Figure 8*, where it will be seen that the simple structure is again the same for the two factors that remained in the system. The primary factors are again identified by test *1* and the combination of tests *2* and *3*. The physical interpretation of the factor $P_1$ would be the same as before. The interpretation of factors $P_2$ and $P_3$ would be obscured because the investigator would supposedly not know that he was dealing with a freak collection of boxes, which had been so selected that the sum of the width and length of each box was the same for all. In the

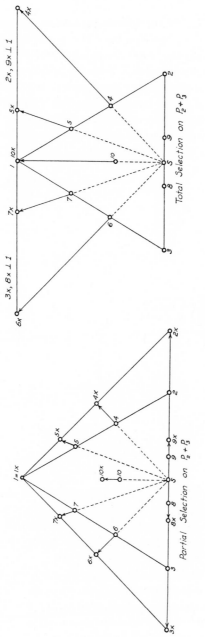

FIGURE 7

first diagram of *Figure 7* it is seen that with partial selection this ambiguity does not arise.

We turn next to an even more stringent selective condition, namely, the composite variable $S=(P_1+P_2+P_3)$. This is the sum of the three box dimensions. In *Figure 9* the inside triangle shows the given configuration as before. The composite variable $S$ is in the middle of the configuration at test *10*. The new configuration, after partial selection on the composite variable $S$, is shown by the outside triangular configuration. The new test vectors all lie in the outside triangle, and their locations are determined by the radial lines from the selection variable as before. It can be seen that the

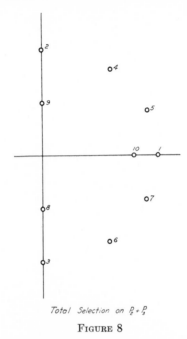

Total Selection on $P_2 + P_3$

FIGURE 8

simple structure is here again retained after selection and that the primary factors are the same, namely, those which are determined by tests *1*, *2*, and *3*. Hence we conclude that partial selection on a linear combination of even all the factors leaves the simple structure, as well as the physical interpretation of the primary factors, invariant.

However, if the boxes are assembled so as to satisfy the conditions of total selection on the composite variable $S$, then the rank is reduced to 2; and in *Figure 10* we have the plot that an investigator would make with the new configuration. Here it is seen that the simple structure has been destroyed, so that the primary factors are no longer identifiable. We conclude, therefore, that conditions of selection can be made so extreme that the simple structure is destroyed. In such a population the primary factors cannot be

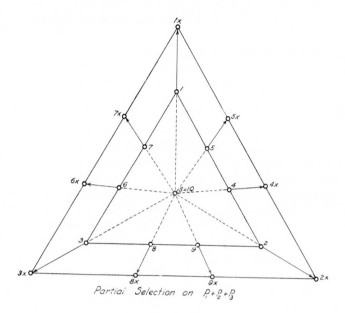

Partial Selection on $P_1 + P_2 + P_3$

FIGURE 9

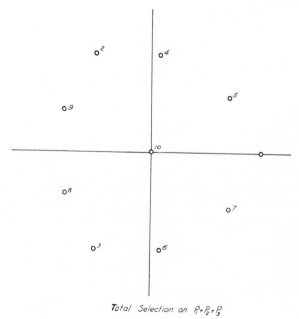

Total Selection on $P_1 + P_2 + P_3$

FIGURE 10

determined. In this case we should be dealing with a set of boxes so selected that the sum of the three box dimensions was the same for every box in the collection. For partial selection, as shown in *Figure 9*, the simple structure remains invariant. Hence we conclude that it is the total selection on this composite variable which destroys the simple structure.

## Multivariate selection of subjects

So far it has been assumed that the selection of subjects is determined by their homogeneity in a *single* criterion variable, even though this variable is itself a linear combination of several factors. Selection of subjects can be made to depend on several variables, with the restriction that the intercorrelations of these variables must have certain prescribed values. In these cases it may not be possible to describe the correlations in the selected group as an alteration in the homogeneity of a single variable, not even a composite selection criterion. We then have *multivariate selection* of subjects. However, multivariate selection can be described in terms of successive univariate selection by the formulae already discussed, provided that the successive variables are properly chosen. This procedure will be illustrated by a numerical example that has been used by Godfrey Thomson in his discussions of multivariate selection.[*]

In analyzing multivariate selection it is convenient to divide the variables into two groups, namely, those which are directly involved in the selection and those which are not directly involved. The former, by which the selection is determined, will be denoted by subscript $j$ and the others will be denoted by subscript $k$. The given correlation matrix can then be sectioned in the following manner:

$$\begin{array}{|c|c|} \hline R_{jj} & R_{jk} \\ \hline R_{kj} & R_{kk} \\ \hline \end{array} \ .$$

The correlations of the selection tests are shown in section $R_{jj}$ before selection. The correlations of the same tests after selection may be symbolized by the matrix $V_{jj}$, which shows the new correlations that are imposed by selection. The new correlation matrix can then be symbolized in sectioned form as follows:

$$\begin{array}{|c|c|} \hline V_{jj} & V_{jk} \\ \hline V_{kj} & V_{kk} \\ \hline \end{array} \ ,$$

[*] *The Factorial Analysis of Human Ability*, p. 187.

which represents the correlations to be expected after selection. The diagonal elements of $V_{jj}$ show the new variances of the selection tests, and the side entries of $V_{jj}$ show the covariances to be imposed by selection.

The problem is, then, to determine the expected correlations in the sections $V_{kk}$ and $V_{jk}$, which is the transpose of $V_{kj}$. A formal matrix solution to this problem has been written by A. C. Aitken and reported by Godfrey Thomson.* The solution is as follows:

$$(42) \qquad V_{jk} = V_{jj}R_{jj}^{-1}R_{jk},$$

$$(43) \qquad V_{kk} = R_{kk} - R_{kj}(R_{jj}^{-1} - R_{jj}^{-1}V_{jj}R_{jj}^{-1})\,R_{jk},$$

$$(44) \qquad V_{kj} = V_{jk}'.$$

Godfrey Thomson's numerical example will be used for the present discussion to illustrate the analysis of multivariate selection in terms of suc-

*Table 10*

*Given Correlation Matrix*

*Table 11*

*Given Factor Matrix*

| | L | M | 1 | 2 | 3 | 4 | 5 | 6 | | I |
|---|---|---|---|---|---|---|---|---|---|---|
| L | 1.0000 | .0000 | .3741 | − .3741 | .0935 | .0802 | .0668 | .0534 | | |
| M | .0000 | 1.0000 | .9274 | .9274 | .6416 | .5500 | .4583 | .3667 | 1 | .9 |
| 1 | .3741 | .9274 | 1.00 | .72 | .63 | .54 | .45 | .36 | 2 | .8 |
| 2 | − .3741 | .9274 | .72 | 1.00 | .56 | .48 | .40 | .32 | 3 | .7 |
| 3 | .0935 | .6416 | .63 | .56 | 1.00 | .42 | .35 | .28 | 4 | .6 |
| 4 | .0802 | .5500 | .54 | .48 | .42 | 1.00 | .30 | .24 | 5 | .5 |
| 5 | .0668 | .4583 | .45 | .40 | .35 | .30 | 1.00 | .20 | 6 | .4 |
| 6 | .0534 | .3667 | .36 | .32 | .28 | .24 | .20 | 1.00 | | |

cessive univariate selection. His numerical example is reproduced in the correlations between the six numbered variables of *Table 10*. The columns $L$ and $M$ have been added, and they will be described presently. The given correlation matrix is of order $6 \times 6$, and it is of unit rank. The corresponding one-column factor matrix is shown in *Table 11*. In order to illustrate multivariate selection, Thomson imposes a change in the variances of tests 1 and 2 and also in the covariance $c_{12}$. The given section of the correlation matrix for these two variables is

$$R_{jj} = \begin{array}{c} 1 \\ 2 \end{array} \begin{array}{|c|c|} \hline 1.00 & .72 \\ \hline .72 & 1.00 \\ \hline \end{array}$$

$$\qquad \begin{array}{cc} 1 & 2 \end{array}$$

* *Ibid.*, p. 189.

where the unit diagonals represent the unit variances of the tests at the start and where the given correlation $r_{12} = .72$. This section of the correlation matrix is to be changed by selection to

$$
V_{jj} = \quad
\begin{array}{c|c|c}
 & 1 & 2 \\
\hline
1 & .36 & .30 \\
\hline
2 & .30 & .36 \\
\end{array}
$$

where the two test variances are depressed to .36 and the covariance to $c_{12} = .30$. The problem is now to determine the expected covariances in the

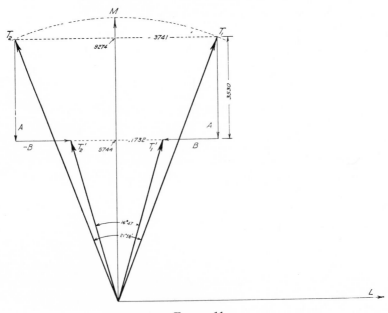

FIGURE 11

rest of the $6 \times 6$ matrix and then to factor the corresponding correlation matrix. The direct method of Aitken can be used to solve the problem. It can also be represented as a form of successive univariate selection.

In *Figure 11* the two unit vectors, $T_1$ and $T_2$, represent the two tests 1 and 2. They have been drawn so that the cosine of the angular separation is .72, which is the given correlation $r_{12}$. The relation between these two tests which is imposed by selection is shown by the two vectors $T_1'$ and $T_2'$, with lengths of .60 and scalar product of .30 as required by the new matrix $V_{jj}$. The two configurations have been arranged in *Figure 11* to utilize the symmetry in this case in order to simplify the transformation from one to the

other. The new orthogonal selection variables are drawn in the figure, namely, $L$ and $M$.

The transformation from the given configuration to the new configuration can be expressed in terms of two successive univariate selections, first
on $M$ and then on $L$. The first selection on $M$ is specified by the restriction
that

$$p = \frac{.5744}{.9274} = .6193 ,$$

so that the new vectors become $(T_1-A)$ and $(T_2-A)$. Then follows a univariate selection on $L$, with the value

$$p = \frac{.1732}{.3741} = .4630 ,$$

so that the new vectors become

(45)                    $$T_1' = (T_1 - A - B) ,$$

(46)                    $$T_2' = (T_2 - A + B) ,$$

which define the new configuration and the covariances.

The first step is to add two rows and columns to the given correlation
matrix for $L$ and $M$ in *Table 10*. The unit vector $M$ bisects the angle between $T_1$ and $T_2$, so that we can write

(47)                    $$M = c_1(T_1 + T_2) .$$

Hence

(48)                    $$r_{jm} = c_1(r_{j1} + r_{j2}) ,$$

where

(49)                    $$c_1 = \frac{1}{\sqrt{2(1 + r_{12})}} .$$

In the same manner the unit vector $L$ is a linear combination of $T_1$ and $T_2$,
orthogonal to $M$, so that

(50)                    $$L = c_2(T_1 - T_2) ;$$

and hence

(51)                    $$r_{jl} = c_2(r_{j1} - r_{j2}) ,$$

where

(52) $$c_2 = \frac{1}{\sqrt{2(1 - r_{12})}}.$$

Having thus determined the correlations of the six tests with $L$ and $M$ in *Table 11*, we determine the new covariances after selection on $M$. These covariances are shown in *Table 12*. The covariances after further selection on $L$ are then computed in the same manner, and these are listed in *Table 13*. It is not necessary here to express *Table 12* in the form of correlation coefficients.

*Table 12*

*Covariance Matrix after Selection on* M

|   | L | M | 1 | 2 | 3 | 4 | 5 | 6 |
|---|---|---|---|---|---|---|---|---|
| L | 1.0000 | .0000 | .3741 | − .3741 | .0935 | .0802 | .0668 | .0534 |
| M | .0000 | .3835 | .3557 | .3557 | .2460 | .2109 | .1757 | .1406 |
| 1 | .3741 | .3557 | .4699 | .1899 | .2632 | .2255 | .1880 | .1504 |
| 2 | − .3741 | .3557 | .1899 | .4699 | .1932 | .1655 | .1380 | .1104 |
| 3 | .0935 | .2460 | .2632 | .1932 | .7462 | .2024 | .1687 | .1350 |
| 4 | .0802 | .2109 | .2255 | .1655 | .2024 | .8135 | .1446 | .1157 |
| 5 | .0668 | .1757 | .1880 | .1380 | .1687 | .1446 | .8705 | .0964 |
| 6 | .0534 | .1406 | .1504 | .1104 | .1350 | .1157 | .0964 | .9171 |

$p = \dfrac{.5744}{.9274} = .6193$

$p^2 = .3835$
$q^2 = .6165$
$q = .7852$

*Table 13*

*Covariance Matrix after Selection on* L

|   | L | M | 1 | 2 | 3 | 4 | 5 | 6 |
|---|---|---|---|---|---|---|---|---|
| L | .2145 | .0000 | .0802 | − .0802 | .0200 | .0172 | .0143 | .0115 |
| M | .0000 | .3835 | .3557 | .3557 | .2460 | .2109 | .1757 | .1406 |
| 1 | .0802 | .3557 | .3599 | .2999 | .2357 | .2019 | .1684 | .1347 |
| 2 | − .0802 | .3557 | .2999 | .3599 | .2207 | .1891 | .1576 | .1261 |
| 3 | .0200 | .2460 | .2357 | .2207 | .7393 | .1965 | .1638 | .1311 |
| 4 | .0172 | .2109 | .2019 | .1891 | .1965 | .8084 | .1404 | .1123 |
| 5 | .0143 | .1757 | .1684 | .1576 | .1638 | .1404 | .8670 | .0936 |
| 6 | .0115 | .1406 | .1347 | .1261 | .1311 | .1123 | .0936 | .9149 |

$p = \dfrac{.1732}{.3741} = .4630$

$p^2 = .2144$
$q^2 = .7856$
$q = .8863$

In *Table 14* are recorded the correlation coefficients corresponding to the covariances of *Table 13*, and in *Table 15* we have the final factor matrix after selection, which is also represented in *Figure 12*. It will be seen that the final factor matrix is of unit rank, except for the doublet factor in the selection tests 1 and 2. The nature of this doublet factor is explained in *Table 2* at the beginning of this chapter. The additional test is there a linear combination of the first two tests of the battery. Here the same effect is shown because the two unique factors have been introduced into the common factors to become an incidental common factor. The multivariate selection with the restriction that the new correlation $r_{12}$ shall have an arbitrarily chosen value of $r_{12} = .83$ introduces an incidental factor, namely, the doublet factor II in *Table 15*. This introduction of an incidental factor into the common factors has not disturbed the single common factor, I, with which the problem started in *Tables 10* and *11*. The saturations of the factor I have been altered, but not its identity.

## Summary

Since factor analysis starts with a set of measurements for each individual member of an experimental group, it is evidently of fundamental significance

| | | | | | | | | | |
|---|---|---|---|---|---|---|---|---|---|

*Table 14*

*New Correlation Matrix*

| | 1 | 2 | 3 | 4 | 5 | 6 |
|---|---|---|---|---|---|---|
| 1 | .87 | .83 | .46 | .38 | .30 | .24 |
| 2 | .83 | .78 | .43 | .35 | .28 | .22 |
| 3 | .46 | .43 | .31 | .26 | .21 | .16 |
| 4 | .38 | .35 | .26 | .21 | .17 | .13 |
| 5 | .30 | .28 | .21 | .17 | .14 | .11 |
| 6 | .24 | .22 | .16 | .13 | .11 | .08 |

*Table 15*

*New Factor Matrix*

| | I | II |
|---|---|---|
| 1 | .82 | .45 |
| 2 | .76 | .45 |
| 3 | .56 | 0 |
| 4 | .46 | 0 |
| 5 | .37 | 0 |
| 6 | .29 | 0 |

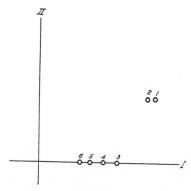

FIGURE 12

to know how the factorial results are affected by the manner in which the experimental individuals are selected. To the extent that a simple structure and its associated primary factors are invariant under changes in selective conditions for the experimental group, we can have confidence that the primary factors represent identifiable processes whose nature transcends the circumstances under which the experimental subjects happen to be selected. It does not follow that these identifiable and interrelated processes are therefore unique in the mathematical sense of being the only set of parameters that can be used for describing the dynamic system that produces the observed individual differences. The invariance of simple structure under changes in selective conditions does imply, however, that the processes so identified are likely to be fruitful landmarks in a logical description of the system.

By *univariate selection* is meant the selection of a group of experimental subjects so that their standard deviation in a selection variable shall be different from unity, which is the dispersion in a set of normalized scores for an initial group of subjects. The criterion or selection variable may be defined by one of the tests in the battery, or it may be a linear combination of several tests or factors of the initial analysis. If the selection criterion is correlated with any of the tests in the battery, then there will be an effect on the correlations between the tests in the selected group of subjects. The expected correlations in the new group can be computed by Godfrey Thomson's equation (18). The new communalities can be determined in an analogous manner.

When the new group of subjects is assembled according to dispersion in a selection variable $L$, so that its standard deviation $s_l$ satisfies the inequality $0 \neq s_l \neq 1$, then the new group is assembled by *partial selection* in the sense that variance in the selection variable is not entirely excluded; but it is different from that of the initial group of subjects. When the new group is assembled so that its dispersion in the selection variable vanishes entirely, then its standard deviation $s_l = 0$, and the new group is then described by *complete or total selection* on the selection variable.

The rank of the reduced correlation matrix for the new group is the same as for the initial group of subjects, except when the selection is complete on the selection variable, in which case the dimensionality is reduced by 1. We then have first-order partial correlation coefficients, with the selection variable constant, and the rank $r$ is then reduced to $(r-1)$.

In partial selection when the rank of the reduced correlation matrix is invariant, the simple structure is also invariant, but the correlations between the primary parameters are altered. The interpretation of the primary factors remains the same in both groups.

In total selection, when the rank of the reduced correlation matrix is reduced by 1, the simple structure may be distorted, depending on the relation of the total selection to the primary factors. The interpretation of the primary factors affected by the total selection may then be obscured.

When the new group is selected so as to satisfy conditions on two independent selection variables, the variances of the selection variables are affected and also their covariances. Such a situation is called *multivariate selection*. Multivariate selection can be described in terms of successive univariate selections. The expected correlations after multivariate selection can be computed by matrix formulae derived by Aitken. The new correlations can also be determined by the univariate formula of Godfrey Thomson applied to represent successive univariate selections.

With partial multivariate selection of a new group of subjects, the rank of the reduced correlation matrix is augmented by one or more incidental factors. The number of incidental selection factors is determined by the number of independent variables that participate in the multivariate selection. The simple structure remains invariant, so that the primary factors can be identified with the same interpretation as for the initial group of subjects. The additional factors may show appreciable variance, but they will not be invariant for differently selected groups, since they are determined by the conditions of selection of each group. If the attempt is made to interpret the incidental selection factors as basic parameters, then the interpretation will fail to be sustained in subsequent factorial studies of the same domain with differently selected subjects. The primary factors should be identified in the differently selected groups.

With total multivariate selection the rank of the correlation matrix is reduced by one or more factors, which depend on the number of successive variables on which the selection is complete; but the rank is also augmented by incidental selection factors, which depend on the number of variables that participate in the selection. With total selection involving the primary factors, the simple structure can be so distorted that the primaries may not be identified. For this reason it is well to allow as much variation as possible among the subjects in the domain to be investigated, thus practically eliminating the possibility of total selection within the parameters that are to be sought. In factorial investigation it is not of any consequence whether any of the groups of experimental subjects are representative of a general population. The important consideration is that the experimental subjects should vary among themselves as much as possible within the domain that is being investigated.

The analysis of these various cases of selection is very encouraging, in that a simple structure has been shown to be invariant under widely different selective conditions. Hence the scientific interpretation of the primary factors as meaningful parameters can be expected to transcend the widely different selective conditions of the objects that are measured and factorially analyzed. This encouraging finding leads to a recommendation for the factorial study of any domain. When a simple structure has been found for a test battery that has been given to an experimental population and when a plausible interpretation of the primary factors has been found, these should be regarded as hypotheses to be verified by giving the same test battery to new experimental populations that should be selected in different ways. If the primary factors are in the nature of basic parameters that are not merely reflections of the experimental conditions or the particular selective conditions, then these factors should be invariant under widely different selective conditions, and their interpretation should be the same for the several experimental groups. New test batteries should be constructed, with prediction as to factorial composition of the new tests, and these should be tried on differently selected subjects in order to determine whether the interpretation of each factor as a meaningful parameter can be sustained.

This is another situation in which the factorial methods depart from the conventions of statistical analysis. It is customary in statistical reasoning to think of a general population from which we merely draw samples, and the worry is then whether the sample is really representative of the universe. In factor analysis the principal concern is to discover an underlying order to be described in terms of meaningful parameters which should represent scientific concepts. The validity of a primary factor is determined by its fruitfulness as a scientific concept. It is inadequate if it serves merely as a regression coefficient. When factor analysis has completed its job of charting a new domain, then it may be of practical importance to establish norms of performance for any specified general population. Then the conventional statistical reasoning is again applicable.

# CHAPTER XX

## THE PRINCIPAL AXES

### Indirect solution

When multiple-factor analysis was first developed, it consisted essentially in a shift of emphasis. The dominant question in previous factorial studies had been as to whether the correlations could be accounted for by a single general factor and whether the general-factor residuals were large enough to justify the recognition of "disturbers," which were called "group factors." These were sometimes frankly admitted at the start of a study, but always with the reservation that they should be regarded as secondary to the general factor, which was invariably postulated. With multiple-factor analysis the fundamental question was formulated without this restriction, namely, to determine how many factors were indicated by the experimentally given correlations. When that question was answered, the next question was naturally to inquire about the nature of all the common factors that determined the correlations. This extension of the factor problem to any number of dimensions made it a question of fact as to whether one or more of the common factors were general in the sense of participating in the variance of every test in the battery.

One of the early objections, raised by Spearman, against multiple-factor analysis was the indeterminacy of the problem when more than one factor was indicated by the correlations. In the author's initial papers describing the multiple-factor approach, this indeterminacy was shown to be associated with the question of where to locate the reference frame in the test configuration.[*] The number of dimensions of that configuration was shown to be equal to the rank of the table of correlation coefficients, which was defined as a square symmetric matrix.[†]

In the author's first papers on multiple-factor analysis the indeterminacy of the location of the reference frame was resolved by placing the first reference axis so as to maximize the sum of the squares of its factor loadings.[‡] The next factor axis was located in the same manner by the first-factor residuals, and so on until the $r$ principal-factor axes had been determined. *Each suc-*

---

[*] L. L. Thurstone, "Multiple Factor Analysis," *Psychological Review*, XXXVIII (1931), 406–27.

[†] L. L. Thurstone, *Theory of Multiple Factors* (Ann Arbor, Mich.: Edwards Bros., 1932), p. 20.

[‡] *Ibid.*, pp. 17–19, 22–27.

cessive reference axis was located so as to maximize the sum of the squares of the factor loadings or test projections. This resolution of the indeterminacy of the reference frame was called the principal-axes solution.* It has an important computational advantage, in that it is unique for any given correlation matrix. This solution was written before the simple-structure principle was developed. The principal-axes solution has considerable theoretical interest for factor analysis, and it is of practical importance in some types of factor problems.

The principal-axes solution will be described here for three dimensions, but this solution is applicable to factor problems in any number of dimensions. It will be assumed, first, that the given correlation matrix $R$ has been factored into the factor matrix $F_0$ with elements $a_{jm}$ and that the reference frame of $F_0$ is arbitrary as determined by the factoring method that happened to be used. It may be assumed also that the diagonal elements were not adjusted for each factor. In this case the correlation matrix with experimentally determined coefficients represents, in general, as many factors as there are tests, so that the $n$th factor residuals are identically zero when $R$ is of order $n \times n$. The problem now is to rotate the arbitrary orthogonal reference frame into that of the principal axes. Later the same solution will be discussed as obtained directly from the correlation matrix without the arbitrary intermediate factor matrix, $F_0$.

Let the unit vectors in each principal axis be denoted $\Lambda_p$ and let the direction cosines of each of these unit vectors be denoted $\lambda_{mp}$. The first or major principal axis is then identified by the unit vector $\Lambda_1$, where $p = 1$ with direction cosines $\lambda_{m1}$ and where the subscript $m$ refers to the arbitrary reference frame of $F_0$. The test vector $j$ is defined by the direction numbers $a_{jm}$.

The projection of the test vector $j$ on the major principal axis $\Lambda_p$ then is

$$(1) \qquad r_{j\Lambda p} = a_{j1}\lambda_{1p} + a_{j2}\lambda_{2p} + a_{j3}\lambda_{3p}.$$

The projection of $j$ on the unit vector $\Lambda_p$ can be denoted $r_{j\Lambda p}$ because this projection is the correlation between test $j$ and what may be regarded as a test $\Lambda_p$ of perfect reliability.

Squaring the test projection on the principal axis, $\Lambda_p$, which is to be determined, and expanding the terms for rank 3, we have

$$(2) \quad \left\{ \begin{aligned} r_{j\Lambda p}^2 = a_{j1}^2\lambda_{1p}^2 + a_{j2}^2\lambda_{2p}^2 + a_{j3}^2\lambda_{3p}^2 + 2a_{j1}a_{j2}\lambda_{1p}\lambda_{2p} + 2a_{j1}a_{j3}\lambda_{1p}\lambda_{3p} \\ + 2a_{j2}a_{j3}\lambda_{2p}\lambda_{3p}. \end{aligned} \right.$$

* The solution of this problem and of the characteristic equation was suggested to the writer in 1931 by Professor Walter Bartky, of the Department of Astronomy at the University of Chicago.

Summing for the $n$ tests $j$,

$$(3) \quad \begin{cases} \sum_j r_{j\Lambda p}^2 = \lambda_{1p}^2 \sum_j a_{j1}^2 + \lambda_{2p}^2 \sum_j a_{j2}^2 + \lambda_{3p}^2 \sum_j a_{j3}^2 \\ \qquad + 2\lambda_{1p}\lambda_{2p} \sum_j a_{j1}a_{j2} + 2\lambda_{1p}\lambda_{3p} \sum_j a_{j1}a_{j3} + 2\lambda_{2p}\lambda_{3p} \sum_j a_{j2}a_{j3} . \end{cases}$$

For convenience, let

$$(4) \qquad \sum_j r_{j\Lambda p}^2 \equiv u .$$

Then the partial derivatives with respect to the direction cosine $\lambda_{1p}$ of $\Lambda_p$ is

$$(5) \qquad \frac{\partial u}{\partial \lambda_{1p}} = 2\lambda_{1p} \sum_j a_{j1}^2 + 2\lambda_{2p} \sum_j a_{j1}a_{j2} + 2\lambda_{3p} \sum_j a_{j1}a_{j3} ,$$

and the other partials are written in the same manner.

The desired values of $\lambda_{mp}$ are subject to the restriction that $\Lambda_p$ shall be unit vectors. Hence we have the conditional equation

$$(6) \qquad v = \lambda_{1p}^2 + \lambda_{2p}^2 + \lambda_{3p}^2 - 1 = 0 .$$

By Lagrange's method of undertermined multipliers we have the following normal equations:

$$(7) \quad \begin{cases} \dfrac{\partial u}{\partial \lambda_{1p}} + \beta \dfrac{\partial v}{\partial \lambda_{1p}} = 0 , \\[2mm] \dfrac{\partial u}{\partial \lambda_{2p}} + \beta \dfrac{\partial v}{\partial \lambda_{2p}} = 0 , \\[2mm] \dfrac{\partial u}{\partial \lambda_{3p}} + \beta \dfrac{\partial v}{\partial \lambda_{3p}} = 0 . \end{cases}$$

The $(r+1)$ unknowns are here the $r$ values, $\lambda_{mp}$ and $\beta$. These are to be determined by the $r$ equations (7) and the conditional equation (6).

The partial derivatives of $v$ are

$$(8) \quad \begin{cases} \dfrac{\partial v}{\partial \lambda_{1p}} = 2\lambda_{1p} , \\[2mm] \dfrac{\partial v}{\partial \lambda_{2p}} = 2\lambda_{2p} , \\[2mm] \dfrac{\partial v}{\partial \lambda_{3p}} = 2\lambda_{3p} . \end{cases}$$

Substituting (5) and (8) in (7), dividing each equation by 2, and rearranging terms, we obtain

$$(9) \quad \begin{cases} \lambda_{1p}\left(\sum_j a_{j1}^2 + \beta\right) + \lambda_{2p}\sum_j a_{j1}a_{j2} + \lambda_{3p}\sum_j a_{j1}a_{j3} = 0, \\ \lambda_{1p}\sum_j a_{j1}a_{j2} + \lambda_{2p}\left(\sum_j a_{j2}^2 + \beta\right) + \lambda_{3p}\sum_j a_{j2}a_{j3} = 0, \\ \lambda_{1p}\sum_j a_{j1}a_{j3} + \lambda_{2p}\sum_i a_{j2}a_{j3} + \lambda_{3p}\left(\sum_j a_{j3}^2 + \beta\right) = 0. \end{cases}$$

This is a set of $r$ homogeneous linear equations in the unknowns $\lambda_{1p}$, $\lambda_{2p}$, $\lambda_{3p}$. The determinant of the coefficients in equations (9) must vanish, in order that a non-trivial solution may exist.* Setting the determinant equal to zero, we have the characteristic equation

$$(10) \quad \Delta = \begin{vmatrix} (\Sigma a_{j1}^2 + \beta) & \Sigma a_{j1}a_{j2} & \Sigma a_{j1}a_{j3} \\ \Sigma a_{j1}a_{j2} & (\Sigma a_{j2}^2 + \beta) & \Sigma a_{j2}a_{j3} \\ \Sigma a_{j1}a_{j3} & \Sigma a_{j2}a_{j3} & (\Sigma a_{j3}^2 + \beta) \end{vmatrix} = 0.$$

It will be seen that the coefficients $a_{jm}$ of this determinant can be written in the form

$$(11) \quad |P| = |F_0'F_0|,$$

where $F_0$ is a factor matrix. The characteristic equation then becomes

$$(12) \quad |F_0'F_0 + \beta I| = 0$$

or

$$(13) \quad |P + \beta I| = 0.$$

By expanding the determinant, this equation can be written in the expanded form

$$(14) \quad \beta^r + c_1\beta^{r-1} + c_2\beta^{r-2} + \cdots + c_r = 0,$$

which is of degree $r$. For the present case the expansion is of third degree, namely,

$$(15) \quad \beta^3 + c_1\beta^2 + c_2\beta + c_3 = 0.$$

---

* A trivial solution for (9) is to set all the unknowns equal to zero.

The coefficients of (15) can be written by expanding the characteristic determinant of (10), or they can be computed from the principal minors of $P$. Each coefficient $c_x$ in (14) is the sum of all the $x$-rowed principal minors of $P$. All the $r$ roots of (14) are real and negative, and they will be denoted $\beta_1, \beta_2, \ldots, \beta_r$.

Each of the roots $\beta_p$ can be substituted, in turn, in (9). Each of the $r$ values of $\beta_p$ gives a set of direction cosines for a principal axis. When a root $\beta_p$ is substituted in (9), the solution gives the direction cosines of $\Lambda_p$, which are $\lambda_{1p}, \lambda_{2p}, \lambda_{3p}$.

The principal axes $\Lambda_p$ are orthogonal. Their direction cosines may be arranged to form a matrix of the transformation $\Lambda$ from the given orthogonal co-ordinates of $F_0$ to those of the principal axes. This transformation may be represented by the equation

$$(16) \qquad F_0\Lambda = F_p ,$$

where $F_p$ is a factor matrix for the principal axes. Each value $-\beta_p$ is the sum of the squares of the projections of the test vectors on a principal axis $\Lambda_p$. These are also the sums of the squares of the factor loadings in the columns of $F_p$.

### Numerical example of indirect solution

In *Table 1* we have a small correlation matrix $R$ and a factor matrix $F_0$ with an arbitrary reference frame. It is desired to find the factor matrix $F_p$ for the principal axes. The first column of $F_p$ will then be such that the sum of the squares of its loadings will be a maximum. We first find the matrix $P = F_0'F_0$, which is of order $2\times2$, since the rank of $F_0$ is 2. The expanded form of the characteristic equation (14) can then be written, and, since $r=2$ in this example, the characteristic equation is the quadratic

$$(17) \qquad \beta^2 + c_1\beta + c_2 = 0 .$$

The coefficient $c_1$ is the sum of the one-rowed principal minors of $P$. These are merely the diagonal terms of $P$, so that

$$(18) \qquad c_1 = 1.87 + 1.06 = 2.93 .$$

The coefficient $c_2$ is the sum of the two-rowed principal minors of $P$. There is only one such principal minor in this example, namely, the determinant $|P|$ itself, and hence

$$(19) \qquad c_2 = |P| = 0.2133 .$$

The numerical form of the characteristic equation then is

$$(20) \qquad \beta^2 + 2.9300 \, \beta + 0.2133 = 0 \,.$$

The two roots of (20) are $-2.855297$ and $-0.074704$. Both roots are real and negative. Writing equation (9) in numerical form, we obtain

$$(21) \qquad \begin{cases} (1.87 - 2.855297) \, \lambda_{1p} + 1.33 \, \lambda_{2p} = 0 \,, \\ 1.33 \, \lambda_{1p} + (1.06 - 2.855297) \, \lambda_{2p} = 0 \,, \end{cases}$$

*Table 1*

| Factor Matrix $F_0$ | I | II |
|---|---|---|
| 1 | .7 | .3 |
| 2 | .5 | .6 |
| 3 | .8 | .5 |
| 4 | .7 | .6 |

| Correlation Matrix R | 1 | 2 | 3 | 4 |
|---|---|---|---|---|
| 1 | .58 | .53 | .71 | .67 |
| 2 | .53 | .61 | .70 | .71 |
| 3 | .71 | .70 | .89 | .86 |
| 4 | .67 | .71 | .86 | .85 |

| Factor Matrix $F_p$ | $\Lambda_1$ | $\Lambda_2$ |
|---|---|---|
| 1 | .741049 | $-.175632$ |
| 2 | .758925 | .184480 |
| 3 | .940456 | $-.074454$ |
| 4 | .919630 | .065425 |
| $-\beta = \Sigma a^2$ | 2.855297 | $-.074703$ |

| Matrix $P = F_0' F_0$ | 1 | 2 |
|---|---|---|
| 1 | 1.87 | 1.33 |
| 2 | 1.33 | 1.06 |

$$|P| = 0.2133$$

| Transformation Matrix $\Lambda$ | $\Lambda_1$ | $\Lambda_2$ |
|---|---|---|
| I | .803525 | $-.595271$ |
| II | .595271 | .803525 |

$$|\Lambda| = +1$$

from which we have

$$(22) \qquad \begin{cases} \lambda_{11} = .803525 \\ \lambda_{21} = .595271 \end{cases} \text{Direction cosines of major principal axis } \Lambda_1 \,,$$

where the subscript $p = 1$ in $\lambda_{mp}$. The major principal axis has the direction cosines $\lambda_{11}$ and $\lambda_{21}$. It can be identified in the latent roots because the numerical value of $-\beta$ is the sum of the squares of the factor loadings of a column of $F_p$. The principal factor $p$, for which $\Sigma a_{jp}^2$ is a maximum, is called the *major principal axis*. The principal axis for which the sum of the squares $\Sigma a_{jp}^2$ is a minimum is called the *mean principal axis*. This axis is also of considerable interest in some factor problems.

The direction cosines of the mean principal axis for the present numerical example are computed in the same manner from equation (13), in which we substitute the second largest root $\beta_2$. We then have

$$(23) \quad \begin{cases} (1.87 - 0.074704)\,\lambda_{12} + 1.33\,\lambda_{22} = 0\,, \\ 1.33\,\lambda_{12} + (1.06 - 0.074704)\,\lambda_{22} = 0\,, \end{cases}$$

from which we have

$$(24) \quad \begin{cases} \lambda_{12} = -.595271 \\ \lambda_{22} = .803525 \end{cases} \begin{array}{l} \text{Direction cosines of mean} \\ \text{principal axes } \Lambda_2\,, \end{array}$$

where the subscript $p = 2$ in $\lambda_{mp}$.

Having found the direction cosines of the two principal axes of the test configuration, we write the transformation matrix, $\Lambda$, which is

$$(25) \quad \Lambda = \begin{array}{c} \\ \mathrm{I} \\ \mathrm{II} \end{array} \begin{array}{cc} \Lambda_1 & \Lambda_2 \\ \left\| \begin{array}{cc} \lambda_{11} & \lambda_{12} \\ \lambda_{21} & \lambda_{22} \end{array} \right\| \end{array} = \left\| \begin{array}{cc} (+.803525) & (-.595271) \\ (+.595271) & (+.803525) \end{array} \right\|.$$

This is an orthogonal matrix by which the test configuration can be described in terms of the principal axes instead of the arbitrary reference frame I, II, in $F_0$. We now have

$$(26) \qquad\qquad F_0\Lambda = F_p\,,$$

which is shown numerically in *Table 1*. It will be seen that $\Lambda$ is an orthogonal matrix. Its determinant $|\Lambda| = 1$. The sum of the squares of the columns of $\Lambda$ are normalized. The geometrical interpretation is that the principal axes vectors are unit reference vectors. The cross products of the columns of $\Lambda$ are zero, which has the geometrical interpretation that the principal axes are orthogonal, their scalar products being zero.

The geometrical interpretation of the present example is shown in *Figure 1*, in which the test configuration is first drawn for the arbitrary orthogonal axes I, II, of $F_0$. When the direction cosines of the major principal axis $\Lambda_1$ have been found $(\lambda_{11}, \lambda_{21})$, they can be represented on the diagram, where $\Lambda_1$ is shown as a unit vector. The sum of the squares of the test vector projections here is a maximum, as seems reasonable from the diagram, since the major principal axis passes through the central part of the test group. On the diagram one may verify by measurement that the test projections on the principal axes agree with the numerical values in $F_p$. The second principal axis $\Lambda_2$ is also shown in the diagram.

The numerical values of $\lambda_{12}$ and $\lambda_{22}$ in (24) can be reversed in sign, since the homogeneous linear equation (23) defines only the ratio of $\lambda_{12}$ to $\lambda_{22}$. Their numerical values are determined by the restriction that $\lambda_{12}^2 + \lambda_{22}^2 = 1$. If the signs of $\lambda_{12}$ and $\lambda_{22}$ in (24) were reversed, then the second column of the transformation matrix $\Lambda$ would also be reversed in sign. In *Figure 1* we would then have the second principal axis reversed in direction. The determinant of the transformation matrix would be reversed in sign, so that $|\Lambda| = -1$. When this determinant is equal to $-1$, we have an odd number of reversals of direction of reference axes. When $|\Lambda| = +1$, there is an even number of reversals of axes, or no reversal. If the reference frame $I$, $II$ is subjected to rigid rotation in *Figure 1* so that $I$ goes to $\Lambda_1$ when $II$ goes to $\Lambda_2$, then the determinant of the orthogonal transformation is $+1$. If there is an odd number of reversals, this determinant is equal to $-1$. Such is the case if we reverse the second column in $\Lambda$ so that the reference vectors be-

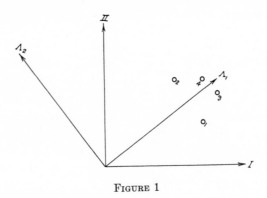

FIGURE 1

come $\Lambda_1$ and $-\Lambda_2$. It can be seen in the figure that the frame $I$, $II$ cannot move to $\Lambda_1$ and $-\Lambda_2$ by a rigid rotation within the dimensionality of $r = 2$. For most factor problems the differentiation between the cases in which $|\Lambda| = +1$ and $|\Lambda| = -1$ is of no practical consequence. It is of some interest to know the relation between the ambiguity of signs in equations (23) and the geometrical interpretation of the problem.

### A direct solution for the principal axes

In previous sections of this chapter we have considered an indirect determination of the principal axes, in that the correlation matrix was first factored into a factor matrix $F_0$ with an arbitrary reference frame which depended on the particular method of factoring that was used on the correlation matrix. That was the author's solution when the principal axes were first described. The principal-axes solution can be written more directly in terms of the correlation matrix and without an intermediate factor matrix $F_0$.

Consider the correlation matrix $R_{jk}$ and the desired factor matrix $F_p$ of

## Table 2

### Correlation Matrix $R_{jk}$

| | 1 | 2 | 3 | 4 |
|---|---|---|---|---|
| 1 | .58 | .53 | .71 | .67 |
| 2 | .53 | .61 | .70 | .71 |
| 3 | .71 | .70 | .89 | .86 |
| 4 | .67 | .71 | .86 | .85 |
| Σ | 2.49 | 2.55 | 3.16 | 3.09 |

### First-Factor Residuals

| | 1 | 2 | 3 | 4 |
|---|---|---|---|---|
| 1 | .030846 | − .032401 | .013076 | − .011491 |
| 2 | − .032401 | .034033 | − .013736 | .012070 |
| 3 | .013076 | − .013736 | .005543 | − .004872 |
| 4 | − .011491 | .012070 | − .004872 | .004281 |

### First Principal Axis ($a_{j1}$)

| | $u_1$ | $v_1$ | $u_2$ | $v_2$ | $u_3$ | $a_{j1}$ |
|---|---|---|---|---|---|---|
| 1 | .7880 | 2.249876 | .787968 | 2.249882 | .787968 | .741049 |
| 2 | .8070 | 2.304148 | .806976 | 2.304156 | .806976 | .758925 |
| 3 | 1.0000 | 2.855288 | 1.000000 | 2.855297 | 1.000000 | .940456 |
| 4 | .9778 | 2.792060 | .977856 | 2.792069 | .977856 | .919630 |
| | 3.5728 | 10.201372 | 3.572800 | 10.201404 | 3.572800 | 3.360060 |

$$k = .35022737 \qquad k = .35022626$$

$$(u_2 v_2) = 9.21777204$$
$$p\beta = \sqrt{u_2 v_2} = 3.03607840$$
$$1/(p\beta) = .32937226$$

### Second Principal Axis ($a_{j2}$)

| | $u_1$ | $v_1$ | $u_2$ | $v_2$ | $u_3$ | $v_3$ | $a_{j2}$ |
|---|---|---|---|---|---|---|---|
| 1 | − .952047 | − .071121 | − .952025 | − .071120 | − .952024 | − .071120 | − .175631 |
| 2 | 1.000000 | .074705 | 1.000000 | .074704 | 1.000000 | .074704 | .184482 |
| 3 | − .403608 | − .030150 | − .403587 | − .030150 | − .403598 | − .030150 | − .074455 |
| 4 | .354656 | .026495 | .354662 | .026494 | .354653 | .026494 | .065427 |

$$k = 13.385985 \qquad k = 13.386164 \qquad k = 13.386164$$

$$(u_3 v_3) = .16397645$$
$$p\beta = \sqrt{u_3 v_3} = .40494006$$
$$1/p\beta = 2.46950128$$

### Factor Matrix $F_p$

| | I | II |
|---|---|---|
| 1 | .741049 | − .175631 |
| 2 | .758925 | .184482 |
| 3 | .940456 | − .074455 |
| 4 | .919630 | .065427 |
| $\beta = \Sigma a^2$ | 2.855298 | .074704 |

*Table 2.* In this table the correlation matrix has only four rows and four columns, and the factor matrix has two factor columns. It is desired to locate the first principal axis so as to maximize the sum of the squares of the test vector projections on that axis. This means that the sum of the squares of the factor loadings $a_{j1}$ in the first column of $F_p$ must be maximized or that the first-factor residuals must be minimized. The first-factor residuals can be written

$$(27) \qquad r_{jk} - a_{j1}a_{k1} = \rho_{jk} \, ,$$

where $\rho_{jk}$ is the residual. Squaring the residuals, we have

$$(28) \qquad r_{jk}^2 - 2a_{j1}a_{k1}r_{jk} + a_{j1}^2 a_{k1}^2 = \rho_{jk}^2 \, ;$$

and, summing for all correlation coefficients, we have

$$(29) \qquad \sum_j \sum_k r_{jk}^2 - 2\sum_j \sum_k a_{j1}a_{k1}r_{jk} + \sum_i \sum_k a_{j1}^2 a_{k1}^2 = \sum \sum_k \rho_{jk}^2 \, .$$

For convenience, let

$$(30) \qquad \sum_j \sum_k \rho_{jk}^2 \equiv z \, .$$

Then

$$(31) \qquad \frac{\partial z}{\partial a_{j1}} = -4\sum_k r_{jk}a_{k1} + 4a_{j1}\sum_k a_{k1}^2 \, .$$

Setting the partial derivatives equal to zero, we obtain

$$(32) \qquad \Sigma r_{jk}a_{k1} = a_{j1}\Sigma a_{k1}^2 \, .$$

In the rest of this chapter the notation $\beta$ will refer to the latent roots with positive signs. Let the sum $\Sigma a_{k1}^2 = \beta$, which is the largest latent root. Writing (32) in matrix form, we obtain

$$(33) \qquad Ra = a\beta \, ,$$

where $R$ is the correlation matrix, $a$ is a column vector, and $\beta$ is a scalar, namely, the first latent root.

Equation (33) is not directly a computing formula, but it is the equation on which Hotelling's iterative factoring method is based.*

* Harold Hotelling, "Analysis of a Complex of Statistical Variables into Principal Components," *Journal of Educational Psychology*, XXIV (September and October, 1933).

### Hotelling's iterative method of factoring

This method of factoring enables us to obtain the desired factor matrix $F_p$ for the principal axes directly from the correlation matrix without the intermediate arbitrary factor matrix $F_0$. Hotelling's iterative method of factoring starts with a trial column vector $u_1$, so that (33) becomes

$$(34) \qquad\qquad Ru_1 = v_1 \text{'},$$

where the product $v_1$ is also a column vector. The next trial vector, $u_2$, is taken proportional to $v_1$, so that $u_2 = kv_1$. Then

$$(35) \qquad\qquad Ru_2 = v_2 \text{ ,}$$

which gives the new trial vector, $u_3 = kv_2$, for the next trial. The stretching factor $k$ is arbitrary for each trial. This process continues until the product numbers $v_q$ are proportional to the next preceding trial numbers $u_q$ to any required degree of accuracy. The column vectors $u_q$ and $v_q$ are then both proportional to the desired column vector $a$. Let the proportionality be represented by

$$(36) \qquad\qquad u = pa \text{ ,}$$

so that $Ru = v$ becomes

$$(37) \qquad\qquad R(pa) = (pa\beta) \text{ .}$$

The scalar product $(uv)$ then is

$$(38) \qquad\qquad (uv) = (pa)(pa\beta) = p^2\beta\Sigma a^2 = p^2\beta^2 \text{ .}$$

Hence

$$(39) \qquad\qquad \frac{v}{\sqrt{(uv)}} = \frac{pa\beta}{\sqrt{p^2\beta^2}} = a \text{ ,}$$

which reduces $v$ to the desired column vector $a_{j1}$.

The latent root $\beta$ can be determined at the solution by the simple relation

$$(40) \qquad\qquad \beta = \frac{\Sigma v}{\Sigma u} \text{ .}$$

When the first-factor residuals have been determined by equation (27), the residual correlation matrix $\rho_{jk}$ can be factored by the same process to give the second column of $F_p$, whose elements are $a_{j2}$. The sum of their squares is

$$(41) \qquad \sum_j a_{j2}^2 = \beta_2 ,$$

which is the second latent root. This is Hotelling's iterative method of factoring the correlation matrix. It is an improvement on the writer's original method of finding the principal-axes solution by the indirect method of first finding an arbitrary factor matrix $F_0$ and then rotating the reference frame to the principal axes. The principal-axes solution can be written to represent the whole factor matrix $F_p$ instead of one column at a time, as was done here. Then the interpretation of the characteristic equation and the latent roots are the same as in the writer's original paper on the principal axes. Hotelling has renamed the principal-axes solution the *principal components*. Sometimes this term refers to the factor loadings $a_{jp}$ in $F_p$ and sometimes to Hotelling's iterative method of factoring. This method and the writer's original indirect method give numerically identical results, as will be seen in the accompanying example. In computational work the indirect solution requires less labor with the computing methods now available, but the direct solution is theoretically the more interesting.

Hotelling restricts himself to the case of unit diagonals in the correlation matrix, but his method is applicable when other values, such as reliabilities or communalities, are written into the diagonals. It should be carefully noted that the rank of the correlation matrix, the number of common factors, and the latent roots are markedly affected by the diagonal values. The rank of $R$ is lowest when communalities are used in the diagonal cells. When unit diagonals are written, the rank generally becomes equal to the order of the correlation matrix.

An important characteristic of Hotelling's iterative method of factoring is that the convergence is slow when the larger latent roots are nearly the same. The convergence is rapid when the latent roots differ markedly in numerical values. In the numerical example of this chapter we have chosen a case in which the latent roots are numerically quite different, so that the convergence is rapid and the solution is reached in a few trials. The reader should not expect such rapid convergence in many practical problems in which the roots may have nearly equal numerical values.

### Numerical example of Hotelling's iterative method

In *Table 2* we have a small correlation matrix of order $4 \times 4$, whose latent roots are widely separated so as to give a rapidly convergent example of the iterative process. The first trial vector, $u_1$, is taken proportional to the column sums of $R$, so that the largest numerical value of $u_1$ is unity. The matrix multiplication, $Ru_1 = v_1$, is shown in the next column. The reciprocal of the largest entry in column $v_1$ is recorded as the arbitrary stretching factor $k$, and we then have $u_2 = kv_1$ in the next column. The matrix multiplication, $Ru_2 = v_2$, is recorded in the next column. The process terminates when the two successive values $u_2$ and $u_3$ are found to be identical within the required degree of accuracy.

The reduction of $v_2$ to the desired column vector $a_{j1}$ is shown under the table. The scalar product $(u_2v_2)$ is computed and recorded as shown. The square root of this number is $p\beta$, as shown. Finally, the reciprocal $1/p\beta$ is computed and recorded. The final column $a_{j1}$ is computed from $v_2$ by the relation $a_{j1} = v/p\beta$.

The first-factor residuals are then computed and are shown in the lower section of *Table 2*. The same process of factoring is applied to this table, with the resulting column vector $a_{j2}$ as shown. Finally, the two column vectors $a_{jp}$ are recorded in the desired factor matrix $F_p$. The first trial vector for a residual correlation matrix can be taken proportional to the absolute sum of the residuals in each column, including or excluding the diagonals. One can also justify taking as trial values the square roots of the diagonal residuals.

The factor matrix for the principal axes has two properties of interest. The sum of the squares of each column of the factor matrix $F_p$ is a latent root. Further, the cross product of each pair of columns is zero. We then have for the sum of the squares of each column

(42) $$\sum_j a_{jp}^2 = \beta_p ,$$

and for the cross product of any pair of columns, $p$ and $q$,

(43) $$\sum_j a_{jp}a_{jq} = 0 .$$

Both these properties can be easily verified numerically in the factor matrix $F_p$.

The present example does not show the problem that arises when the convergence is slow. The wide separation of the latent roots in this example produces the rapid convergence shown here. When the latent roots are nearly alike, the slow convergence makes it desirable to introduce other devices to increase the convergence to the desired solution.

### The squaring process

When the iterative method of factoring for the principal-axes solution is used on a correlation matrix in which the largest latent roots are of nearly the same numerical values, the process converges slowly. The labor required to reach the solution is then so considerable as to be discouraging. The convergence can be increased by the squaring process described by Hotelling as an improvement on the first form of his iterative factoring method.*

Consider the first iteration $Ru_1 = v_1$ (equation [34]), with a column vector $u_1$ which is either arbitrarily chosen as a start or chosen by inspection of the correlation matrix $R$. If, now, this product $v_1$ is used as the next trial vector, we have

$$(44) \qquad\qquad Rv_1 = v_2 .$$

Substituting (34) in (44), we get

$$(45) \qquad\qquad R(Ru_1) = v_2$$

or

$$(46) \qquad\qquad R^2 u_1 = v_2 .$$

Using $v_2$ as the next trial vector, we get

$$(47) \qquad\qquad Rv_2 = v_3 ,$$

and then

$$(48) \qquad\qquad Rv_3 = v_4 .$$

By (47) this becomes

$$(49) \qquad\qquad R(Rv_2) = v_4 ,$$

and, by (46),

$$(50) \qquad\qquad R^4 u_1 = v_4 .$$

This process can be continued, so that

$$(51) \qquad\qquad R^x u = v_x ,$$

where $x$ denotes any power of $R$. If $R$ is raised to a sufficiently high power, the product vector $v_x$ is proportional to the desired solution $a_{j1}$, even if the arbitrary trial vector is badly chosen. A reservation may be made about the choice of the trial vector $u$. If this trial vector is exactly proportional to any column of $F_p$, including the secondary roots, the equation (51) is satisfied. This situation is not likely to happen in practice, so that the iterations will practically always lead to the major principal axis. A simple example of this

* Harold Hotelling, "Simplified Calculation of Principal Components," *Psychometrika*, I (1936), 27–35.

effect in which iteration does not lead to the major principal axis is the following $2\times2$ correlation matrix:

$$
\begin{bmatrix} 1.00 & -\ .80 \\ -\ .80 & 1.00 \end{bmatrix}_{R} \quad \begin{bmatrix} +1 \\ +1 \end{bmatrix}_{u}.
$$

Iteration with the trial vector $(+1, +1)$, as shown, leads to the mean principal axis, whereas iteration with the trial vector $(+1, -1)$ leads to the major principal axis. Examples of this kind arise very rarely with experimental data, because it is very unlikely that a trial vector will be proportional to one of the secondary columns in $F_p$.

From (46) it is evident that one iteration on $R^2$ gives the same result as two iterations on $R$. From (50) we see that one iteration on $R^4$ gives the same result as four iterations on $R$, and so on for any power of $R$. The more rapid convergence of this process is offset to some extent by the labor of multiplying the correlation matrix by itself several times, and it must also be considered in relation to the fact that a large number of decimals are carried in this process in order to retain its full effectiveness.

The relation of this process to the characteristic root $\beta$ can be seen if we write $Ra = a\beta$ (equation [33]), where $a$ is the desired column vector and $\beta$ is the largest latent root of $R$ or of a residual matrix. This can be written

$$(52) \qquad \frac{1}{\beta}\, Ra = a ,$$

from which we have

$$(53) \qquad \frac{1}{\beta}\, R\!\left(\frac{1}{\beta}\, Ra\right) = a ,$$

so that

$$(54) \qquad \frac{1}{\beta^2}\, R^2 a = a .$$

Repeating this process gives

$$(55) \qquad R^x a = \beta^x a ,$$

from which it is seen that if $R$ is raised to the power $x$, the iteration with $a$ gives the product numbers $\beta^x a$.

An interesting property of the correlation matrix is that when it is raised to a sufficiently high power it approaches unit rank to any required degree of approximation.[*] The factor matrix corresponding to such an augmented

* Cyril Burt, "The Unit Hierarchy and Its Properties," *Psychometrika*, III (1938), 151–68.

correlation matrix has only one column. This symmetric matrix $R^x$, which is of unit rank, can be factored by a single-column factor matrix, which may be represented by the column vector $F_x = A$, so that

$$(56) \qquad R^x = AA' \; ;$$

and it is of some interest to see the relation between the single-column factor matrix $A$ of $R^x$ and the first-column $a$ of the factor matrix $F_p$. Let

$$(57) \qquad a = pA \; ,$$

and substitute in (55), which becomes

$$(58) \qquad R^x(pA) = \beta^x(pA) \; ;$$

and this can be written

$$(59) \qquad pR^xA = p\beta^xA \; ;$$

but $R^x$ can be factored by analogy with (55),

$$(60) \qquad R^xA = kA \; ,$$

where $k$ is the largest characteristic root of $R^x$, namely,

$$(61) \qquad k = A'A \; .$$

From (59) and (60) we get

$$(62) \qquad pkA = p\beta^xA \; ,$$

and hence

$$(63) \qquad k = \beta^x \; .$$

We can then re-write (60) in the form

$$(64) \qquad R^xA = \beta^xA \; .$$

From (56) we find

$$(65) \qquad AA'A = \beta^xA \; ,$$

and by (57),

$$(66) \qquad \frac{1}{p^3} aa'a = \frac{1}{p} \beta^xa \; ;$$

and, since $\beta = a'a$,

$$(67) \qquad \frac{\beta}{p^3} a = \frac{\beta^x}{p} a \,,$$

so that

$$(68) \qquad \beta^{\frac{x-1}{2}} = \frac{1}{p} \,.$$

Hence by (57),

$$(69) \qquad a = \beta^{\frac{1-x}{2}} A = k^{\frac{1-x}{2x}} A \,,$$

so that the desired column vector $a_{j1}$ of $R$ can be obtained from the single-factor loadings of $R^x$. This is not the usual procedure in the squaring process. The generally recommended procedure is to continue the squaring until the column sums of two successive squarings, $R^x$ to $R^{2x}$, are proportional to any required degree of approximation. The column sums of $R^x$, or numbers proportional to them, are then used as a trial vector $u$ on the original correlation matrix $R$, so that $Ru = v$. The column vectors $u$ and $v$ may then be expected to be proportional, so that $u$ or $v$ is proportional to the desired column vector $a_{j1}$. If proportionality is not attained, the iteration may be continued on $R$. The actual reduction from $v$ to $a$ is done by noting that the ratio

$$(70) \qquad \frac{v_j}{u_j} = \beta \,;$$

and if one of the trial numbers $u_j$ is unity, then $\beta$ can be read directly from the corresponding value of $v_j$. If one of the trial numbers $u_j$ is not unity, the root $\beta$ can be determined from the ratio $\beta = \Sigma |v| / \Sigma |u|$ for the last iteration. A useful device, especially when it is desired to reduce $v$ to a unit vector in the configuration before reaching the final principal-axes solution, is to compute the desired loadings from the relation

$$(71) \qquad a_{j1} = cv_j = \frac{v_j}{\sqrt{\Sigma uv}} \,,$$

where

$$(72) \qquad c = \frac{1}{\sqrt{\Sigma uv}} \,.$$

When the correlation matrix has been raised to some power $x$, so that the column sums of $R^x$ are proportional to the column sums of the next previous matrix $R^{x/2}$ to the required degree of approximation, then $R^x$ is of unit rank to the same approximation. The single-factor loadings $a_j$ of $R^z$ can be found by the centroid method, which gives the unique values

$$(73) \qquad a_j = \frac{m_j t_j}{\sqrt{\Sigma t_j}},$$

in which

$\quad$ $t_j$ = sum of absolute values of cell entries in row $j$ of $R^z$,

$\quad$ $m_j = \pm 1$, according to the sign of $s_j$,

$\quad$ $s_j$ = algebraic column sums of $R^z$.

The desired factor loadings $a_{j1}$ can be obtained from the column sums $s_j$ of $R^z$ without an additional iteration on $R$. If the column sums $S_z$ of $R^z$, or the single-factor loadings $a_j$ of $R^z$, are used in the iteration $Ru = v$, then it is expected that $u$ and $v$ will be proportional and that these will also be proportional to $a_{j1}$. Therefore, we write

$$(74) \qquad a = pu.$$

Let $s_1$ denote column sums of $R$. Then

$$(75) \qquad \Sigma s_1 u = T,$$

where $T$ is the column sum of the product numbers $Ru = V$. The ratio of this column sum $T$ to the column sum $\Sigma u$ is the largest characteristic root $\beta$. Hence by equation (70),

$$(76) \qquad \frac{T}{\Sigma u} = \beta.$$

From (75) we have

$$(77) \qquad \frac{\Sigma s_1 u}{\Sigma u} = \beta.$$

From (74) we have

$$(78) \qquad \Sigma a^2 = \beta = p^2 \Sigma u^2,$$

so that

$$(79) \qquad \frac{\Sigma s_1 u}{\Sigma u} = p^2 \Sigma u^2;$$

and hence

$$(80) \qquad p = \sqrt{\frac{\Sigma s_1 u}{\Sigma u \, \Sigma u^2}}.$$

By (74) we then have

$$(81) \qquad a = u\sqrt{\frac{\Sigma s_1 u}{\Sigma u \, \Sigma u^2}},$$

where $u$ is proportional to the column sums of $R^x$ and $s_1$ represents the corresponding column sums of $R$. It is good computational practice to verify the determination of $a_{j1}$ by the iteration $Ra = \beta a$ for any method of obtaining the values of $a$. An alternative procedure is to carry out the iteration $Ru = v$ and then reduce $v$ to $a_{j1}$ by equation (71). Several relations have been described here, but it is not necessary in practice to verify all of them on each numerical problem in finding the solution $a_{j1}$. The same procedures are used on the correlation matrix residuals for determining each column of the factor matrix $F_p$.

### Numerical example of the squaring process

In order to illustrate the squaring process, we shall use a small example which does not converge so rapidly as the previous example with Hotelling's original iterative method of factoring. This example is shown in the factor matrix $F_p$ of *Table 3*. The two characteristic roots are 1.26 and .33 as shown. The two columns represent principal axes, as can be seen from the fact that $\Sigma a_{j1} a_{j2} = 0$. The corresponding correlation matrix $R$ is shown in the same table.

The expected column sums $s_j$ of $R^2$ are computed from $R$, and, since these are not proportional to the column sums of $R$, the complete matrix $R^2$ is computed. Under each matrix we have reduced the column sums $s_j$ to the proportional values $ks_j$, in which the largest value is unity. This facilitates comparison of successive sets of column sums.

The expected column sums of $R^4$ are computed from $R^2$, and these are again not proportional to those of $R^2$, so that $R^4$ is computed in full as shown. Next we compute column sums of $R^8$ and compare with column sums of $R^4$. These two sets approach proportionality, but they still differ in the second decimal. Hence $R^8$ is computed as shown. The column sums of $R^{16}$ agree closely with those of $R^8$, and hence it is not necessary to compute $R^{16}$ in full. The discrepancies here do not exceed .0002.

In *Table 4* we have a summary of numerical examples. The trial values $u = ks_j$ from $R^{16}$ are used in the iteration $Ru = v$, as shown. The computation $\Sigma uv = 3.2400000$ leads to the values of $a_{j1}$ by equation (71).

In the same table we have the computation of $a_{j1}$ from column sums of $R^{16}$. In the first column of this table we list $u = ks_{16}$ of $R^{16}$. The values of $a_{j1}$ are then obtained from equation (81). For check purposes these values should be verified by the iteration $Ra = \beta a$ for one or more rows of $R$.

Table 3

Factor Matrix $F_p$

| | I | II |
|---|---|---|
| 1 | .7 | .0 |
| 2 | − .6 | − .4 |
| 3 | .5 | − .4 |
| 4 | − .4 | .1 |
| $\Sigma a$ | .2 | − .7 |
| $\Sigma a^2$ | 1.26 | .33 |

Correlation Matrix R

| | 1 | 2 | 3 | 4 |
|---|---|---|---|---|
| 1 | .49 | − .42 | .35 | − .28 |
| 2 | − .42 | .52 | − .14 | .20 |
| 3 | .35 | − .14 | .41 | − .24 |
| 4 | − .28 | .20 | − .24 | .17 |
| $s_j$ | .14 | .16 | .38 | − .15 |
| $ks_j$ | .37 | .42 | 1.00 | − .39 |

Matrix $R^2$

| | 1 | 2 | 3 | 4 |
|---|---|---|---|---|
| 1 | .6174 | − .5292 | .4410 | − .3528 |
| 2 | − .5292 | .5064 | − .3252 | .2892 |
| 3 | .4410 | − .3252 | .3678 | − .2652 |
| 4 | − .3528 | .2892 | − .2652 | .2049 |
| $s_j$ | .1764 | − .0588 | .2184 | − .1239 |
| $ks_j$ | .8077 | − .2692 | 1.0000 | − .5673 |

Matrix $R^4$

| | 1 | 2 | 3 | 4 |
|---|---|---|---|---|
| 1 | .98018424 | − .84015792 | .70013160 | − .56010528 |
| 2 | − .84015792 | .72588528 | − .59436288 | .47865276 |
| 3 | .70013160 | − .59436288 | .50584392 | − .40151268 |
| 4 | − .56010528 | .47865276 | − .40151268 | .32041953 |
| $s_j$ | .28005264 | − .22998276 | .21009996 | − .16254567 |
| $ks_j$ | 1.00000000 | − .82121261 | .75021596 | − .58041113 |

Matrix $R^8$

| | 1 | 2 | 3 | 4 |
|---|---|---|---|---|
| 1 | 2.47052866 | −2.11759599 | 1.76466333 | −1.41173066 |
| 2 | −2.11759599 | 1.81515047 | −1.51250038 | 1.21003780 |
| 3 | 1.76466333 | −1.51250038 | 1.26054199 | −1.00839609 |
| 4 | −1.41173066 | 1.21003780 | −1.00839609 | .80670750 |
| $s_j$ | .70586534 | − .60490810 | .50430885 | − .40338145 |
| $ks_j$ | 1.00000000 | − .85697380 | .71445476 | − .57147083 |
| $t_j$ | 7.76451864 | 6.65528464 | 5.54610179 | 4.43687205 |

Matrix $R^{16}$

| | 1 | 2 | 3 | 4 |
|---|---|---|---|---|
| $s_j$ | 4.48421281 | −3.84361097 | 3.20300917 | −2.56240732 |
| $ks_j$ | 1.00000000 | − .85714285 | .71428572 | − .57142857 |

## The principal-axes residuals

When one factor column of $F_p$ has been determined, the extraction of the next factor from the correlation matrix is usually done by computing the residual correlation matrix,

$$(82) \qquad\qquad R_1 = R - aa' \, ,$$

where $R_1$ denotes here the first-factor residual matrix from $R$. These residuals can be computed in the same manner as for any other factoring method. The residual correlation matrix is then used for determining the next factor

*Table 4*

*Computation of $a_{j1}$ by Iteration $Ru = V$*

| | $u$ | $v$ | $a_{j1}$ | |
|---|---|---|---|---|
| 1 | 1.00000000 | 1.26000000 | .70000000 | $\Sigma uv = 3.24000000$ |
| 2 | − .85714285 | −1.08000000 | − .60000000 | $1/\Sigma uv = .30864198$ |
| 3 | .71428572 | .90000000 | .50000000 | $1/\sqrt{\Sigma uv} = .55555556$ |
| 4 | − .57142857 | − .72000000 | − .40000000 | |

*Computation of $a_{j1}$ from Column*
*Sums $u = ks_{16}$ of $R^{16}$*

| | $u$ | $a_{j1}$ | |
|---|---|---|---|
| 1 | 1.00000000 | .70000000 | $\Sigma u = .28571430$ |
| 2 | − .85714285 | − .60000000 | $\Sigma u^2 = 2.57142857$ |
| 3 | .71428572 | .50000000 | $\Sigma s_1 u = .36000000$ |
| 4 | − .57142857 | − .40000000 | $p^2 = .48999998$ |
| | | | $p = .70000000$ |

column $a_{j2}$ of $F_p$. The procedures on $R_1$ are the same as those which have been described for the first factor.

In addition to the customary method of computing residuals, we shall describe two methods, namely, (1) Hotelling's adaptation of the squaring process to the computation of residuals and (2) Tucker's method of computing the subsequent principal-factor loadings without computing residuals.

If the squaring process has been used in the determination of the first-factor loadings $a_{j1}$ of $F_p$, then the augmented correlation matrix $R^x$ can be used also for writing the residual correlation matrix raised to the same power with considerable reduction in computational labor. For this purpose we shall first prove several useful relations.

Let

$$(83) \qquad\qquad Q \equiv aa' \, ,$$

where $Q$ is a square symmetric matrix of unit rank produced by the column vector $a$, which has been determined. The residual matrix $R_1$ is then

$$(84) \qquad R_1 = R - Q = R - aa' .$$

We also have the two relations previously established, namely,

$$(33) \qquad Ra = \beta a ,$$

and

$$(85) \qquad \beta = a'a .$$

From (33) and (83) we have

$$(86) \qquad RQ = Raa' = \beta aa' ,$$

$$(87) \qquad RQ = \beta Q .$$

From (83) and (85) we can write

$$Q^2 = (aa')(aa')$$
$$= a(a'a)a'$$
$$= a\beta a'$$
$$= \beta aa'$$
$$(88) \qquad Q^2 = \beta Q .$$

Applying these relations to the augmented correlation matrix $R^z$, we have, starting with $R^3$ and using (87),

$$R^3Q = R^2(RQ) = R^2\beta Q = \beta R^2 Q$$
$$= \beta R(RQ) = \beta R(\beta Q) = \beta^2 RQ$$
$$= \beta^2(\beta Q)$$
$$(89) \qquad R^3Q = \beta^3 Q ,$$

and, in general,

$$(90) \qquad R^z Q = \beta^z Q .$$

Another relation involving $R^x$ can be shown from (87) and (88) by writing

$$R^3Q = R^2(RQ) = R^2Q^2$$
$$= R(RQ)Q = RQ^2Q$$

(91) $$R^3Q = RQ^3 ,$$

or, in general,

(92) $$R^xQ = RQ^x .$$

Powers of $Q$ can be reduced from (88) by writing

$$Q^3 = QQ^2 = Q(\beta Q) = \beta Q^2 ,$$

(93) $$Q^3 = \beta(\beta Q) = \beta^2 Q ,$$

or, in general,

(94) $$Q^x = \beta^{x-1}Q .$$

The residuals can be expressed by (84), (87), and (88) from the squaring process by writing

$$R_1^2 = (R - Q)^2 = R^2 - 2RQ + Q^2$$
$$= R^2 - 2\beta Q + \beta Q ,$$

(95) $$R_1^2 = R^2 - \beta Q ,$$

or, in general,

(96) $$R_1^x = R^x - \beta^{x-1}Q ,$$

by which the residuals $R_1^x$ raised to the power $x$ can be obtained from the already computed matrix $R^x$. In using (96) the procedure is as follows:

1) The column sums $s$ of $R^x$ are used as trial numbers in the iteration $Rs = v$. Several iterations are taken, if necessary, until $a_{j1}$ are determined.
2) Determine characteristic root $\beta$.
3) Compute the product numbers $R^xa = \beta^xa$, in which

$$\frac{\beta^xa}{a} = \beta^x .$$

Table 5

### Correlation Matrix R₂

|   | 1 | 2 | 3 | 4 | I |
|---|---|---|---|---|---|
| 1 | $r_{11}$ | $r_{12}$ | $r_{13}$ | $r_{14}$ | $a_{11}\sqrt{\beta_1}\,i$ |
| 2 | $r_{21}$ | $r_{22}$ | $r_{23}$ | $r_{24}$ | $a_{21}\sqrt{\beta_1}\,i$ |
| 3 | $r_{31}$ | $r_{32}$ | $r_{33}$ | $r_{34}$ | $a_{31}\sqrt{\beta_1}\,i$ |
| 4 | $r_{41}$ | $r_{42}$ | $r_{43}$ | $r_{44}$ | $a_{41}\sqrt{\beta_1}\,i$ |
| I | $a_{11}\sqrt{\beta_1}\,i$ | $a_{21}\sqrt{\beta_1}\,i$ | $a_{31}\sqrt{\beta_1}\,i$ | $a_{41}\sqrt{\beta_1}\,i$ | $-\beta$ |

### Factor Matrix F_p

|   | I | II | III |
|---|---|---|---|
| 1 | $a_{11}$ | $a_{12}$ | $a_{13}$ |
| 2 | $a_{21}$ | $a_{22}$ | $a_{23}$ |
| 3 | $a_{31}$ | $a_{32}$ | $a_{33}$ |
| 4 | $a_{41}$ | $a_{42}$ | $a_{43}$ |
| I | $\sqrt{\beta_1}\,i$ | 0 | 0 |

### Correlation Matrix R₁

|   | 1 | 2 | 3 | 4 |
|---|---|---|---|---|
| 1 | .04 | .04 | .08 | −.10 |
| 2 | .04 | .29 | .18 | .08 |
| 3 | .08 | .18 | .56 | .16 |
| 4 | −.10 | .08 | .16 | .61 |

$a_{j1}$

|   |   |
|---|---|
| 1 | .0 |
| 2 | .3 |
| 3 | .6 |
| 4 | .6 |

$\beta_1 = .81$
$\sqrt{\beta_1} = .90$

### Correlation Matrix R₂

|   | 1 | 2 | 3 | 4 | I |
|---|---|---|---|---|---|
| 1 | .04 | .04 | .08 | −.10 | .00$i$ |
| 2 | .04 | .29 | .18 | .08 | .27$i$ |
| 3 | .08 | .18 | .56 | .16 | .54$i$ |
| 4 | −.10 | .08 | .16 | .61 | .54$i$ |
| I | .00$i$ | .27$i$ | .54$i$ | .54$i$ | −.81 |

$a_{j2}$

|   |   |
|---|---|
| 1 | .2 |
| 2 | .2 |
| 3 | .4 |
| 4 | −.5 |
| I | .0 |

$\beta_2 = .49$
$\sqrt{\beta_2} = .70$

### Correlation Matrix R₃

|   | 1 | 2 | 3 | 4 | I | II |
|---|---|---|---|---|---|---|
| 1 | .04 | .04 | .08 | −.10 | .00$i$ | .14$i$ |
| 2 | .04 | .29 | .18 | .08 | .27$i$ | .14$i$ |
| 3 | .08 | .18 | .56 | .16 | .54$i$ | .28$i$ |
| 4 | −.10 | .08 | .16 | .61 | .54$i$ | −.35$i$ |
| I | .00$i$ | .27$i$ | .54$i$ | .54$i$ | −.81$i$ | .00 |
| II | .14$i$ | .14$i$ | .28$i$ | −.35$i$ | .00 | −.49 |

$a_{j3}$

|   |   |
|---|---|
| 1 | .0 |
| 2 | .4 |
| 3 | −.2 |
| 4 | .0 |
| I | .0 |
| II | .0 |

### Factor Matrix F_p

|   | I | II | III |
|---|---|---|---|
| 1 | .0 | .2 | .0 |
| 2 | .3 | .2 | .4 |
| 3 | .6 | .4 | −.2 |
| 4 | .6 | −.5 | .0 |

4) Determine $\beta^{x-1}$ by the division

$$\beta^{x-1} = \frac{\beta^x}{\beta}\,.$$

5) Compute $R_1^x$ by equation (96).

The squaring process has advantages in rapid convergence, but it is also quite laborious in practice, especially when large correlation matrices are to be raised to a high power.

Another solution for the principal-axes problem without residuals has recently been proposed by Ledyard Tucker.* It is ingenious and looks promising, but it has not yet been tried extensively. In *Table 5* we have a 4×4 correlation matrix $R_1$, which gives the first principal-factor loadings in the adjacent column $a_{j1}$. The sum of the squares of this column is $\beta_1 = .81$. When this first factor has been determined, the usual procedure is to write another matrix of correlation residuals. The present method avoids the necessity of computing residuals. Instead, the original correlation matrix is merely bordered, as shown in literal notation at the top of *Table 5*. The indicated elements of the bordering column and row have the effect of reducing the largest characteristic root to zero. Then the major principal factor of the bordered matrix $R_2$ is the second principal factor of the original matrix $R_1$. The corresponding factor matrix $F_p$ is also shown in literal form at the top of *Table 5* with an added row. The sum of the squares of the first column of this factor matrix is identically zero, so that the major principal factor now becomes the second column of $F_p$.

The bordered matrix $R_2$ is shown in numerical form in the same table. Hotelling's iterative process on this correlation matrix gives the second-factor column $a_{j2}$, as shown, with the second characteristic root $\beta_2 = .49$. The matrix $R_3$ is constructed by bordering $R_1$ with two additional rows and columns. Hotelling's process on this matrix $R_3$ gives the third-factor column $a_{j3}$. The three factor columns are assembled in the numerical factor matrix $F_p$ at the bottom of the table.

### Graphical aids in factoring the correlation matrix

In the iterative process of determining the principal axes the computations can be reduced by graphical methods, at least in the first few trials.† The iterative process depends on the relation

(97) $$Ru = v\Sigma u^2\,,$$

* "The Determination of Successive Principal Components without Computation of Tables of Residual Correlation Coefficients," *Psychometrika*, IX (September, 1944), 149–53.

† L. L. Thurstone, "Graphical Method of Factoring the Correlation Matrix," *Proceedings of the National Academy of Sciences*, XXX, No. 6 (June, 1944), 129–34.

## Table 6

### Correlation Matrix R

|   | 1 | 2 | 3 | 4 | 5 | 6 | 7 | 8 | 9 | 10 |
|---|---|---|---|---|---|---|---|---|---|----|
| 1 | 0.37 | 0.33 | -0.29 | 0.11 | 0.10 | 0.16 | -0.33 | -0.09 | 0.20 | -0.03 |
| 2 | 0.33 | 0.46 | -0.31 | 0.18 | 0.22 | 0.05 | -0.15 | -0.14 | 0.20 | 0.18 |
| 3 | -0.29 | -0.31 | 0.30 | -0.05 | -0.04 | 0.04 | 0.34 | 0.27 | 0.03 | 0.15 |
| 4 | 0.11 | 0.18 | -0.05 | 0.14 | 0.18 | 0.15 | 0.11 | 0.14 | 0.28 | 0.30 |
| 5 | 0.10 | 0.22 | -0.04 | 0.18 | 0.24 | 0.16 | 0.20 | 0.18 | 0.34 | 0.42 |
| 6 | 0.16 | 0.05 | 0.04 | 0.15 | 0.16 | 0.45 | 0.08 | 0.43 | 0.54 | 0.33 |
| 7 | -0.33 | -0.15 | 0.34 | 0.11 | 0.20 | 0.08 | 0.70 | 0.43 | 0.27 | 0.63 |
| 8 | -0.09 | -0.14 | 0.27 | 0.14 | 0.18 | 0.43 | 0.43 | 0.62 | 0.56 | 0.54 |
| 9 | 0.20 | 0.20 | 0.03 | 0.28 | 0.34 | 0.54 | 0.27 | 0.56 | 0.77 | 0.66 |
| 10 | -0.03 | 0.18 | 0.15 | 0.30 | 0.42 | 0.33 | 0.63 | 0.54 | 0.66 | 0.90 |
| Σ | 0.53 | 1.02 | 0.44 | 1.54 | 2.00 | 2.39 | 2.28 | 2.94 | 3.85 | 4.08 |

### Factor Matrix $F_p$

|   | I | II | III |
|---|---|----|-----|
| 1 | 0.00 | 0.60 | 0.10 |
| 2 | 0.10 | 0.60 | -0.30 |
| 3 | 0.20 | -0.50 | -0.10 |
| 4 | 0.30 | 0.20 | -0.10 |
| 5 | 0.40 | 0.20 | -0.20 |
| 6 | 0.50 | 0.20 | -0.40 |
| 7 | 0.60 | -0.50 | -0.30 |
| 8 | 0.70 | -0.20 | -0.30 |
| 9 | 0.80 | 0.30 | 0.20 |
| 10 | 0.90 | 0.00 | -0.30 |
| Σ | 4.50 | 0.90 | -0.10 |

### Factor I

|   | Trial 1 | | Trial 2 | | Trial 3 | |
|---|---|---|---|---|---|---|
|   | $u_1$ | $v_1$ | $y_1 = u_2$ | $v_2$ | $y_2 = u_3$ | $v_3$ |
| 1 | 0.10 | 0.05 | 0.05 | 0.10 | 0.10 | 0.00 |
| 2 | 0.25 | 0.15 | 0.16 | 0.10 | 0.10 | 0.10 |
| 3 | 0.10 | 0.15 | 0.16 | 0.20 | 0.20 | 0.20 |
| 4 | 0.40 | 0.30 | 0.33 | 0.30 | 0.30 | 0.30 |
| 5 | 0.50 | 0.40 | 0.44 | 0.40 | 0.40 | 0.40 |
| 6 | 0.60 | 0.50 | 0.55 | 0.50 | 0.51 | 0.50 |
| 7 | 0.60 | 0.50 | 0.55 | 0.60 | 0.61 | 0.60 |
| 8 | 0.70 | 0.60 | 0.66 | 0.70 | 0.71 | 0.70 |
| 9 | 0.90 | 0.80 | 0.87 | 0.80 | 0.81 | 0.80 |
| 10 | 1.00 | 0.85 | 0.93 | 0.90 | 0.91 | 0.90 |
| Σ | 5.15 | 4.30 | 4.70 | 4.60 | | |
| m | | 0.8850 | | 0.9787 | | |
| k | | 0.9138 | | 0.9893 | | |

### Factor II

|   | Trial 1 | | Trial 2 | | Trial 3 | |
|---|---|---|---|---|---|---|
|   | $u_1$ | $v_1$ | $y_1 = u_2$ | $v_2$ | $y_2 = u_3$ | $v_3$ |
| 1 | 0.37 | 1.00 | 0.59 | 0.60 | 0.61 | 0.60 |
| 2 | 0.33 | 1.00 | 0.59 | 0.62 | 0.63 | 0.60 |
| 3 | -0.29 | -0.80 | -0.47 | -0.50 | -0.51 | -0.50 |
| 4 | 0.11 | 0.35 | 0.21 | 0.15 | 0.15 | 0.20 |
| 5 | 0.10 | 0.35 | 0.21 | 0.20 | 0.20 | 0.20 |
| 6 | 0.16 | 0.50 | 0.30 | 0.20 | 0.20 | 0.20 |
| 7 | -0.33 | -0.90 | -0.53 | -0.50 | -0.51 | -0.50 |
| 8 | -0.09 | -0.30 | -0.18 | -0.20 | -0.20 | -0.20 |
| 9 | -0.20 | -0.55 | -0.33 | -0.30 | 0.31 | -0.30 |
| 10 | -0.03 | 0.00 | 0.00 | 0.00 | 0.00 | 0.00 |
| Σ | 2.01 | 5.75 | 3.41 | 3.27 | | |
| m | | 2.860 | | 0.959 | | |
| k | | 1.691 | | 0.979 | | |

where $R$ is the given correlation matrix, $u$ is the trial column vector, and $v$ is here a column vector proportional to the product $Ru$. Consider in particular the scalar product of row $j$ of $R_{jk}$ and the trial column vector $u$. This scalar product is

(98) $$R_j u = v_j \Sigma u^2 ,$$

from which we have

(99) $$v_j = \frac{R_j u}{\Sigma u^2} ;$$

but this is also the well-known equation for the slope of the regression line $r$ on $u$ through the origin for a plot of $r$ against $u$. If we plot columns of $r_{jk}$ against the trial values $u_k$, we get a plot with $n$ points. The best-fitting straight line through the origin (regression $r$ on $u$) can be drawn by inspection, and the slope of the line is easily read graphically with sufficient accuracy for the first few iterations. That slope is the value $v_j$. To plot, say, thirty points and to draw by inspection the best-fitting straight line through the origin takes less time than to obtain the cumulative sum of thirty cross products on a calculating machine.

By equation (97) it is evident that at the solution the values $v_j = u_j = a_{j1}$. When a set of values of $v$ has been determined graphically, we plot $v$ against $u$ and find the slope $m$. In the first few graphical iterations, this slope will not be unity because the trial values $u$ are probably too large or too small. If the true values are better represented by $ku$, in which $k$ is a stretching factor, then a plot of $r$ against $ku$ will give a slope of $v/k$ instead of $v$. When these graphs have been drawn, the slope of $v/k$ against $ku$ should be unity. But the obtained slope of $v$ against $u$ is $m$ for the values actually used. Hence the observed slope $m = k^2$. Having found the slope $m$ of the plot of $v$ against $u$, we find $k = \sqrt{m}$. Then if we should take a new set of trial numbers $x_j = ku_j$, the iteration would give, instead of equation (99),

(100) $$\frac{Rx}{\Sigma x^2} = y ,$$

where $y = v/k$. The slope of $y$ against $x$ should now be unity, and the values of $y$ should be used as the trial vector for the next graphical iteration. The determination of $m$ and $k$ can be done with a slide rule, and the new trial values $y = v/k$ can be similarly determined. The slope $m$ can be found either by inspection or by simple summing with the method of averages, in which $m = \Sigma v / \Sigma u$ for like signed pairs of $v$ and $u$.

A numerical example is shown in *Table 6*, which starts with the correlation matrix $R$ of order $10 \times 10$ and rank 3. The corresponding factor matrix $F_p$ for the principal axes is shown in the same table. It is the solution to be found from $R$. The latent roots of $R$ are 2.85, 1.47, and 0.63. These are the sums of the squares of the columns of $F_p$. In the same table the initial trial vector $u$ for the major principal factor is taken roughly proportional to the sums of the columns of $R$. Column 1 of $R$ is plotted against column $u_1$, and the slope is estimated to be approximately $+.05$ and is recorded in column $v_1$. Ten such plots give the values in column $v_1$. The slope is read directly from each graph by noting the ordinate of a straight-line fit at $u_1 = 1$. Next obtain the two column sums, $\Sigma u_1$ and $\Sigma v_1$. The ratio $\Sigma v / \Sigma u = m$, and $k = \sqrt{m}$. This summation can be absolute sums for like signed pairs of $u$ and $v$. Then compute $y_1 = v_1/k$ with a slide rule. These are also the trial values $u_2$ for the next trial. Proceed likewise for three trials, which give the desired values of $a_{j1}$ to two decimals.

The first-factor residuals are then computed. These are $\rho_{jk} = r_{jk} - a_{j1}a_{k1}$. Choose as a starting vector that column of the first-factor residuals which has the largest absolute sum, ignoring diagonals. This is column 1. Its values are recorded in column $u_1$ for factor II. The procedure is now the same as before. The third iteration was taken on a calculating machine, and it gave the second-factor loadings $a_{j2}$, the second column of $F_p$, to two decimals. The last iterations for each factor can be done on a calculating machine to obtain greater accuracy, while the first few iterations can be done graphically to save time and labor. The computation for the third column of $F_p$ was done in the same manner.

Occasionally, when two or three latent roots are nearly the same, the iterative process will be found to oscillate, or the convergence will be slow. This is an indication that the test configuration has nearly equal thicknesses in these dimensions, so that the configuration is nearly circular or spherical in these dimensions. If the purpose is to extract the maximum variance from the correlation matrix, it does not matter where we place a set of orthogonal axes in those dimensions which are represented by nearly equal latent roots. In such a situation it is desirable to reduce the obtained vector $v$ to a unit vector in the system without waiting for complete convergence. That can be done with a stretching factor $c$ on $v$ so that $cv = a$, where $a$ are the desired factor loadings. The value of $c$ can be found from equation (72). By this device the computer need not be unduly delayed by slow convergence in obtaining a factorially useful solution. The graphical method here described can be applied to a variety of computational problems.

### Additional theorems

We shall consider here some additional properties of the principal-axes solution which are of theoretical and computational interest.[*] Starting with the relation of equation (32), we write

(101)                         $$R_{jk}a_{j1} = a_{j1}\beta_1$$

---

[*] The theorems in this section were assembled by Ledyard Tucker.

for the first column $a_{j1}$ of the factor matrix $F_p$ for the principal axes. For the second column we have, similarly,

$$(102) \qquad R_{jk}a_{j2} = a_{j2}\beta_2 ,$$

and, in general,

$$(103) \qquad R_{jk}a_{jp} = a_{jp}\beta_p .$$

The elements of $F_p$ are $a_{jp}$, and the characteristic roots $\beta_p$ may be taken as diagonal elements in the diagonal matrix $D$. Then, in matrix form,

$$(104) \qquad RF_p = F_pD .$$

The matrix $F_p$ is orthogonal by columns, so that $\sum_j a_{jp}a_{jq}=0$, where $p$ and $q$ represent any pair of columns. Since $\sum_j a_{jp}^2=\beta_p$, the columns of $F_p$ can be normalized by the postmultiplication $F_pD^{-\frac{1}{2}}$. The matrix $F_pD^{-\frac{1}{2}}$ is then an orthogonal matrix, which may be denoted $\Lambda$,

$$(105) \qquad F_pD^{-\frac{1}{2}} \equiv \Lambda \qquad \text{or} \qquad F_p = \Lambda D^{\frac{1}{2}} ,$$

by which we see that the columns of $\Lambda$ are proportional to the columns of the factor matrix $F_p$. From (104) and (105) we have

$$(106) \qquad RF_pD^{-\frac{1}{2}} = F_pDD^{-\frac{1}{2}} ,$$

and hence

$$(107) \qquad R\Lambda = \Lambda D .$$

Premultiplying (107) by $\Lambda'$, we have

$$(108) \qquad \Lambda'R\Lambda = \Lambda'\Lambda D ;$$

but, since $\Lambda$ is an orthogonal matrix, we get

$$(109) \qquad \Lambda'R\Lambda = D$$

or

$$(110) \qquad R = \Lambda D\Lambda' .$$

Since $\Lambda\Lambda'=I$, we get from (105)

$$(111) \qquad F_p'F_p = D .$$

Several useful relations of the characteristic roots $\beta_p$ are as follows: The sum of the squares of each row $j$ in any factor matrix $F$ is the communality $h_j^2$. Hence the sum of the squares in the whole factor matrix $F$ is equal to the sum of the diagonal elements in $R$. The sum of the squares in each column $p$ of $F_p$ is the root $\beta_p$. Hence the sum of the squares of all the elements in $F_p$ is equal to the sum of the roots $\beta_p$, and this is also the sum of the diagonal elements of $R$.

The sum of the squares of the correlations in $R$ is equal to the sum of the squares of the entries in the matrix $P = F'F$, where $F$ is any factor matrix for $R$. We write

$$(112) \qquad r_{jk} = \sum_m a_{jm} a_{km} ,$$

and then

$$(113) \qquad \sum_j \sum_k r_{jk}^2 = \sum_j \sum_k \left( \sum_m a_{jm} a_{km} \right)^2 ,$$

which becomes

$$(114) \qquad \sum_j \sum_k r_{jk}^2 = \sum_m \sum_M \left( \sum_j a_{jm} a_{jM} \right) \left( \sum_k a_{km} a_{kM} \right)$$

or

$$(115) \qquad \sum_j \sum_k r_{jk}^2 = \sum_m \sum_M \left( \sum_j a_{jm} a_{jM} \right)^2 :$$

but

$$(116) \qquad P = F'F ,$$

in which the elements are

$$(117) \qquad p_{mM} = \sum_j a_{jm} a_{jM} ,$$

and hence

$$(118) \qquad \sum_j \sum_k r_{jk}^2 = \sum_m \sum_M p_m^2 {}_M .$$

For the principal axes we have, by (105),

$$(119) \qquad F_p'F_p = (\Lambda D^{\frac{1}{2}})'(\Lambda D^{\frac{1}{2}})$$
$$= D^{\frac{1}{2}} \Lambda' \Lambda D^{\frac{1}{2}} .$$

But $\Lambda$ is an orthogonal transformation, and hence

$$(120) \qquad F_p'F_p = D = P_p .$$

Hence the diagonal elements of $P$ are the characteristic roots of $R$. It can be shown that the characteristic roots of $R$ and $P$ are identical.

If, in applying Hotelling's iterative method of factoring, the first trial vector is orthogonal to the first $s$ principal axes, it can be shown that all succeeding trial vectors will also remain orthogonal to the first $s$ principal axes, and they will approach the $(s+1)$th principal axis.

It can also be shown that if we subtract a number $k$ from each diagonal element of $R$, then the characteristic roots are reduced by the same scalar $k$, but the solution $\Lambda$ of equation (110) remains unaltered. The introduction of the decrement $k$ on the diagonal elements of $R$ can be used for accelerating the iterative process. The iterations can be made to approach the mean principal axis instead of the major principal axis by this device. The mean principal axis can also be determined by iteration on $P^{-1}$, which has the characteristic roots $1/\beta_p$, and these are the diagonal elements of $D^{-1}$.

## Advantages and limitations of the principal-axes solution

The principal-axes solution for the factor problem has an intrinsic interest because of its many mathematical properties, including the fact that it is a unique solution for any given correlation matrix. That was the writer's motivation in the original formulation of the principal-axes solution in 1932. Soon after publication of the solution, it was realized that the solution did not satisfy the psychological requirements for which the simple-structure solution was devised. Because of the rather general confusion about the controversial issues in this problem, we shall summarize briefly the advantages and the limitations of the principal-axes solution, including a description of the types of problem for which the principal-axes solution is applicable and of those to which the principal-axes solution is not applicable.

A factorial analysis can be made for one of two purposes, namely, (1) to condense the test scores by expressing them in terms of a relatively small number of linearly independent factors or (2) to discover the underlying functional unities which operate to produce the test performances and to describe the individual differences eventually in terms of these distinguishable functions. Many arguments about factorial methods could be resolved if the participants would indicate which purpose they have in mind, because, strictly speaking, there is no intrinsically correct factorial method except in terms of what the investigator is trying to do. According to the first purpose, factor analysis becomes essentially a statistical method of condensing the test scores. According to the second purpose, factor analysis becomes essentially a scientific method for sustaining or rejecting hypotheses about the nature of the underlying processes that produce the test scores. These two points of view are both legitimate in their respective places. There is trouble, however, when two investigators have these different points of view and proceed to argue about factorial method without recognizing that they imply entirely different objectives with their analyses. It is the second objective that has guided the writer, since 1931, in developing multiple-factor methods. It is the first objective that is usually implied by mathematical statisticians who write on factorial problems. This difference in objectives is largely responsible for controversies about factorial method. Many misunderstandings in this field would probably be resolved if we all recognized that a factorial analysis should be judged in terms of the purpose for which it is made and that multiple-factor analysis is a flexible and powerful tool that can serve as a guide in a variety of scientific problems.

Let us consider, first, a table of scores $s_{ji}$ for individuals $i$ in tests $j$. This is the score matrix of order $n \times N$. For convenience let the scores be recorded in standard form, with unit standard deviation and with origin at the mean. This table shows $n$ scores for each of the $N$ individuals. If the tests are correlated, we may undertake a factor analysis in order to condense a large score matrix so that each individual may be described as to the same domain in terms of a relatively small number $(r)$ of linearly independent factor scores instead of the large number $(n)$ of test scores with which we start in the score matrix. This is essentially a statistical problem, and, as such, there is no demand that the factor scores shall have any particular interpretation in terms of the processes that produce the scores. This situation is very similar to that of writing a regression equation in which we want a set of coefficients for the independent variables which will give that linear combination of them which minimizes the residuals in estimating the dependent variable. When we solve the least-squares problem and write a regression equation, we demand only that the regression coefficients shall be numbers which minimize the residuals. We usually make no demand that the regression coefficients shall be interpreted in terms of the processes which produced the dependent variable scores. If that is ever done, we can expect each of the regression coefficients to be complex in nature, in that it is affected by all or by many of the processes which affect the problem. However, it is just as legitimate to ask for a condensation of the test scores into a relatively small number of indices to replace the original test scores as it is to ask for a linear combination of the independent variables for the purpose of making the best-possible prediction of the dependent variable, without any reference to the question of what the regression coefficients might mean in terms of the processes that fundamentally determine them.

Starting with the score matrix of order $n \times N$, it is our object, according to the first purpose of factor analysis, to write another score matrix of order $r \times N$ in which $r < n$, and we want to describe each individual in terms of this smaller number $(r)$ of indices so as to cover essentially the same domain which is covered by the larger number $(n)$ of tests in the whole test battery. The fundamental factor theorem which was first formulated in 1931 applies here, namely, that the number of linearly independent factors in a correlation matrix is the rank of the correlation matrix.* The correlation matrix for this statistical problem has unit diagonals because the correlation matrix $R = (1/N)SS'$, where the elements of $S$ are standard scores.

The score elements in $S$ are fallible, in that they are experimentally determined, and hence there is at least some part of the variance of each test which is fortuitous and attributable to variable errors. The rank of the correlation matrix with experimentally determined correlation coefficients is necessarily of rank equal to the order of the correlation matrix. Hence, strictly speaking, $n = r$ with experimentally determined correlations. If we carry out the factor analysis with this literal interpretation, then we shall have as many factors as there are tests. We might as well use the tests as they stand for the description of each individual, since we have gained nothing in the economy of description. However, there is a gain in the statistical sense in that the new factors would be uncorrelated, whereas the tests are correlated. The investigator may consider it worth while to use a set of $n$ uncorrelated factor scores for each individual instead of a set of $n$ correlated test scores. That may be his choice.

Economy of description of each individual can be obtained in most practical problems, so that $r$ is less than $n$, even with the present formulation, because it may be possible to select a relatively small number of factor scores or indices which cover most of the variances of the tests in the battery. This is, in fact, the objective when the principal-axes solution is used without rotation of axes. The investigator then makes a factor analysis in terms of a relatively small number of factors which account for the test scores with residuals that are so small that he is willing to ignore them. The number of factors to be used in such a description depends on the size of the residuals that are judged to be negligible.

In the writer's first attempt to solve this problem, the first column of the factor matrix was so determined that it accounted for the maximum possible amount of the variance in one factor. Geometrically, this solution is found by placing the first axis in the test configuration so as to maximize the sums of squares of the test vector projections on the first axis. This is, in fact, the major principal axis. The next column was so determined that it accounted for the maximum possible amount of the variance from the first-factor residuals. The process can be continued until the residuals are negligible. It is evident that the principal-axes solution is exactly the desired solution for this problem. At first, it was necessary to factor the correlation matrix with an arbitrary orthogonal reference frame, which was rotated to the principal axes. Then, only the first few principal axes were used to describe the test battery, leaving the remaining variance unaccounted for in the form of residuals. With the publication of Hotelling's iterative method of factoring, it

* L. L. Thurstone, "Multiple Factor Analysis," *Psychological Review*, Vol. XXXVIII, No. 5 (September, 1931).

became possible to determine the principal axes directly from the correlation matrix, one at a time and starting with the major principal axis. The factoring need continue only until the residuals are judged to be negligible. The solution is in such a form that we can say with confidence that no other set of $r$ linearly independent factors can be determined for the given set of test scores which accounts for more of the variance. In this statistical sense the first $r$ principal factors constitute the best description that can be found for the test scores with this number of factors. In practice, there is a limitation of excessive labor with a large correlation matrix. A practical compromise is to determine a factor matrix with one of the centroid methods and to determine one or two more factors than would be required by the principal axes in order to cover the same total variance. This centroid frame can then be rotated to the principal axes when that is the desired solution.

We consider, next, the second purpose for which a factorial analysis can be undertaken, namely, to discover the underlying functional unities which operate to produce the test performances. A verbalism is frequently given as an objection to the mere statement of this purpose, namely, that no method of analyzing data can discover factors. Let us meet such a triviality by acknowledging that no method of analyzing data can ever discover anything in science or give any interpretation of the data. Discovering anything or interpreting experimental findings of any kind always implies the subjective functions of a human being, the experimenter. Analytical methods can aid his thinking, but they never write the interpretations for him. The analytical methods that he selects depend on his purposes.

As an example of the second purpose, namely, to discover functional unities and their nature, let us consider a set of tests of visual perception. The correlations between the tests might indicate that more than one factor is involved and hence that visual perceptual efficiency cannot be adequately described as a single function but rather as a complex of several or of many functions. On the basis of previous factorial experiments, two visual functions, such as visual acuity and visual perceptual closure, might be postulated among many other factors. Every visual test will involve visual acuity to some extent in its variance; but, if the figures to be seen are reasonably large and distinct and sufficiently illuminated, the factor of visual acuity will be represented in only a small and negligible part of the total variance in studying individual differences in such tasks. Similarly, the factor of visual perceptual closure will be represented in most visual tasks, but most of the tests may have little or almost none of their variances accounted for by individual differences in visual closure. If such factors operate to produce individual differences in performance on visual tasks of considerable variety, it should be possible to predict with some confidence that the relative variances will be large or small in these two factors by merely examining the psychological nature of each test. If the battery of visual perceptual tests be

# CHAPTER XXI

## THE APPRAISAL OF INDIVIDUAL ABILITIES

In previous chapters the main problem has been to devise factorial methods which would be sufficiently powerful to deal with the complexities of multiple factors so as to reveal functional unities, with a minimum of restriction as to their nature and the interrelations of the factors. To discover the factors and to sustain or refute postulated factors have been the principal purposes. The development of the factorial methods has been a continuous process of compromising between the theoretically complete and ideal solutions and those solutions that can be made available with a reasonable amount of labor, time, and cost. We turn, now, to the problem of appraising individuals as to the factors that may have been identified, either as reasonably pure factors or at least as functional unities that are practically useful in dealing with individual differences.

In dealing with this problem of appraising individuals as to their profiles of abilities, we shall develop, first, what seems now to be a rather complete statement of the solution for the factors that have been identified and which can be tested for; and then we shall consider the compromises that will be necessary in practical situations which will rarely allow a complete solution.

### The regression $x$ on $s$

Let us assume that a set of $n$ tests is available for which the factorial compositions are known and that the whole battery of tests is given to each subject for the purpose of writing his profile of $r$ factorial abilities. Here, as before, let the standard score of individual $i$ in the primary ability $p$ be denoted $x_{pi}$. Similarly, let the standard score of individual $i$ on test $j$ be denoted $s_{ji}$. The problem then is to estimate the standard factorial scores $x_{pi}$ in terms of the given and known test scores $s_{ji}$. This is a conventional form of statistical problem which calls for the regression $x_{pi}$ on $s_{ji}$. The given test scores are the independent variables in terms of which the individual factorial scores are to be estimated. We then have the equation

$$(1) \qquad x_{pi} = \sum_j w_{pj}s_{ji} + \epsilon_{pi} \, ,$$

where the subscript $p$ refers to primary factors, $j$ refers to tests, $i$ refers to individuals, and $w$ is the regression coefficient or weight of the score $s_{ji}$ in test $j$ in the estimation of the primary factor $p$. The residual or discrepancy between the true value of $x_{pi}$ and the best value that can be obtained as a linear combination of test scores is denoted $\epsilon_{pi}$. It is assumed here that the true individual factor scores are the values $x_{pi}$.

Equation (1) is a regression equation, in which the test scores $s_{ji}$ are the $n$ independent variables and $x_{pi}$ is the dependent variable to be estimated by the best linear combination of the test scores. The problem of finding the best linear combination of the test scores is that of finding the regression weights $w_{pj}$ for tests $j$ in estimating the dependent variable which is the score $x_{pi}$ in the primary factor $p$. The weights $w$ are to be so determined as to minimize the discrepancies. The discrepancies can be written by (1) in the matrix form

$$(2) \qquad X - WS = E ,$$

where $X$ of order $r \times N$ is the matrix of factor scores with elements $x_{pi}$, $W$ of order $r \times n$ is the matrix of regression weights $w_{pj}$, $S$ of order $n \times N$ is the standard test score matrix with elements $s_{ji}$, and $E$ of order $r \times N$ is the matrix of residuals in which the sum of the squares of each row is minimized. The problem can be solved separately for each primary factor $p$. Then in equation (2) the matrices $X$, $WS$, and $E$ are reduced to row vectors of order $1 \times N$. Then it is the $n$ values of $w_{pj}$ in the row vector $W$ of order $1 \times n$ which are to be determined so as to minimize the residuals.*

For each primary factor $p$ that is to be estimated in the subjects, we have a residual $\epsilon_{pi}$ for each individual. These residuals are the $N$ elements in the row vector $E$. The sum of the squares of these residuals is given by the matrix product $EE'$, which is a scalar. From (2) we have

$$(3) \qquad EE' = (X - WS)(X - WS)' ,$$

which becomes

$$(4) \qquad EE' = XX' - XS'W' - WSX' + WSS'W' .$$

Since these terms represent scalars, we can write

$$(5) \qquad EE' = XX' - 2WSX' + WSS'W' .$$

From this we obtain the normal equation for $W$,

$$(6) \qquad XS' = WSS' .$$

Multiplying both sides by $1/N$, we have

$$(7) \qquad \frac{1}{N} XS' = W\left(\frac{1}{N} SS'\right) .$$

---

* H. W. Turnbull and A. C. Aitken, *Canonical Matrices* (London: Blackie & Sons, 1932), p. 173.

But

$$(8) \qquad \frac{1}{N} XS' = R_{pj} ,$$

where $R_{pj}$ is a row vector whose elements are the correlations between the test scores $s_{ji}$ and the primary-factor scores $x_{pi}$. These are the correlations between the tests and the primary factor $p$, and hence they are, in a sense, the validity coefficients of the tests for the primary factor $p$. Similarly,

$$(9) \qquad \frac{1}{N} SS' = R_{jk} ,$$

where $R_{jk}$ is the correlation matrix with unit diagonals.* From (7), (8), and (9) we get

$$(10) \qquad R_{pk} = W_{pj}R_{jk} ;$$

and from this we have the desired equation,

$$(11) \qquad R_{pj}R_{jk}^{-1} = W_{pk} ,$$

where $w_{pk}$ (or $w_{pj}$) are the desired regression coefficients in equation (1).

Equation (11) has interesting interpretations for statistical and psychological problems. In order to determine the regression weights $w$, we need the inverse, $R_{jk}^{-1}$. This inverse does not exist if $R_{jk}$ is singular. Hence the correlation matrix $R_{jk}$ with unit diagonals for the independent variables must be of rank equal to its order. The number of terms in $WS$ of the regression equation (2) is equal to the number of independent variables.

If the situation should arise in which a set of supposedly independent variables is not linearly independent, then the inverse, $R_{jk}^{-1}$, could not be determined. In dealing with experimental data it may happen that the independent variables owe their linear independence to fortuitous variable errors. If the variable errors were then eliminated, the set of supposedly independent variables would no longer be linearly independent. If, in spite of such a situation, the regression equation were computed with as many regression weights as there are supposedly independent variables, we should expect to see absurdities in the regression weights. They would express only the fortuitous variable errors. This situation is not unlikely when a regression equation is written in terms of a large number of independent variables.

The difficulty with correlated independent variables whose true rank may be less than the order can be avoided by an application of multiple-factor analysis. The correlation matrix for the independent variables should be

---

* The unit diagonals are called for here because we are now dealing with a conventional regression equation.

factored with reliability coefficients in the diagonals. These diagonals include not only the common-factor variances of the independent variables but also those parts of the unique variances which the independent variables may share with the dependent variable. These diagonals exclude, however, the unreliabilities of the independent variables. When the residuals are judged to be vanishingly small, the number of factors is also the number of terms which may be written legitimately in the regression equation.

Having determined the number of terms which can be written in the regression equation, one proceeds next to arrange the independent variables in the same number of groups as there are number of terms in $WS$, which is also the rank of the independent variables. The grouping should be done so that closely correlated variables are in the same group as far as possible. A new set of independent variables can then be written as centroids of the groups. These, in turn, constitute the independent variables $R_{jk}$ in equation (11), with unit diagonals for determining the $r$ weights $w_{pk}$.*

In application to a psychological problem, equation (11) gives results which are of theoretical, as well as of practical, interest. Suppose that the number factor $N$ is to be appraised by a large battery of tests which represent several factors. If the instructions for the number tests include some variance on the verbal comprehension factor $V$, then this factor will have small saturation on the number tests. In writing the regression equation for the appraisal of the number factor, one might find a small negative regression weight on the verbal factor $V$. The interpretation then would be that the number factor $N$ is a linear combination of the number test composite $N_t$ and the verbal test composite $V_t$, in which the number test composite $N_t$ is coplanar with $N$ and $V_t$ and between them. It is as if the number factor $N$ would be determined from $N$ and $V$ by subtracting a correction for the verbal component in the number tests. This is illustrative of the system of weights that may arise in a complete solution for primary-factor scores as linear combinations of the tests in a diversified battery.

Much thought has been given by some students of factorial theory to this problem of appraising the primary-factor scores of individuals on the basis of their scores in a diversified test battery. The solution to this problem is given by the regression equation (1) and equation (11) for the regression coefficients, but in practical application it is rarely feasible or even desirable to use the theoretically complete solution.

The regression equation (1), or its variants, presupposes that a complete test battery has been given to each subject, and it implies that the battery represents all the relevant primary factors. In practice it is desirable that the tests for each factor be as far as possible self-contained, so that a subject

* This is the problem which was discussed in a different setting by Ragnar Frisch in his monograph, *Statistical Confluence Analysis by Means of Complete Regression Systems* (Pub. No. 5 [University of Oslo Economic Institute, 1934]).

can be examined for one factor without corrections for the other factors which may be irrelevant for the occasion. In order to prepare tests to satisfy this requirement we merely select several tests which have high saturation on the desired factor, and the score in such a composite may then be used in practical situations as the subject's factor score. The additional refinement that could be brought into the appraisal by giving the tests for all other known factors in order that a regression equation might be solved for each individual for each factor is rarely, if ever, worth the extra trouble. In most situations this complete procedure would even be absurd.

In selecting the subtests which are to constitute a composite test for any primary factor, it is useful to distribute as far as possible the variances on the factors which are irrelevant for the composite. Thus in subtests for a composite to appraise the space factor $S$, the several subtests would probably be found to be impure, in that each of them would have some variance attributable to verbal comprehension $V$ in the test instruction, to the number factor $N$ if a part of the task induces numerical thinking, and so on. Now, if all the space tests had an appreciable secondary saturation on the verbal factor $V$, then evidently the composite would represent a linear combination of $S$ and $V$ with major variance in $S$. This effect is reduced by selecting the subtests so that the irrelevant variance is scattered among different factors.

When a test composite for a primary factor has been selected, it can be used as a test for the factor in question quite independently of test composites for other primary factors that may or may not be given to the same subjects. It should be specially noted that the correlations between the test composites for the several primary factors will generally have higher intercorrelations than the primary factors themselves. Further, if the primary-factor scores are estimated by the regression equation (1) for a factorially diversified test battery, the correlations between such factor scores may be expected to be lower than the correlations between the corresponding test composites. Nevertheless, the problem of appraising an individual as to each of several factors is best solved in the practical situation by using a test composite for each factor. In theoretical studies of the intrinsic correlations between the factors it is preferable to use the more complete factorial methods previously described.

We turn next to the other regression, namely, to predict the test scores $s_{ji}$ when the individual factor scores $x_{pi}$ are known.

### The regression $s$ on $x$

This regression implies that the primary abilities of an individual are known and that it is desired to estimate what his performance will be on a test with known factorial weightings. This is the reverse of the previous regression $x$ on $s$, in which it was assumed that an individual's scores are known and that his primary abilities are to be appraised.

The case in which $s_{ji}$ is to be estimated by $x_{pi}$ can be written in the form

$$(12) \qquad\qquad s_{ji} = \sum_p w_{jp} x_{pi} + \epsilon_{ji} ,$$

in which the notation is the same as in the previous case. By similar reasoning we get, for the regression coefficients,

$$(13) \qquad\qquad w_{jp} = R_{jp} R_{pq}^{-1} .$$

The matrix $R_{jp}$ is of order $n \times r$, and it shows the correlation between each test $j$ and each primary factor $p$. These correlations are, in a sense, validity coefficients, because these are the best available correlations between the tests and the factors that the tests are intended to appraise. The matrix $R_{pq}^{-1}$ is of order $r \times r$, and it is determined from the intercorrelations $R_{pq}$. The matrix $R_{pq}$ has unit diagonals because it shows correlations between factors of unit variance in the common-factor space. Since the primary abilities are linearly independent, it follows that the rank of $R_{pq}$ is $r$ and hence that $R_{pq}$ is non-singular.

If the primary abilities are uncorrelated, the matrix $R_{pq}$ becomes an identity matrix and its inverse is then also the identity matrix. The regression weights then become

$$(14) \qquad\qquad w_{jp} = R_{jp} = F \qquad \text{(orthogonal case) ;}$$

and in this case the regression weights are, in fact, the elements of the factor matrix $F$, whose elements show the correlations between the tests and the orthogonal unit reference factors. The corresponding regression equation for the simplest case in which all the contributing factors are common then is

$$(15) \qquad\qquad s_{ji} = F_{jp} x_{pi} \qquad \text{(orthogonal case) ,}$$

which is also the fundamental observation equation with which we started the development of multiple-factor theory.

# INDEX

[The numbers refer to the pages]